S0-AGE-103

ELECTRIC CIRCUITS FUNDAMENTALS

Custom Seventh Edition

Thomas L. Floyd

Taken from:

Electric Circuits Fundamentals, Seventh Edition
by Thomas L. Floyd

Learning Solutions

New York   Boston   San Francisco
London   Toronto   Sydney   Tokyo   Singapore   Madrid
Mexico City   Munich   Paris   Cape Town   Hong Kong   Montreal

Cover Art: Courtesy of PhotoDisc/Getty Images

Taken from:

Electric Circuits Fundamentals, Seventh Edition
by Thomas L. Floyd
Copyright © 2007, 2004, 2001, 1998, 1995, 1991, 1987 by Pearson Education, Inc.
Published by Prentice Hall
Upper Saddle River, New Jersey 07458

All rights reserved. No part of this book may be reproduced, in any form or by any means, without permission in writing from the publisher.

This special edition published in cooperation with Pearson Learning Solutions.

All trademarks, service marks, registered trademarks, and registered service marks are the property of their respective owners and are used herein for identification purposes only.

Pearson Learning Solutions, 501 Boylston Street, Suite 900, Boston, MA 02116
A Pearson Education Company
www.pearsoned.com

Printed in the United States of America

2 3 4 5 6 7 8 9 10 XXXX 14 13 12 11 10

2009280147

KW

ISBN 10: 0-558-56410-0
ISBN 13: 978-0-558-56410-0

DEDICATION

Once again, to Sheila
With love

PREFACE

This seventh edition of *Electric Circuits Fundamentals* provides a comprehensive and clear coverage of basic electrical and electronic concepts, practical applications, and troubleshooting. In this edition many topics have been strengthened and improved, and some new topics and features have been added. A set of innovative and interactive PowerPoint® slides by Dave Buchla are new with this edition and are available to instructors. Please check your courseware for location of and access to PPTs. The Multisim circuit files needed for your course are found on the CD-ROM packaged with this textbook. Additionally, a new text design makes the book more visually interesting and easier to use.

This textbook is divided into two parts: DC Circuits in Chapters 1 through 7 and AC Circuits in Chapters 8 through 15. The traditional topics of resistive, capacitive, and inductive circuits with both dc and ac sources are covered.

As in previous editions, *Electric Circuits Fundamentals* Seventh Edition, uses the electron flow direction for current assignments. The two widely accepted views concerning the assumed direction of current for the purpose of envisioning and analyzing circuit behavior are electron flow direction and conventional current direction. There is no difference between the two approaches in terms of the outcome of circuit analysis. Electron flow current direction is from the negative side of a voltage source, through a circuit, and back to the positive side of the source, which is the actual direction in which electrons move through a circuit. Conventional current direction is from the positive side of a voltage source, through the circuit, and back to the negative side of the source. Although the effects of current are observable, current itself is never seen; so the direction that one assumes makes no difference as long as consistency is applied. The choice is usually a matter of preference or familiarity.

Features

Math level is limited to basic algebra and right-triangle trigonometry.

Full-color format

Chapter opener includes an introduction, a chapter outline, a list of chapter objectives, a list of key terms, an Application Assignment preview, and a website reference.

An introduction and list of objectives for each section in the chapter

Numerous worked examples throughout each chapter, each containing a related problem with answers at the end of the chapter

A Multisim exercise in many examples

Section review questions with answers at the end of the chapter

Troubleshooting sections in many of the chapters

- An application assignment in each chapter (except Chapter 1)

- Margin features such as Safety Point, Hands On Tip, and Biography appear throughout.

- A summary, key term glossary, and formula list at the end of each chapter

- A self-test at the end of each chapter with answers

- A set of exercises that help develop thought processes essential to troubleshooting (*Troubleshooting: Symptom and Cause*) at the end of most chapters with answers

- Problems organized into basic and advanced categories are at the end of each chapter. Most chapters also have a set of Multisim problems, many with faults. Answers to odd-numbered problems are at the end of the book.

- A comprehensive glossary at the end of the book includes all boldface terms.

- Standard resistor and capacitor values are used throughout.

Student Resources

Multisim® CD-ROM   A CD-RO, containing Multisim circuit files needed for this course, is packaged with the textbook.

These Multisim circuit files are provided for use by anyone who has Multisim software. Anyone who does not have Multisim software and wishes to purchase it in order to use the circuit files may do so by ordering it from *www.prenhall.com/ewb*. However, although the circuit files are intended to complement classroom, textbook, and laboratory study, it is not necessary to use these files in order to successfully study electric circuits or use Floyd's *Electric Circuits Fundamentals,* Seventh Edition.

Lab Manual   DC/AC Electronics Lab Manua, Custom Edition.

Companion Website (www.prenhall.com/floyd)   For the student, this website offers the opportunity to test his or her own progress and practice answering sample test questions.

Instructor Resources

Please check your courseware document for location of and access to these supplements.

PowerPoint® Slides   A completely new set of PowerPoint® slides, created by David M. Buchla, dynamically illustrates key concepts in the text. Each slide contains a summary with examples, key term definitions, and a quiz for each chapter. This is an excellent tool for classroom presentation to supplement the textbook.

Instructor's Resource Manual   This manual contains solutions to chapter problems from the text, solutions to Application Assignments, Summary of Multisim Circuit results, a test item file, lab manual solutions, and a partial list of CEMA skills.

Suggestions for Using This Textbook

As mentioned before, this book is divided into two parts: DC Circuits and AC Circuits. The text can accommodate a variety of scheduling and program requirements. Some suggestions follow:

Option 1 A two-term dc/ac sequence should allow sufficient time to cover all or most of the topics in the book. Chapters 1 through 7 can be covered in the first term and Chapters 8 through 15 in the second term.

Option 2 A modification of Option 1 is to add the coverage of capacitors through Section 9-5 and inductors through Section 11-5 to the first-term dc course.

Option 3 Yet another modification to Option 1 for those who prefer to cover reactive components before covering reactive circuits is to cover Chapter 11 on inductors immediately after Chapter 9 on capacitors. Then follow with Chapter 10, Chapter 12, and so on.

Option 4 A one-term dc/ac sequence. Obviously, this approach will require selective and faster-paced coverage of much of the material. Since program requirements vary greatly, it is difficult to make specific suggestions for selective coverage.

Chapter Pedagogical Features

Chapter Opener Each chapter begins with an outline, a list of objectives, a list of key terms, an Application Assignment preview, a website reference and an introduction. A typical chapter opener is shown in Figure P–1.

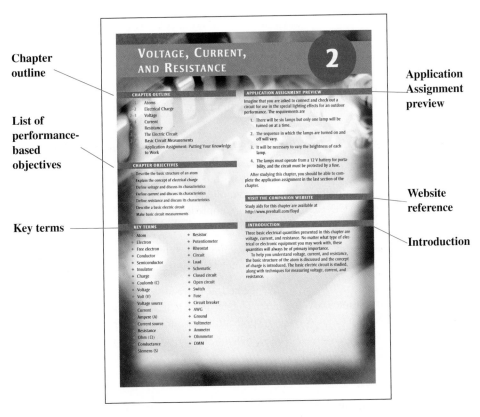

▲ FIGURE P–1

Chapter opener.

Section Opener Each section in a chapter begins with a brief introduction that includes a general overview and section objectives. An example is shown in Figure P–2.

▶ FIGURE P–2

Section review, section opener, and Hands On Tip.

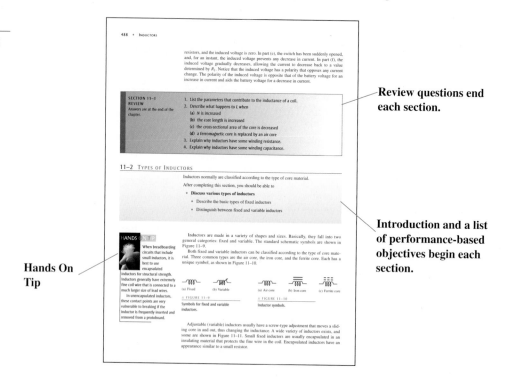

Hands On Tip

Section Review Each section ends with questions or exercises that emphasize the main concepts presented in the chapter, as illustrated in Figure P–2. Answers are given at the end of the chapter.

Worked Example, Related Problem, and Multisim Exercise Numerous worked examples illustrate and clarify basic concepts or specific procedures. Each example ends with a Related Problem that reinforces or expands on the example by requiring the student to work through a similar problem. Selected examples have a Multisim exercise that references a circuit file on the CD-ROM. A typical example is shown in Figure P–3. Answers to the related problems are at the end of the chapter.

Troubleshooting Section Many chapters include a troubleshooting section related to chapter coverage. Each emphasizes logical thought and presents a structured approach.

Application Assignment This feature, located at the end of most chapters, presents a practical application of topics covered in the chapter in an activities format that requires the student to perform certain tasks. A typical Application Assignment, as shown in Figure P–4, conveys certain practical aspects of a technician's job. Application Assignments are not intended to be laboratory exercises.

To the Student

Any career training requires hard work, and electronics is no exception. The best way to learn new material is by reading, thinking, and doing. This text is designed to help you along the way by providing an overview and objectives for each section, numerous worked-out examples, exercises, and review questions.

Read each section of the text carefully and think about what you have read. Sometimes you may need to read the section more than once. Work through each example problem step by step before you try the related problem that goes with the example. After each section, answer the review questions. Answers to the related problems and the section review questions are at the end of the chapter.

◀ FIGURE P–3

An example with a related problem and a Multisim exercise.

Examples are set off from text.

Each example includes a related problem.

Selected examples have a Multisim exercise keyed to the CD-ROM.

ANALYSIS OF SERIES *RC* CIRCUITS ♦ 431

EXAMPLE 10–3 Determine the current in the *RC* circuit of Figure 10–9.

▶ FIGURE 10–9

Solution The capacitive reactance is

$$X_C = \frac{1}{2\pi fC} = \frac{1}{2\pi(1.5 \text{ kHz})(0.022 \text{ } \mu F)} = 4.82 \text{ k}\Omega$$

The impedance is

$$Z = \sqrt{R^2 + X_C^2} = \sqrt{(2.2 \text{ k}\Omega)^2 + (4.82 \text{ k}\Omega)^2} = 5.30 \text{ k}\Omega$$

Applying Ohm's law yields

$$I = \frac{V}{Z} = \frac{10 \text{ V}}{5.30 \text{ k}\Omega} = \textbf{1.89 mA}$$

Related Problem Determine the phase angle between V_s and I in Figure 10–9.

Open Multisim file E10-03 on your CD-ROM. Measure the current and the voltages across the resistor and the capacitor.

Phase Relationships of the Current and Voltages

In a series *RC* circuit, the current is the same through both the resistor and the capacitor. Thus, the resistor voltage is in phase with the current, and the capacitor voltage lags the current by 90°. Therefore, there is a phase difference of 90° between the resistor voltage, V_R, and the capacitor voltage, V_C, as shown in the waveform diagram of Figure 10–10.

▲ FIGURE 10–10
Phase relation of the voltages and current in a series *RC* circuit.

An Application Assignment is set off from text.

Realistic instrument and circuit board graphics.

▲ FIGURE P–4

A typical Application Assignment.

Review the chapter summary, the key term definitions, and the formula list. Take the multiple choice self-test and the Troubleshooting: Symptom and Cause quiz. Check your answers against those at the end of the chapter. Finally, work the problems. Working problems is the most important way to check your comprehension and solidify concepts. Verify your answers to the odd-numbered problems with those provided at the end of the book.

Careers in Electronics

The field of electronics is very diverse, and career opportunities are available in many areas. Because electronics is currently found in so many different applications and new technology is being developed at a fast rate, its future appears limitless. There is hardly an area of our lives that is not enhanced to some degree by electronics technology. Those who acquire a sound, basic knowledge of electrical and electronic principles and are willing to continue learning will always be in demand.

The importance of obtaining a thorough understanding of the basic principles contained in this text cannot be overemphasized. Most employers prefer to hire people who have both a thorough grounding in the basics and the ability and eagerness to grasp new concepts and techniques. If you have a good training in the basics, an employer will train you in the specifics of the job to which you are assigned.

There are many types of job classifications for which a person with training in electronics technology may qualify. A few of the most common job functions are discussed briefly in the following paragraphs.

Service Shop Technician   Technical personnel in this category are involved in the repair or adjustment of both commercial and consumer electronic equipment that is returned to the dealer or manufacturer for service. Specific areas include TVs, VCRs, CD and DVD players, stereo equipment, CB radios, and computer hardware. This area also offers opportunities for self-employment.

Industrial Manufacturing Technician   Manufacturing personnel are involved in the testing of electronic products at the assembly-line level or in the maintenance and troubleshooting of electronic and electromechanical systems used in the testing and manufacturing of products. Virtually every type of manufacturing plant, regardless of its product, uses automated equipment that is electronically controlled.

Laboratory Technician   These technicians are involved in breadboarding, prototyping, and testing new or modified electronic systems in research and development laboratories. They generally work closely with engineers during the development phase of a product.

Field Service Technician   Field service personnel service and repair electronic equipment—for example, computer systems, radar installations, automatic banking equipment, and security systems—at the user's location.

Engineering Assistant/Associate Engineer   Personnel in this category work closely with engineers in the implementation of a concept and in the basic design and development of electronic systems. Engineering assistants are frequently involved in a project from its initial design through the early manufacturing stages.

Technical Writer   Technical writers compile technical information and then use the information to write and produce manuals and audiovisual materials. A broad knowledge of a particular system and the ability to clearly explain its principles and operation are essential.

Technical Sales   Technically trained people are in demand as sales representatives for high-technology products. The ability both to understand technical concepts and to communicate the technical aspects of a product to a potential customer is very valuable. In this area, as in technical writing, competency in expressing yourself orally and in writing is essential. Actually, being able to communicate well is very important in any technical job category because you must be able to record data clearly and explain procedures, conclusions, and actions taken so that others can readily understand what you are doing.

Milestones in Electronics

Before you begin your study of electric circuits fundamentals, let's briefly look at some of the important developments that led to the electronics technology we have today. The names of many of the early pioneers in electricity and electromagnetics still live on in terms of familiar units and quantities. Names such as Ohm, Ampere, Volta, Farad, Henry, Coulomb, Oersted, and Hertz are some of the better known examples. More widely known names such as Franklin and Edison are also significant in the history of electricity and electronics because of their tremendous contributions. Short biographies of some of these pioneers are located throughout the text.

The Beginning of Electronics   Early experiments with electronics involved electric currents in vacuum tubes. Heinrich Geissler (1814–1879) removed most of the air from a glass tube and found that the tube glowed when there was current through it. Later, Sir William Crookes (1832–1919) found the current in vacuum tubes seemed to consist of particles. Thomas Edison (1847–1931) experimented with carbon filament bulbs with plates and discovered that there was a current from the hot filament to a positively charged plate. He patented the idea but never used it.

Other early experimenters measured the properties of the particles that flowed in vacuum tubes. Sir Joseph Thompson (1856–1940) measured properties of these particles, later called *electrons.*

Although wireless telegraphic communication dates back to 1844, electronics is basically a 20th century concept that began with the invention of the vacuum tube amplifier. An early vacuum tube that allowed current in only one direction was constructed by John A. Fleming in 1904. Called the Fleming valve, it was the forerunner of vacuum tube diodes. In 1907, Lee deForest added a grid to the vacuum tube. The new device, called the audiotron, could amplify a weak signal. By adding the control element, deForest ushered in the electronics revolution. It was with an improved version of his device that made transcontinental telephone service and radios possible. In 1912, a radio amateur in San Jose, California, was regularly broadcasting music!

In 1921, the secretary of commerce, Herbert Hoover, issued the first license to a broadcast radio station; within two years over 600 licenses were issued. By the end of the 1920s radios were in many homes. A new type of radio, the superheterodyne radio, invented by Edwin Armstrong, solved problems with high-frequency communication. In 1923, Vladimir Zworykin, an American researcher, invented the first television picture tube, and in 1927 Philo T. Farnsworth applied for a patent for a complete television system.

The 1930s saw many developments in radio, including metal tubes, automatic gain control, "midget sets," directional antennas, and more. Also started in this decade was the development of the first electronic computers. Modern computers trace their origins to the work of John Atanasoff at Iowa State University. Beginning in 1937, he envisioned a binary machine that could do complex mathematical work. By 1939, he and graduate student Clifford Berry had constructed a binary machine called ABC, (for Atanasoff-Berry Computer) that used vacuum tubes for logic and condensers (capacitors) for memory. In 1939, the magnetron, a microwave oscillator, was invented in Britain by Henry Boot and John Randall. In the same year, the klystron microwave tube was invented in America by Russell and Sigurd Varian.

During World War II, electronics developed rapidly. Radar and very high-frequency communication were made possible by the magnetron and klystron. Cathode ray tubes were improved for use in radar. Computer work continued during the war. By 1946, John von Neumann had developed the first stored program computer, the Eniac, at the University of Pennsylvania. The decade ended with one of the most important inventions ever, the transistor.

Solid-State Electronics   The crystal detectors used in early radios were the forerunners of modern solid-state devices. However, the era of solid-state electronics began with the invention of the transistor in 1947 at Bell Labs. The inventors were Walter Brattain, John Bardeen, and William Shockley. PC (printed circuit) boards were introduced in 1947, the year the transistor was invented. Commercial manufacturing of transistors began in Allen-town, Pennsylvania, in 1951.

The most important invention of the 1950s was the integrated circuit. On September 12, 1958, Jack Kilby, at Texas Instruments, made the first integrated circuit. This invention literally created the modern computer age and brought about sweeping changes in medicine, communication, manufacturing, and the entertainment industry. Many billions of "chips"—as integrated circuits came to be called—have since been manufactured.

The 1960s saw the space race begin and spurred work on miniaturization and computers. The space race was the driving force behind the rapid changes in electronics that followed. The first successful "op-amp" was designed by Bob Widlar at Fairchild Semiconductor in 1965. Called the mA709, it was very successful but suffered from "latch-up" and other problems. Later, the most popular op-amp ever, the 741, was taking shape at Fairchild. This op-amp became the industry standard and influenced design of op-amps for years to come.

By 1971, a new company that had been formed by a group from Fairchild introduced the first microprocessor. The company was Intel and the product was the 4004 chip, which had the same processing power as the Eniac computer. Later in the same year, Intel announced the first 8-bit processor, the 8008. In 1975, the first personal computer was introduced by Altair, and Popular Science magazine featured it on the cover of the January, 1975, issue. The 1970s also saw the introduction of the pocket calculator and new developments in optical integrated circuits.

By the 1980s, half of all U.S. homes were using cable hookups instead of television antennas. The reliability, speed, and miniaturization of electronics continued throughout the 1980s, including automated testing and calibrating of PC boards. The computer became a part of instrumentation and the virtual instrument was created. Computers became a standard tool on the workbench.

The 1990s saw a widespread application of the Internet. In 1993, there were 130 websites, and now there are millions. Companies scrambled to establish a home page and many of the early developments of radio broadcasting had parallels with the Internet. In 1995, the FCC allocated spectrum space for a new service called Digital Audio Radio Service. Digital television standards were adopted in 1996 by the FCC for the nation's next generation of broadcast television.

The 21st century dawned in January 2001. One of the major technology stories has been the continuous and explosive growth of the Internet. Internet usage in North America has increased by over 100% from 2000 to 2005. The rest of the world experienced almost 200% growth during the same period. The processing speed of computers is increasing at a steady rate and data storage media capacity is increasing at an amazing pace. Carbon nanotubes are seen to be the next step forward for computer chips, eventually replacing transistor technology.

Acknowledgments

Many excellent reviews and surveys have contributed to making this revision of *Electric Circuits Fundamentals* better than ever. My thanks to each of the following reviewers and survey participants: Kevin E. Boiter, Piedmont Technical College; Barry Fahnstock, Macomb Community College; Michael Kregg, College of DuPage; Ravi Manimaran, Lake Michigan College; David Mayo, South Georgia Technical College; Greg Presley, Ranken Technical College; Alan Rux, University of Massachusetts; and Karim Salman, Middle Tennessee State University.

Rex Davidson is my production editor at Prentice Hall, and I can't commend him enough for his hard work and dedication. Lois Porter, my manuscript editor, has done the best job ever on this project and to her goes my undying gratitude. Dave Buchla, my coauthor on other books, has contributed tremendously during the preparation of this revision, and Gary Snyder has done another excellent job in creating the Multisim circuit files. Last but not least, Jane Lopez again provided beautiful renderings for the numerous illustrations in the book. My thanks to all.

Tom Floyd

CONTENTS

APPENDICES

DC Circuits

QUANTITIES AND UNITS

1

CHAPTER OUTLINE

CHAPTER OBJECTIVES

◆ Use scientific notation to represent quantities

◆ Work with electrical units and metric prefixes

◆ Convert from one unit with a metric prefix to another

◆ Express measured data with the proper number of significant digits

◆ Recognize electrical hazards and practice proper safety procedures

KEY TERMS

◆ Scientific notation

◆ Power of ten

◆ Exponent

◆ Engineering notation

◆ SI

◆ Metric prefix

◆ Accuracy

◆ Precision

◆ Significant digit

◆ Round off

◆ Electrical shock

APPLICATION ASSIGNMENT PREVIEW

At the beginning of each chapter starting with Chapter 2, you will find an application assignment preview that relates to that chapter. The application assignments described by the previews present a variety of practical situations that you might encounter in industry.

As you study each chapter, think about how to approach the application assignment that appears as the last section in each chapter. When you have completed each chapter, you should have a sufficient knowledge of the topics covered to enable you to complete the assignment.

VISIT THE COMPANION WEBSITE

Study aids for this chapter are available at
http://www.prenhall.com/floyd

INTRODUCTION

You must be familiar with the units used in electronics and know how to express electrical quantities in various ways using metric prefixes. Scientific notation and engineering notation are indispensable tools whether you use a computer, a calculator, or do computations the old-fashioned way.

1–1 SCIENTIFIC AND ENGINEERING NOTATION

In the electrical and electronics fields, you will encounter both very small and very large quantities. For example, electrical current can range from hundreds of amperes in power applications to a few thousandths or millionths of an ampere in many electronic circuits. This range of values is typical of many other electrical quantities also. Engineering notation is a specialized form of scientific notation. It is used widely in technical fields to express large and small quantities. In electronics, engineering notation is used to express values of voltage, current, power, resistance, and other quantities.

After completing this section, you should be able to

◆ **Use scientific notation to represent quantities**

   ◆ Express any number using a power of ten

   ◆ Do calculations with powers of ten

Scientific notation* provides a convenient method for expressing large and small numbers and for performing calculations involving such numbers. In scientific notation, a quantity is expressed as a product of a number between 1 and 10 (one digit to the left of the decimal point) and a power of ten. For example, the quantity 150,000 is expressed in scientific notation as 1.5×10^5, and the quantity 0.00022 is expressed as 2.2×10^{-4}.

Powers of Ten

Table 1–1 lists some powers of ten, both positive and negative, and the corresponding decimal numbers. The **power of ten** is expressed as an *exponent* of the *base* 10 in each case.

$$\underset{10^x}{\overset{\text{Base} \diagdown \quad \diagup \text{Exponent}}{}}$$

An **exponent** is a number to which a base number is raised. It exponent indicates the number of places that the decimal point is moved to the right or left to produce the decimal number. For a positive power of ten, move the decimal point to the right to get the equivalent decimal number. As an example, for an exponent of 4,

$$10^4 = 1 \times 10^4 = 1.0000. = 10{,}000.$$

▼ TABLE 1–1

Some positive and negative powers of ten.

$10^6 = 1{,}000{,}000$	$10^{-6} = 0.000001$
$10^5 = 100{,}000$	$10^{-5} = 0.00001$
$10^4 = 10{,}000$	$10^{-4} = 0.0001$
$10^3 = 1{,}000$	$10^{-3} = 0.001$
$10^2 = 100$	$10^{-2} = 0.01$
$10^1 = 10$	$10^{-1} = 0.1$
$10^0 = 1$	

***All bold terms are in the end-of-book glossary. The bold terms in color are key terms and are also defined at the end of the chapter.**

For a negative power of ten, move the decimal point to the left to get the equivalent decimal number. As an example, for an exponent of -4,

$$10^{-4} = 1 \times 10^{-4} = .0001. = 0.0001$$

The negative exponent does not make a number negative; it simply moves the decimal point to the left.

EXAMPLE 1–1

Express each number in scientific notation:

(a) 200   **(b)** 5000   **(c)** 85,000   **(d)** 3,000,000

Solution   In each case, move the decimal point an appropriate number of places to the left to determine the positive power of ten.

(a) $200 = 2 \times 10^2$ **(b)** $5000 = 5 \times 10^3$

(c) $85,000 = 8.5 \times 10^4$ **(d)** $3,000,000 = 3 \times 10^6$

*Related Problem**   Express 750,000,000 in scientific notation.

*Answers are at the end of the chapter.

EXAMPLE 1–2

Express each number in scientific notation:

(a) 0.2   **(b)** 0.005   **(c)** 0.00063   **(d)** 0.000015

Solution   In each case, move the decimal point an appropriate number of places to the right to determine the negative power of ten.

(a) $0.2 = 2 \times 10^{-1}$ **(b)** $0.005 = 5 \times 10^{-3}$

(c) $0.00063 = 6.3 \times 10^{-4}$ **(d)** $0.000015 = 1.5 \times 10^{-5}$

Related Problem   Express 0.00000093 in scientific notation.

EXAMPLE 1–3

Express each of the following numbers as a normal decimal number:

(a) 1×10^5 **(b)** 2×10^3 **(c)** 3.2×10^{-2} **(d)** 2.5×10^{-6}

Solution   Move the decimal point to the right or left a number of places indicated by the positive or the negative power of ten respectively.

(a) $1 \times 10^5 = 100,000$ **(b)** $2 \times 10^3 = 2000$

(c) $3.2 \times 10^{-2} = 0.032$ **(d)** $2.5 \times 10^{-6} = 0.0000025$

Related Problem   Express 8.2×10^8 as a normal decimal number.

Calculations Using Powers of Ten

The advantage of scientific notation is in addition, subtraction, multiplication, and division of very small or very large numbers.

Addition The steps for adding numbers in powers of ten are as follows:

1. Express the numbers to be added in the same power of ten.

2. Add the numbers without their powers of ten to get the sum.

3. Bring down the common power of ten, which is the power of ten of the sum.

EXAMPLE 1–4

Add 2×10^6 and 5×10^7 and express the result in scientific notation.

Solution
1. Express both numbers in the same power of ten: $(2 \times 10^6) + (50 \times 10^6)$

2. Add $2 + 50 = 52$.

3. Bring down the common power of ten (10^6); the sum is $52 \times 10^6 = \mathbf{5.2 \times 10^7}$.

Related Problem Add 4.1×10^3 and 7.9×10^2.

Subtraction The steps for subtracting numbers in powers of ten are as follows:

1. Express the numbers to be subtracted in the same power of ten.

2. Subtract the numbers without their powers of ten to get the difference.

3. Bring down the common power of ten, which is the power of ten of the difference.

EXAMPLE 1–5

Subtract 2.5×10^{-12} from 7.5×10^{-11} and express the result in scientific notation.

Solution
1. Express each number in the same power of ten: $(7.5 \times 10^{-11}) - (0.25 \times 10^{-11})$

2. Subtract $7.5 - 0.25 = 7.25$.

3. Bring down the common power of ten (10^{-11}); the difference is $\mathbf{7.25 \times 10^{-11}}$.

Related Problem Subtract 3.5×10^{-6} from 2.2×10^{-5}.

Multiplication The steps for multiplying numbers in powers of ten are as follows:

1. Multiply the numbers directly without their powers of ten.

2. Add the powers of ten algebraically (the exponents do not have to be the same).

EXAMPLE 1–6

Multiply 5×10^{12} by 3×10^{-6} and express the result in scientific notation.

Solution Multiply the numbers, and algebraically add the powers.

$$(5 \times 10^{12})(3 \times 10^{-6}) = 15 \times 10^{12+(-6)} = 15 \times 10^6 = \mathbf{1.5 \times 10^7}$$

Related Problem Multiply 1.2×10^3 by 4×10^2.

Division   The steps for dividing numbers in powers of ten are as follows:

1. Divide the numbers directly without their powers of ten.

2. Subtract the power of ten in the denominator from the power of ten in the numerator (the exponents do not have to be the same).

EXAMPLE 1–7

Divide 5.0×10^8 by 2.5×10^3 and express the result in scientific notation.

Solution   Write the division problem with a numerator and denominator.

$$\frac{5.0 \times 10^8}{2.5 \times 10^3}$$

Divide the numbers and subtract the powers of ten (3 from 8).

$$\frac{5.0 \times 10^8}{2.5 \times 10^3} = 2 \times 10^{8-3} = \mathbf{2 \times 10^5}$$

Related Problem   Divide 8×10^{-6} by 2×10^{-10}.

Scientific Notation on a Calculator   Entering a number in scientific notation is accomplished on most calculators using the EE key as follows: Enter the number with one digit to the left of the decimal point, press EE, and enter the power of ten. This method requires that the power of ten be determined before entering the number. Some calculators can be placed in a mode that will automatically convert any decimal number entered into scientific notation.

EXAMPLE 1–8

Enter 23,560 in scientific notation using the EE key.

Solution   Move the decimal point four places to the left so that it comes after the digit 2. This results in the number expressed in scientific notation as

$$2.3560 \times 10^4$$

Enter this number on your calculator as follows:

Related Problem   Enter the number 573,946 using the EE key.

Engineering Notation

Engineering notation is similar to scientific notation. However, in **engineering notation** a number can have from one to three digits to the left of the decimal point and the power-of-ten exponent must be a multiple of three. For example, the number 33,000 expressed in engineering notation is 33×10^3. In scientific notation, it is expressed as 3.3×10^4. As another example, the number 0.045 is expressed in engineering notation as 45×10^{-3}. In scientific notation, it is expressed as 4.5×10^{-2}.

EXAMPLE 1–9

Express the following numbers in engineering notation:

(a) 82,000   (b) 243,000   (c) 1,956,000

Solution   In engineering notation,

(a) 82,000 is expressed as 82×10^3.

(b) 243,000 is expressed as 243×10^3.

(c) 1,956,000 is expressed as 1.956×10^6.

Related Problem   Express 36,000,000,000 in engineering notation.

EXAMPLE 1–10

Convert each of the following numbers to engineering notation:

(a) 0.0022   (b) 0.000000047   (c) 0.00033

Solution   In engineering notation,

(a) 0.0022 is expressed as 2.2×10^{-3}.

(b) 0.000000047 is expressed as 47×10^{-9}.

(c) 0.00033 is expressed as 330×10^{-6}.

Related Problem   Express 0.0000000000056 in engineering notation.

Engineering Notation on a Calculator   Use the EE key to enter the number with one, two, or three digits to the left of the decimal point, press EE, and enter the power of ten that is a multiple of three. This method requires that the appropriate power of ten be determined before entering the number.

EXAMPLE 1–11

Enter 51,200,000 in engineering notation using the EE key.

Solution   Move the decimal point six places to the left so that it comes after the digit 1. This results in the number expressed in engineering notation as

$$51.2 \times 10^6$$

Enter this number on your calculator as follows:

Related Problem   Enter the number 273,900 in engineering notation using the EE key.

SECTION 1–1
REVIEW
Answers are at the end of the chapter.

1. Scientific notation uses powers of ten. (True or False)
2. Express 100 as a power of ten.
3. Express the following numbers in scientific notation:
   (a) 4350   **(b)** 12,010   **(c)** 29,000,000
4. Express the following numbers in scientific notation:
   (a) 0.760   **(b)** 0.00025   **(c)** 0.000000597
5. Do the following operations:
   (a) $(1 \times 10^5) + (2 \times 10^5)$ **(b)** $(3 \times 10^6)(2 \times 10^4)$
   (c) $(8 \times 10^3) \div (4 \times 10^2)$ **(d)** $(2.5 \times 10^{-6}) - (1.3 \times 10^{-7})$
6. Enter the numbers expressed in scientific notation in Problem 3 into your calculator.
7. Express the following numbers in engineering notation:
   (a) 0.0056   **(b)** 0.0000000283   **(c)** 950,000   **(d)** 375,000,000,000
8. Enter the numbers in Problem 7 into your calculator using engineering notation.

1–2   UNITS AND METRIC PREFIXES

In electronics, you must deal with measurable quantities. For example, you must be able to express how many volts are measured at a certain test point in a circuit, how much current there is through a conductor, or how much power a certain amplifier delivers. In this section, you are introduced to the units and symbols for most of the electrical quantities that are used throughout the book. Metric prefixes are used in conjunction with engineering notation as a "shorthand" for the certain powers of ten that commonly are used.

After completing this section, you should be able to

- ◆ **Work with electrical units and metric prefixes**

   - ◆ Name the units for twelve electrical quantities

   - ◆ Specify the symbols for the electrical units

   - ◆ List the metric prefixes

   - ◆ Change a power of ten in engineering notation to a metric prefix

   - ◆ Use metric prefixes to express electrical quantities

   - ◆ Convert one metric prefix to another

Electrical Units

Letter symbols are used in electronics to represent both quantities and their units. One symbol is used to represent the name of the quantity, and another is used to represent the unit of measurement of that quantity. For example, *P* stands for *power,* and W stands for *watt,* which is the unit of power. Table 1–2 lists the most important electrical quantities, along with their SI units and symbols. These will be used throughout the text. The term **SI** is the French abbreviation for *International System* (*Système International* in French).

▶ TABLE 1–2

Electrical quantities and their corresponding units with SI symbols.

QUANTITY	SYMBOL	SI UNIT	SYMBOL
capacitance	C	farad	F
charge	Q	coulomb	C
conductance	G	siemens	S
current	I	ampere	A
energy	W	joule	J
frequency	f	hertz	Hz
impedance	Z	ohm	Ω
inductance	L	henry	H
power	P	watt	W
reactance	X	ohm	Ω
resistance	R	ohm	Ω
voltage	V	volt	V

Metric Prefixes

In engineering notation **metric prefixes** represent each of the most commonly used powers of ten. These metric prefixes are listed in Table 1–3 with their symbols and corresponding powers of ten.

▶ TABLE 1–3

Metric prefixes with their symbols and corresponding powers of ten and values.

METRIC PREFIX	SYMBOL	POWER OF TEN	VALUE
Femto	f	10^{-15}	one-quadrillionth
pico	p	10^{-12}	one-trillionth
nano	n	10^{-9}	one-billionth
micro	μ	10^{-6}	one-millionth
milli	m	10^{-3}	one-thousandth
kilo	k	10^{3}	one thousand
mega	M	10^{6}	one million
giga	G	10^{9}	one billion
tera	T	10^{12}	one trillion

Metric prefixes are used only with numbers that have a unit of measure, such as volts, amperes, and ohms, and precede the unit symbol. For example, 0.025 amperes can be expressed in engineering notation as 25×10^{-3} A. This quantity expressed using a metric prefix is 25 mA, which is read 25 milliamps. The metric prefix *milli* has replaced 10^{-3}. As another example, 100,000,000 ohms can be expressed as 100×10^{6} Ω. This quantity expressed using a metric prefix is 100 MΩ, which is read 100 megohms. The metric prefix *mega* has replaced 10^{6}.

EXAMPLE 1–12

Express each quantity using a metric prefix:

(a) 50,000 V   **(b)** 25,000,000 Ω   **(c)** 0.000036 A

Solution   **(a)** 50,000 V = 50×10^{3} V = **50 kV**   **(b)** 25,000,000 Ω = 25×10^{6} Ω = **25 MΩ**

(c) 0.000036 A = 36×10^{-6} A = **36 μA**

Related Problem   Express each quantity using metric prefixes:

(a) 56,000,000 Ω   **(b)** 0.000470 A

SECTION 1–2
REVIEW

1. List the metric prefix for each of the following powers of ten: 10^6, 10^3, 10^{-3}, 10^{-6}, 10^{-9}, and 10^{-12}

2. Use an appropriate metric prefix to express 0.000001 A.

3. Use an appropriate metric prefix to express 250,000 W.

1–3 METRIC UNIT CONVERSIONS

It is sometimes necessary or convenient to convert a quantity from one unit with a metric prefix to another, such as from milliamperes (mA) to microamperes (μA). Moving the decimal point in the number an appropriate number of places to the left or to the right, depending on the particular conversion, results in a metric unit conversion.

After completing this section, you should be able to

◆ **Convert from one unit with a metric prefix to another**

  ◆ Convert between milli, micro, nano, and pico

  ◆ Convert between kilo and mega

The following basic rules apply to metric unit conversions:

1. When converting from a larger unit to a smaller unit, move the decimal point to the right.

2. When converting from a smaller unit to a larger unit, move the decimal point to the left.

3. Determine the number of places to move the decimal point by finding the difference in the powers of ten of the units being converted.

For example, when converting from milliamperes (mA) to microamperes (μA), move the decimal point three places to the right because there is a three-place difference between the two units (mA is 10^{-3} A and μA is 10^{-6} A). The following examples illustrate a few conversions.

EXAMPLE 1–13

Convert 0.15 milliampere (0.15 mA) to microamperes (μA).

Solution   Move the decimal point three places to the right.

$$0.15\,\text{mA} = 0.15 \times 10^{-3}\,\text{A} = 150 \times 10^{-6}\,\text{A} = \mathbf{150\ \mu A}$$

Related Problem   Convert 1 mA to microamperes.

EXAMPLE 1–14

Convert 4500 microvolts (4500 μV) to millivolts (mV).

Solution   Move the decimal point three places to the left.

$$4500\,\mu\text{V} = 4500 \times 10^{-6}\,\text{V} = 4.5 \times 10^{-3}\,\text{V} = \mathbf{4.5\,mV}$$

Related Problem   Convert 1000 μV to millivolts.

EXAMPLE 1–15

Convert 5000 nanoamperes (5000 nA) to microamperes (μA).

Solution   Move the decimal point three places to the left.

$$5000\,\text{nA} = 5000 \times 10^{-9}\,\text{A} = 5 \times 10^{-6}\,\text{A} = \textbf{5}\,\boldsymbol{\mu}\textbf{A}$$

Related Problem   Convert 893 nA to microamperes.

EXAMPLE 1–16

Convert 47,000 picofarads (47,000 pF) to microfarads (μF).

Solution   Move the decimal point six places to the left.

$$47,000\,\text{pF} = 47,000 \times 10^{-12}\,\text{F} = 0.047 \times 10^{-6}\,\text{F} = \textbf{0.047}\,\boldsymbol{\mu}\textbf{F}$$

Related Problem   Convert 10,000 pF to microfarads.

EXAMPLE 1–17

Convert 0.00022 microfarad (0.00022 μF) to picofarads (pF).

Solution   Move the decimal point six places to the right.

$$0.00022\,\mu\text{F} = 0.00022 \times 10^{-6}\,\text{F} = 220 \times 10^{-12}\,\text{F} = \textbf{220 pF}$$

Related Problem   Convert 0.0022 μF to picofarads.

EXAMPLE 1–18

Convert 1800 kilohms (1800 kΩ) to megohms (MΩ).

Solution   Move the decimal point three places to the left.

$$1800\,\text{k}\Omega = 1800 \times 10^{3}\,\Omega = 1.8 \times 10^{6}\,\Omega = \textbf{1.8 M}\boldsymbol{\Omega}$$

Related Problem   Convert 2.2 kΩ to megohms.

When adding (or subtracting) quantities with different metric prefixes, first convert one of the quantities to the same prefix as the other quantity.

EXAMPLE 1–19

Add 15 mA and 8000 μA and express the result in milliamperes.

Solution   Convert 8000 μA to 8 mA and add.

$$15\,\text{mA} + 8000\,\mu\text{A} = 15\,\text{mA} + 8\,\text{mA} = \textbf{23 mA}$$

Related Problem   Add 2873 mA to 10,000 μA.

SECTION 1–3 REVIEW	1. Convert 0.01 MV to kilovolts (kV).
	2. Convert 250,000 pA to milliamperes (mA).
	3. Add 0.05 MW and 75 kW and express the result in kW.
	4. Add 50 mV and 25,000 μV and express the result in mV.

1–4 MEASURED NUMBERS

Whenever a quantity is measured, there is uncertainty in the result due to limitations of the instruments used. When a measured quantity contains approximate numbers, the digits known to be correct are called significant digits. When reporting measured quantities, the number of digits that should be retained are the significant digits and no more than one uncertain digit.

After completing this section, you should be able to

◆ **Express measured data with the proper number of significant digits**

   ◆ Define *accuracy, error,* and *precision*

   ◆ Round numbers properly

Error, Accuracy, and Precision

Data taken in experiments are not perfect because the accuracy of the data depends on the accuracy of the test equipment and the conditions under which the measurement was made. In order to properly report measured data, the error associated with the measurement should be taken into account. Experimental error should not be thought of as a mistake. All measurements that do not involve counting are approximations of the true value. The difference between the true or best-accepted value of some quantity and the measured value is the **error**. A measurement is said to be accurate if the error is small. **Accuracy** refers to the difference between the measured and accepted or "true" value. For example, if you measure thickness of a 10.00 mm gauge block with a micrometer and find that it is 10.8 mm, the reading is not accurate because a gauge block is considered to be a working standard. If you measure 10.02 mm, the reading is accurate because it is in reasonable agreement with the standard.

Another term associated with the quality of a measurement is *precision.* **Precision** is a measure of the repeatability (or consistency) of a measurement of some quantity. It is possible to have a precise measurement in which a series of readings are not scattered, but each measurement is inaccurate because of an instrument error. For example, a meter may be out of calibration and produce inaccurate but consistent (precise) results. However, it is not possible to have an accurate instrument unless it is also precise.

Significant Digits

The digits in a measured number that are known to be correct are called **significant digits**. Most measuring instruments show the proper number of significant digits, but some instruments can show digits that are not significant, leaving it to the user to determine what should be reported. This may occur because of an effect called *loading* (discussed in Section 6–4). A meter can change the actual reading in a circuit by its very presence. It is important to recognize when a reading may be inaccurate; you should not report digits that are known to be inaccurate.

Another problem with significant digits occurs when you perform mathematical operations with numbers. The number of significant digits should never exceed the number in the original measurement. For example, if 1.0 V is divided by 3.0 Ω, a calculator will show 0.33333333. Since the original numbers each contain 2 significant digits, the answer should be reported as 0.33 A, the same number of significant digits.

The rules for determining if a reported digit is significant are

1. Nonzero digits are always considered to be significant.

2. Zeros to the left of the first nonzero digit are never significant.

3. Zeros between nonzero digits are always significant.

4. Zeros to the right of the decimal point for a decimal number are significant.

5. Zeros to the left of the decimal point with a whole number may or may not be significant depending on the measurement. For example, the number 12,100 Ω has 3, 4, or 5 significant figures. To clarify the significant digits, scientific notation (or a metric prefix) should be used. For example, 12.10 kΩ has 4 significant figures.

When a measured value is reported, one uncertain digit may be retained but other uncertain digits should be discarded. To find the number of significant digits in a number, ignore the decimal point, and count the number of digits from left to right starting with the first nonzero digit and ending with the last digit to the right. All of the digits counted are significant except zeros to the right end of the number, which may or may not be significant. In the absence of other information, the significance of the right-hand zeros is uncertain. Generally, zeros that are placeholders, and not part of a measurement, are considered to be not significant. To avoid confusion, numbers should be shown using scientific or engineering notation if it is necessary to show the significant zeros.

EXAMPLE 1–20

Express the measured number 4300 with 2, 3, and 4 significant digits.

Solution Zeros to the right of the decimal point in a decimal number are significant. Therefore, to show two significant digits, write

$$4.3 \times 10^3$$

To show three significant digits, write

$$4.30 \times 10^3$$

To show four significant digits, write

$$4.300 \times 10^3$$

Related Problem How would you show the number 10,000 showing three significant digits?

EXAMPLE 1–21

Underline the significant digits in each of the following measurements:

(a) 40.0   (b) 0.3040   (c) 1.20×10^5 (d) 120,000   (e) 0.00502

Solution (a) 40.0 has three significant digits; see rule 4.

(b) 0.3040 has four significant digits; see rules 2 and 3.

(c) 1.20×10^5 has three significant digits; see rule 4.

(d) 120,000 has at least two significant digits. Although the number has the same value as in (c), zeros in this example are uncertain; see rule 5. This is *not* a recommended method for reporting a measured quantity; use scientific notation or a metric prefix in this case. See Example 1–20.

(e) 0.00<u>502</u> has three significant digits; see rules 2 and 3.

Related Problem   What is the difference between a measured quantity of 10 and 10.0?

Rounding Off Numbers

Since they always contain approximate numbers, measurements should be shown only with those digits that are significant plus no more than one uncertain digit. The number of digits shown is indicative of the precision of the measurement. For this reason, you should **round off** a number by dropping one or more digits to the right of the last significant digit. Use only the most significant dropped digit to decide how to round off. The rules for rounding off are

1. If the most significant digit dropped is greater than 5 or a 5 is followed by any nonzero digits, increase the last retained digit by 1.

2. If the most significant digit dropped is less than 5, do not change the last retained digit.

3. If the most significant digit dropped is 5 and there are no following nonzero digits, increase the last retained digit by 1 if it makes the number even. If it makes the number odd, do not change the retained digit. This is called the "round-to-even" rule.

EXAMPLE 1–22   Round each of the following numbers to three significant digits:

(a) 10.071   **(b)** 29.961   **(c)** 6.3948   **(d)** 123.5   **(e)** 122.5   **(f)** 328.52

Solution   **(a)** 10.071 rounds to **10.1.**   **(b)** 29.961 rounds to **30.0.**

(c) 6.3948 rounds to **6.39.**   **(d)** 123.5 rounds to **124.**

(e) 122.5 rounds to **122.**   **(f)** 328.52 rounds to **329.**

Related Problem   Why is the round-to-even rule used?

In most electronics work, components have tolerances greater than 1% (5% and 10% are common). Most measuring instruments have accuracy specifications better than this, but it is unusual for measurements to be made with higher accuracy than 1 part in 1000. For this reason, three significant digits are appropriate for numbers that represent measured quantities in all but the most exacting work. If you are working with a problem with several intermediate results, keep all digits in your calculator, but round the answers to three when reporting a result.

SECTION 1–4 REVIEW

1. What is the rule for showing zeros to the right of the decimal point?
2. What is the round-to-even rule?
3. On schematics, you will frequently see a 1000 Ω resistor listed as 1.0 kΩ. What does this imply about the value of the resistor?
4. If a power supply is required to be set to 10.00 V, what does this imply about the accuracy needed for the measuring instrument?
5. How can scientific or engineering notation be used to show the correct number of significant digits in a measurement?

1–5   ELECTRICAL SAFETY

Safety is a major concern when working with electricity. The possibility of an electric shock or a burn is always present, so caution should always be used. You provide a current path when voltage is applied across two points on your body, and current produces electrical shock. Electrical components often operate at high temperatures, so you can sustain skin burns when you come in contact with them. Also, the presence of electricity creates a potential fire hazard.

After completing this section, you should be able to

◆ **Recognize electrical hazards and practice proper safety procedures**

   ◆ Describe the cause of electrical shock

   ◆ List the groups of current paths through the body

   ◆ Discuss the effects of current on the human body

   ◆ List the safety precautions that you should observe when you work with electricity

Electrical Shock

Current through your body, not the voltage, is the cause of **electrical shock**. Of course, it takes voltage across a resistance to produce current. When a point on your body comes in contact with a voltage and another point comes in contact with a different voltage or with ground, such as a metal chassis, there will be current through your body from one point to the other. The path of the current depends on the points across which the voltage occurs. The severity of the resulting electrical shock depends on the amount of voltage and the path that the current takes through your body.

The current path through the body determines which tissues and organs will be affected. The current paths can be placed into three groups which are referred to as *touch potential, step potential,* and *touch/step potential.* These are illustrated in Figure 1–1.

▶ FIGURE 1–1

Shock hazard in terms of three basic current path groups.

Touch potential   Step potential   Touch/Step potential

Effects of Current on the Human Body   The amount of current is dependent on voltage and resistance. The human body has resistance that depends on many factors, which include body mass, skin moisture, and points of contact of the body with a voltage potential. Table 2–5 shows the effects for various values of current in milliamperes.

Body Resistance   Resistance of the human body is typically between $10\,k\Omega$ and $50\,k\Omega$ and depends on the two points between which it is measured. The moisture of the skin also affects the resistance between two points. The resistance determines the amount of voltage required to produce each of the effects listed in Table 1–4. For example, if you have a resistance of $10\,k\Omega$ between two given points on your body, 90 V across those two points will produce enough current (9 mA) to cause painful shock.

CURRENT (mA)	PHYSICAL EFFECT
0.4	Slight sensation
1.1	Perception threshold
1.8	Shock, no pain, no loss of muscular control
9	Painful shock, no loss of muscular control
16	Painful shock, let-go threshold
23	Severe painful shock, muscular contractions, breathing difficulty
75	Ventricular fibrillation, threshold
235	Ventricular fibrillation, usually fatal for duration of 5 seconds or more
4,000	Heart paralysis (no ventricular fibrillation)
5,000	Tissue burn

◀ TABLE 1–4

Physical effects of electrical current. Values vary depending on body mass.

Safety Precautions

There are many practical things that you should do when you work with electrical and electronic equipment. Some important precautions are listed here.

- ◆ Avoid contact with any voltage source. Turn power off before you work on circuits when you need to touch circuit parts.

- ◆ Do not work alone. A telephone should be available for emergencies.

- ◆ Do not work when tired or taking medications that make you drowsy.

- ◆ Remove rings, watches, and other metallic jewelry when you work on circuits.

- ◆ Do not work on equipment until you know proper procedures and are aware of potential hazards.

- ◆ Use equipment with three-wire power cords (three-prong plug).

- ◆ Make sure power cords are in good condition and grounding pins are not missing or bent.

- ◆ Keep your tools properly maintained. Make sure the insulation on metal tool handles is in good condition.

- ◆ Handle tools properly and maintain a neat work area.

- ◆ Wear safety glasses when appropriate, particularly when soldering and clipping wires.

- ◆ Always shut off power and discharge capacitors before you touch any part of a circuit with your hands.

- ◆ Know the location of the emergency power-off switch and emergency exits.

- ◆ Never try to override or tamper with safety devices such as an interlock switch.

- ◆ Always wear shoes and keep them dry. Do not stand on metal or wet floors.

- ◆ Never handle instruments when your hands are wet.

- ◆ Never assume that a circuit is off. Double-check it with a reliable meter before handling.

◆ Set the limiter on electronic power supplies to prevent currents larger than necessary to supply the circuit under test.

◆ Some devices such as capacitors can store a lethal charge for long periods after power is removed. They must be properly discharged before you work with them.

◆ When making circuit connections, always make the connection to the point with the highest voltage as your last step.

◆ Avoid contact with the terminals of power supplies.

◆ Always use wires with insulation and connectors or clips with insulating shrouds.

◆ Keep cables and wires as short as possible. Connect polarized components properly.

◆ Report any unsafe condition.

◆ Be aware of and follow all workplace and laboratory rules. Do not have drinks or food near equipment.

◆ If another person cannot let go of an energized conductor, switch the power off immediately. If that is not possible, use any available nonconductive material to try to separate the body from the contact.

SECTION 1–5 REVIEW

1. What causes physical pain and/or damage to the body when electrical contact is made?
2. It's OK to wear a ring when working on an electrical circuit.   (T or F)
3. Standing on a wet floor presents no safety hazard when working with electricity.   (T or F)
4. A circuit can be rewired without removing the power if you are careful.   (T or F)
5. Electrical shock can be extremely painful or even fatal.   (T or F)

SUMMARY

◆ Scientific notation is a method for expressing very large and very small numbers as a number between one and ten (one digit to left of decimal point) times a power of ten.

◆ Engineering notation is a form of scientific notation in which quantities are expressed with one, two, or three digits to the left of the decimal point times a power of ten that is a multiple of three.

◆ Metric prefixes are symbols used to represent powers of ten that are multiples of three.

◆ The uncertainty of a measured quantity depends on the accuracy and precision of the measurement.

◆ The number of significant digits in the result of a mathematical operation should never exceed the significant digits in the original numbers.

KEY TERMS

These key terms are also defined in the end-of-book glossary.

Accuracy   The difference between the measured and accepted or "true" value of a measurement.

Electrical shock   The physical sensation resulting from current through the body.

Engineering notation   A system for representing any number as a one-, two-, or three-digit number times a power of ten with an exponent that is a multiple of 3.

Exponent   The number to which a base number is raised.

Metric prefix   A symbol that is used to replace the power of ten in numbers expressed in engineering notation.

Power of ten   A numerical representation consisting of a base of 10 and an exponent; the number 10 raised to a power.

Precision   A measure of the repeatability (or consistency) of a series of measurements.

Round off   The process of dropping one or more digits to the right of the last significant digit in a number.

Scientific notation   A system for representing any number as a number between 1 and 10 times an appropriate power of ten.

SI   Standardized international system of units used for all engineering and scientific work; abbreviation for French *Le Systeme International d'Unites.*

Significant digit   A digit known to be correct in a number.

SELF-TEST

Answers are at the end of the chapter.

1. The quantity 4.7×10^3 is the same as
   (a) 470   (b) 4700   (c) 47,000   (d) 0.0047

2. The quantity 56×10^{-3} is the same as
   (a) 0.056   (b) 0.560   (c) 560   (d) 56,000

3. The number 3,300,000 can be expressed in engineering notation as
   (a) 3300×10^3 (b) 3.3×10^{-6} (c) 3.3×10^6 (d) either (a) or (c)

4. Ten milliamperes can be expressed as
   (a) 10 MA   (b) $10\,\mu$A   (c) 10 kA   (d) 10 mA

5. Five thousand volts can be expressed as
   (a) 5000 V   (b) 5 MV   (c) 5 kV   (d) either (a) or (c)

6. Twenty million ohms can be expressed as
   (a) $20\,m\Omega$ (b) 20 MW   (c) $20\,M\Omega$ (d) $20\,\mu\Omega$

7. 15,000 W is the same as
   (a) 15 mW   (b) 15 kW   (c) 15 MW   (d) $15\,\mu$W

8. Which of the following is not an electrical quantity?
   (a) current   (b) voltage   (c) time   (d) power

9. The unit of current is
   (a) volt   (b) watt   (c) ampere   (d) joule

10. The unit of voltage is
    (a) ohm   (b) watt   (c) volt   (d) farad

11. The unit of resistance is
    (a) ampere   (b) henry   (c) hertz   (d) ohm

12. Hertz is the unit of
    (a) power   (b) inductance   (c) frequency   (d) time

13. How many significant digits are in the number 0.1050
    (a) two   (b) three   (c) four   (d) five

PROBLEMS

Answers to odd-numbered problems are at the end of the book.

BASIC PROBLEMS

SECTION 1–1   **Scientific and Engineering Notation**

1. Express each of the following numbers in scientific notation:
   (a) 3000   (b) 75,000   (c) 2,000,000

2. Express each fractional number in scientific notation:
   (a) 1/500   (b) 1/2000   (c) 1/5,000,000

3. Express each of the following numbers in scientific notation:
   (a) 8400   (b) 99,000   (c) 0.2×10^6

4. Express each of the following numbers in scientific notation:

   (a) 0.0002   (b) 0.6   (c) 7.8×10^{-2}

5. Express each of the following as a regular decimal number:

   (a) 2.5×10^{-6} (b) 5.0×10^{2} (c) 3.9×10^{-1}

6. Express each number in regular decimal form:

   (a) 4.5×10^{-6} (b) 8×10^{-9} (c) 4.0×10^{-12}

7. Add the following numbers:

   (a) $(9.2 \times 10^{6}) + (3.4 \times 10^{7})$ (b) $(5 \times 10^{3}) + (8.5 \times 10^{-1})$

   (c) $(5.6 \times 10^{-8}) + (4.6 \times 10^{-9})$

8. Perform the following subtractions:

   (a) $(3.2 \times 10^{12}) - (1.1 \times 10^{12})$ (b) $(2.6 \times 10^{8}) - (1.3 \times 10^{7})$

   (c) $(1.5 \times 10^{-12}) - (8 \times 10^{-13})$

9. Perform the following multiplications:

   (a) $(5 \times 10^{3})(4 \times 10^{5})$ (b) $(1.2 \times 10^{12})(3 \times 10^{2})$ (c) $(2.2 \times 10^{-9})(7 \times 10^{-6})$

10. Divide the following:

    (a) $(1.0 \times 10^{3}) \div (2.5 \times 10^{2})$ (b) $(2.5 \times 10^{-6}) \div (5.0 \times 10^{-8})$

    (c) $(4.2 \times 10^{8}) \div (2 \times 10^{-5})$

11. Express each of the following numbers in engineering notation:

    (a) 89,000   (b) 450,000   (c) 12,040,000,000,000

12. Express each number in engineering notation:

    (a) 2.35×10^{5} (b) 7.32×10^{7} (c) 1.333×10^{9}

13. Express each number in engineering notation:

    (a) 0.000345   (b) 0.025   (c) 0.00000000129

14. Express each number in engineering notation:

    (a) 9.81×10^{-3} (b) 4.82×10^{-4} (c) 4.38×10^{-7}

15. Add the following numbers and express each result in engineering notation:

    (a) $2.5 \times 10^{-3} + 4.6 \times 10^{-3}$ (b) $68 \times 10^{6} + 33 \times 10^{6}$

    (c) $1.25 \times 10^{6} + 250 \times 10^{3}$

16. Multiply the following numbers and express each result in engineering notation:

    (a) $(32 \times 10^{-3})(56 \times 10^{3})$ (b) $(1.2 \times 10^{-6})(1.2 \times 10^{-6})$ (c) $100(55 \times 10^{-3})$

17. Divide the following numbers and express each result in engineering notation:

    (a) $50 \div (2.2 \times 10^{3})$ (b) $(5 \times 10^{3}) \div (25 \times 10^{-6})$ (c) $560 \times 10^{3} \div (660 \times 10^{3})$

SECTION 1–2   **Units and Metric Prefixes**

18. Express each number in Problem 11 in ohms using a metric prefix.

19. Express each number in Problem 13 in amperes using a metric prefix.

20. Express each of the following as a quantity having a metric prefix:

    (a) 31×10^{-3} A   (b) 5.5×10^{3} V   (c) 20×10^{-12} F

21. Express the following using metric prefixes:

    (a) 3×10^{-6} F   (b) $3.3 \times 10^{6} \, \Omega$ (c) 350×10^{-9} A

22. Express each quantity with a power of ten:

    (a) $5 \, \mu$A   (b) 43 mV   (c) 275 kΩ (d) 10 MW

SECTION 1–3   **Metric Unit Conversions**

23. Perform the indicated conversions:

    (a) 5 mA to microamperes   (b) 3200 μW to milliwatts

    (c) 5000 kV to megavolts   (d) 10 MW to kilowatts

24. Determine the following:

    (a) The number of microamperes in 1 milliampere

    (b) The number of millivolts in 0.05 kilovolt

    (c) The number of megohms in 0.02 kilohm

    (d) The number of kilowatts in 155 milliwatts

25. Add the following quantities:

    (a) $50\,\text{mA} + 680\,\mu\text{A}$ **(b)** $120\,\text{k}\Omega + 2.2\,\text{M}\Omega$ **(c)** $0.02\,\mu\text{F} + 3300\,\text{pF}$

26. Do the following operations:

    (a) $10\,\text{k}\Omega \div (2.2\,\text{k}\Omega + 10\,\text{k}\Omega)$ **(b)** $250\,\text{mV} \div 50\,\mu\text{V}$ **(c)** $1\,\text{MW} \div 2\,\text{kW}$

SECTION 1–4   Measured Numbers

27. How many significant digits are in each of the following numbers?

    (a) 1.00×10^3 **(b)** 0.0057   **(c)** 1502.0

    (d) 0.000036   **(e)** 0.105   **(f)** 2.6×10^2

28. Round each of the following numbers to three significant digits. Use the "round-to-even" rule.

    (a) 50,505   **(b)** 220.45   **(c)** 4646   **(d)** 10.99   **(e)** 1.005

ANSWERS

SECTION REVIEWS

SECTION 1–1   Scientific and Engineering Notation

1. True

2. 10^2

3. **(a)** 4.35×10^3 **(b)** 1.201×10^4 **(c)** 2.9×10^7

4. **(a)** 7.6×10^{-1} **(b)** 2.5×10^{-4} **(c)** 5.97×10^{-7}

5. **(a)** 3×10^5 **(b)** 6×10^{10} **(c)** 2×10^1 **(d)** 2.37×10^{-6}

6. Enter the digits, press EE, and enter the power of ten.

7. **(a)** 5.6×10^{-3} **(b)** 28.3×10^{-9} **(c)** 950×10^3 **(d)** 375×10^9

8. Enter the digits, press EE, and enter the power of ten.

SECTION 1–2   Units and Metric Prefixes

1. Mega (M), kilo (k), milli (m), micro (μ), nano (n), and pico (p)

2. $1\,\mu\text{A}$ (one microampere)

3. 250 kW (250 kilowatts)

SECTION 1–3   Metric Unit Conversions

1. 0.01 MV = 10 kV

2. 250,000 pA = 0.00025 mA

3. 125 kW

4. 75 mV

SECTION 1–4   Measured Numbers

1. Zeros should be retained only if they are significant because if they are shown, they are considered significant.

2. If the digit dropped is 5, increase the last retained digit *if* it makes it even, otherwise do not.

3. A zero to the right of the decimal point implies that the resistor is accurate to the nearest $100\,\Omega$ (0.1 kΩ).

4. The instrument must be accurate to four significant digits.

5. Scientific and engineering notation can show any number of digits to the right of a decimal. Numbers to the right of the decimal are always considered significant.

SECTION 1–5 Electrical Safety

1. Current
2. F
3. F
4. F
5. T

RELATED PROBLEMS FOR EXAMPLES

1–1 7.5×10^8

1–2 9.3×10^{-7}

1–3 820,000,000

1–4 4.89×10^3

1–5 1.85×10^{-5}

1–6 4.8×10^5

1–7 4×10^4

1–8 Enter 5.73946; press EE, enter 5.

1–9 36×10^9

1–10 5.6×10^{-12}

1–11 Enter 273.9, press EE, enter 3.

1–12 (a) $56 \, \text{M}\Omega$ (b) $470 \, \mu\text{A}$

1–13 $1000 \, \mu\text{A}$

1–14 $1 \, \text{mV}$

1–15 $0.893 \, \mu\text{A}$

1–16 $0.01 \, \mu\text{F}$

1–17 $2200 \, \text{pF}$

1–18 $0.0022 \, \text{M}\Omega$

1–19 $2883 \, \text{mA}$

1–20 10.0×10^3

1–21 The number 10 has two significant digits; the number 10.0 has three.

1–22 There are four numbers larger than 5 and four numbers smaller than 5 (not counting zero). Ideally, 5 should be retained half the time to avoid weighting rounded numbers too high or too low; hence the round-to-even rule.

SELF-TEST

1. (b)   **2.** (a)   **3.** (c)   **4.** (d)   **5.** (d)   **6.** (c)   **7.** (b)

8. (c)   **9.** (c)   **10.** (c)   **11.** (d)   **12.** (c)   **13.** (c)

VOLTAGE, CURRENT, AND RESISTANCE

2

CHAPTER OUTLINE

CHAPTER OBJECTIVES

◆ Describe the basic structure of an atom

◆ Explain the concept of electrical charge

◆ Define *voltage* and discuss its characteristics

◆ Define *current* and discuss its characteristics

◆ Define *resistance* and discuss its characteristics

◆ Describe a basic electric circuit

◆ Make basic circuit measurements

KEY TERMS

◆ Atom
◆ Electron
◆ Free electron
◆ Conductor
◆ Semiconductor
◆ Insulator
◆ Charge
◆ Coulomb (C)
◆ Voltage
◆ Volt (V)
◆ Voltage source
◆ Current
◆ Ampere (A)
◆ Current source
◆ Resistance
◆ Ohm (Ω)
◆ Conductance
◆ Siemens (S)

◆ Resistor
◆ Potentiometer
◆ Rheostat
◆ Circuit
◆ Load
◆ Schematic
◆ Closed circuit
◆ Open circuit
◆ Switch
◆ Fuse
◆ Circuit breaker
◆ AWG
◆ Ground
◆ Voltmeter
◆ Ammeter
◆ Ohmmeter
◆ DMM

APPLICATION ASSIGNMENT PREVIEW

Imagine that you are asked to connect and check out a circuit for use in the special lighting effects for an outdoor performance. The requirements are

1. There will be six lamps but only one lamp will be turned on at a time.

2. The sequence in which the lamps are turned on and off will vary.

3. It will be necessary to vary the brightness of each lamp.

4. The lamps must operate from a 12 V battery for portability, and the circuit must be protected by a fuse.

After studying this chapter, you should be able to complete the application assignment in the last section of the chapter.

VISIT THE COMPANION WEBSITE

Study aids for this chapter are available at
http://www.prenhall.com/floyd

INTRODUCTION

Three basic electrical quantities presented in this chapter are voltage, current, and resistance. No matter what type of electrical or electronic equipment you may work with, these quantities will always be of primary importance.

To help you understand voltage, current, and resistance, the basic structure of the atom is discussed and the concept of charge is introduced. The basic electric circuit is studied, along with techniques for measuring voltage, current, and resistance.

2–1 Atoms

All matter is made of atoms; and all atoms consist of electrons, protons, and neutrons. The configuration of certain electrons in an atom is the key factor in determining how well a conductive or semiconductive material conducts electric current.

After completing this section, you should be able to

◆ **Describe the basic structure of an atom**

    ◆ Define *nucleus, proton, neutron,* and *electron*

    ◆ Define *atomic number*

    ◆ Define *shell*

    ◆ Explain what a valence electron is

    ◆ Describe ionization

    ◆ Explain what a free electron is

    ◆ Define *conductor, semiconductor,* and *insulator*

An **atom** is the smallest particle of an **element** that retains the characteristics of that element. Each of the known 109 elements has atoms that are different from the atoms of all other elements. This gives each element a unique atomic structure. According to the classic Bohr model, an atom is visualized as having a planetary type of structure that consists of a central nucleus surrounded by orbiting electrons, as illustrated in Figure 2–1. The **nucleus** consists of positively charged particles called **protons** and uncharged particles called **neutrons.** The basic particles of negative charge are called **electrons**.

Each type of atom has a certain number of electrons and protons that distinguishes it from the atoms of all other elements. For example, the simplest atom is that of hydrogen, which has one proton and one electron, as pictured in Figure 2–2(a). As another example, the helium atom, shown in Figure 2–2(b), has two protons and two neutrons in the nucleus and two electrons orbiting the nucleus.

▶ FIGURE 2–1

The Bohr model of an atom showing electrons in circular orbits around the nucleus. The "tails" on the electrons indicate they are moving.

⊖ Electron   ⊕ Proton   ◯ Neutron

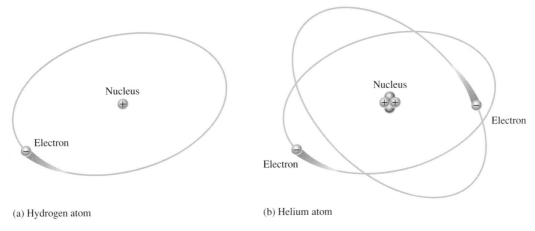

(a) Hydrogen atom   (b) Helium atom

▲ FIGURE 2–2

The two simplest atoms, hydrogen and helium.

Atomic Number

All elements are arranged in the periodic table of the elements in order according to their **atomic number.** The atomic number equals the number of protons in the nucleus. For example, hydrogen has an atomic number of 1 and helium has an atomic number of 2. In their normal (or neutral) state, all atoms of a given element have the same number of electrons as protons; the positive charges cancel the negative charges, and the atom has a net charge of zero, making it electrically balanced.

Electron Shells and Orbits

Electrons orbit the nucleus of an atom at certain distances from the nucleus. Electrons near the nucleus have less energy than those in more distant **orbits.** It is known that only discrete (separate and distinct) values of electron energies exist within atomic structures. Therefore, electrons must orbit only at discrete distances from the nucleus.

Energy Levels   Each discrete distance (orbit) from the nucleus corresponds to a certain energy level. In an atom, the orbits are grouped into energy bands known as **shells.** A given atom has a fixed number of shells. Each shell has a fixed maximum number of electrons at permissible energy levels (orbits). The shells are designated 1, 2, 3, and so on, with 1 being closest to the nucleus. This energy band concept is illustrated in Figure 2–3, which shows two energy levels. Additional shells may exist in other types of atoms, depending on the element.

     The number of electrons in each shell follows a predictable pattern according to the formula, $2N^2$, where N is the number of the shell. The first shell of any atom can have up to 2 electrons, the second shell up to 8 electrons, the third shell up to 18 electrons, and the fourth shell up to 32 electrons.

Valence Electrons

Electrons that are in orbits farther from the nucleus have higher energy and are less tightly bound to the atom than those closer to the nucleus. This is because the force of attraction between the positively charged nucleus and the negatively charged electron decreases with increasing distance from the nucleus. Electrons with the highest energy levels exist in the outermost shell of an atom and are relatively loosely bound to the atom. This outermost shell is known as the **valence** shell, and electrons in this shell are called **valence electrons.** These valence electrons contribute to chemical reactions and bonding within the structure of a material, and they determine a material's electrical properties.

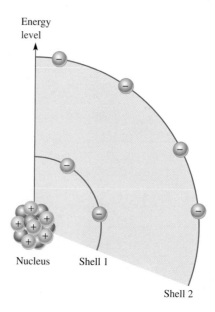

Energy levels increase as the distance from the nucleus increases.

Energy Levels and Ions

If an electron absorbs a photon with sufficient energy, it escapes from the atom and becomes a **free electron**. Any time an atom or group of atoms is left with a net charge, it is called an **ion**. When an electron escapes from the neutral hydrogen atom (designated H), the atom is left with a net positive charge and becomes a *positive ion* (designated H$^+$). In some cases, an atom or group of atoms can acquire an electron, in which case it is called a *negative ion*.

The Copper Atom

Copper is the most commonly used metal in **electrical** applications. The copper atom has 29 electrons that orbit the nucleus in four shells, as shown in Figure 2–4. Notice that the fourth or outermost shell, the valence shell, has only one valence electron. When the valence electron in the outer shell of the copper atom gains sufficient thermal energy, it can break away from the parent atom and become a free electron. In a piece of copper at room temperature, a "sea" of these free electrons is present. These electrons are not bound to a given

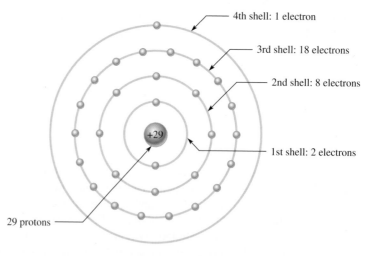

The copper atom.

atom but are free to move in the copper material. Free electrons make copper an excellent conductor and make electrical current possible.

Categories of Materials

Three categories of materials are used in electronics: conductors, semiconductors, and insulators.

Conductors **Conductors** are materials that readily allow current. They have a large number of free electrons and are characterized by one to three valence electrons in their structure. Most metals are good conductors. Silver is the best conductor, and copper is next. Copper is the most widely used conductive material because it is less expensive than silver. Copper wire is commonly used as a conductor in electric circuits.

Semiconductors **Semiconductors** are classed below the conductors in their ability to carry current because they have fewer free electrons than do conductors. Semiconductors have four valence electrons in their atomic structures. However, because of their unique characteristics, certain semiconductor materials are the basis for **electronic** devices such as the diode, transistor, and integrated circuit. Silicon and germanium are common semiconductive materials.

Insulators Insulating materials are poor conductors of electric current. In fact, **insulators** are used to prevent current where it is not wanted. Compared to conductive materials, insulators have very few free electrons and are characterized by more than four valence electrons in their atomic structures.

SECTION 2–1 REVIEW Answers are at the end of the chapter.	1. What is the basic particle of negative charge? 2. Define *atom*. 3. What does an atom consist of? 4. Define *atomic number*. 5. Do all elements have the same types of atoms? 6. What is a free electron? 7. What is a shell in the atomic structure? 8. Name two conductive materials.

2–2 ELECTRICAL CHARGE

As you know, an electron is the smallest particle that exhibits negative electrical charge. When an excess of electrons exists in a material, there is a net negative electrical charge. When a deficiency of electrons exists, there is a net positive electrical charge.

After completing this section, you should be able to

◆ **Explain the concept of electrical charge**

  ◆ Name the unit of charge

  ◆ Name the types of charge

  ◆ Describe the forces between charges

  ◆ Determine the amount of charge on a given number of electrons

BIOGRAPHY

Charles
Augustin
Coulomb,
1736–1806

Coulomb, a Frenchman, spent
many years as a military engineer.
When bad health forced him to
retire, he devoted his time to
scientific research. He is best
known for his work on electricity
and magnetism due to his
development of the inverse square
law for the force between two
charges. The unit of electrical
charge is named in his honor.
(Photo credit: Courtesy of the
Smithsonian Institution. Photo
number 52,597.)

The charge of an electron and that of a proton are equal in magnitude. Electrical **charge**, an electrical property of matter that exists because of an excess or deficiency of electrons, is symbolized by Q. Static electricity is the presence of a net positive or negative charge in a material. Everyone has experienced the effects of static electricity from time to time, for example, when attempting to touch a metal surface or another person or when the clothes in a dryer cling together.

Materials with charges of opposite polarity are attracted to each other; materials with charges of the same polarity are repelled, as indicated symbolically in Figure 2–5. A force acts between charges, as evidenced by the attraction or repulsion. This force, called an *electric field*, consists of invisible lines of force as represented in Figure 2–6.

(a) Uncharged: (b) Opposite   (c) Like positive   (d) Like negative
    no force   charges   charges repel   charges repel
                      attract

▲ FIGURE 2–5

Attraction and repulsion of electrical charges.

▶ FIGURE 2–6

Electric field between two oppositely
charged surfaces.

Coulomb: The Unit of Charge

Electrical charge is measured in coulombs, symbolized by C.

One coulomb is the total charge possessed by 6.25×10^{18} electrons.

A single electron has a charge of 1.6×10^{-19} C. The total charge Q, expressed in coulombs, for a given number of electrons is found by the following formula:

Equation 2–1

$$Q = \frac{\text{number of electrons}}{6.25 \times 10^{18} \text{ electrons/C}}$$

Positive and Negative Charge

Consider a neutral atom—that is, one that has the same number of electrons and protons and thus has no net charge. As you know, when a valence electron is pulled away from the atom by the application of energy, the atom is left with a net positive charge (more protons than electrons) and becomes a positive ion. If an atom acquires an extra electron in its outer shell, it has a net negative charge and becomes a negative ion.

The amount of energy required to free a valence electron is related to the number of electrons in the outer shell. An atom can have up to eight valence electrons. The more complete the outer shell, the more stable the atom and thus the more energy is required to release an electron. Figure 2–7 illustrates the creation of a positive ion and a negative ion when a hydrogen atom gives up its single valence electron to a chlorine atom, forming gaseous hydrogen chloride (HCl). When the gaseous HCl is dissolved in water, hydrochloric acid is formed.

Example of the formation of positive and negative ions.

Hydrogen atom
(1 proton, 1 electron)

Chlorine atom
(17 protons, 17 electrons)

(a) The neutral hydrogen atom has a single valence electron.

(b) The atoms combine by sharing the valence electron to form gaseous hydrogen chloride (HCl).

Positive hydrogen ion
(1 proton, no electrons)

Negative chloride ion
(17 protons, 18 electrons)

(c) When dissolved in water, hydrogen chloride gas separates into positive hydrogen ions and negative chloride ions. The chlorine atom retains the electron given up by the hydrogen atom forming both positive and negative ions in the same solution.

EXAMPLE 2–1

How many coulombs of charge do 93.8×10^{16} electrons represent?

Solution $Q = \dfrac{\text{number of electrons}}{6.25 \times 10^{18} \text{ electrons/C}} = \dfrac{93.8 \times 10^{16} \text{ electrons}}{6.25 \times 10^{18} \text{ electrons/C}} = 15 \times 10^{-2}\,\text{C} = \textbf{0.15 C}$

*Related Problem** How many electrons does it take to have 3 C of charge?

*Answers are at the end of the chapter.

SECTION 2–2 REVIEW

1. What is the symbol used for charge?
2. What is the unit of charge, and what is the unit symbol?
3. What are the two types of charge?
4. How much charge, in coulombs, is there in 10×10^{12} electrons?

2–3 VOLTAGE

As you have learned, a force of attraction exists between a positive and a negative charge. A certain amount of energy must be exerted in the form of work to overcome the force and move the charges a given distance apart. All opposite charges possess a certain potential energy because of the separation between them. The difference in potential energy of the charges is the potential difference or **voltage**. Voltage is the driving force in electric circuits and is what establishes current.

After completing this section, you should be able to

◆ **Define *voltage* and discuss its characteristics**

    ◆ State the formula for voltage

    ◆ Name and define the unit of voltage

    ◆ Describe the basic sources of voltage

Voltage is defined as energy per unit of charge and is expressed as

Equation 2–2

$$V = \frac{W}{Q}$$

where: V = voltage in volts (V)

           W = energy in joules (J)

           Q = charge in coulombs (C)

As a simple analogy, you can think of voltage as corresponding to the pressure difference created by a pump that causes the water to flow through a pipe in a water system.

Volt: The Unit of Voltage

The unit of voltage is the volt, symbolized by V.

One volt is the potential difference (voltage) between two points when one joule of energy is used to move one coulomb of charge from one point to the other.

EXAMPLE 2–2	If 50 J of energy are available for every 10 C of charge, what is the voltage?
Solution	$$V = \frac{W}{Q} = \frac{50\,J}{10\,C} = \textbf{5 V}$$
Related Problem	How much energy is used to move 50 C from one point in a circuit to another when the voltage between the two points is 12 V?

The Voltage Source

A **voltage source** provides electrical energy or electromotive force (emf), more commonly known as voltage. Voltage is produced by means of chemical energy, light energy, and magnetic energy combined with mechanical motion.

The Ideal Voltage Source   An ideal voltage source can provide a constant voltage for any current required by a circuit. The ideal voltage source does not exist but can be closely approximated in practice. We will assume ideal unless otherwise specified.

    Voltage sources can be either dc or ac. A common symbol for a dc voltage source is shown in Figure 2–8.

▲ FIGURE 2–8

Symbol for dc voltage sources.

    A graph showing current versus voltage for an ideal dc voltage source is called the *IV* characteristic and is illustrated in Figure 2–9. As you can see, the voltage is constant for any current (within limits) from the source. For a practical voltage source connected in a circuit, the voltage decreases slightly as the current increases. Current is always drawn from a voltage source when a load such as a resistance is connected to it.

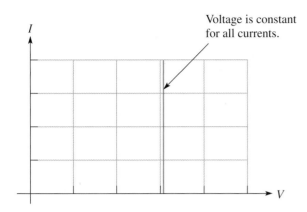

Voltage is constant for all currents.

IV characteristic of an ideal voltage source.

Types of DC Voltage Sources

Batteries   A **battery** is a type of voltage source that converts chemical energy into electrical energy. A battery consists of one or more electrochemical cells that are electrically connected. A cell consists of four basic components: a positive electrode, a negative electrode, an electrolyte, and a porous separator. The *positive electrode* has a deficiency of electrons due to chemical reaction, the *negative electrode* has a surplus of electrons due to chemical reaction, the *electrolyte* provides a mechanism for charge flow between positive and negative electrodes, and the *separator* electrically isolates the positive and negative electrodes. A basic diagram of a battery cell is shown in Figure 2–10.

◀ FIGURE 2–10

Diagram of a battery cell.

BIOGRAPHY

Alessandro Volta 1745–1827

Volta, an Italian, invented a device to generate static electricity and he discovered methane gas. Volta investigated reactions between dissimilar metals and developed the first battery in 1800. Electrical potential, more commonly known as voltage, and the unit of voltage, the volt, are named in his honor. (Photo credit: Giovita Garavaglia, courtesy AIP Emilio Segrè Visual Archives, Landé Collection.)

The materials used in a battery cell determine the voltage that it produces. The chemical reaction at each of the electrodes produces a fixed potential at each electrode. For example, in a lead-acid cell, a potential of −1.685 V is produced at the positive electrode and a potential of +0.365 V is produced at the negative electrode. This means that the voltage between two electrodes of a cell is 2.05 V, which is the standard lead-acid electrode potential. Factors such as acid concentration will affect this value to some degree so that the typical voltage of a commercial lead-acid cell is 2.15 V. The voltage of any battery cell depends on the cell chemistry. Nickel-cadmium cells are about 1.2 V and lithium cells can be as high as almost 4 V.

Although the voltage of a battery cell is fixed by its chemistry, the capacity is variable and depends on the quantity of materials in the cell. Essentially, the *capacity* of a cell is the number of electrons that can be obtained from it and is measured by the amount of current (defined in Section 2–4) that can be supplied over time.

Batteries normally consist of multiple cells that are electrically connected together internally. The way that the cells are connected and the type of cells determine the voltage and capacity of the battery. If the positive electrode of one cell is connected to the negative electrode of the next and so on, as illustrated in Figure 2–11(a), the battery voltage is the sum of the individual cell voltages. This is called a *series connection*. To increase battery capacity, the positive electrodes of several cells are connected together and all the negative electrodes are connected together, as illustrated in Figure 2–11(b). This is called a *parallel connection*.

Cells connected to form batteries.

(a) Series-connected battery   (b) Parallel-connected battery

Also, by using larger cells, which have a greater quantity of material, the ability to supply current can be increased but the voltage is not affected.

Batteries are divided into two major classes, primary and secondary. Primary batteries are used once and discarded because their chemical reactions are irreversible. Secondary batteries can be recharged and reused many times because they are characterized by reversible chemical reactions.

There are many types, shapes, and sizes of batteries. Some of the sizes that you are most familiar with are AAA, AA, C, D, and 9 V, as shown in Figure 2–12. There is also a less common size called AAAA, which is smaller than the AAA.

Sizes of common batteries.

In addition to these common sizes, there are many other physical configurations for various applications from hearing aids to lanterns. Batteries for hearing aids, watches, and other miniature applications are usually in a flat round configuration and are often called button batteries or coin batteries. Large multicell batteries are used in lanterns and industrial applications and, of course, there is the familiar automotive battery.

In addition to the many sizes and shapes, batteries are usually classified according to their chemical makeup as follows. Each of these classifications are typically available in several physical configurations.

◆ *Alkaline-MnO$_2$.* This is a primary battery that is commonly used in palm-type computers, photographic equipment, toys, radios, and recorders.

◆ *Lithium-MnO$_2$.* This is a primary battery that is commonly used in photographic and electronic equipment, smoke alarms, personal organizers, memory backup, and communications equipment.

◆ *Zinc air.* This is a primary battery that is commonly used in hearing aids, medical monitoring instruments, pagers, and other frequency-use applications.

◆ *Silver oxide.* This is a primary battery that is commonly used in watches, photographic equipment, hearing aids, and electronics requiring high-capacity batteries.

◆ *Nickel-metal hydride.* This is a secondary (rechargable) battery that is commonly used in portable computers, cell phones, camcorders, and other portable consumer electronics.

◆ *Lead-acid.* This is a secondary (rechargable) battery that is commonly used in automotive, marine, and other similar applications.

Solar Cells   The operation of solar cells is based on the **photovoltaic effect,** which is the process whereby light energy is converted directly into electrical energy. A basic solar cell consists of two layers of different types of semiconductive materials joined together to form a junction. When one layer is exposed to light, many electrons acquire enough energy to break away from their parent atoms and cross the junction. This process forms negative ions on one side of the junction and positive ions on the other, and thus a potential difference (voltage) is developed. Figure 2–13 shows the construction of a basic solar cell.

▲ FIGURE 2–13

Construction of a basic solar cell.

Generator   Electrical **generators** convert mechanical energy into electrical energy using a principle called *electromagnetic induction* (see Chapter 7). A conductor is rotated through a magnetic field, and a voltage is produced across the conductor. A typical generator is pictured in Figure 2–14.

▲ FIGURE 2–14

Cutaway view of a dc voltage generator.

The Electronic Power Supply   **Electronic power supplies** convert the ac voltage from the wall outlet to a constant (dc) voltage that is available across two terminals, as indicated in Figure 2–15(a). Typical commercial power supplies are shown in Figure 2–15(b).

Thermocouples   The **thermocouple** is a thermoelectric type of voltage source that is commonly used to sense temperature. A thermocouple is formed by the junction of two

(a)

(b)

▲ FIGURE 2–15

Electronic power supplies. (b) Courtesy of B+K precision.

dissimilar metals, and its operation is based on the **Seebeck effect** that describes the voltage generated at the junction of the metals as a function of temperature.

Standard types of thermocouples are characterized by the specific metals used. These standard thermocouples produce predictable output voltages for a range of temperatures. The most common is type K, made of chromel and alumel. Other types are also designated by letters as E, J, N, B, R, and S. Most thermocouples are available in wire or probe form.

Piezoelectric sensors   These sensors act as voltage sources and are based on the **piezoelectric effect** where a voltage is generated when a piezoelectric material is mechanically deformed by an external force. Quartz and ceramic are two types of piezoelectric material. Piezoelectric sensors are used in applications such as pressure sensors, force sensors, accelerometers, microphones, ultrasonic devices, and many others.

SECTION 2–3 REVIEW	1. Define *voltage*.
	2. What is the unit of voltage?
	3. What is the voltage when there are 24 J of energy for 10 C of charge?
	4. List six sources of voltage.

2–4 CURRENT

Voltage provides energy to electrons that allows them to move through a circuit. This movement of electrons is the current, which results in work being done in an electric circuit.

After completing this section, you should be able to

- **Define *current* and discuss its characteristics**
  - Explain the movement of electrons
  - State the formula for current
  - Name and define the unit of current

As you have learned, free electrons are available in all conductive and semiconductive materials. These electrons drift randomly in all directions, from atom to atom, within the structure of the material, as indicated in Figure 2–16.

◀ FIGURE 2–16

Random motion of free electrons in a material.

If a voltage is placed across a conductive or semiconductive material, one end becomes positive and the other negative, as indicated in Figure 2–17. The repulsive force produced by the negative voltage at the left end causes the free electrons (negative charges) to move toward the right. The attractive force produced by the positive voltage at the right end pulls the free electrons to the right. The result is a net movement of the free electrons from the negative end of the material to the positive end, as shown in Figure 2–17.

▲ FIGURE 2–17

Electrons flow from negative to positive when a voltage is applied across a conductive or semiconductive material.

The movement of the free electrons from the negative end of a material to the positive end is the electrical current, symbolized by *I*.

Electrical current is the rate of flow of charge.

Current in a conductive material is measured by the number of electrons (amount of charge) that flow past a point in a unit of time.

$$I = \frac{Q}{t}$$

Equation 2–3

where: I = current in amperes (A)

Q = the charge of the electrons in coulombs (C)

t = time in seconds (s)

BIOGRAPHY

André Marie Ampère 1775–1836

In 1820 Ampère, a Frenchman, developed a theory of electricity and magnetism that was fundamental for 19th century developments in the field. He was the first to build an instrument to measure charge flow (current). The unit of electrical current is named in his honor. (Photo credit: AIP Emilio Segrè Visual Archives.)

As a simple analogy, you can think of current as corresponding to water flowing through a pipe in a water system when pressure (corresponding to voltage) is applied by a pump (corresponding to a voltage source). *Voltage causes current.*

Ampere: The Unit of Current

Current is measured in a unit called the *ampere* or *amp* for short, symbolized by A.

> **One ampere (1 A) is the amount of current that exists when a number of electrons having a total charge of one coulomb (1 C) move through a given cross-sectional area in one second (1 s).**

See Figure 2–18. Remember, one coulomb is the charge carried by 6.25×10^{18} electrons.

◤ FIGURE 2–18

Illustration of 1 A of current (1 C/s) in a material.

When a number of electrons having a total charge of 1 C pass
through a cross-sectional area in 1 s, there is 1 A of current.

EXAMPLE 2–3

Ten coulombs of charge flow past a given point in a wire in 2 s. What is the current in amperes?

Solution

$$I = \frac{Q}{t} = \frac{10\,C}{2\,s} = 5\,A$$

Related Problem

If there are 8 A of direct current through the filament of a light bulb, how many coulombs have moved through the filament in 1.5 s?

The Current Source

The Ideal Current Source   As you know, an ideal voltage source can provide a constant voltage for any load. An ideal **current source** can provide a constant current in any load. Just as in the case of a voltage source, the ideal current source does not exist but can be approximated in practice. We will assume ideal unless otherwise specified.

The symbol for a current source is shown in Figure 2–19(a). The *IV* characteristic for an ideal current source is a horizontal line as illustrated in Figure 2–19(b). Notice that the current is constant for any voltage across the current source.

◤ FIGURE 2–19

The current source.

(a) Symbol   (b) *IV* characteristic

Actual Current Sources   Power supplies are normally thought of as voltage sources because they are the most common source in the laboratory. However, current sources can also be considered a type of power supply. Typical commercial constant-current sources are illustrated in Figure 2–20.

(a)   (b)

▲ FIGURE 2–20

Typical commercial current sources. (Courtesy of Lake Shore Cryotronics)

In most transistor circuits, the transistor acts as a current source because part of the *IV* characteristic curve is a horizontal line as shown by the transistor characteristic in Figure 2–21. The flat part of the graph indicates where the transistor current is constant over a range of voltages. The constant-current region is used to form a constant-current source.

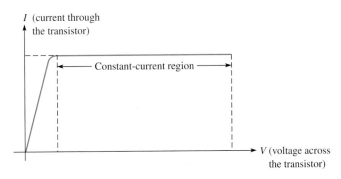

◀ FIGURE 2–21

Characteristic curve of a transistor showing the constant-current region.

One common application of a constant-current source is in constant-current battery chargers, as illustrated in a simplified way in Figure 2–22. The rectifier is a circuit that acts as a dc voltage source by converting the ac voltage from a standard wall outlet to a constant dc voltage. This voltage is effectively applied in parallel with a battery that is to be charged and in series with a constant-current source. The battery voltage is initially low but increases over time due to the constant charging current. The total voltage across the current source is the voltage from the rectifier minus the voltage of the battery, which increases as the battery charges.

▲ FIGURE 2–22

Battery charger as an example of a current source application.

SECTION 2–4 REVIEW	1. Define *current* and state its unit.
	2. How many electrons make up one coulomb of charge?
	3. What is the current in amperes when 20 C flow past a point in a wire in 4 s?

2–5   RESISTANCE

When there is current through a material, the free electrons move through the material and occasionally collide with atoms. These collisions cause the electrons to lose some of their energy, and thus their movement is restricted. The more collisions, the more the flow of electrons is restricted. This restriction varies and is determined by the type of material. The property of a material that restricts the flow of electrons is called *resistance,* designated with an *R*.

After completing this section, you should be able to

♦ **Define *resistance* and discuss its characteristics**

  ♦ Name and define the unit of resistance

  ♦ Describe the basic types of resistors

  ♦ Determine resistance value by color code or labeling

R

▲ FIGURE 2–23

Resistance/resistor symbol.

Resistance is the opposition to current.

The schematic symbol for resistance is shown in Figure 2–23.

When there is current through any material that has resistance, heat is produced by the collisions of free electrons and atoms. Therefore, wire, which typically has a very small resistance, can become warm or even hot when there is sufficient current through it.

As a simple analogy, you can think of a resistor as corresponding to a partially open valve in a closed water system that restricts the amount of water flowing through a pipe. If the valve is opened more (corresponding to less resistance), the water flow (corresponding to current) increases. If the valve is closed a little (corresponding to more resistance), the water flow (corresponding to current) decreases.

Ohm: The Unit of Resistance

Resistance, *R*, is expressed in the unit of ohms, which is symbolized by the Greek letter omega (Ω).

One ohm (1 Ω) of resistance exists when there is one ampere (1 A) of current in a material with one volt (1 V) applied across the material.

Conductance   The reciprocal of resistance is **conductance**, symbolized by *G*. It is a measure of the ease with which current is established. The formula is

Equation 2–4

$$G = \frac{1}{R}$$

The unit of conductance is the **siemens**, symbolized by S. For example, the conductance of a 22 kΩ resistor is

$$G = \frac{1}{22 \text{ k}\Omega} = 45.5 \, \mu\text{S}$$

Occasionally, the obsolete unit of *mho* is still used for conductance.

Resistors

Components that are specifically designed to have a certain amount of resistance are called **resistors**. The principal applications of resistors are to limit current, divide voltage, and, in certain cases, generate heat. Although different types of resistors come in many shapes and sizes, they can all be placed in one of two main categories: fixed or variable.

Fixed Resistors Fixed resistors are available with a large selection of resistance values that are set during manufacturing and cannot be changed easily. Fixed resistors are constructed using various methods and materials. Figure 2–24 shows several common types.

One common fixed resistor is the carbon-composition type, which is made with a mixture of finely ground carbon, insulating filler, and a resin binder. The ratio of carbon to insulating filler sets the resistance value. The mixture is formed into rods which are cut into short lengths, and lead connections are made. The entire resistor is then encapsulated in an insulated coating for protection. Figure 2–25(a) shows the construction of a typical carbon-composition resistor.

BIOGRAPHY

Georg Simon Ohm
1787–1854

Ohm was born in Bavaria and struggled for years to gain recognition for his work in formulating the relationship of current, voltage, and resistance. This mathematical relationship is known today as Ohm's law and the unit of resistance is named in his honor. (Photo credit: Library of Congress, LC-USZ62-40943.)

(a) Carbon-composition

(b) Metal film chip resistor

(c) Chip resistor array

(d) Resistor network (simm)

(e) Resistor network (surface mount)

(f) Radial-lead for PC board insertion

▲ FIGURE 2–24

Typical fixed resistors.

Color bands

Resistance material (carbon composition)

Insulated coating

Leads

(a) Cutaway view of a carbon-composition resistor

Protective glass overcoat

External electrode (solder)

Secondary electrode

Ceramic substrate   Resistive material

Internal electrode

(b) Cutaway view of a tiny chip resistor

▲ FIGURE 2–25

Two types of fixed resistors (not to scale).

B I O G R A P H Y

Ernst Werner
von Siemens
1816–1892

Siemens was born in Prussia.
While in prison for acting as a
second in a duel, he began
experiments with chemistry, which
led to his invention of the first
electroplating system. In 1837,
Siemens began making
improvements in the early
telegraph and contributed greatly
to the development of telegraphic
systems. The unit of conductance
is named in his honor. (Photo
credit: AIP Emilio Segrè Visual
Archives, E. Scott Barr Collection.)

The chip resistor is another type of fixed resistor and is in the category of SMT (surface-mount technology) components. It has the advantage of a very small size for compact assemblies. Figure 2–25(b) shows the construction of a chip resistor.

Other types of fixed resistors include carbon film, metal film, metal-oxide film, and wirewound. In film resistors, a resistive material is deposited evenly onto a high-grade ceramic rod. The resistive film may be carbon (carbon film) or nickel chromium (metal film). In these types of resistors, the desired resistance value is obtained by removing part of the resistive material in a helical pattern along the rod using a spiraling technique, as shown in Figure 2–26(a). Very close **tolerance** can be achieved with this method. Film resistors are also available in the form of resistor networks, as shown in Figure 2–26(b).

(a) Film resistor showing spiraling technique

(b) Resistor network

▲ FIGURE 2–26

Construction views of typical film resistors.

Wirewound resistors are constructed with resistive wire wound around an insulating rod and then sealed. Normally, wirewound resistors are used because of their relatively high power ratings. Since they are constructed with a coil of wire, wirewound resistors have significant inductance and are not used at higher frequencies. Some typical wirewound resistors are shown in Figure 2–27.

▲ FIGURE 2–27

Typical wirewound power resistors.

Resistor Color Codes   Some types of fixed resistors with value tolerances of 5% or 10% are color coded with four bands to indicate the resistance value and the tolerance. This color-code band system is shown in Figure 2–28, and the **color code** is listed in Table 2–1. The bands are always located closer to one end.

The 4-band color code is read as follows:

1. Start with the band closest to one end of the resistor. The first band is the first digit of the resistance value. If it is not clear which is the banded end, start from the end that does not begin with a gold or silver band.

Color-code bands on a 4-band resistor.

1st digit

2nd digit

Multiplier (Number of zeros following 2nd digit)

Percent tolerance

▼ TABLE 2–1

4-band resistor color code.

	Digit		Color
Resistance value, first three bands: First band—1st digit Second band—2nd digit *Third band—multiplier (number of zeros following the 2nd digit)	0		Black
	1		Brown
	2		Red
	3		Orange
	4		Yellow
	5		Green
	6		Blue
	7		Violet
	8		Gray
	9		White
Fourth band—tolerance	±5%		Gold
	±10%		Silver

* For resistance values less than 10 Ω, the third band is either gold or silver. Gold is for a multiplier of 0.1 and silver is for a multiplier of 0.01.

2. The second band is the second digit of the resistance value.

3. The third band is the number of zeros following the second digit, or the *multiplier*.

4. The fourth band indicates the percent tolerance and is usually gold or silver. If there is no fourth band, the tolerance is ±20%.

For example, a 5% tolerance means that the *actual* resistance value is within ±5% of the color-coded value. Thus, a 100 Ω resistor with a tolerance of ±5% can have an acceptable range of values from a minimum of 95 Ω to a maximum of 105 Ω.

As indicated in the table, for resistance values less than 10 Ω, the third band is either gold or silver. Gold in the third band represents a multiplier of 0.1, and silver represents 0.01. For example, a color code of red, violet, gold, and silver represents 2.7 Ω with a tolerance of ±10%. A table of standard resistance values is in Appendix A.

EXAMPLE 2–4

Find the resistance values in ohms and the percent tolerance for each of the color-coded resistors shown in Figure 2–29.

(a)   (b)   (c)

▲ FIGURE 2–29

Solution

(a) First band is red = 2, second band is violet = 7, third band is orange = 3 zeros, fourth band is silver = ±10% tolerance.

$$R = 27,000 \ \Omega \pm 10\%$$

(b) First band is brown = 1, second band is black = 0, third band is brown = 1 zero, fourth band is silver = ±10% tolerance.

$$R = 100 \ \Omega \pm 10\%$$

(c) First band is green = 5, second band is blue = 6, third band is green = 5 zeros, fourth band is gold = ±5% tolerance.

$$R = 5,600,000 \ \Omega \pm 5\%$$

Related Problem

A certain resistor has a yellow first band, a violet second band, a red third band, and a gold fourth band. Determine the value in ohms and its percent tolerance.

Five-Band Color Code   Certain precision resistors with tolerances of 2%, 1%, or less are generally color coded with five bands, as shown in Figure 2–30. Begin at the band closest to one end. The first band is the first digit of the resistance value, the second band is the second digit, the third band is the third digit, the fourth band is the multiplier (number of zeros after the third digit), and the fifth band indicates the tolerance. Table 2–2 shows the 5-band color code.

1st digit
2nd digit
3rd digit
Multiplier (Number of zeros following 3rd digit)
Percent tolerance

▲ FIGURE 2–30

Color-code bands on a 5-band resistor.

Resistor Reliability Band   An extra band on some color-coded resistors indicates the resistor's reliability in percent of failures per 1000 hours (1000 h) of use. The reliability color code is listed in Table 2–3. For example, a brown fifth band on a 4-band color-coded resistor means that if a group of like resistors is operated under standard conditions for 1000 h, 1% of the resistors in that group will fail.

Resistors, as well as other components, should be operated substantially below their rated values to enhance their reliability.

	DIGIT	COLOR
Resistance value, first four bands:	0	Black
	1	Brown
	2	Red
First band—1st digit	3	Orange
Second band—2nd digit	4	Yellow
Third band—3rd digit	5	Green
Fourth band—multiplier	6	Blue
(number of zeros	7	Violet
following 3rd digit)	8	Gray
	9	White
Fourth band—multiplier	0.1	Gold
	0.01	Silver
Fifth band—tolerance	±2%	Red
	±1%	Brown
	±0.5%	Green
	±0.25%	Blue
	±0.1%	Violet

COLOR	FAILURES DURING 1000 h OF OPERATION
Brown	1.0%
Red	0.1%
Orange	0.01%
Yellow	0.001%

EXAMPLE 2–5

Find the resistance value in ohms and the percent tolerance for each of the color-coded resistors shown in Figure 2–31.

FIGURE 2–31

(a)   (b)   (c)

Solution

(a) First band is red = 2, second band is violet = 7, third band is black = 0, fourth band is gold = ×0.1, fifth band is red = ±2% tolerance.

$$R = 270 \times 0.1 = \textbf{27 } \Omega \pm \textbf{2\%}$$

(b) First band is yellow = 4, second band is black = 0, third band is red = 2, fourth band is black = 0, fifth band is brown = ±1% tolerance.

$$R = \textbf{402 } \Omega \pm \textbf{1\%}$$

(c) First band is orange = 3, second band is orange = 3, third band is red = 2, fourth band is orange = 3, fifth band is green = ±0.5% tolerance.

$$R = \textbf{332,000 } \Omega \pm \textbf{0.5\%}$$

Related Problem A certain resistor has a yellow first band, a violet second band, a green third band, a gold fourth band, and a red fifth band. Determine its value in ohms and its percent tolerance.

Resistor Label Codes

Not all types of resistors are color coded. Many, including surface-mount resistors, use typographical marking to indicate the resistance value and tolerance. These label codes consist of either all numbers (numeric) or a combination of numbers and letters (alphanumeric). In some cases when the body of the resistor is large enough, the entire resistance value and tolerance are stamped on it in standard form. For example, a 33,000 Ω resistor may be labeled as 33 kΩ.

Numeric Labeling   This type of marking uses three digits to indicate the resistance value, as shown in Figure 2–32 using a specific example. The first two digits give the first two digits of the resistance value, and the third digit gives the multiplier or number of zeros that follow the first two digits. This code is limited to values of 10 Ω or greater.

▶ FIGURE 2–32

Example of three-digit labeling for a resistor.

Alphanumeric Labeling   Another common type of marking is a three- or four-character label that uses both digits and letters. This type of label typically consists of only three digits or two or three digits and one of the letters R, K, or M. The letter is used to indicate the multiplier, and the position of the letter indicates the decimal point placement. The letter R indicates a multiplier of 1 (no zeros after the digits), the K indicates a multiplier of 1000 (three zeros after the digits), and the M indicates a multiplier of 1,000,000 (six zeros after the digits). In this format, values from 100 to 999 consist of three digits and no letter to represent the three digits in the resistance value. Figure 2–33 shows three examples of this type of resistor label.

▲ FIGURE 2–33

Examples of the alphanumeric resistor label.

EXAMPLE 2–6

Interpret the following alphanumeric resistor labels:

(a) 470   (b) 5R6   (c) 68K   (d) 10M   (e) 3M3

Solution   (a) 470 = **470 Ω**   (b) 5R6 = **5.6 Ω**   (c) 68K = **68 kΩ**

(d) 10M = **10 MΩ**   (e) 3M3 = **3.3 MΩ**

Related Problem   What is the resistance indicated by 1K25?

One system of labels for resistance tolerance values uses the letters F, G, and J:

$$F = \pm 1\% \qquad G = \pm 2\% \qquad J = \pm 5\%$$

For example, 620F indicates a 620 Ω resistor with a tolerance of ±1%, 4R6G is a 4.6 Ω ± 2% resistor, and 56KJ is a 56 kΩ ± 5% resistor.

Variable Resistors

Variable resistors are designed so that their resistance values can be changed easily with a manual or an automatic adjustment.

Two basic uses for variable resistors are to divide voltage and to control current. The variable resistor used to divide voltage is called a **potentiometer**. The variable resistor used to control current is called a **rheostat**. Schematic symbols for these types are shown in Figure 2–34. The potentiometer is a three-terminal device, as indicated in part (a). Terminals 1 and 2 have a fixed resistance between them, which is the total resistance. Terminal 3 is connected to a moving contact **(wiper).** You can vary the resistance between 3 and 1 or between 3 and 2 by moving the contact.

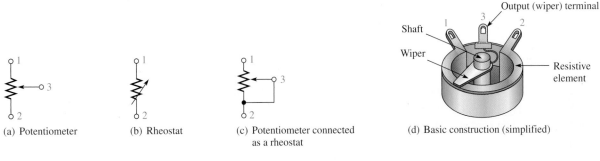

(a) Potentiometer   (b) Rheostat   (c) Potentiometer connected as a rheostat   (d) Basic construction (simplified)

▲ FIGURE 2–34

Potentiometer and rheostat symbols and basic construction of one type of potentiometer.

Figure 2–34(b) shows the rheostat as a two-terminal variable resistor. Part (c) shows how you can use a potentiometer as a rheostat by connecting terminal 3 to either terminal 1 or terminal 2. Parts (b) and (c) are equivalent symbols. Part (d) shows a simplified construction diagram of a potentiometer. Some typical potentiometers are pictured in Figure 2–35.

▲ FIGURE 2–35

Typical potentiometers and two construction views.

Potentiometers and rheostats can be classified as linear or tapered, as shown in Figure 2–36, where a potentiometer with a total resistance of 100 Ω is used as an example. As shown in part (a), in a linear potentiometer, the resistance between either terminal and the moving contact varies linearly with the position of the moving contact. For example, one-half of a turn results in one-half the total resistance. Three-quarters of a turn results in three-quarters of the total resistance between the moving contact and one terminal, or one-quarter of the total resistance between the other terminal and the moving contact.

(a) Linear

1. Quarter turn   2. Half turn   3. Three-quarter turn

(b) Tapered (nonlinear)

1. Quarter turn   2. Half turn   3. Three-quarter turn

▲ FIGURE 2–36

Examples of (a) linear and (b) tapered potentiometers.

HANDS ON TIP

A special type of resistor is used for sensing forces ranging from the pressure of a finger tip on a keyboard to the weight of a truck on a scale. These specialized resistors are known as force sensing resistors (FSRs) and are a type of transducer. The FSR exhibits a change in resistance in response to an applied force. The resistance change is used to indicate the amount of force.

In a **tapered** potentiometer, the resistance varies nonlinearly with the position of the moving contact, so that one-half of a turn does not necessarily result in one-half the total resistance. This concept is illustrated in Figure 2–36(b), where the nonlinear values are arbitrary.

The potentiometer is used as a voltage-control device. When a fixed voltage is applied across the end terminals, a variable voltage is obtained at the wiper contact with respect to either end terminal. The rheostat is used as a current-control device; the current can be changed by changing the wiper position.

Two Types of Automatically Variable Resistors   A **thermistor** is a type of variable resistor that is temperature-sensitive. When its temperature coefficient is negative, the resistance changes inversely with temperature. When its temperature coefficient is positive, the resistance changes directly with temperature.

The resistance of a **photoconductive cell** changes with a change in light intensity. This cell also has a negative temperature coefficient, which means that resistance decreases with increasing temperature. Symbols for both of these devices are shown in Figure 2–37. Sometimes the Greek letter lamda (λ) is used with the photoconductive cell symbol.

▶ FIGURE 2–37

Symbols for resistive devices with sensitivities to temperature and light.

(a) Thermistor

(b) Photoconductive cell

SECTION 2–5 REVIEW

1. Define *resistance* and name its unit.
2. What are the two main categories of resistors? Briefly explain the difference between them.
3. In the 4-band resistor color code, what does each band represent?

4. Determine the resistance and percent tolerance for each of the following color codes:
   (a) yellow, violet, red, gold   (b) blue, red, orange, silver
   (c) brown, gray, black, gold   (d) red, red, blue, red, green
5. What resistance value is indicated by each alphanumeric label:
   (a) 33R   (b) 5K6   (c) 900   (d) 6M8
6. What is the basic difference between a rheostat and a potentiometer?
7. What is a thermistor?

2–6 THE ELECTRIC CIRCUIT

A basic electric circuit is an arrangement of physical components that use voltage, current, and resistance to perform some useful function.

After completing this section, you should be able to

◆ **Describe a basic electric circuit**

   ◆ Relate a schematic to a physical circuit

   ◆ Define *open circuit* and *closed circuit*

   ◆ Describe various types of protective devices

   ◆ Describe various types of switches

   ◆ Explain how wire sizes are related to gauge numbers

   ◆ Define *ground* or *common*

Basically, an electric **circuit** consists of a voltage source, a load, and a path for current between the source and the load. The **load** is a device on which work is done by the current through it. Figure 2–38 shows an example of a simple electric circuit: a battery connected to a lamp with two conductors (wires). The battery is the voltage source, the lamp is the load on the battery because it draws current from the battery, and the two wires provide the current path from the negative terminal of the battery to the lamp and back to the positive terminal of the battery, as indicated by the red arrows. There is current through the filament of the lamp (which has a resistance), causing it to become hot enough to emit visible light. Current through the battery is produced by chemical action.

SAFETY POINT

To avoid electrical shock, never touch a circuit while it is connected to a voltage source. If you need to handle a circuit, remove a component, or change a component, first make sure the voltage source is disconnected.

Wire conductor (current path)

Battery
(voltage source)

Lamp
(load)

◀ FIGURE 2–38

A simple electric circuit.

In many practical cases, one terminal of the battery is connected to a ground (common) point. For example, in automobiles, the negative battery terminal is generally connected to the metal chassis of the car. The chassis is the ground for the automobile electrical system and provides a current path for the circuit. (The concept of *ground* is covered later in this chapter.)

An electric circuit can be represented by a **schematic**, a diagram that shows the interconnection of components, using standard symbols for each element, as shown in Figure 2–39 for the simple circuit in Figure 2–38. A schematic shows, in an organized manner, how the various components in a given circuit are interconnected so that the operation of the circuit can be determined.

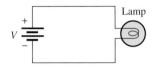

▲ FIGURE 2–39

A schematic for the circuit in Figure 2–38.

Circuit Current Control and Protection

The circuit in Figure 2–40(a) illustrates a **closed circuit**—that is, a circuit in which the current has a complete path. An **open circuit** is a circuit in which the current path is broken so that there is no current, as shown in part (b). An open circuit is considered to have infinite resistance (*infinite* means immeasurably large).

Mechanical Switches **Switches** are commonly used for controlling the opening or closing of circuits. For example, a switch is used to turn a lamp on or off, as illustrated in Figure 2–40. Each circuit pictorial is shown with its associated schematic. The type of switch indicated is a *single-pole–single-throw* (SPST) toggle switch. The term *pole* refers to the movable arm in a switch, and the term *throw* indicates the number of contacts that are affected (either opened or closed) by a single switch action (a single movement of a pole).

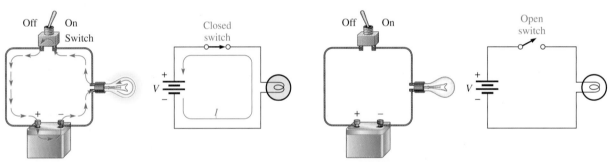

(a) There is current in a *closed* circuit because there is a complete current path (switch is ON or in the *closed* position). Current is always indicated by a red arrow in this text.

(b) There is no current in an *open* circuit because the path is broken (switch is OFF or in the *open* position).

▲ FIGURE 2–40

Illustration of closed and open circuits using an SPST switch for control.

Figure 2–41 shows a somewhat more complicated circuit using a *single-pole–double-throw* (SPDT) type of switch to control the current to two different lamps. When one lamp is on, the other is off, and vice versa, as illustrated by the two schematics that represent each of the switch positions.

In addition to the SPST and the SPDT switches (symbols are shown in Figure 2–42(a) and (b)), the following other types of switches are also important:

- *Double-pole–single-throw (DPST).* The DPST switch permits simultaneous opening or closing of two sets of contacts. The symbol is shown in Figure 2–42(c). The dashed line indicates that the contact arms are mechanically linked so that both move with a single switch action.

- *Double-pole–double-throw (DPDT).* The DPDT switch provides connection from one set of contacts to either of two other sets. The schematic symbol is shown in Figure 2–42(d).

- *Push button (PB).* In the normally open push-button switch (NOPB), shown in Figure 2–42(e), connection is made between two contacts when the button is

(a) Pictorial

(b) A schematic showing
Lamp 1 on and Lamp 2 off

(c) A schematic showing
Lamp 2 on and Lamp 1 off

▲ FIGURE 2–41

An example of an SPDT switch controlling two lamps.

(a) SPST   (b) SPDT   (c) DPST   (d) DPDT   (e) NOPB   (f) NCPB   (g) Single-pole rotary
(6-position)

▲ FIGURE 2–42

Switch symbols.

depressed, and connection is broken when the button is released. In the normally closed push-button switch (NCPB), shown in Figure 2–42(f), connection between the two contacts is broken when the button is depressed.

◆ *Rotary.*   In a rotary switch, a knob is turned to make a connection between one contact and any one of several others. A symbol for a simple six-position rotary switch is shown in Figure 2–42(g).

Figure 2–43 shows several varieties of switches, and Figure 2–44 shows a construction view of a typical toggle switch. In addition to mechanical switches, a transistor

Toggle switch   Rocker switch   Push-button switches   PC board mounted push-button switches

Rotary switches   DIP switches for mounting on PC boards

▲ FIGURE 2–43

Typical mechanical switches.

▲ FIGURE 2–44

Construction view of a typical toggle switch.

can be used as the equivalent of a single-pole–single-throw switch in certain applications.

Protective Devices **Fuses** and **circuit breakers** are placed in the current path and are used to deliberately create an open circuit when the current exceeds a specified number of amperes due to a malfunction or other abnormal condition in a circuit. For example, a fuse or circuit breaker with a 20 A rating will open a circuit when the current exceeds 20 A.

The basic difference between a fuse and a circuit breaker is that when a fuse is "blown," it must be replaced; but when a circuit breaker opens, it can be reset and reused repeatedly. Both of these devices protect against damage to a circuit due to excess current or prevent a hazardous condition created by the overheating of wires and other components when the current is too great. Because fuses cut off excess current more quickly than circuit breakers, fuses are used whenever delicate electronic equipment needs to be protected. Several typical fuses and circuit breakers, along with their schematic symbols, are shown in Figure 2–45.

Two basic categories of fuses in terms of their physical configuration are cartridge type and plug type (screw in). Cartridge type fuses have various shaped housings with leads or other types of contacts as shown in Figure 2–45(a). A typical plug type fuse is shown in part (b). Fuse operation is based on the melting temperature of a wire or other metal element. As current increases, the fuse element heats up and when the rated current is exceeded, the element reaches its melting temperature and opens, thus removing power from the circuit.

Two common types of fuses are the fast-acting and the time-delay (slow blow). Fast-acting fuses are type F and time-delay fuses are type T. In normal operation, most fuses are subjected to intermittent current surges that exceed the rated current, such as when power to a circuit is turned on. Over time, this reduces the fuse's ability to withstand short surges or even current at the rated value. A slow blow fuse can tolerate greater and longer duration surges of current than the typical fast-acting fuse. A fuse symbol is shown in Figure 2–45(c).

Typical circuit breakers are shown in Figure 2–45(d) and the symbol is shown in part (e). Generally, a circuit breaker detects excess current either by the heating effect of the current or by the magnetic field it creates. In a circuit breaker based on the heating effect, a bimetallic spring opens the contacts when the rated current is exceeded. Once opened, the contact is held open by mechanical means until manually reset. In a circuit breaker based on a magnetic field, the contacts are opened by a sufficient magnetic force created by excess current and must be mechanically reset.

Wires

Wires are the most common form of conductive material used in electrical applications. They vary in diameter size and are arranged according to standard gauge numbers, called **AWG** (American Wire Gauge) sizes. As the gauge number increases, the wire diameter decreases. The size of a wire is also specified in terms of its cross-sectional area, as illustrated

(a) Cartridge fuses

(b) Plug fuse

(c) Fuse symbol

(d) Circuit breakers

(e) Circuit breaker symbol

▲ FIGURE 2–45

Typical fuses and circuit breakers and their symbols.

in Figure 2–46. The unit of cross-sectional area is the **circular mil,** abbreviated CM. One circular mil is the area of a wire with a diameter of 0.001 inch (0.001 in., or 1 mil). You can find the cross-sectional area in circular mils by expressing the diameter in thousandths of an inch (mils) and squaring it, as follows:

$$A = d^2$$

Equation 2–5

where A is the cross-sectional area in circular mils and d is the diameter in mils. Table 2–4 lists the AWG sizes with their corresponding cross-sectional area and resistance in ohms per 1000 ft at 20°C.

Cross-sectional area, A

0.001 in.

$A = 1$ CM

▲ FIGURE 2–46

Cross-sectional area of a wire.

▼ TABLE 2–4

AWG (American Wire Gauge) sizes and resistances for solid round copper.

AWG #	AREA (CM)	RESISTANCE (Ω/1000 FT AT 20°C)	AWG #	AREA (CM)	RESISTANCE (Ω/1000 FT AT 20°C)
0000	211,600	0.0490	19	1,288.1	8.051
000	167,810	0.0618	20	1,021.5	10.15
00	133,080	0.0780	21	810.10	12.80
0	105,530	0.0983	22	642.40	16.14
1	83,694	0.1240	23	509.45	20.36
2	66,373	0.1563	24	404.01	25.67
3	52,634	0.1970	25	320.40	32.37
4	41,742	0.2485	26	254.10	40.81
5	33,102	0.3133	27	201.50	51.47
6	26,250	0.3951	28	159.79	64.90
7	20,816	0.4982	29	126.72	81.83
8	16,509	0.6282	30	100.50	103.2
9	13,094	0.7921	31	79.70	130.1
10	10,381	0.9989	32	63.21	164.1
11	8,234.0	1.260	33	50.13	206.9
12	6,529.0	1.588	34	39.75	260.9
13	5,178.4	2.003	35	31.52	329.0
14	4,106.8	2.525	36	25.00	414.8
15	3,256.7	3.184	37	19.83	523.1
16	2,582.9	4.016	38	15.72	659.6
17	2,048.2	5.064	39	12.47	831.8
18	1,624.3	6.385	40	9.89	1049.0

EXAMPLE 2–7

What is the cross-sectional area of a wire with a diameter of 0.005 inch?

Solution

$$d = 0.005 \text{ in.} = 5 \text{ mils}$$

$$A = d^2 = (5 \text{ mils})^2 = \textbf{25 CM}$$

Related Problem What is the cross-sectional area of a 0.0201 in. diameter wire? What is the AWG # for this wire from Table 2–4?

Wire Resistance Although copper wire conducts current extremely well, it still has some resistance, as do all conductors. The resistance of a wire depends on three physical characteristics: (a) type of material, (b) length of wire, and (c) cross-sectional area. In addition, temperature can also affect the resistance.

Each type of conductive material has a characteristic called its *resistivity,* which is represented by the Greek letter rho (ρ). For each material, ρ is a constant value at a given temperature. The formula for the resistance of a wire of length l and cross-sectional area A is

Equation 2–6

$$R = \frac{\rho l}{A}$$

This formula shows that resistance increases with an increase in resistivity and length and decreases with an increase in cross-sectional area. For resistance to be calculated in ohms, the length must be in feet (ft), the cross-sectional area in circular mils (CM), and the resistivity in CM-Ω/ft.

EXAMPLE 2–8

Find the resistance of a 100 ft length of copper wire with a cross-sectional area of 810.1 CM. The resistivity of copper is 10.37 CM-Ω/ft at 20°C.

Solution

$$R = \frac{\rho l}{A} = \frac{(10.37\ \text{CM-}\Omega\text{/ft})(100\ \text{ft})}{810.1\ \text{CM}} = \mathbf{1.280\ \Omega}$$

Related Problem Use Table 2–4 to determine the resistance of 100 ft of copper wire with a cross-sectional area of 810.1 CM. Compare with the calculated value.

As mentioned, Table 2–4 lists the resistance of the various standard wire sizes in ohms per 1000 ft at 20°C. For example, a 1000 ft length of 14-gauge copper wire has a resistance of 2.525 Ω. A 1000 ft length of 22-gauge wire has a resistance of 16.14 Ω. For a given length, the smaller-gauge wire has more resistance. Thus, for a given voltage, larger-gauge wires can carry more current than smaller ones.

Ground

Ground is the reference point in an electric circuit. The term *ground* originated from the fact that one conductor of a circuit was typically connected with an 8-foot long metal rod driven into the earth itself. Today, this type of connection is referred to as an *earth ground*. In household wiring, earth ground is indicated with a green or bare copper wire. Earth ground is normally connected to the metal chassis of an appliance or a metal electrical box for safety. Unfortunately, there have been exceptions to this rule, which can present a safety hazard if a metal chassis is not at earth ground. It is a good idea to confirm that a metal chassis is actually at earth ground potential before doing any work on an instrument or appliance.

Another type of ground is called a *reference ground*. Voltages are always specified with respect to another point. If that point is not stated explicitly, the reference ground is understood. Reference ground defines 0 V for the circuit. The reference ground can be at a completely different potential than the earth ground. Reference ground is also called **common** and labeled COM or COMM because it represents a common conductor. When you are wiring a protoboard in the laboratory, you will normally reserve one of the bus strips (a long line along the length of the board) for this common conductor.

Three ground symbols are shown in Figure 2–47. Unfortunately, there is not a separate symbol to distinguish between earth ground and reference ground. The symbol in (a) represents either an earth ground or a reference ground, (b) shows a chassis ground, and (c) is an alternate reference symbol typically used when there is more than one common connection (such as analog and digital ground in the same circuit). In this book, the symbol in part (a) will be used throughout.

Figure 2–48 illustrates a simple circuit with ground connections. The current is from the negative terminal of the 12 V source, through the common ground connection, through the lamp, and through the wire back to the positive terminal of the source. Ground provides a path for the current from the source because all of the ground points are electrically the same point and provide a zero resistance (ideally) current path. The voltage at the top of the circuit is +12 V with respect to ground. You can think of all the ground points in a circuit as being connected together by a conductor.

(a)   (b)   (c)

▲ FIGURE 2–47

Symbols for ground.

▲ FIGURE 2–48

A simple circuit with ground connections.

SECTION 2–6 REVIEW

1. What are the basic elements of an electric circuit?
2. Define *open circuit*.
3. Define *closed circuit*.
4. What is the resistance of an open switch? Ideally, what is the resistance of a closed switch?
5. What is the purpose of a fuse?
6. What is the difference between a fuse and a circuit breaker?
7. Which wire is larger in diameter, AWG #3 or AWG #22?
8. What is ground in an electric circuit?

2–7 BASIC CIRCUIT MEASUREMENTS

In electronics technology, you cannot function without knowing how to measure voltage, current, and resistance.

After completing this section, you should be able to

◆ **Make basic circuit measurements**

- ◆ Properly measure voltage in a circuit
- ◆ Properly measure current in a circuit
- ◆ Properly measure resistance
- ◆ Set up and read basic meters

Voltage, current, and resistance measurements are commonly required in electronics work. The instrument used to measure voltage is a **voltmeter**, the instrument used to measure current is an **ammeter**, and the instrument used to measure resistance is an **ohmmeter**. Commonly, all three instruments are combined into a single instrument known as a **multimeter,** in which you can choose the specific quantity to measure by selecting the appropriate function with a switch.

Typical portable multimeters are shown in Figure 2–49. Part (a) shows a digital multimeter (DMM), which provides a digital readout of the measured quantity; and part (b) shows an analog meter with a needle pointer. Many digital multimeters also include a bar graph display.

Meter Symbols

Throughout this book, certain symbols will be used in circuits to represent meters, as shown in Figure 2–50. You may see any of four types of symbols for voltmeters, ammeters, and ohmmeters, depending on which symbol most effectively conveys the information required. The digital meter symbol is used when specific values are to be indicated in a circuit. The bar graph meter symbol and sometimes the analog meter symbol are used to illustrate the operation of a circuit when *relative* measurements or changes in quantities, rather than specific values, need to be depicted. A changing quantity may be indicated by an arrow in the display showing an increase or decrease. The generic symbol is used to indicate placement of meters in a circuit when no values or value changes need to be shown.

(a) Digital multimeter   (b) Analog multimeter

▲ FIGURE 2–49

Typical portable multimeters. (a) Courtesy of Fluke Corporation. Reproduced with permission. (b) Courtesy of B+K Precision.

(a) Digital   (b) Bar graph   (c) Analog   (d) Generic

▲ FIGURE 2–50

Examples of meter symbols used in this book. Each of the symbols can be used to represent either an ammeter (A), a voltmeter (V), or an ohmmeter (Ω).

Measuring Current

Figure 2–51 illustrates how to measure current with an ammeter. Part (a) shows a simple circuit in which the current through a resistor is to be measured. Connect an ammeter in the current path by first opening the circuit, as shown in part (b). Then insert the meter as shown in part (c). Such a connection is a *series* connection. The polarity of the meter must be such that the current is in at the negative terminal and out at the positive terminal.

Measuring Voltage

To measure voltage, connect a voltmeter across the component for which the voltage is to be found. Such a connection is a *parallel* connection. The negative terminal of the meter must be connected to the negative side of the circuit, and the positive terminal of the meter must be connected to the positive side of the circuit. Figure 2–52 shows a voltmeter connected to measure the voltage across the resistor.

Measuring Resistance

To measure resistance, connect an ohmmeter across the resistor. *The resistor must first be removed or disconnected from the circuit.* This procedure is shown in Figure 2–53.

SAFETY POINT

Never wear rings or any type of metallic jewelry while working on a circuit. These items may accidentally come in contact with the circuit, causing shock and/or damage to the circuit.

(a) Circuit in which the current is to be measured

(b) Open the circuit either between the resistor and the positive terminal or between the resistor and the negative terminal of source.

(c) Install the ammeter in the current path with polarity as shown (negative to negative, positive to positive).

▲ FIGURE 2–51

Example of an ammeter connection to measure current in a simple circuit.

▲ FIGURE 2–52

Example of a voltmeter connection to measure voltage in a simple circuit.

► FIGURE 2–53

Example of using an ohmmeter to measure resistance.

(a) Disconnect the resistor from the circuit to avoid damage to the meter and/or incorrect measurement.

(b) Measure the resistance. (Polarity is not important.)

Digital Multimeters (DMMs)

A **DMM** is an electronic instrument that combines meters for measurement of voltage, current, and resistance. DMMs are the most widely used type of electronic measuring instrument. Generally, DMMs provide more functions, better accuracy, greater ease of reading, and greater reliability than do analog meters, which are covered next. Analog meters have at least one advantage over DMMs, however. They can track short-term variations and trends in a measured quantity that many DMMs are too slow to respond to. Typical DMMs are shown in Figure 2–54. Many DMMs are autoranging types in which the proper range is automatically selected by internal circuitry.

(a)   (b)

◄ FIGURE 2–54

Typical digital multimeters (DMMs). (Courtesy of B+K Precision)

DMM Functions   The basic functions found on most DMMs are

+ Ohms

+ DC voltage and current

+ AC voltage and current

Some DMMs provide additional functions such as analog bar graph displays, transistor or diode tests, power measurement, and decibel measurement for audio amplifier tests.

DMM Displays   DMMs are available with either LCD (liquid-crystal display) or LED (light-emitting diode) readouts. The LCD is the most commonly used readout in battery-powered instruments because it requires only very small amounts of current. A typical battery-powered DMM with an LCD readout operates on a 9 V battery that will last from a few hundred hours to 2000 hours and more. The disadvantages of LCD readouts are that (a) they are difficult or impossible to see in low-light conditions and (b) they are relatively slow to respond to measurement changes. LEDs, on the other hand, can be seen in the dark and respond quickly to changes in measured values. LED displays require much more current than LCD displays; and, therefore, battery life is shortened when LEDs are used in portable equipment.

Both LCD and LED DMM displays are in a seven-segment format. Each digit in the display consists of seven separate segments, as shown in Figure 2–55(a). Each of the ten

◄ FIGURE 2–55

Seven-segment display.

(a)   (b)

decimal digits is formed by the activation of appropriate segments, as illustrated in Figure 2–55(b). In addition to the seven segments, there is also a decimal point.

Resolution   The **resolution** of a DMM is the smallest increment of a quantity that the DMM can measure. The smaller the increment, the better the resolution. One factor that determines the resolution of a meter is the number of digits in the display.

Because many DMMs have 3½ digits in their display, we will use this case for illustration. A 3½-digit multimeter has three digit positions that can indicate from 0 through 9, and one digit position that can indicate only a value of 1. This latter digit, called the *half-digit*, is always the most significant digit in the display. For example, suppose that a DMM is reading .999 V, as shown in Figure 2–56(a). If the voltage increases by 0.001 V to 1 V, the display correctly shows 1.000 V, as shown in part (b). The "1" is the half-digit. Thus, with 3½ digits, a variation of 0.001 V, which is the resolution, can be observed.

(a) Resolution: 0.001 V

(b) Resolution: 0.001 V

(c) Resolution: 0.001 V

(d) Resolution: 0.01 V

▲ **FIGURE 2–56**

A 3½-digit DMM illustrates how the resolution changes with the number of digits in use.

Now, suppose that the voltage increases to 1.999 V. This value is indicated on the meter as shown in Figure 2–56(c). If the voltage increases by 0.001 V to 2 V, the half-digit cannot display the "2," so the display shows 2.00. The half-digit is blanked and only three digits are active, as indicated in part (d). With only three digits active, the resolution is 0.01 V rather than 0.001 V as it is with 3½ active digits. The resolution remains 0.01 V up to 19.99 V. The resolution goes to 0.1 V for readings of 20.0 V to 199.9 V. At 200 V, the resolution goes to 1 V, and so on.

The resolution capability of a DMM is also determined by the internal circuitry and the rate at which the measured quantity is sampled. DMMs with displays of 4½ through 8½ digits are also available.

Accuracy   As defined in Chapter 1, accuracy is an indication, usually expressed in percentage, of the range of error which is the difference in the measured and true or accepted value of a quantity. The accuracy of a DMM is established strictly by its internal circuitry and calibration. For typical meters, accuracies range from 0.01% to 0.5%, with some precision laboratory-grade meters going to 0.002%.

Reading Analog Multimeters

Although the DMM is predominately used, you may have to use on analog meter on occasion.

Functions   The face of a typical analog (needle-type) multimeter is represented in Figure 2–57. This particular instrument can be used to measure both direct current (dc)

HANDS ON TIP

When reading the scales on an analog meter, always view the scale and "needle" directly from the front and not from an angle. This practice will avoid *parallax*, which is an apparent change in position of the needle relative to the meter scale and results in inaccurate readings.

◀ FIGURE 2–57

A typical analog multimeter.

and alternating current (ac) quantities as well as resistance values. It has four selectable functions: dc volts (DC VOLTS), dc milliamperes (DC mA), ac volts (AC VOLTS), and OHMS. Many analog multimeters are similar to this one, although range selections and scales may vary.

Ranges Within each function there are several ranges, as indicated by the brackets around the selector switch. For example, the DC VOLTS function has 0.3 V, 3 V, 12 V, 60 V, 300 V, and 600 V ranges. Thus, dc voltages from 0.3 V full-scale to 600 V full-scale can be measured. On the DC mA function, direct currents from 0.06 mA full-scale to 120 mA full-scale can be measured. On the ohm scale, the range settings are ×1, ×10, ×100, ×1000, and ×100,000.

The Ohm Scale Ohms are read on the top scale of the meter. This scale is nonlinear; that is, the values represented by each division (large or small) vary as you go across the scale. In Figure 2–57, notice how the scale becomes more compressed as you go from right to left.

To read the actual value in ohms, multiply the number on the scale as indicated by the pointer by the factor selected by the switch. For example, when the switch is set at ×100 and the pointer is at 20, the reading is $20 \times 100 = 2000 \ \Omega$.

As another example, assume that the switch is at ×10 and the pointer is at the seventh small division between the 1 and 2 marks, indicating 17 Ω (1.7 × 10). Now, if the meter remains connected to the same resistance and the switch setting is changed to ×1, the pointer will move to the second small division between the 15 and 20 marks. This, of course, is also a 17 Ω reading, illustrating that a given resistance value can often be read at more than one switch setting. However, the meter should be *zeroed* each time the range is changed by touching the leads together and adjusting the needle.

The AC-DC and DC mA Scales The second, third, and fourth scales from the top (labeled "AC" and "DC") are used in conjunction with the DC VOLTS and AC VOLTS functions. The upper ac-dc scale ends at the 300 mark and is used with range settings such as 0.3, 3, and 300. For example, when the switch is at 3 on the DC VOLTS function, the 300 scale has a full-scale value of 3 V; at the range setting of 300, the full-scale value is 300 V. The middle ac-dc scale ends at 60. This scale is used in conjunction with range settings such as 0.06, 60, and 600. For example, when the switch is at 60 on the DC VOLTS function, the full-scale value is 60 V. The lower ac-dc scale ends at 12 and is used in conjunction with switch settings such as 1.2, 12, and 120. The three DC mA scales are used in a similar way to measure current.

HANDS ON TIP

When you are using a multimeter, such as the analog multimeter illustrated in Figure 2–57, where you manually select the voltage and current ranges, it is good practice to always set the multimeter on the maximum range before you measure an unknown voltage or current. You can then reduce the range until you get an acceptable reading.

EXAMPLE 2–9

In Figure 2–58, determine the quantity (voltage, current, or resistance) that is being measured and its value for each of the following specified switch settings on the meter in Figure 2–57.

(a) DC volts: 60   **(b)** DC mA: 12   **(c)** OHMS: ×1K

▲ FIGURE 2–58

Solution

(a) The reading taken from the middle AC-DC scale is **18 V.**

(b) The reading taken from the lower AC-DC scale is **3.8 mA.**

(c) The reading taken from the ohms scale (top) is **10 kΩ.**

Related Problem

For part (c) in this example, the switch is moved to the ×100 ohms setting. Assuming that the same resistance is being measured, what will the needle do?

SECTION 2–7 REVIEW

1. Name the multimeter functions for measuring
   (a) current   **(b)** voltage   **(c)** resistance

2. Show how to place two ammeters in the circuit of Figure 2–41 to measure the current through either lamp (be sure to observe the polarities). How can the same measurements be accomplished with only one ammeter?

3. Show how to place a voltmeter to measure the voltage across lamp 2 in Figure 2–41.

4. List two common types of DMM displays, and discuss the advantages and disadvantages of each.

5. Define *resolution* in a DMM.

6. The multimeter in Figure 2–57 is set on the 3 V range to measure dc voltage. Assume the pointer is at 150 on the upper ac-dc scale. What voltage is being measured?

7. How do you set up the multimeter in Figure 2–57 to measure 275 V dc, and on what scale do you read the voltage?

8. If you expect to measure a resistance in excess of 20 kΩ with the multimeter in Figure 2–57, where do you set the switch?

Application Assignment

You are to connect and check out a circuit for use in the special lighting effects for an outdoor performance. You will go through a step-by-step process of working through this assignment using things that you've learned in this chapter. Recall that the requirements from the application assignment preview were

1. The lighting system will consist of six lamps that are controlled so that only one is turned on at a time.

2. The sequence can be in any order.

3. A method must be provided for varying the brightness of the lamp that is on.

4. The system must be fused and operate from a 12 V battery.

Step 1: The Circuit

Select the circuit that meets the requirements from the four configurations in Figure 2–59. Explain why the rejected circuits will not meet the requirements. Explain the purpose of each component in your circuit.

Step 2: Connecting the Circuit

From the selection of components in Figure 2–60, specify the quantity of each component required for the lighting circuit. Connect the lighting circuit by developing a point-to-point (From–To) wiring list using component designations and pin numbers.

Step 3: Determining the Current Rating of the Fuse

The fuse protects the circuit by burning open when there is excessive current. The type of lamp to be used draws

(a)   (b)   (c)   (d)

▲ FIGURE 2–59

Lamp (L) 12 V battery (V) Fuse (F) SPST toggle switch (SWA) Rotary switch (SWB) Potentiometer (R)

▲ FIGURE 2–60

Component selection.

approximately 5 A when 12 V are applied. Choose a fuse based on its ampere rating that is the most appropriate for your circuit from the following ratings: 1 A, 2 A, 3 A, 4 A, 5 A, 6 A, 7 A, 8 A, 9 A, 10 A, 20 A, and 30 A. Explain your choice.

Step 4: Determining the Capacity of the Battery

A battery can provide a certain amount of current for a certain period of time at its rated voltage. The amount of amps that a battery can deliver to a load for a given number of hours at its rated voltage is its *ampere-hour rating*. Determine the minimum ampere-hour rating of the battery if the lighting circuit must operate for four hours before the battery is recharged. If necessary, see Section 3–7 for a discussion of the ampere-hour rating.

Step 5: Troubleshooting the Circuit

Once you have connected all the components, it is time to check out the operation to verify that everything is functioning properly.

◆ Write a brief description of the procedure you would use to thoroughly test the circuit. This is called a *test procedure*.

◆ For each of the following cases where the circuit is not working properly, determine the possible fault or faults and specify how you would correct it:

1. Each lamp can be turned on except one.

2. None of the lamps can be turned on.

3. Each lamp is too dim and cannot be brightened by adjusting the rheostat.

4. Each lamp is too dim; however, the amount of light can be varied with the rheostat, but not to full brightness.

Review

1. If the resistance of the rheostat in your lighting circuit is reduced, does the brightness of the selected lamp increase or decrease?

2. Does removing any one of the lamps affect the operation of any of the other lamps?

3. What is the current from the battery when no lamps are on?

4. What will happen if you try to turn on two lamps at the same time? Explain.

SUMMARY

◆ An atom is the smallest particle of an element that retains the characteristics of that element.

◆ The electron is the basic particle of negative electrical charge.

◆ The proton is the basic particle of positive charge.

◆ An ion is an atom that has gained or lost an electron and is no longer neutral.

◆ When electrons in the outer orbit of an atom (valence electrons) break away, they become free electrons.

◆ Free electrons make current possible.

◆ Like charges repel each other, and opposite charges attract each other.

◆ Voltage must be applied to a circuit before there can be current.

◆ Resistance limits the current.

◆ Basically, an electric circuit consists of a source, a load, and a current path.

◆ An open circuit is one in which the current path is broken.

◆ A closed circuit is one which has a complete current path.

◆ An ammeter is connected in line (series) with the current path to measure current.

◆ A voltmeter is connected across (parallel) the current path to measure voltage.

◆ An ohmmeter is connected across a resistor to measure resistance. The resistor must be disconnected from the circuit.

◆ Figure 2–61 shows the electrical symbols introduced in this chapter.

◆ One coulomb is the charge on 6.25×10^{18} electrons.

◆ One volt is the potential difference (voltage) between two points when one joule of energy is used to move one coulomb of charge from one point to the other.

◆ One ampere is the amount of current that exists when one coulomb of charge moves through a given cross-sectional area of a material in one second.

◆ One ohm is the resistance when there is one ampere of current in a material with one volt applied across the material.

▲ FIGURE 2–61

KEY TERMS

Key terms and other bold terms in the chapter are defined in the end-of-book glossary.

Ammeter   An electrical instrument used to measure current.

Ampere (A)   The unit of electrical current.

Atom   The smallest particle of an element possessing the unique characteristics of that element.

AWG   American Wire Gauge; a standardization based on wire diameter.

Charge   An electrical property of matter that exists because of an excess or a deficiency of electrons. Charge can be either positive or negative.

Circuit   An interconnection of electrical components designed to produce a desired result. A basic circuit consists of a source, a load, and an interconnecting current path.

Circuit breaker   A resettable protective device used for interrupting excessive current in an electric circuit.

Closed circuit   A circuit with a complete current path.

Conductance   The ability of a circuit to allow current. The unit is the siemens (S).

Conductor   A material in which electric current is easily established. An example is copper.

Coulomb (C)   The unit of electrical charge; the total charge possessed by 6.25×10^{18} electrons.

Current   The rate of flow of charge (free electrons).

Current source   A device that produces a constant current for a varying load.

DMM   Digital multimeter; an electronic instrument that combines meters for measurement of voltage, current, and resistance.

Electron   A basic particle of electrical charge in matter. The electron possesses negative charge.

Free electron   A valence electron that has broken away from its parent atom and is free to move from atom to atom within the atomic structure of a material.

Fuse   A protective device that burns open when there is excessive current in a circuit.

Ground   The common or reference point in a circuit.

Insulator   A material that does not allow current under normal conditions.

Load   An element (resistor or other component) connected across the output terminals of a circuit that draws current from the source and upon which work is done.

Ohm (Ω)   The unit of resistance.

Ohmmeter   An instrument for measuring resistance.

Open circuit   A circuit in which there is not a complete current path.

Potentiometer   A three-terminal variable resistor.

Resistance   Opposition to current. The unit is the ohm (Ω).

Resistor   An electrical component designed specifically to have a certain amount of resistance.

Rheostat   A two-terminal variable resistor.

Schematic   A symbolized diagram of an electrical or electronic circuit.

Semiconductor   A material that has a conductance value between that of a conductor and an insulator. Silicon and germanium are examples.

Siemens (S)   The unit of conductance.

Switch   An electrical or electronic device for opening and closing a current path.

Volt (V)   The unit of voltage or electromotive force.

Voltage   The amount of energy per charge available to move electrons from one point to another in an electric circuit.

Voltage source   A device that produces a constant voltage for a varying load.

Voltmeter   An instrument used to measure voltage.

FORMULAS

2–1	$Q = \dfrac{\text{number of electrons}}{6.25 \times 10^{18} \text{ electrons/C}}$	Charge
2–2	$V = \dfrac{W}{Q}$	Voltage in volts equals energy in joules divided by charge in coulombs.
2–3	$I = \dfrac{Q}{t}$	Current in amperes equals charge in coulombs divided by time in seconds.
2–4	$G = \dfrac{1}{R}$	Conductance in siemens is the reciprocal of resistance in ohms.
2–5	$A = d^2$	Cross-sectional area in circular mils equals the diameter in mils squared.
2–6	$R = \dfrac{\rho l}{A}$	Resistance is resistivity in CM Ω/ft times length in feet divided by cross-sectional area in circular mils.

SELF-TEST

Answers are at the end of the chapter.

1. A neutral atom with an atomic number of three has how many electrons?

   (a) 1   **(b)** 3   **(c)** none   **(d)** depends on the type of atom

2. Electron orbits are called

   (a) shells   **(b)** nuclei   **(c)** waves   **(d)** valences

3. Materials in which current cannot be established are called

   (a) filters   **(b)** conductors   **(c)** insulators   **(d)** semiconductors

4. When placed close together, a positively charged material and a negatively charged material will

   (a) repel   **(b)** become neutral   **(c)** attract   **(d)** exchange charges

5. The charge on a single electron is

   (a) 6.25×10^{-18} C   **(b)** 1.6×10^{-19} C   **(c)** 1.6×10^{-19} J   **(d)** 3.14×10^{-6} C

6. *Potential difference* is another term for

   (a) energy   **(b)** voltage   **(c)** distance of an electron from the nucleus   **(d)** charge

7. The unit of energy is the

   (a) watt   **(b)** coulomb   **(c)** joule   **(d)** volt

8. Which one of the following is not a type of energy source?

    (a) battery   (b) solar cell   (c) generator   (d) potentiometer

9. Which one of the following is generally not a possible condition in an electric circuit?

    (a) voltage and no current   (b) current and no voltage

    (c) voltage and current   (d) no voltage and no current

10. Electrical current is defined as

    (a) free electrons   (b) the rate of flow of free electrons

    (c) the energy required to move electrons   (d) the charge on free electrons

11. There is no current in a circuit when

    (a) a series switch is closed   (b) a series switch is open   (c) there is no source voltage

    (d) both (a) and (c)   (e) both (b) and (c)

12. The primary purpose of a resistor is to

    (a) increase current   (b) limit current   (c) produce heat   (d) resist current change

13. Potentiometers and rheostats are types of

    (a) voltage sources   (b) variable resistors   (c) fixed resistors   (d) circuit breakers

14. The current in a given circuit is not to exceed 22 A. Which value of fuse is best?

    (a) 10 A   (b) 25 A   (c) 20 A   (d) a fuse is not necessary

PROBLEMS

Answers to odd-numbered problems are at the end of the book.

BASIC PROBLEMS

SECTION 2–2 Electrical Charge

1. How many coulombs of charge do 50×10^{31} electrons possess?
2. How many electrons does it take to make $80\,\mu C$ of charge?
3. What is the charge in coulombs of the nucleus of a copper atom?
4. What is the charge in coulombs of the nucleus of a chlorine atom?

SECTION 2–3 Voltage

5. Determine the voltage in each of the following cases:

    (a) 10 J/C   (b) 5 J/2 C   (c) 100 J/25 C

6. Five hundred joules of energy are used to move 100 C of charge through a resistor. What is the voltage across the resistor?
7. What is the voltage of a battery that uses 800 J of energy to move 40 C of charge through a resistor?
8. How much energy does a 12 V battery in your car use to move 2.5 C through the electrical circuit?

SECTION 2–4 Current

9. Determine the current in each of the following cases:

    (a) 75 C in 1 s   (b) 10 C in 0.5 s   (c) 5 C in 2 s

10. Six-tenths coulomb passes a point in 3 s. What is the current in amperes?
11. How long does it take 10 C to flow past a point if the current is 5 A?
12. How many coulombs pass a point in 0.1 s when the current is 1.5 A?

SECTION 2–5 Resistance

13. Figure 2–62(a) shows color-coded resistors. Determine the resistance value and the tolerance of each.

(a)

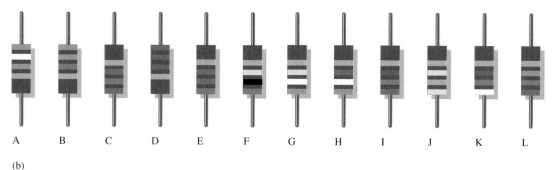

A   B   C   D   E   F   G   H   I   J   K   L

(b)

▲ FIGURE 2–62

14. Find the minimum and the maximum resistance within the tolerance limits for each resistor in Figure 2–62(a).

15. (a) If you need a 270 Ω resistor with 5% tolerance, what color bands should you look for?

    (b) From the selection of resistors in Figure 2–62(b), choose the following values: 330 Ω, 2.2 kΩ, 39 kΩ, 56 kΩ, and 100 kΩ.

16. Determine the resistance value and tolerance for each resistor in Figure 2–63.

▶ FIGURE 2–63

(a)   (b)   (c)

17. Determine the resistance and tolerance of each of the following 4-band resistors:

    (a) brown, black, black, gold   (b) green, brown, green, silver

    (c) blue, gray, black, gold

18. Determine the color bands for each of the following 4-band resistors. Assume each has a 5% tolerance.

    (a) 0.47 Ω   (b) 270 kΩ   (c) 5.1 MΩ

19. Determine the resistance and tolerance of each of the following 5-band resistors:

    (a) red, gray, violet, red, brown

    (b) blue, black, yellow, gold, brown

    (c) white, orange, brown, brown, brown

20. Determine the color bands for each of the following 5-band resistors. Assume each has a 1% tolerance.

    (a) 14.7 kΩ   (b) 39.2 Ω   (c) 9.76 kΩ

21. Determine the resistance value represented by the numeric labels in parts (a), (b), and (c) and the alphanumeric labels in parts (d), (e), and (f).

    (a) 220   (b) 472   (c) 823   (d) 3K3   (e) 560   (f) 10M

22. The adjustable contact of a linear potentiometer is set at the mechanical center of its adjustment. If the total resistance is 1000 Ω, what is the resistance between each end terminal and the adjustable contact?

SECTION 2–6 The Electric Circuit

23. Trace the current path in the lamp circuit of Figure 2–41(a) with the switch making contact between the middle and lower pins.

24. With the switch in either position, redraw the lamp circuit in Figure 2–41(b) with a fuse connected to protect the circuit against excessive current.

SECTION 2–7 Basic Circuit Measurements

25. Show the placement of an ammeter and a voltmeter to measure the current and the source voltage in Figure 2–64.

26. Show how you would measure the resistance of R_2 in Figure 2–64.

27. In Figure 2–65 what does each voltmeter indicate when the switch (SW) is in position 1? In position 2?

28. In Figure 2–65, show how to connect an ammeter to measure the current from the voltage source regardless of the switch (SW) position.

▲ FIGURE 2–64   ▲ FIGURE 2–65

29. What is the voltage reading of the meter in Figure 2–66?

▶ FIGURE 2–66

30. How much resistance is the meter in Figure 2–67 measuring?

▶ FIGURE 2–67

31. Determine the resistance indicated by each of the following ohmmeter readings and range settings:

(a) pointer at 2, range setting at R × 100

(b) pointer at 15, range setting at R × 10M

(c) pointer at 45, range setting at R × 100

32. A multimeter has the following ranges: 1 mA, 10 mA, 100 mA; 100 mV, 1 V, 10 V; R × 1, R × 10, R × 100. Indicate schematically how you would connect the multimeter in Figure 2–68 to measure the following quantities:

(a) I_{R1} **(b)** V_{R1} **(c)** R_1

In each case indicate the *function* to which you would set the meter and the *range* that you would use.

▶ FIGURE 2–68

ADVANCED PROBLEMS

33. A resistor with a current of 2 A through it in an amplifier circuit converts 1000 J of electrical energy to heat energy in 15 s. What is the voltage across the resistor?

34. If 574×10^{15} electrons flow through a speaker wire in 250 ms, what is the current in amperes?

35. A 120 V source is to be connected to a 1500 Ω resistive load by two lengths of wire as shown in Figure 2–69. The voltage source is to be located 50 ft from the load. Using Table 2–4, determine the gauge number of the *smallest* wire that can be used if the total resistance of the two lengths of wire is not to exceed 6 Ω.

▶ FIGURE 2–69

36. Determine the resistance and tolerance of each resistor labeled as follows:

(a) 4R7J   (b) 560KF   (c) 1M5G

37. There is only one circuit in Figure 2–70 in which it is possible to have all lamps on at the same time. Determine which circuit it is.

▲ FIGURE 2–70

38. Through which resistor in Figure 2–71 is there always current, regardless of the position of the switches?

▶ FIGURE 2–71

39. In Figure 2–71, show the proper placement of ammeters to measure the current through each resistor and the current out of the battery.

40. Show the proper placement of voltmeters to measure the voltage across each resistor in Figure 2–71.

41. Devise a switch arrangement whereby two voltage sources V_{S1} and V_{S2} can be connected simultaneously to either of two resistors (R_1 and R_2) as follows:

V_{S1} connected to R_1 and V_{S2} connected to R_2

V_{S1} connected to R_2 and V_{S2} connected to R_1

42. The different sections of a stereo system are represented by the blocks in Figure 2–72. Show how a single switch can be used to connect the phonograph, the CD (compact disk) player, the tape deck, the AM tuner, or the FM tuner to the amplifier by a single knob control. Only one section can be connected to the amplifier at any time.

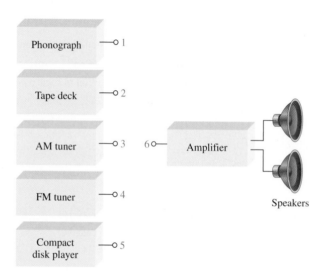

▲ FIGURE 2–72

ANSWERS

SECTION REVIEWS

SECTION 2–1 Atoms

1. The electron is the basic particle of negative charge.

2. An atom is the smallest particle of an element that retains the unique characteristics of the element.

3. An atom is a positively charged nucleus surrounded by orbiting electrons.

4. Atomic number is the number of protons in a nucleus.

5. No, each element has a different type of atom.

6. A free electron is an outer-shell electron that has drifted away from the parent atom.

7. Shells are energy bands in which electrons orbit the nucleus of an atom.

8. Copper and silver

SECTION 2–2 Electrical Charge

1. Q is the symbol for charge.

2. Coulomb is the unit of charge, and C is the symbol for coulomb.

3. The two types of charge are positive and negative.

4. $Q = \dfrac{10 \times 10^{12} \text{ electrons}}{6.25 \times 10^{18} \text{ electrons/C}} = 1.6 \times 10^{-6}\,\text{C} = 1.6\,\mu\text{C}$

SECTION 2–3 Voltage

1. Voltage is energy per unit charge.
2. The unit of voltage is the volt.
3. $V = W/Q = 24 \text{ J}/10 \text{ C} = 2.4 \text{ V}$
4. Battery, electronic power supply, solar cell, generator, thermocouple, and piezoelectric sensors are voltage sources.

SECTION 2–4 Current

1. Current is the rate of flow of charge; the unit of current is the ampere (A).
2. There are 6.25×10^{18} electrons in one coulomb.
3. $I = Q/t = 20 \text{ C}/4 \text{ s} = 5 \text{ A}$

SECTION 2–5 Resistance

1. Resistance is opposition to current and its unit is the ohm (Ω).
2. Two resistor categories are fixed and variable. The value of a fixed resistor cannot be changed, but that of a variable resistor can.
3. *First band:* first digit of resistance value.

   Second band: second digit of resistance value.

   Third band: number of zeros following the 2nd digit.

   Fourth band: percent tolerance.
4. (a) Yellow, violet, red, gold = $4700 \, \Omega \pm 5\%$

   (b) Blue, red, orange, silver = $62{,}000 \, \Omega \pm 10\%$

   (c) Brown, gray, black, gold = $18 \, \Omega \pm 5\%$

   (d) Red, red, blue, red, green = $22.5 \, \text{k}\Omega \pm 0.5\%$
5. (a) 33R = $33 \, \Omega$

   (b) 5K6 = $5.6 \, \text{k}\Omega$

   (c) 900 = $900 \, \Omega$

   (d) 6M8 = $6.8 \, \text{M}\Omega$
6. A rheostat has two terminals; a potentiometer has three terminals.
7. A thermistor is a temperature-sensitive resistor.

SECTION 2–6 The Electric Circuit

1. A basic electric circuit consists of source, load, and current path between source and load.
2. An open circuit is one that has no path for current.
3. A closed circuit is one that has a complete path for current.
4. $R = \infty$ (infinite); $R = 0 \, \Omega$
5. A fuse protects a circuit against excessive current.
6. A fuse must be replaced once blown. A circuit breaker can be reset once tripped.
7. AWG #3 is larger than AWG #22.
8. Ground is the reference point with zero voltage with respect to other points.

SECTION 2–7 Basic Circuit Measurements

1. (a) Ammeter measures current.

   (b) Voltmeter measures voltage.

   (c) Ohmmeter measures resistance.

▶ FIGURE 2–73

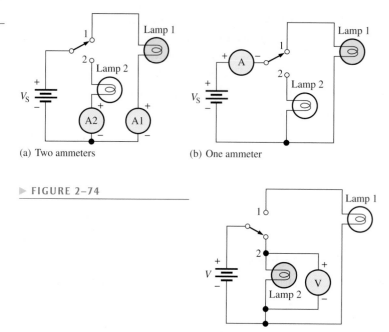

(a) Two ammeters   (b) One ammeter

▶ FIGURE 2–74

2. See Figure 2–73.

3. See Figure 2–74.

4. Two types of DMM displays are LED and LCD. The LCD requires little current, but it is difficult to see in low light and is slow to respond. The LED can be seen in the dark, and it responds quickly; however, it requires much more current than does the LCD.

5. Resolution is the smallest increment of a quantity that a meter can measure.

6. The voltage being measured is 1.5 V.

7. DC VOLTS, 600 setting; 275 V is read on the 60 scale near midpoint.

8. OHMS × 1000

Application Assignment

1. The brightness increases.

2. No

3. There is no current when all lights are off.

4. The total current would increase, possibly causing the fuse to blow.

RELATED PROBLEMS FOR EXAMPLES

2–1 1.88×10^{19} electrons

2–2 600 J

2–3 12 C

2–4 4700 Ω ± 5%

2–5 47.5 Ω ± 2%

2–6 1.25 kΩ

2–7 404.01 CM; #24

2–8 1.280 Ω; same as calculated result

2–9 The needle will indicate 100 on the top scale.

SELF-TEST

1. (b)   2. (a)   3. (c)   4. (c)   5. (b)   6. (b)   7. (c)

8. (d)   9. (b)   10. (b)   11. (e)   12. (b)   13. (b)   14. (c)

Ohm's Law, Energy, and Power

3

CHAPTER OBJECTIVES

◆ Explain Ohm's law

◆ Use Ohm's law to determine voltage, current, or resistance

◆ Define *energy* and *power*

◆ Calculate power in a circuit

◆ Properly select resistors based on power consideration

◆ Explain energy conversion and voltage drop

◆ Discuss power supplies and their characteristics

◆ Describe a basic approach to troubleshooting

KEY TERMS

◆ Ohm's law
◆ Linear
◆ Energy
◆ Power
◆ Joule (J)
◆ Watt (W)
◆ Kilowatt-hour (kWh)
◆ Watt's law
◆ Power rating
◆ Voltage drop
◆ Power supply
◆ Ampere-hour rating
◆ Efficiency
◆ Troubleshooting
◆ Half-splitting

APPLICATION ASSIGNMENT PREVIEW

You are assigned the task of modifying an existing test fixture for use in a new application. The test fixture is a resistance box with an array of switch-selectable resistors of various values. Your assignment will be to determine and specify the changes to be made in the existing circuit and develop a procedure to test the box once the modifications have been made. To complete the assignment, you will

1. Determine color-coded resistor values.

2. Determine resistor power ratings.

3. Draw the schematic of the existing circuit.

4. Draw the schematic to meet the new requirements.

5. Use Watt's law power formulas to determine required power ratings.

6. Use Ohm's law to determine resistor values to meet specifications.

After studying this chapter, you should be able to complete the application assignment.

VISIT THE COMPANION WEBSITE

Study aids for this chapter are available at
http://www.prenhall.com/floyd

INTRODUCTION

Georg Simon Ohm (1787–1854) experimentally found that voltage, current, and resistance are all related in a specific way. This basic relationship, known as *Ohm's law,* is one of the most fundamental and important laws in the fields of electricity and electronics. In this chapter, Ohm's law is examined, and its use in practical circuit applications is discussed and demonstrated by numerous examples.

In addition to Ohm's law, the concepts and definitions of energy and power in electric circuits are introduced and the Watt's law power formulas are given. A general approach to troubleshooting using the analysis, planning, and measurement (APM) method is also introduced.

3–1   OHM'S LAW

Ohm's law describes mathematically how voltage, current, and resistance in a circuit are related. Ohm's law can be written in three equivalent forms; the formula you use depends on the quantity you need to determine.

After completing this section, you should be able to

◆ **Explain Ohm's law**

    ◆ Describe how voltage (*V*), current (*I*), and resistance (*R*) are related

    ◆ Express *I* as a function of *V* and *R*

    ◆ Express *V* as a function of *I* and *R*

    ◆ Express *R* as a function of *V* and *I*

Ohm determined experimentally that if the voltage across a resistor is increased, the current through the resistor will increase; and, likewise, if the voltage is decreased, the current will decrease. For example, if the voltage is doubled, the current will double. If the voltage is halved, the current will also be halved. This relationship is illustrated in Figure 3–1, with relative meter indications of voltage and current.

(a) Less *V*, less *I*   (b) More *V*, more *I*

▲ FIGURE 3–1

Effect on the current of changing the voltage with the resistance at a constant value.

Ohm also determined that if the voltage is kept constant, less resistance results in more current, and more resistance results in less current. For example, if the resistance is halved, the current doubles. If the resistance is doubled, the current is halved. This concept is illustrated by the meter indications in Figure 3–2, where the resistance is increased and the voltage is held constant.

▲ FIGURE 3–2

Effect on the current of changing the resistance with the voltage at a constant value.

Ohm's law states that current is directly proportional to voltage and inversely proportional to resistance.

$$I = \frac{V}{R}$$

Equation 3–1

where: I = current in amperes (A)
         V = voltage in volts (V)
         R = resistance in ohms (Ω)

This formula describes the relationship illustrated by the action in the circuits of Figures 3–1 and 3–2.

For a constant resistance, if the voltage applied to a circuit is increased, the current will increase; and if the voltage is decreased, the current will decrease.

$$I = \frac{V}{R} \qquad\qquad I = \frac{V}{R} \qquad\qquad R \text{ constant}$$

Increase V, I increases   Decrease V, I decreases

For a constant voltage, if the resistance in a circuit is increased, the current will decrease; and if the resistance is decreased, the current will increase.

$$I = \frac{V}{R} \qquad\qquad I = \frac{V}{R} \qquad\qquad V \text{ constant}$$

Increase R, I decreases   Decrease R, I increases

EXAMPLE 3–1

Using the Ohm's law formula in Equation 3–1, verify that the current through a 10 Ω resistor increases when the voltage is increased from 5 V to 20 V.

Solution   For $V = 5$ V,

$$I = \frac{V}{R} = \frac{5\ V}{10\ \Omega} = \textbf{0.5 A}$$

For $V = 20$ V,

$$I = \frac{V}{R} = \frac{20\ V}{10\ \Omega} = \textbf{2 A}$$

Related Problem*   Show that the current decreases when the resistance is increased from 5 Ω to 20 Ω and the voltage is a constant 10 V.

* Answers are at the end of the chapter.

Ohm's law can also be stated another equivalent way. By multiplying both sides of Equation 3–1 by R and transposing terms, you obtain an equivalent form of Ohm's law, as follows:

$$V = IR$$

Equation 3–2

With this formula, you can calculate voltage in volts if you know the current in amperes and resistance in ohms.

EXAMPLE 3–2

Use the Ohm's law formula in Equation 3–2 to calculate the voltage across a 100 Ω resistor when the current is 2 A.

Solution

$$V = IR = (2\text{ A})(100\ \Omega) = \textbf{200 V}$$

Related Problem   Find the voltage across a 1.0 kΩ resistor when the current is 1 mA.

There is a third equivalent way to state Ohm's law. By dividing both sides of Equation 3–2 by I and transposing terms, you obtain the following formula:

Equation 3–3

$$R = \frac{V}{I}$$

This expression of the Ohm's law formula is used to determine resistance in ohms if you know the values of voltage in volts and current in amperes.

Remember, the three expressions—Equations 3–1, 3–2, and 3–3—are all equivalent. They are simply three ways of using Ohm's law.

EXAMPLE 3–3

Use the Ohm's law formula in Equation 3–3 to calculate the resistance in a circuit when the voltage is 12 V and the current is 0.5 A.

Solution

$$R = \frac{V}{I} = \frac{12\text{ V}}{0.5\text{ A}} = \textbf{24 }\boldsymbol{\Omega}$$

Related Problem   Find the resistance when the voltage is 9 V and the current is 10 mA.

The Linear Relationship of Current and Voltage

In resistive circuits, current and voltage are linearly proportional. **Linear** means that if one is increased or decreased by a certain percentage, the other will increase or decrease by the same percentage, assuming that the resistance is constant in value. For example, if the voltage across a resistor is tripled, the current will triple. If the voltage is reduced by half, the current will decrease by half.

EXAMPLE 3–4

Show that if the voltage in the circuit of Figure 3–3 is increased to three times its present value, the current will triple in value.

▶ FIGURE 3–3

Solution   With 10 V, the current is

$$I = \frac{V}{R} = \frac{10\text{ V}}{100\ \Omega} = 0.1\text{ A}$$

If the voltage is increased to 30 V, the current will be

$$I = \frac{V}{R} = \frac{30\,V}{100\,\Omega} = 0.3\,A$$

The current went from 0.1 A to 0.3 A when the voltage was tripled to 30 V.

Related Problem   If the voltage in Figure 3–3 is quadrupled, will the current also quadruple?

Let's take a constant value of resistance, for example, 10 Ω, and calculate the current for several values of voltage ranging from 10 V to 100 V in the circuit in Figure 3–4(a). The current values obtained are shown in Figure 3–4(b). The graph of the *I* values versus the *V* values is shown in Figure 3–4(c). Note that it is a straight line graph. This graph shows that a change in voltage results in a linearly proportional change in current. No matter what value *R* is, assuming that *R* is constant, the graph of *I* versus *V* will always be a straight line.

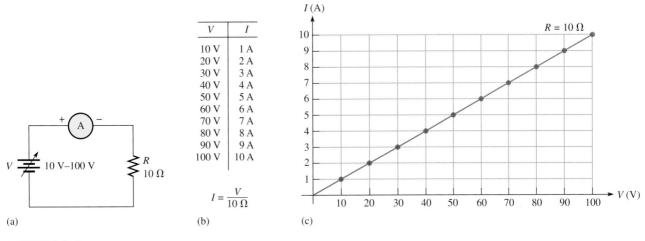

V	I
10 V	1 A
20 V	2 A
30 V	3 A
40 V	4 A
50 V	5 A
60 V	6 A
70 V	7 A
80 V	8 A
90 V	9 A
100 V	10 A

$$I = \frac{V}{10\,\Omega}$$

(a)   (b)   (c)

▲ FIGURE 3–4

Graph of current versus voltage for the circuit in part (a).

A Graphic Aid for Ohm's Law

You may find the graphic aid in Figure 3–5 helpful for applying Ohm's law. It is a way to remember the formulas.

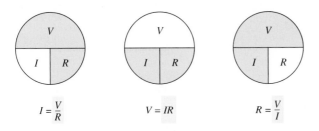

$$I = \frac{V}{R}$$ $$V = IR$$ $$R = \frac{V}{I}$$

▲ FIGURE 3–5

A graphic aid for the Ohm's law formulas.

**SECTION 3–1
REVIEW**
Answers are at the end of the chapter.

1. Briefly state Ohm's law in words.
2. Write the Ohm's law formula for calculating current.
3. Write the Ohm's law formula for calculating voltage.
4. Write the Ohm's law formula for calculating resistance.
5. If the voltage across a resistor is tripled, does the current increase or decrease? By how much?
6. There is a fixed voltage across a variable resistor, and you measure a current of 10 mA. If you double the resistance, how much current will you measure?
7. What happens to the current in a linear circuit where both the voltage and the resistance are doubled?

3–2 Application of Ohm's Law

This section provides examples of the application of Ohm's law for calculating voltage, current, and resistance in electric circuits. You will also see how to use quantities expressed with metric prefixes in circuit calculations.

After completing this section, you should be able to

◆ **Use Ohm's law to determine voltage, current, or resistance**

 ◆ Use Ohm's law to find current when you know voltage and resistance

 ◆ Use Ohm's law to find voltage when you know current and resistance

 ◆ Use Ohm's law to find resistance when you know voltage and current

 ◆ Use quantities with metric prefixes

Calculating Current

In these examples you will learn to determine current values when you know the values of voltage and resistance. In these problems, the formula $I = V/R$ is used. In order to get current in amperes, you must express the value of V in volts and the value of R in ohms.

EXAMPLE 3–5

How many amperes of current are in the circuit of Figure 3–6?

▶ FIGURE 3–6

Solution   Use the Ohm's law formula $I = V/R$ to find the current. Substitute the values for the source voltage and resistance shown in the figure.

$$I = \frac{V_S}{R} = \frac{100 \text{ V}}{22 \text{ }\Omega} = \mathbf{4.55 \text{ A}}$$

Related Problem   What is the current in Figure 3–6 if the voltage is reduced to 50 V?

Open Multisim file E03-05 on your CD-ROM. Connect the multimeter to the circuit and verify the value of current calculated in this example.

In electronics, resistance values of thousands or millions of ohms are common. The metric prefixes *kilo* (k) and *mega* (M) are used to indicate large values. Thus, thousands of ohms are expressed in kilohms (kΩ), and millions of ohms are expressed in megohms (MΩ). The following examples illustrate how to use kilohms and megohms when you use Ohm's law to calculate current.

EXAMPLE 3–6

Calculate the current in milliamperes for the circuit of Figure 3–7.

▶ FIGURE 3–7

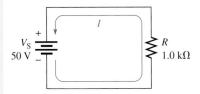

Solution   Remember that $1.0\,\text{k}\Omega$ is the same as $1.0 \times 10^3\,\Omega$. Use the formula $I = V/R$ and substitute 50 V for V and $1.0 \times 10^3\,\Omega$ for R.

$$I = \frac{V_S}{R} = \frac{50\,\text{V}}{1.0\,\text{k}\Omega} = \frac{50\,\text{V}}{1.0 \times 10^3\,\Omega} = 50 \times 10^{-3}\,\text{A} = \mathbf{50\,mA}$$

Related Problem   If the resistance in Figure 3–7 is increased to $10\,\text{k}\Omega$, what is the current?

Open Multisim file E03-06 on your CD-ROM. Connect the multimeter to the circuit and verify the value of current calculated in this example.

In Example 3–6, the current is expressed as 50 mA. Thus, *when volts (V) are divided by kilohms (kΩ), the current is in milliamperes (mA).*

When volts (V) are divided by megohms (MΩ), the current is in microamperes (μA), as Example 3–7 illustrates.

EXAMPLE 3–7

Determine the amount of current in microamperes for the circuit of Figure 3–8.

▶ FIGURE 3–8

Solution Recall that 4.7 MΩ equals 4.7 × 10⁶ Ω. Use the formula $I = V/R$ and substitute 25 V for V and 4.7 × 10⁶ Ω for R.

$$I = \frac{V_S}{R} = \frac{25 \text{ V}}{4.7 \text{ M}\Omega} = \frac{25 \text{ V}}{4.7 \times 10^6 \, \Omega} = 5.32 \times 10^{-6} \text{ A} = \mathbf{5.32 \, \mu A}$$

Related Problem If the resistance in Figure 3–8 is decreased to 1.0 MΩ, what is the current?

 Open Multisim file E03-07 on your CD-ROM. Connect the multimeter to the circuit and verify the value of current calculated in this example.

Small voltages, usually less than 50 V, are common in electronic circuits. Occasionally, however, large voltages are encountered. For example, the high-voltage supply in a television receiver is around 20,000 V (20 kV). Transmission voltages generated by the power companies may be as high as 345,000 V (345 kV).

EXAMPLE 3–8

How much current in microamperes is there through a 100 MΩ resistor when 50 kV are applied across it?

Solution Divide 50 kV by 100 MΩ to get the current. Substitute 50 × 10³ V for 50 kV and 100 × 10⁶ Ω for 100 MΩ in the formula for current. V_R is the voltage across the resistor.

$$I = \frac{V_R}{R} = \frac{50 \text{ kV}}{100 \text{ M}\Omega} = \frac{50 \times 10^3 \text{ V}}{100 \times 10^6 \, \Omega} = 0.5 \times 10^{-3} \text{ A} = 500 \times 10^{-6} = \mathbf{500 \, \mu A}$$

Related Problem How much current is there through 10 MΩ when 2 kV are applied?

Calculating Voltage

In these examples you will learn how to determine voltage values when you know the current and resistance using the formula $V = IR$. To obtain voltage in volts, you must express the value of I in amperes and the value of R in ohms.

EXAMPLE 3–9

In the circuit of Figure 3–9, how much voltage is needed to produce 5 A of current?

▲ FIGURE 3–9

Solution Substitute 5 A for I and 100 Ω for R into the formula $V = IR$.

$$V_S = IR = (5\text{ A})(100\text{ Ω}) = \textbf{500 V}$$

Thus, 500 V are required to produce 5 A of current through a 100 Ω resistor.

Related Problem How much voltage is required to produce 8 A in the circuit of Figure 3–9?

EXAMPLE 3–10

How much voltage will be measured across the resistor in Figure 3–10?

▶ FIGURE 3–10

Solution Note that 5 mA equals 5×10^{-3} A. Substitute the values for I and R into the formula $V = IR$.

$$V_R = IR = (5\text{ mA})(56\text{ Ω}) = (5 \times 10^{-3}\text{ A})(56\text{ Ω}) = \textbf{280 mV}$$

When milliamperes are multiplied by ohms, the result is millivolts.

Related Problem Change the resistor in Figure 3–10 to 22 Ω and determine the voltage required to produce 10 mA.

EXAMPLE 3–11

The circuit in Figure 3–11 has a current of 10 mA. What is the source voltage?

▶ FIGURE 3–11

Solution Note that 10 mA equals 10×10^{-3} A and that 3.3 kΩ equals 3.3×10^{3} Ω. Substitute these values into the formula $V = IR$.

$$V_S = IR = (10\text{ mA})(3.3\text{ kΩ}) = (10 \times 10^{-3}\text{ A})(3.3 \times 10^{3}\text{ Ω}) = \textbf{33 V}$$

When milliamperes and kilohms are multiplied, the result is volts.

Related Problem What is the voltage in Figure 3–11 if the current is 5 mA?

Calculating Resistance

In these examples you will learn how to determine resistance values when you know the voltage and current using the formula $R = V/I$. To find resistance in ohms, you must express the value of V in volts and the value of I in amperes.

EXAMPLE 3–12

In the circuit of Figure 3–12 how much resistance is needed to draw 3 A of current from the battery?

▶ FIGURE 3–12

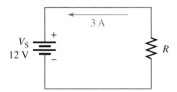

Solution   Substitute 12 V for V and 3 A for I into the formula $R = V/I$.

$$R = \frac{V_S}{I} = \frac{12\ V}{3\ A} = \mathbf{4\ \Omega}$$

Related Problem   How much resistance is required to draw 3 mA from the battery in Figure 3–12?

EXAMPLE 3–13

The ammeter in Figure 3–13 indicates 5 mA of current and the voltmeter reads 150 V. What is the value of R?

▶ FIGURE 3–13

Solution   Note that 5 mA equals 5×10^{-3} A. Substitute the voltage and current values into the formula $R = V/I$.

$$R = \frac{V_S}{I} = \frac{150\ V}{5\ mA} = \frac{150\ V}{5 \times 10^{-3}\ A} = 30 \times 10^3\ \Omega = \mathbf{30\ k\Omega}$$

Thus, if volts are divided by milliamperes, the resistance will be in kilohms.

Related Problem   Determine the value of R if $V_S = 50$ V and $I = 500$ mA in Figure 3–13.

**SECTION 3–2
REVIEW**

1. $V = 10$ V and $R = 4.7\ \Omega$. Find I.
2. If a 4.7 MΩ resistor has 20 kV across it, how much current is there?
3. How much current will 10 kV across a 2 kΩ resistance produce?
4. $I = 1$ A and $R = 10\ \Omega$. Find V.
5. What voltage do you need to produce 3 mA of current in a 3 kΩ resistance?
6. A battery produces 2 A of current through a 6 Ω resistive load. What is the battery voltage?
7. $V = 10$ V and $I = 2$ A. Find R.
8. In a stereo amplifier circuit there is a resistor across which you measure 25 V, and your ammeter indicates 50 mA of current through the resistor. What is the resistor's value in kilohms? In ohms?

3–3   ENERGY AND POWER

When there is current through a resistance, electrical energy is converted to heat or other form of energy, such as light. A common example of this is a light bulb that becomes too hot to touch. The current through the filament that produces light also produces unwanted heat because the filament has resistance. Electrical components must be able to dissipate a certain amount of energy in a given period of time.

After completing this section, you should be able to

◆ **Define** *energy* **and** *power*

  ◆ Express power in terms of energy

  ◆ State the unit of power

  ◆ State the common units of energy

  ◆ Perform energy and power calculations

Energy is the ability to do work, and power is the rate at which energy is used.

In other words, power, P, is a certain amount of energy, W, used in a certain length of time (t), expressed as follows:

$$P = \frac{W}{t}$$

Equation 3–4

where: P = power in watts (W)

   W = energy in joules (J)

   t = time in seconds (s)

Note that an italic W is used to represent energy in the form of work and a nonitalic W is used for watts, the unit of power. The **joule** is the SI unit for energy.

Energy in joules divided by time in seconds gives power in watts. For example, if 50 J of energy are used in 2 s, the power is 50 J/2 s = 25 W. By definition,

One watt is the amount of power when one joule of energy is used in one second.

Thus, the number of joules used in 1 s is always equal to the number of watts. For example, if 75 J are used in 1 s, the power is

$$P = \frac{W}{t} = \frac{75 \text{ J}}{1 \text{ s}} = 75 \text{ W}$$

Amounts of power much less than one watt are common in certain areas of electronics. As with small current and voltage values, metric prefixes are used to designate small amounts of power. Thus, milliwatts (mW) and microwatts (μW) are commonly found in some applications.

In the electrical utilities field, kilowatts (kW) and megawatts (MW) are common units. Radio and television stations also use large amounts of power to transmit signals. Electric motors are commonly rated in horsepower (hp) where 1 hp = 746 W.

Since power is the rate at which energy is used, power utilized over a period of time represents energy consumption. If you multiply power in watts and time in seconds, you have energy in joules, symbolized by W.

$$W = Pt$$

B I O G R A P H Y

James Prescott Joule
1818–1889

Joule, a British physicist, is known for his research in electricity and thermodynamics. He formulated the relationship that states that the amount of heat energy produced by an electrical current in a conductor is proportional to the conductor's resistance and the time. The unit of energy is named in his honor. (Photo credit: Library of Congress.)

EXAMPLE 3–14   An amount of energy equal to 100 J is used in 5 s. What is the power in watts?

Solution
$$P = \frac{\text{energy}}{\text{time}} = \frac{W}{t} = \frac{100 \text{ J}}{5 \text{ s}} = \textbf{20 W}$$

Related Problem   If 100 W of power occurs for 30 s, how much energy in joules is used?

EXAMPLE 3–15   Express the following powers using appropriate metric prefixes:

(a) 0.045 W   (b) 0.000012 W   (c) 3500 W   (d) 10,000,000 W

Solution   (a) $0.045 \text{ W} = 45 \times 10^{-3} \text{ W} = \textbf{45 mW}$

(b) $0.000012 \text{ W} = 12 \times 10^{-6} \text{ W} = \textbf{12 } \boldsymbol{\mu}\textbf{W}$

(c) $3500 \text{ W} = 3.5 \times 10^{3} \text{ W} = \textbf{3.5 kW}$

(d) $10,000,000 \text{ W} = 10 \times 10^{6} \text{ W} = \textbf{10 MW}$

Related Problem   Express the following amounts of power in watts without metric prefixes:

(a) 1 mW   (b) 1800 μW   (c) 3 MW   (d) 10 kW

The Kilowatt-hour (kWh) Unit of Energy

The joule has been defined as the unit of energy. However, there is another way to express energy. Since power is expressed in watts and time can be expressed in hours, a unit of energy called the kilowatt-hour (kWh) can be used.

When you pay your electric bill, you are charged on the basis of the amount of energy you use. Because power companies deal in huge amounts of energy, the most practical unit is the kilowatt-hour. You use a **kilowatt-hour** of energy when you use the equivalent of 1000 W of power for 1 h. For example, a 100 W light bulb burning for 10 h uses 1 kWh of energy.

$$W = Pt = (100 \text{ W})(10 \text{ h}) = 1000 \text{ Wh} = 1 \text{ kWh}$$

EXAMPLE 3–16   Determine the number of kilowatt-hours (kWh) for each of the following energy consumptions:

(a) 1400 W for 1 hr   (b) 2500 W for 2 h   (c) 100,000 W for 5 h

Solution   (a) $1400 \text{ W} = 1.4 \text{ kW}$
$$W = Pt = (1.4 \text{ kW})(1 \text{ h}) = \textbf{1.4 kWh}$$

(b) $2500 \text{ W} = 2.5 \text{ kW}$
$$\text{Energy} = (2.5 \text{ kW})(2 \text{ h}) = \textbf{5 kWh}$$

(c) $100,000 \text{ W} = 100 \text{ kW}$
$$\text{Energy} = (100 \text{ kW})(5 \text{ h}) = \textbf{500 kWh}$$

Related Problem   How many kilowatt-hours of energy are used by a 250 W light bulb burning for 8 h?

Table 3–1 lists the typical power rating in watts for several household appliances. You can determine the maximum kWh for various appliances by using the power rating in Table 3–1 converted to kilowatts times the number of hours it is used.

APPLIANCE	POWER RATING (WATTS)
Air conditioner	860
Blow dryer	1300
Clock	2
Clothes dryer	4800
Dishwasher	1200
Heater	1322
Microwave oven	800
Range	12,200
Refrigerator	1800
Television	250
Washing machine	400
Water heater	2500

◀ TABLE 3–1

B I O G R A P H Y

James Watt
1736–1819

Watt was a Scottish inventor and was well known for his improvements to the steam engine, which made it practical for industrial use. Watt patented several inventions, including the rotary engine. The unit of power is named in his honor. (Photo credit: Library of Congress.)

EXAMPLE 3–17

During a typical 24-hour period, you use the following appliances for the specified lengths of time:

air conditioner: 15 hours   microwave oven: 15 minutes

blow dryer: 10 minutes   refrigerator: 12 hours

clock: 24 hours   television: 2 hours

clothes dryer: 1 hour   water heater: 8 hours

dishwasher: 45 minutes

Determine the total kilowatt-hours and the electric bill for the time period. The rate is 10 cents per kilowatt-hour.

Solution   Determine the kWh for each appliance used by converting the watts in Table 3–1 to kilowatts and multiplying by the time in hours:

air conditioner: $0.860\,\text{kW} \times 15\,\text{h} = 12.9\,\text{kWh}$

blow dryer: $1.3\,\text{kW} \times 0.167\,\text{h} = 0.217\,\text{kWh}$

clock: $0.002\,\text{kW} \times 24\,\text{h} = 0.048\,\text{kWh}$

clothes dryer: $4.8\,\text{kW} \times 1\,\text{h} = 4.8\,\text{kWh}$

dishwasher: $1.2\,\text{kW} \times 0.75\,\text{h} = 0.9\,\text{kWh}$

microwave: $0.8\,\text{kW} \times 0.25\,\text{h} = 0.2\,\text{kWh}$

refrigerator: $1.8\,\text{kW} \times 12\,\text{h} = 21.6\,\text{kWh}$

television: $0.25\,\text{kW} \times 2\,\text{h} = 0.5\,\text{kWh}$

water heater: $2.5\,\text{kW} \times 8\,\text{h} = 20\,\text{kWh}$

Now, add up all the kilowatt-hours to get the total energy for the 24-hour period.

$$\text{Total energy} = (12.9 + 0.217 + 0.048 + 4.8 + 0.9 + 0.2 + 21.6 + 0.5 + 20)\,\text{kWh}$$
$$= \mathbf{61.165\,kWh}$$

At 10 cents/kilowatt-hour, the cost of energy to run the appliances for the 24-hour period is

$$\text{Energy cost} = 61.165\,\text{kWh} \times 0.1\,\text{\$/kWh} = \mathbf{\$6.12}$$

Related Problem   In addition to the appliances, suppose you used two 100 W light bulbs for 2 hours and one 75 W bulb for 3 hours. Calculate your cost for the 24-hour period for both appliances and lights.

**SECTION 3–3
REVIEW**

1. Define *power*.
2. Write the formula for power in terms of energy and time.
3. Define *watt*.
4. Express each of the following values of power in the most appropriate units:
     (a) 68,000 W   (b) 0.005 W   (c) 0.000025 W
5. If you use 100 W of power for 10 h, how much energy (in kilowatt-hours) have you used?
6. Convert 2000 W to kilowatts.
7. How much does it cost to run a heater (1322 W) for 24 hours if energy cost is 9¢ per kilowatt-hour?

3–4   Power in an Electric Circuit

The generation of heat, which occurs when electrical energy is converted to heat energy, in an electric circuit is often an unwanted by-product of current through the resistance in the circuit. In some cases, however, the generation of heat is the primary purpose of a circuit as, for example, in an electric resistive heater. In any case, you must frequently deal with power in electrical and electronic circuits.

After completing this section, you should be able to

◆ **Calculate power in a circuit**

  ◆ Determine power when you know *I* and *R*

  ◆ Determine power when you know *V* and *I*

  ◆ Determine power when you know *V* and *R*

When there is current through a resistance, the collisions of the electrons as they move through the resistance give off heat, resulting in a conversion of electrical energy to thermal energy as indicated in Figure 3–14. The amount of power dissipated in an electrical circuit is dependent on the amount of resistance and on the amount of current, expressed as follows:

Equation 3–5

$$P = I^2R$$

where: P = power in watts (W)

           V = voltage in volts (V)

           I = current in amperes (A)

◀ FIGURE 3–14

Power dissipation in an electric circuit is seen as heat given off by the resistance. The power dissipation is equal to the power produced by the voltage source.

Heat produced by current through resistance is a result of energy conversion.

You can get an equivalent expression for power in terms of voltage and current by substituting $I \times I$ for I^2 and V for IR.

$$P = I^2R = (I \times I)R = I(IR) = (IR)I$$

$$P = VI$$

Equation 3–6

You can obtain another equivalent expression by substituting V/R for I (Ohm's law).

$$P = VI = V\left(\frac{V}{R}\right)$$

$$P = \frac{V^2}{R}$$

Equation 3–7

The three power expressions in Equations 3–5, 3–6, and 3–7 are known as **Watt's law**. To calculate the power in a resistance, you can use any one of the three equivalent Watt's law power formulas, depending on what information you have. For example, assume that you know the values of current and voltage; in this case, calculate the power with the formula $P = VI$. If you know I and R, use the formula $P = I^2R$. If you know V and R, use the formula $P = V^2/R$.

An aid for using both Ohm's law and Watt's law is found in the chapter summary, Figure 3–26.

EXAMPLE 3–18

Calculate the power in each of the three circuits of Figure 3–15.

▶ FIGURE 3–15

(a) (b) (c)

Solution In circuit (a), you know V and I. The power is determined as follows:

$$P = VI = (10\text{ V})(2\text{ A}) = \textbf{20 W}$$

In circuit (b), you know I and R. Therefore,

$$P = I^2R = (2\text{ A})^2(47\text{ }\Omega) = \textbf{188 W}$$

In circuit (c), you know V and R. Therefore,

$$P = \frac{V^2}{R} = \frac{(5\text{ V})^2}{10\text{ }\Omega} = \textbf{2.5 W}$$

Related Problem Determine the power in each circuit of Figure 3–15 for the following changes: In circuit (a), I is doubled and V remains the same; in circuit (b), R is doubled and I remains the same; in circuit (c), V is halved and R remains the same.

EXAMPLE 3–19

A 100 W light bulb operates on 120 V. How much current does it require?

Solution
Use the formula $P = VI$ and solve for I by first transposing the terms to get I on the left side of the equation.

$$VI = P$$

Rearranging,

$$I = \frac{P}{V}$$

Substitute 100 W for P and 120 V for V.

$$I = \frac{P}{V} = \frac{100 \text{ W}}{120 \text{ V}} = 0.833 \text{ A} = \mathbf{833 \text{ mA}}$$

Related Problem
A light bulb draws 545 mA from a 110 V source. What is the power dissipated?

**SECTION 3–4
REVIEW**

1. If there are 10 V across a resistor and a current of 3 A through it, what is the power dissipated?
2. If there is a current of 5 A through a 47 Ω resistor, what is the power dissipated?
3. How much power is produced by 20 mA through a 5.1 kΩ resistor?
4. Five volts are applied to a 10 Ω resistor. What is the power dissipated?
5. How much power does a 2.2 kΩ resistor with 8 V across it produce?
6. What is the resistance of a 55 W bulb that draws 0.5 A?

3–5   THE POWER RATING OF RESISTORS

As you know, a resistor gives off heat when there is current through it. There is a limit to the amount of heat that a resistor can give off, which is specified by its power rating.

After completing this section, you should be able to

◆ **Properly select resistors based on power consideration**

  ◆ Define *power rating*

  ◆ Explain how physical characteristics of resistors determine their power rating

  ◆ Check for resistor failure with an ohmmeter

The **power rating** is the maximum amount of power that a resistor can dissipate without being damaged by excessive heat buildup. The power rating is not related to the ohmic value (resistance) but rather is determined mainly by the physical composition, size, and shape of the resistor. All else being equal, the larger the surface area of a resistor, the more power it can dissipate. *The surface area of a cylindrically shaped resistor is equal to the length (l) times the circumference (c),* as indicated in Figure 3–16. The area of the ends is not included.

Surface area = $l \times c$

▲ FIGURE 3–16

The power rating of a resistor is directly related to its surface area.

Metal-film resistors are available in standard power ratings from $\frac{1}{8}$ W to 1 W, as shown in Figure 3–17. Available power ratings for other types of resistors vary. For example, wirewound resistors have ratings up to 225 W or greater. Figure 3–18 shows some of these resistors.

SAFETY POINT

Resistors can become very hot in normal operation. To avoid a burn, do not touch a circuit component while the power is connected to the circuit. After power has been turned off, allow time for the components to cool down.

◀ FIGURE 3–17

Relative sizes of metal-film resistors with standard power ratings of $\frac{1}{8}$ W, $\frac{1}{4}$ W, $\frac{1}{2}$ W, and 1 W.

(a) Axial-lead wirewound   (b) Adjustable wirewound   (c) Radial-lead for PC board insertion

▲ FIGURE 3–18

Typical resistors with high power ratings.

When a resistor is used in a circuit, its power rating should be greater than the maximum power that it will have to handle to create a safety margin. Generally, the next higher standard value is used. For example, if a metal-film resistor is to dissipate 0.75 W in a circuit application, its rating should be the next higher standard value which is 1 W.

EXAMPLE 3–20

Choose an adequate power rating ($\frac{1}{8}$ W, $\frac{1}{4}$ W, $\frac{1}{2}$ W, or 1 W) for each of the metal-film resistors represented in Figure 3–19.

FIGURE 3–19

V_S 10 V R 120 Ω   (a)

V_S 10 mA R 1000 Ω   (b)

Solution   For the circuit in Figure 3–19(a), the actual power is

$$P = \frac{V_S^2}{R} = \frac{(10\,\text{V})^2}{120\,\Omega} = \frac{100\,\text{V}^2}{120\,\Omega} = 0.833\,\text{W}$$

Select a resistor with a power rating higher than the actual power dissipation. In this case, a **1 W resistor** should be used.

For the circuit in Figure 3–19(b), the actual power is

$$P = I^2R = (10\,\text{mA})^2(1000\,\Omega) = 0.1\,\text{W}$$

A ⅛ W **(0.125 W) resistor** should be used in this case.

Related Problem   A certain resistor is required to dissipate 0.25 W (¼ W). What standard rating should be used?

When the power dissipated in a resistor is greater than its rating, the resistor will become excessively hot. As a result, either the resistor will burn open or its resistance value will be greatly altered.

A resistor that has been damaged because of overheating can often be detected by the charred or altered appearance of its surface. If there is no visual evidence, a resistor that is suspected of being damaged can be checked with an ohmmeter for an open or increased resistance value. Recall that a resistor should be disconnected from the circuit to measure resistance.

EXAMPLE 3–21   Determine whether the resistor in each circuit of Figure 3–20 has possibly been damaged by overheating.

FIGURE 3–20

Solution   For the circuit in Figure 3–20(a),

$$P = \frac{V^2}{R} = \frac{(9\,\text{V})^2}{100\,\Omega} = 0.81\,\text{W}$$

The rating of the resistor is ¼ W (0.25 W), which is insufficient to handle the power. The resistor has been overheated and may be burned out, making it an open.

For the circuit in Figure 3–20(b),

$$P = \frac{V^2}{R} = \frac{(24\,\text{V})^2}{1.5\,\text{k}\Omega} = 0.384\,\text{W}$$

The rating of the resistor is ½ W (0.5 W), which is sufficient to handle the power.

For the circuit in Figure 3–20(c),

$$P = \frac{V^2}{R} = \frac{(5 \text{ V})^2}{10 \text{ } \Omega} = 2.5 \text{ W}$$

The rating of the resistor is 1 W, which is insufficient to handle the power. The resistor has been overheated and may be burned out, making it an open.

Related Problem A ¼ W, 1.0 kΩ resistor is connected across a 12 V battery. Will it overheat?

SECTION 3–5
REVIEW

1. Name two important parameters associated with a resistor.
2. How does the physical size of a resistor determine the amount of power that it can handle?
3. List the standard power ratings of metal-film resistors.
4. A resistor must handle 0.3 W. What standard size metal-film resistor should be used to dissipate the energy properly?

3–6 ENERGY CONVERSION AND VOLTAGE DROP IN A RESISTANCE

As you have learned, when there is current through a resistance, electrical energy is converted to heat energy. This heat is caused by collisions of the free electrons within the atomic structure of the resistive material. When a collision occurs, heat is given off; and the electron gives up some of its acquired energy as it moves through the material.

After completing this section, you should be able to

◆ **Explain energy conversion and voltage drop**

  ◆ Discuss the cause of energy conversion in a circuit

  ◆ Define *voltage drop*

  ◆ Explain the relationship between energy conversion and voltage drop

Figure 3–21 illustrates charge in the form of electrons flowing from the negative terminal of a battery, through a circuit, and back to the positive terminal. As they emerge from the negative terminal, the electrons are at their highest energy level. The electrons flow through each of the resistors that are connected together to form a current path (this type of connection is called series, as you will learn in Chapter 4). As the electrons flow through each resistor, some of their energy is given up in the form of heat. Therefore, the electrons have more energy when they enter a resistor than when they exit the resistor, as illustrated in the figure by the decrease in the intensity of the red color. When they have traveled through the circuit back to the positive terminal of the battery, the electrons are at their lowest energy level.

Recall that voltage equals energy per charge ($V = W/Q$) and that charge is a property of electrons. Based on the voltage of the battery, a certain amount of energy is imparted to all of the electrons that flow out of the negative terminal. The same number of electrons flow at each point throughout the circuit, but their energy decreases as they move through the resistance of the circuit.

A loss of energy by electrons (charge) as they flow through a resistance creates a voltage drop because voltage equals energy divided by charge.

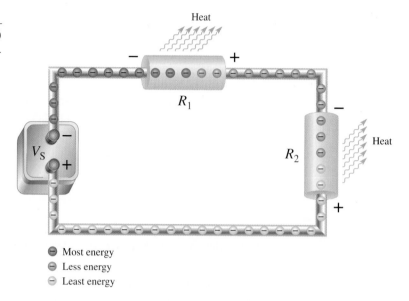

In Figure 3–21, the voltage at the left end of R_1 is equal to W_{enter}/Q, and the voltage at the right end of R_1 is equal to W_{exit}/Q. The same number of electrons that enter R_1 also exit R_1, so Q is constant. However, the energy W_{exit} is less than W_{enter}, so the voltage at the right end of R_1 is less than the voltage at the left end. This decrease in voltage across the resistor due to a loss of energy is called a **voltage drop**. The voltage at the right end of R_1 is less negative (or more positive) than the voltage at the left end. The voltage drop is indicated by $-$ and $+$ signs (the $+$ implies a less negative or more positive voltage).

The electrons have lost some energy in R_1 and now they enter R_2 with a reduced energy level. As they flow through R_2, they lose more energy, resulting in another voltage drop across R_2.

SECTION 3–6 REVIEW	1. What is the basic reason for energy conversion in a resistor?
	2. What is a voltage drop?
	3. What is the polarity of a voltage drop in relation to current direction?

3–7   Power Supplies

A **power supply** is a device that provides power to a load. Recall that a load is any electrical device or circuit that is connected to the output of the power supply and draws current from the supply.

After completing this section, you should be able to

◆ **Discuss power supplies and their characteristics**

   ◆ Define *ampere-hour rating*

   ◆ Discuss power supply efficiency

Figure 3–22 shows a representation of a power supply with a loading device connected to its output. The load can be anything from a light bulb to a computer. The power supply produces a voltage across its two output terminals and provides current through the load, as

◀ FIGURE 3–22

Power supply and load.

Power supply

$+ V_{\text{OUT}} -$

I

Load

Power $= I V_{\text{OUT}}$

indicated in the figure. The product IV_{OUT} is the amount of power produced by the supply and consumed by the load. For a given output voltage (V_{OUT}), more current drawn by the load means more power from the supply.

Power supplies range from simple batteries to regulated electronic circuits where an accurate output voltage is automatically maintained. A battery is a dc power supply that converts chemical energy into electrical energy. Electronic power supplies normally convert 110 V ac (alternating current) from a wall outlet into a regulated dc (direct current) voltage at a level suitable for electronic components. A regulated voltage is one that remains essentially constant with changes in input voltage or load.

HANDS ON TIP

An electronic power supply provides both output voltage and current. You should make sure the voltage range is sufficient for your applications. Also, you must have sufficient current capacity to assure proper circuit operation. The current capacity is the maximum current that a power supply can provide to a load at a given voltage.

Ampere-hour Ratings of Batteries

Batteries convert chemical energy into electrical energy. Because of their limited source of chemical energy, batteries have a certain capacity that limits the amount of time over which they can produce a given power level. This capacity is measured in ampere-hours (Ah). The **ampere-hour rating** determines the length of time that a battery can deliver a certain amount of average current to a load at the rated voltage.

A rating of one ampere-hour means that a battery can deliver an average of one ampere of current to a load for one hour at the rated voltage output. This same battery can deliver an average of two amperes for one-half hour. The more current the battery is required to deliver, the shorter the life of the battery. In practice, a battery usually is rated for a specified current level and output voltage. For example, a 12 V automobile battery may be rated for 70 Ah at 3.5 A. This means that it can supply an average of 3.5 A for 20 h at the rated voltage.

EXAMPLE 3–22

For how many hours can a battery deliver 2 A if it is rated at 70 Ah?

Solution The ampere-hour rating is the current times the number of hours, x.

$$70 \text{ Ah} \times (2 \text{ A})(x \text{ h})$$

Solving for the number of hours, x, yields

$$x = \frac{70 \text{ Ah}}{2 \text{ A}} = \textbf{35 h}$$

Related Problem A certain battery delivers 10 A for 6 h. What is its minimum Ah rating?

Power Supply Efficiency

An important characteristic of electronic power supplies is efficiency. **Efficiency** is the ratio of the output power, P_{OUT}, to the input power, P_{IN}.

Equation 3–8

$$\text{Efficiency} = \frac{P_{OUT}}{P_{IN}}$$

Efficiency is often expressed as a percentage. For example, if the input power is 100 W and the output power is 50 W, the efficiency is (50 W/100 W) × 100% = 50%.

All electronic power supplies are energy converters and require that power be put into them in order to get power out. For example, an electronic dc power supply might use the ac power from a wall outlet as its input. Its output is usually regulated dc voltage. The output power is *always* less than the input power because some of the total power is used internally to operate the power supply circuitry. This internal power dissipation is normally called the *power loss*. The output power is the input power minus the power loss.

Equation 3–9

$$P_{OUT} = P_{IN} - P_{LOSS}$$

High efficiency means that very little power is dissipated in the power supply and there is a higher proportion of output power for a given input power.

EXAMPLE 3–23

A certain electronic power supply requires 25 W of input power. It can produce an output power of 20 W. What is its efficiency, and what is the power loss?

Solution

$$\text{Efficiency} = \frac{P_{OUT}}{P_{IN}} = \left(\frac{20\ W}{25\ W}\right) = \mathbf{0.8}$$

Expressed as a percentage,

$$\text{Efficiency} = \frac{20\ W}{25\ W} = 80\%$$

$$P_{LOSS} = P_{IN} - P_{OUT} = 25\ W - 20\ W = \mathbf{5\ W}$$

Related Problem A power supply has an efficiency of 92%. If P_{IN} is 50 W, what is P_{OUT}?

**SECTION 3–7
REVIEW**

1. When a loading device draws an increased amount of current from a power supply, does this change represent a greater or a smaller load on the supply?

2. A power supply produces an output voltage of 10 V. If the supply provides 0.5 A to a load, what is the power output?

3. If a battery has an ampere-hour rating of 100 Ah, how long can it provide 5 A to a load?

4. If the battery in Question 3 is a 12 V device, what is its power output for the specified value of current?

5. An electronic power supply used in the lab operates with an input power of 1 W. It can provide an output power of 750 mW. What is its efficiency?

3–8 INTRODUCTION TO TROUBLESHOOTING

Technicians must be able to diagnose and repair malfunctioning circuits and systems. In this section, you learn a general approach to troubleshooting using a simple example. Troubleshooting coverage is an important part of this textbook, so you will find a troubleshooting section in many of the chapters as well as troubleshooting problems for skill building.

After completing this section, you should be able to

♦ **Describe a basic approach to troubleshooting**

  ♦ List three steps in troubleshooting

  ♦ Explain what is meant by half-splitting

  ♦ Discuss and compare the three basic measurements of voltage, current, and resistance

Troubleshooting is the application of logical thinking combined with a thorough knowledge of circuit or system operation to correct a malfunction. The basic approach to troubleshooting consists of three steps: *analysis, planning,* and *measuring.* We will refer to this 3-step approach as APM.

Analysis

The first step in troubleshooting a circuit is to analyze clues or symptoms of the failure. The analysis can begin by determining the answer to certain questions:

1. Has the circuit ever worked?

2. If the circuit once worked, under what conditions did it fail?

3. What are the symptoms of the failure?

4. What are the possible causes of failure?

Planning

The second step in the troubleshooting process, after analyzing the clues, is formulating a logical plan of attack. Much time can be saved by proper planning. A working knowledge of the circuit is a prerequisite to a plan for troubleshooting. If you are not certain how the circuit is supposed to operate, take time to review circuit diagrams (schematics), operating instructions, and other pertinent information. A schematic with proper voltages marked at various test points is particularly useful. Although logical thinking is perhaps the most important tool in troubleshooting, it rarely can solve the problem by itself.

Measuring

The third step is to narrow the possible failures by making carefully thought out measurements. These measurements usually confirm the direction you are taking in solving the problem, or they may point to a new direction that you should take. Occasionally, you may find a totally unexpected result.

An APM Example

The thought process that is part of the APM approach can be illustrated with a simple example. Suppose you have a string of eight decorative 12 V bulbs connected in series to a

◆ FIGURE 3–23

A string of bulbs connected to a voltage source.

120 V source V_S, as shown in Figure 3–23. Assume that this circuit worked properly at one time but stopped working after it was moved to a new location. When plugged in at the new location, the bulbs fail to turn on. How do you go about finding the trouble?

The Analysis Thought Process   You may think like this as you proceed to analyze the situation:

- Since the circuit worked before it was moved, the problem could be that there is no voltage at the new location.

- Perhaps the wiring was loose and pulled apart when moved.

- It is possible that a bulb is burned out or loose in its socket.

With this reasoning, you have considered possible causes and failures that may have occurred. The thought process continues:

- The fact that the circuit once worked eliminates the possibility that the original circuit was improperly wired.

- If the fault is due to an open path, it is unlikely that there is more than one break which could be either a bad connection or a burned out bulb.

You have now analyzed the problem and are ready to plan the process of finding the fault in the circuit.

The Planning Thought Process   The first part of your plan is to measure for voltage at the new location. If the voltage is present, then the problem is in the string of lights. If voltage is not present, check the circuit breaker at the distribution box in the house. Before resetting breakers, you should think about why a breaker may be tripped. Let's assume that you find the voltage is present. This means that the problem is in the string of lights.

The second part of your plan is to measure either the resistance in the string of lights or to measure voltages across the bulbs. The decision whether to measure resistance or voltage is a toss-up and can be made based on the ease of making the test. Seldom is a troubleshooting plan developed so completely that all possible contingencies are included. You will frequently need to modify the plan as you go along.

The Measurement Process   You proceed with the first part of your plan by using a multimeter to check the voltage at the new location. Assume the measurement shows a voltage of 120 V. Now you have eliminated the possibility of no voltage. You know that, since you have voltage across the string and there is no current because no bulb is on, there must be an open in the current path. Either a bulb is burned out, a connection at the lamp socket is broken, or the wire is broken.

Next, you decide to locate the break by measuring resistance with your multimeter. Applying logical thinking, you decide to measure the resistance of each half of the string instead of measuring the resistance of each bulb. By measuring the resistance of half the bulbs at once, you can usually reduce the effort required to find the open. This technique is a type of troubleshooting procedure called **half-splitting**.

Once you have identified the half in which the open occurs, as indicated by an infinite resistance, you use half-splitting again on the faulty half and continue until you narrow the fault down to a faulty bulb or connection. This process is shown in Figure 3–24, assuming for purposes of illustration that the seventh bulb is burned out.

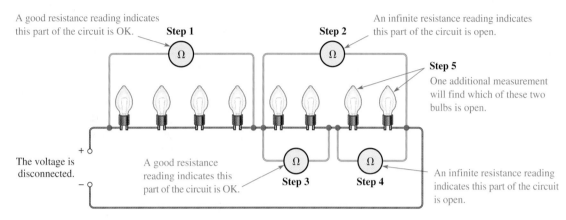

▲ FIGURE 3–24

Illustration of the half-splitting method of troubleshooting. The numbered steps indicate the sequence in which the multimeter is moved from one position to another.

As you can see in the figure, the half-splitting approach in this particular case takes a maximum of five measurements to identify the open bulb. If you had decided to measure each bulb individually and had started at the left, you would have needed seven measurements. So, sometimes half-splitting saves steps; sometimes it doesn't. The number of steps required depends on where you make your measurements and in what sequence.

Unfortunately, most troubleshooting is more difficult than this example. However, analysis and planning are essential for effective troubleshooting in any situation. As measurements are made, the plan is often modified; the experienced troubleshooter narrows the search by fitting the symptoms and measurements into a probable cause. In some cases, low-cost equipment is simply discarded when troubleshooting and repair costs are comparable to replacement costs.

Comparison of *V*, *R*, and *I* Measurements

As you know from Section 2–7, you can measure voltage, current, or resistance in a circuit. To measure voltage, place the voltmeter in parallel across the component; that is, place one lead on each side of the component. This makes voltage measurements the easiest of the three types of measurements.

To measure resistance, connect the ohmmeter across a component; however, the voltage must be first disconnected, and sometimes the component itself must be removed from the circuit. Therefore, resistance measurements are generally more difficult than voltage measurements.

To measure current, place the ammeter in series with the component; that is, the ammeter must be in line with the current path. To do this you must disconnect a component lead or a wire before you connect the ammeter. This usually makes a current measurement the most difficult to perform.

SECTION 3–8 REVIEW	1. Name the three steps in the APM approach to troubleshooting.
	2. Explain the basic idea of the half-splitting technique.
	3. Why are voltages easier to measure than currents in a circuit?

Application Assignment

In this assignment, an existing resistance box that is to be used as part of a test setup in the lab is to be checked out and modified. Your task is to modify the circuit so that it will meet the requirements of the new application. You will have to apply your knowledge of Ohm's law and Watt's law in order to complete this assignment.

The specifications are as follows:

1. Each resistor is switch selectable and only one resistor is selected at a time.

2. The lowest resistor value is to be 10 Ω.

3. Each successively higher resistance in the switch sequence must be a decade (10 times) increase over the previous one.

4. The maximum resistor value must be 1.0 MΩ.

5. The maximum voltage across any resistor in the box will be 4 V.

6. Two additional resistors are required, one to limit the current to 10 mA ± 10% with a 4 V drop and the other to limit the current to 5 mA ± 10% with a 4 V drop.

Step 1: Inspect the Existing Resistance Box

The existing resistance box is shown in both top and bottom views in Figure 3–25. The switch is a rotary type. The resistors all have a power rating of 1 W.

Step 2: Draw the Schematic

From Figure 3–25, determine the resistor values and draw the schematic for the existing circuit so that you will know what you

have to work with. Determine the resistor numbering from the R labels on the top view.

Step 3: Modify the Schematic to Meet New Requirements

Change the schematic from Step 2 so the circuit will accomplish the following:

1. One resistor at a time is to be connected by the switch between terminals 1 and 2 of the box.

2. Provide switch selectable resistor values beginning with 10 Ω and increasing in decade increments to 1.0 MΩ.

3. Each of the resistors from Step 1 must be selectable by a sequence of adjacent switch positions in ascending order.

4. In addition to the resistors in Step 1, there must be two switch-selectable resistors, one is in switch position 1 (shown in Figure 3–25, bottom view) and must limit the current to 10 mA ± 10% with a 4 V drop and the other is in switch position 8 and must limit the current to 5 mA ± 10% with a 4 V drop.

5. All the resistors must be standard values with 10% tolerance and have a sufficient power rating for the 4 V operating requirement. See Appendix A for standard resistor values.

Step 4: Modify the Circuit

State the modifications that must be made to the existing box to meet the specifications and develop a detailed list of the changes including resistance values, power ratings, wiring, and new components. You should number each point in the schematic for easy reference.

(a) Top view

(b) Bottom view

▲ FIGURE 3–25

Step 5: Develop a Test Procedure

After the box has been modified to meet the new specifications, it must be tested to see if it is working properly. Determine how you would test the resistance box and what instruments you would use and then detail your test procedure in a step-by-step format.

Step 6: Troubleshoot the Circuit

When an ohmmeter is connected across terminals 1 and 2 of the resistance box, determine the most likely fault in each of the following cases:

1. The ohmmeter shows an infinitely high resistance when the switch is in position 3.

2. The ohmmeter shows an infinitely high resistance in all switch positions.

3. The ohmmeter shows an incorrect value of resistance when the switch is in position 6.

Review

1. Explain how you applied Watt's law to this application assignment.

2. Explain how you applied Ohm's law to this application assignment.

3. How did you determine the power ratings of the resistors in the existing box?

SUMMARY

- ◆ Voltage and current are linearly proportional.
- ◆ Ohm's law gives the relationship of voltage, current, and resistance.
- ◆ Current is inversely proportional to resistance.
- ◆ A kilohm (kΩ) is one thousand ohms.
- ◆ A megohm (MΩ) is one million ohms.
- ◆ A microampere (μA) is one-millionth of an ampere.
- ◆ A milliampere (mA) is one-thousandth of an ampere.
- ◆ Use $I = V/R$ to calculate current.
- ◆ Use $V = IR$ to calculate voltage.
- ◆ Use $R = V/I$ to calculate resistance.
- ◆ One watt equals one joule per second.
- ◆ Watt is the unit of power, and joule is the unit of energy.
- ◆ The power rating of a resistor determines the maximum power that it can handle safely.
- ◆ Resistors with a larger physical size can dissipate more power in the form of heat than smaller ones.
- ◆ A resistor should have a power rating as high or higher than the maximum power that it is expected to handle in the circuit.
- ◆ Power rating is not related to resistance value.
- ◆ A resistor usually opens when it overheats and fails.
- ◆ Energy is equal to power multiplied by time.
- ◆ The kilowatt-hour is a unit of energy.
- ◆ An example of one kilowatt-hour is one thousand watts used for one hour.
- ◆ A power supply is an energy source used to operate electrical and electronic devices.
- ◆ A battery is one type of power supply that converts chemical energy into electrical energy.
- ◆ An electronic power supply converts commercial energy (ac from the power company) to regulated dc at various voltage levels.
- ◆ The output power of a power supply is the output voltage times the load current.
- ◆ A load is a device that draws current from the power supply.
- ◆ The capacity of a battery is measured in ampere-hours (Ah).
- ◆ One ampere-hour equals one ampere used for one hour, or any other combination of amperes and hours that has a product of one.
- ◆ An electronic power supply with a high efficiency has a smaller percentage power loss than one with a lower efficiency.

◆ The formula wheel in Figure 3–26 gives the Ohm's law and Watt's law relationships.

◆ APM (analysis, planning, and measurement) provides a logical approach to troubleshooting.

◆ The half-splitting method of troubleshooting generally results in fewer measurements.

▶ FIGURE 3–26

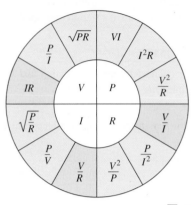

☐ Ohm's law   ☐ Watt's law

KEY TERMS

Key terms and other bold terms in the chapter are defined in the end-of-book glossary.

Ampere-hour rating   A number given in ampere-hours (Ah) determined by multiplying the current (A) times the length of time (h) a battery can deliver that current to a load.

Efficiency   The ratio of the output power to the input power of a circuit, usually expressed as a percent.

Energy   The ability to do work. The unit is the joule (J).

Half-splitting   A troubleshooting procedure where one starts in the middle of a circuit or system and, depending on the first measurement, works toward the output or toward the input to find the fault.

Joule (J)   The SI unit of energy.

Kilowatt-hour (kWh)   A large unit of energy used mainly by utility companies.

Linear   Characterized by a straight-line relationship.

Ohm's law   A law stating that current is directly proportional to voltage and inversely proportional to resistance.

Power   The rate of energy usage.

Power rating   The maximum amount of power that a resistor can dissipate without being damaged by excessive heat buildup.

Power supply   A device that provides power to a load.

Troubleshooting   A systematic process of isolating, identifying, and correcting a fault in a circuit or system.

Voltage drop   The decrease in voltage across a resistor due to a loss of energy.

Watt (W)   The unit of power. One watt is the power when 1 J of energy is used in 1 s.

Watt's law   A law that states the relationships of power to current, voltage, and resistance.

FORMULAS

3–1 $I = \dfrac{V}{R}$ Form of Ohm's law for calculating current

3–2 $V = IR$ Form of Ohm's law for calculating voltage

3–3 $R = \dfrac{V}{I}$ Form of Ohm's law for calculating resistance

3–4 $\quad P = \dfrac{W}{t}$ Power equals energy divided by time.

3–5 $\quad P = I^2R$ Power equals current squared times resistance.

3–6 $\quad P = VI$ Power equals voltage times current.

3–7 $\quad P = \dfrac{V^2}{R}$ Power equals voltage squared divided by resistance.

3–8 $\quad \text{Efficiency} = \dfrac{P_{OUT}}{P_{IN}}$ Power supply efficiency

3–9 $\quad P_{OUT} = P_{IN} - P_{LOSS}$ Output power

SELF-TEST

Answers are at the end of the chapter.

1. Ohm's law states that
   (a) current equals voltage times resistance
   (b) voltage equals current times resistance
   (c) resistance equals current divided by voltage
   (d) voltage equals current squared times resistance

2. When the voltage across a resistor is doubled, the current will
   (a) triple   (b) halve   (c) double   (d) not change

3. When 10 V are applied across a 20 Ω resistor, the current is
   (a) 10 A   (b) 0.5 A   (c) 200 A   (d) 2 A

4. When there are 10 mA of current through a 1.0 kΩ resistor, the voltage across the resistor is
   (a) 100 V   (b) 0.1 V   (c) 10 kV   (d) 10 V

5. If 20 V are applied across a resistor and there are 6.06 mA of current, the resistance is
   (a) 3.3 kΩ   (b) 33 kΩ   (c) 330 Ω   (d) 3.03 kΩ

6. A current of 250 μA through a 4.7 kΩ resistor produces a voltage drop of
   (a) 53.2 V   (b) 1.175 mV   (c) 18.8 V   (d) 1.175 V

7. A resistance of 2.2 MΩ is connected across a 1 kV source. The resulting current is approximately
   (a) 2.2 mA   (b) 455 μA   (c) 45.5 μA   (d) 0.455 A

8. Power can be defined as
   (a) energy   (b) heat
   (c) the rate at which energy is used   (d) the time required to use energy

9. For 10 V and 50 mA, the power is
   (a) 500 mW   (b) 0.5 W   (c) 500,000 μW   (d) answers (a), (b), and (c)

10. When the current through a 10 kΩ resistor is 10 mA, the power is
    (a) 1 W   (b) 10 W   (c) 100 mW   (d) 1 mW

11. A 2.2 kΩ resistor dissipates 0.5 W. The current is
    (a) 15.1 mA   (b) 227 μA   (c) 1.1 mA   (d) 4.4 mA

12. A 330 Ω resistor dissipates 2 W. The voltage is
    (a) 2.57 V   (b) 660 V   (c) 6.6 V   (d) 25.7 V

13. The power rating of a resistor that is to handle up to 1.1 W should be
    (a) 0.25 W   (b) 1 W   (c) 2 W   (d) 5 W

14. A 22 Ω half-watt resistor and a 220 Ω half-watt resistor are connected across a 10 V source. Which one(s) will overheat?
    (a) 22 Ω   (b) 220 Ω   (c) both   (d) neither

15. When the needle of an analog ohmmeter indicates infinity, the resistor being measured is
    (a) overheated   (b) shorted   (c) open   (d) reversed

TROUBLESHOOTING: SYMPTOM AND CAUSE

The purpose of these exercises is to help develop thought processes essential to troubleshooting. Answers are at the end of the chapter.

Determine the cause for each set of symptoms. Refer to Figure 3–27.

▶ FIGURE 3–27

The meters indicate the correct readings for this circuit.

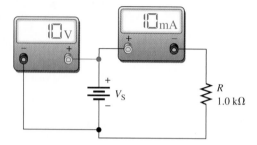

1. *Symptom:* The ammeter reading is zero, and the voltmeter reading is 10 V.
   Cause:
   (a) R is shorted.
   (b) R is open.
   (c) The voltage source is faulty.

2. *Symptom:* The ammeter reading is zero, and the voltmeter reading is 0 V.
   Cause:
   (a) R is open.
   (b) R is shorted.
   (c) The voltage source is turned off or faulty.

3. *Symptom:* The ammeter reading is 10 mA, and the voltmeter reading is 0 V.
   Cause:
   (a) The voltmeter is defective.
   (b) The ammeter is faulty.
   (c) The voltage source is turned off or faulty.

4. *Symptom:* The ammeter reading is 1 mA, and the voltmeter reading is 10 V.
   Cause:
   (a) The voltmeter is defective.
   (b) The resistor value is higher than it should be.
   (c) The resistor value is lower than it should be.

5. *Symptom:* The ammeter reading is 100 mA, and the voltmeter reading is 10 V.
   Cause:
   (a) The voltmeter is defective.
   (b) The resistor value is higher than it should be.
   (c) The resistor value is lower than it should be.

PROBLEMS

Answers to odd-numbered problems are at the end of the book.

BASIC PROBLEMS

SECTION 3–1 Ohm's Law

1. The current in a circuit is 1 A. Determine what the current will be when
   (a) the voltage is tripled
   (b) the voltage is reduced by 80%
   (c) the voltage is increased by 50%

2. The current in a circuit is 100 mA. Determine what the current will be when

   (a) the resistance is increased by 100%

   (b) the resistance is reduced by 30%

   (c) the resistance is quadrupled

3. The current in a circuit is 10 mA. What will the current be if the voltage is tripled and the resistance is doubled?

SECTION 3–2 Application of Ohm's Law

4. Determine the current in each case.

   (a) $V = 5\,V, R = 1.0\,\Omega$ (b) $V = 15\,V, R = 10\,\Omega$

   (c) $V = 50\,V, R = 100\,\Omega$ (d) $V = 30\,V, R = 15\,k\Omega$

   (e) $V = 250\,V, R = 4.7\,M\Omega$

5. Determine the current in each case.

   (a) $V = 9\,V, R = 2.7\,k\Omega$ (b) $V = 5.5\,V, R = 10\,k\Omega$

   (c) $V = 40\,V, R = 68\,k\Omega$ (d) $V = 1\,kV, R = 2\,k\Omega$

   (e) $V = 66\,kV, R = 10\,M\Omega$

6. A 10 Ω resistor is connected across a 12 V battery. How much current is there through the resistor?

7. A resistor is connected across the terminals of a dc voltage source in each part of Figure 3–28. Determine the current in each resistor.

8. A 5-band resistor is connected across a 12 V source. Determine the current if the resistor color code is orange, violet, yellow, gold, brown.

(a)

(b)

(c)

▲ FIGURE 3–28

9. If the voltage in Problem 8 is doubled, will a 0.5 A fuse blow? Explain your answer.

10. Calculate the voltage for each value of I and R.

(a) $I = 2$ A, $R = 18 \, \Omega$ (b) $I = 5$ A, $R = 47 \, \Omega$ (c) $I = 2.5$ A, $R = 620 \, \Omega$

(d) $I = 0.6$ A, $R = 47 \, \Omega$ (e) $I = 0.1$ A, $R = 470 \, \Omega$

11. Calculate the voltage for each value of I and R.

(a) $I = 1$ mA, $R = 10 \, \Omega$ (b) $I = 50$ mA, $R = 33 \, \Omega$

(c) $I = 3$ A, $R = 4.7 \, k\Omega$ (d) $I = 1.6$ mA, $R = 2.2 \, k\Omega$

(e) $I = 250 \, \mu A$, $R = 1.0 \, k\Omega$ (f) $I = 500$ mA, $R = 1.5 \, M\Omega$

(g) $I = 850 \, \mu A$, $R = 10 \, M\Omega$ (h) $I = 75 \, \mu A$, $R = 47 \, \Omega$

12. Three amperes of current are measured through a 27 Ω resistor connected across a voltage source. How much voltage does the source produce?

13. Assign a voltage value to each source in the circuits of Figure 3–29 to obtain the indicated amounts of current.

(a)   (b)   (c)

▲ FIGURE 3–29

14. Calculate the resistance for each value of V and I.

(a) $V = 10$ V, $I = 2$ A   (b) $V = 90$ V, $I = 45$ A   (c) $V = 50$ V, $I = 5$ A

(d) $V = 5.5$ V, $I = 10$ A   (e) $V = 150$ V, $I = 0.5$ A

15. Calculate R for each set of V and I values.

(a) $V = 10$ kV, $I = 5$ A   (b) $V = 7$ V, $I = 2$ mA   (c) $V = 500$ V, $I = 250$ mA

(d) $V = 50$ V, $I = 500 \, \mu A$ (e) $V = 1$ kV, $I = 1$ mA

16. Six volts are applied across a resistor. A current of 2 mA is measured. What is the value of the resistor?

17. Choose the correct value of resistance to get the current values indicated in each circuit of Figure 3–30.

(a)   (b)   (c)

▲ FIGURE 3–30

SECTION 3–3   **Energy and Power**

18. What is the power when energy is used at the rate of 350 J/s?

19. What is the power in watts when 7500 J of energy are used in 5 h?

20. Convert the following in kilowatts:

(a) 1000 W   (b) 3750 W   (c) 160 W   (d) 50,000 W

21. Convert the following to megawatts:

(a) 1,000,000 W   (b) 3×10^6 W   (c) 15×10^7 W   (d) 8700 kW

22. Convert the following to milliwatts:

(a) 1 W   (b) 0.4 W   (c) 0.002 W   (d) 0.0125 W

23. Convert the following to microwatts:

(a) 2 W   (b) 0.0005 W   (c) 0.25 mW   (d) 0.00667 mW

24. Convert the following to watts:

(a) 1.5 kW   (b) 0.5 MW   (c) 350 mW   (d) 9000 μW

25. Prove that the unit for power (the watt) is equivalent to 1 V $\times$ 1 A.

26. Show that there are 3.6×10^6 joules in a kilowatt-hour.

SECTION 3–4 **Power in an Electric Circuit**

27. If a resistor has 5.5 V across it and 3 mA through it, what is the power dissipation?

28. An electric heater works on 115 V and draws 3 A of current. How much power does it use?

29. What is the power when there are 500 mA of current through a 4.7 kΩ resistor?

30. Calculate the power dissipated by a 10 kΩ resistor carrying 100 μA.

31. If there are 60 V across a 620 Ω resistor, what is the power dissipation?

32. A 56 Ω resistor is connected across the terminals of a 1.5 V battery. What is the power dissipation in the resistor?

33. If a resistor is to carry 2 A of current and handle 100 W of power, how many ohms must it be? Assume that the voltage can be adjusted to any required value.

34. Convert 5×10^6 watts used for 1 minute to kWh.

35. Convert 6700 watts used for 1 second to kWh.

36. How many kilowatt-hours do 50 W used for 12 h equal?

37. Assume that an alkaline D-cell battery can maintain an average voltage of 1.25 V for 90 h in a 10 Ω load before becoming unusable. What average power is delivered to the load during the life of the battery?

38. What is the total energy in joules that is delivered during the 90 hours for the battery in Problem 37?

SECTION 3–5 **The Power Rating of Resistors**

39. A 6.8 kΩ resistor has burned out in a circuit. You must replace it with another resistor with the same resistance value. If the resistor carries 10 mA, what should its power rating be? Assume that you have available resistors in all the standard power ratings.

40. A certain type of power resistor comes in the following ratings: 3 W, 5 W, 8 W, 12 W, 20 W. Your particular application requires a resistor that can handle approximately 8 W. Which rating would you use for a minimum safety margin of 20% above the rated value? Why?

SECTION 3–6 **Energy Conversion and Voltage Drop in a Resistance**

41. For each circuit in Figure 3–31, assign the proper polarity for the voltage across the resistor.

▶ FIGURE 3–31

(a)　　　　　　　　(b)　　　　　　　　(c)

SECTION 3–7   Power Supplies

42. A 50 Ω load consumes 1 W of power. What is the output voltage of the power supply?

43. A battery can provide an average of 1.5 A of current for 24 h. What is its ampere-hour rating?

44. How much average current can be drawn from an 80 Ah battery for 10 h?

45. If a battery is rated at 650 mAh, how much average current will it provide for 48 h?

46. If the input power is 500 mW and the output power is 400 mW, what is the power loss? What is the efficiency of this power supply?

47. To operate at 85% efficiency, how much output power must a source produce if the input power is 5 W?

SECTION 3–8   Introduction to Troubleshooting

48. In the light circuit of Figure 3–32, identify the faulty bulb based on the series of ohmmeter readings shown.

49. Assume you have a 32-light string and one of the bulbs is burned out. Using the half-splitting approach and starting in the left half of the circuit, how many resistance measurements will it take to find the faulty bulb if it is seventeenth from the left.

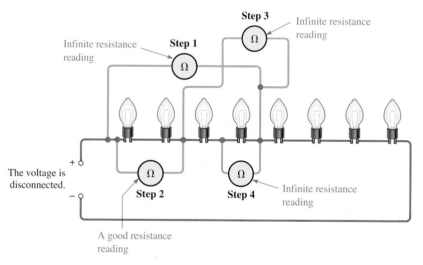

▲ FIGURE 3–32

ADVANCED PROBLEMS

50. A certain power supply provides a continuous 2 W to a load. It is operating at 60% efficiency. In a 24 h period, how many kilowatt-hours does the power supply use?

51. The filament of a light bulb in the circuit of Figure 3–33(a) has a certain amount of resistance, represented by an equivalent resistance in Figure 3–33(b). If the bulb operates with 120 V and 0.8 A of current, what is the resistance of its filament?

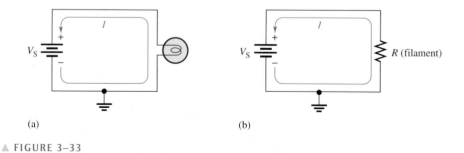

(a)   (b)

▲ FIGURE 3–33

52. A certain electrical device has an unknown resistance. You have available a 12 V battery and an ammeter. How would you determine the value of the unknown resistance? Draw the necessary circuit connections.

53. A variable voltage source is connected to the circuit of Figure 3–34. Start at 0 V and increase the voltage in 10 V steps up to 100 V. Determine the current at each voltage value, and plot a graph of V versus I. Is the graph a straight line? What does the graph indicate?

54. In a certain circuit, $V_S = 1$ V and $I = 5$ mA. Determine the current for each of the following voltages in a circuit with the same resistance:

   (a) $V_S = 1.5$ V   (b) $V_S = 2$ V   (c) $V_S = 3$ V   (d) $V_S = 4$ V   (e) $V_S = 10$ V

55. Figure 3–35 is a graph of current versus voltage for three resistance values. Determine R_1, R_2, and R_3.

▲ FIGURE 3–34

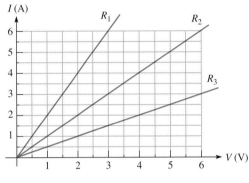

▲ FIGURE 3–35

56. You are measuring the current in a circuit that is operated on a 10 V battery. The ammeter reads 50 mA. Later, you notice that the current has dropped to 30 mA. Eliminating the possibility of a resistance change, you must conclude that the voltage has changed. How much has the voltage of the battery changed, and what is its new value?

57. If you wish to increase the amount of current in a resistor from 100 mA to 150 mA by changing the 20 V source, by how many volts should you change the source? To what new value should you set it?

58. By varying the rheostat (variable resistor) in the circuit of Figure 3–36, you can change the amount of current. The setting of the rheostat is such that the current is 750 mA. What is the resistance value of this setting? To adjust the current to 1 A, to what resistance value must you set the rheostat? The rheostat must never be adjusted to 0 Ω. Why?

▶ FIGURE 3–36

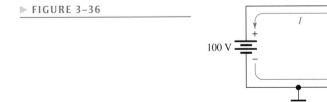

59. A certain resistor has the following color code: orange, orange, red, gold. Determine the maximum and minimum currents you should expect to measure when a 12 V source is connected across the resistor.

60. A 6 V source is connected to a 100 Ω resistor by two 12 ft lengths of 18-gauge copper wire. Refer to Table 2–4 to determine the following:

   (a) current   (b) resistor voltage   (c) voltage across each length of wire

61. If a 300 W bulb is allowed to burn continuously for 30 days, how many kilowatt-hours of energy does it use?

62. At the end of a 31-day period, your utility bill shows that you have used 1500 kWh. What is the average daily power?

63. A certain type of power resistor comes in the following ratings: 3 W, 5 W, 8 W, 12 W, 20 W. Your particular application requires a resistor that can handle approximately 10 W. Which rating would you use? Why?

64. A 12 V source is connected across a 10 Ω resistor for 2 min.

    (a) What is the power dissipation?

    (b) How much energy is used?

    (c) If the resistor remains connected for an additional minute, does the power dissipation increase or decrease?

65. The rheostat in Figure 3–37 is used to control the current to a heating element. When the rheostat is adjusted to a value of 8 Ω or less, the heating element can burn out. What is the rated value of the fuse needed to protect the circuit if the voltage across the heating element at the point of maximum current is 100 V?

    ▶ FIGURE 3–37

Fuse R_1 120 V Resistive heating element

MULTISIM TROUBLESHOOTING PROBLEMS

66. Open file P03-66 on your CD-ROM. Determine whether or not the circuit is operating properly. If not, find the fault.

67. Open file P03-67 on your CD-ROM. Determine whether or not the circuit is operating properly. If not, find the fault.

68. Open file P03-68 on your CD-ROM. Determine whether or not the circuit is operating properly. If not, find the fault.

69. Open file P03-69 on your CD-ROM. Determine whether or not the circuit is operating properly. If not, find the fault.

70. Open file P03-70 on your CD-ROM. Determine whether or not the circuit is operating properly. If not, find the fault.

ANSWERS

SECTION REVIEWS

SECTION 3–1   Ohm's Law

1. Ohm's law states that current varies directly with voltage and inversely with resistance.

2. $I = V/R$ **3.** $V = IR$ **4.** $R = V/I$

5. The current increases; three times when V is tripled

6. Doubling R cuts I in half to 5 mA.

7. No change in I if V and R are doubled.

SECTION 3–2   Application of Ohm's Law

1. $I = 10\,V/4.7\,Ω = 2.13\,A$

2. $I = 20\,kV/4.7\,MΩ = 4.26\,mA$

3. $I = 10\,kV/2\,kΩ = 5\,A$

4. $V = (1\,A)(10\,Ω) = 10\,V$

5. $V = (3\,\text{mA})(3\,\text{k}\Omega) = 9\,\text{V}$

6. $V = (2\,\text{A})(6\,\Omega) = 12\,\text{V}$

7. $R = 10\,\text{V}/2\,\text{A} = 5\,\Omega$

8. $R = 25\,\text{V}/50\,\text{mA} = 0.5\,\text{k}\Omega = 500\,\Omega$

SECTION 3–3 Energy and Power

1. Power is the rate at which energy is used.

2. $P = W/t$

3. Watt is the unit of power. One watt is the power when 1 J of energy is used in 1 s.

4. (a) $68,000\,\text{W} = 68\,\text{kW}$ **(b)** $0.005\,\text{W} = 5\,\text{mW}$ **(c)** $0.000025 = 25\,\mu\text{W}$

5. $(100\,\text{W})(10\,\text{h}) = 1\,\text{kWh}$

6. $2000\,\text{W} = 2\,\text{kW}$

7. $(1.322\,\text{kW})(24\,\text{h}) = 31.73\,\text{kWh}$; $(0.09\,\$/\text{kWh})(31.73\,\text{kWh}) = \$2.86$

SECTION 3–4 Power in an Electric Circuit

1. $P = (10\,\text{V})(3\,\text{A}) = 30\,\text{W}$

2. $P = (5\,\text{A})^2(47\,\Omega) = 1175\,\text{W}$

3. $P = (20\,\text{mA})^2(5.1\,\text{k}\Omega) = 2.04\,\text{W}$

4. $P = (5\,\text{V})^2/10\,\Omega = 2.5\,\text{W}$

5. $P = (8\,\text{V})^2/2.2\,\text{k}\Omega = 29.1\,\text{mW}$

6. $R = 55\,\text{W}/(0.5\,\text{A})^2 = 220\,\Omega$

SECTION 3–5 The Power Rating of Resistors

1. Two resistor parameters are resistance and power rating.

2. A larger resistor physical size dissipates more energy.

3. Standard ratings of metal-film resistors are 0.125 W, 0.25 W, 0.5 W, and 1 W.

4. At least a 0.5 W rating to handle 0.3 W

SECTION 3–6 Energy Conversion and Voltage Drop in a Resistance

1. Energy conversion in a resistor is caused by collisions of free electrons with the atoms in the material.

2. Voltage drop is a decrease in voltage across a resistor due to a loss of energy.

3. Voltage drop is negative to positive in the direction of current.

SECTION 3–7 Power Supplies

1. An increased amount of current represents a greater load.

2. $P_{\text{OUT}} = (10\,\text{V})(0.5\,\text{A}) = 5\,\text{W}$

3. $100\,\text{Ah}/5\,\text{A} = 20\,\text{h}$

4. $P_{\text{OUT}} = (12\,\text{V})(5\,\text{A}) = 60\,\text{W}$

5. Efficiency $= (750\,\text{mW}/1000\,\text{mW})100\% = 75\%$

SECTION 3–8 Introduction to Troubleshooting

1. Analysis, Planning, and Measuring

2. Half-splitting identifies the fault by successively isolating half of the remaining circuit.

3. Voltage is measured across a component. Current is measured in series with the component.

Application Assignment

1. Watt's law was used to find power ratings ($P = V^2/R$).

2. Ohm's law was used to find the two additional resistors ($R = V/I$).

3. Power ratings were determined by the relative sizes of the resistors, given the range of values.

RELATED PROBLEMS FOR EXAMPLES

3–1 $I_1 = 10\text{ V}/5\,\Omega = 2\text{ A}; I_2 = 10\text{ V}/20\,\Omega = 0.5\text{ A}$

3–2 1 V

3–3 900 Ω

3–4 Yes

3–5 2.27 A

3–6 5 mA

3–7 25 μA

3–8 200 μA

3–9 800 V

3–10 220 mV

3–11 16.5 V

3–12 4 kΩ

3–13 100 Ω

3–14 3000 J

3–15 **(a)** 0.001 W   **(b)** 0.0018 W   **(c)** 3,000,000 W   **(d)** 10,000 W

3–16 2 kWh

3–17 $6.12 + $.06 = 6.18

3–18 **(a)** 40 W

   (b) 376 W

   (c) 625 mW

3–19 60 W

3–20 0.5 W (½ W)

3–21 No

3–22 60 Ah

3–23 46 W

SELF-TEST

1. (b)   **2.** (c)   **3.** (b)   **4.** (d)   **5.** (a)   **6.** (d)   **7.** (b)   **8.** (c)

9. (d)   **10.** (a)   **11.** (a)   **12.** (d)   **13.** (c)   **14.** (a)   **15.** (c)

TROUBLESHOOTING: SYMPTOM AND CAUSE

1. (b)

2. (c)

3. (a)

4. (b)

5. (c)

SERIES CIRCUITS

4

CHAPTER OBJECTIVES

◆ Identify a series resistive circuit
◆ Determine total series resistance
◆ Determine the current throughout a series circuit
◆ Apply Ohm's law in series circuits
◆ Determine the total effect of voltage sources connected in series
◆ Apply Kirchhoff's voltage law
◆ Use a series circuit as a voltage divider
◆ Determine power in a series circuit
◆ Measure voltage with respect to ground
◆ Troubleshoot series circuits

KEY TERMS

◆ Series
◆ Series-aiding
◆ Series-opposing
◆ Kirchhoff's voltage law
◆ Voltage divider
◆ Reference ground
◆ Open
◆ Short

APPLICATION ASSIGNMENT PREVIEW

For the application assignment in this chapter, a voltage-divider board will be evaluated and modified if necessary. The voltage divider provides five different voltage levels from a 12 V battery. The voltage divider will be used to supply positive reference voltages to an electronic circuit in an analog-to-digital converter. You will check the circuit to see if it provides the required voltages and, if not, modify it so that it does. Also, the power ratings of the resistors must be adequate for the application. After studying this chapter, you should be able to complete the application assignment.

VISIT THE COMPANION WEBSITE

Study aids for this chapter are available at
http://www.prenhall.com/floyd

INTRODUCTION

Resistive circuits can be of two basic forms: series or parallel. In this chapter series circuits are discussed. Parallel circuits are covered in Chapter 5, and combinations of series and parallel circuits are examined in Chapter 6. In this chapter you will see how Ohm's law is used in series circuits; and you will study another important law, Kirchhoff's voltage law. Also, several important applications of series circuits are presented.

4–1   RESISTORS IN SERIES

When connected in series, resistors form a "string" in which there is only one path for current.

After completing this section, you should be able to

◆ **Identify a series resistive circuit**

   ◆ Translate a physical arrangement of resistors into a schematic diagram

Figure 4–1(a) shows two resistors connected in series between point A and point B. Part (b) shows three resistors in series, and part (c) shows four in series. Of course, there can be any number of resistors in series.

(a)   (b)   (c)

▲ FIGURE 4–1

Resistors in series.

When a voltage source is connected from point A to point B, the only way for current to get from one point to the other in any of the connections of Figure 4–1 is to go through each of the resistors. A series circuit is identified as follows:

A series circuit provides only one path for current between two points so that the current is the same through each series resistor.

In an actual circuit diagram, a series circuit may not always be as easy to identify as those in Figure 4–1. For example, Figure 4–2 shows series resistors drawn in other ways with a voltage applied. Remember, if there is only one current path between two points, the resistors between those two points are in series, no matter how they appear in a diagram.

(a)   (b)   (c)   (d)   (e)

▲ FIGURE 4–2

Some examples of series connections of resistors. Notice that the current must be the same at all points because the current has only one path.

EXAMPLE 4–1

Five resistors are positioned on a protoboard as shown in Figure 4–3. Wire them together in series so that, starting from the negative (−) terminal, R_1 is first, R_2 is second, R_3 is third, and so on. Draw a schematic showing this connection.

▶ FIGURE 4–3

Solution   The wires are connected as shown in Figure 4–4(a), which is the assembly diagram. The schematic is shown in Figure 4–4(b). Note that the schematic does not necessarily show the actual physical arrangement of the resistors as does the assembly diagram. The schematic shows how components are connected electrically; the assembly diagram shows how components are arranged and interconnected physically.

FIGURE 4–4

(a) Assembly diagram   (b) Schematic

Related Problem*   **(a)** Show how you would rewire the circuit board in Figure 4–4(a) so that all the odd-numbered resistors come first starting at point *A* followed by the even-numbered ones. **(b)** Determine the value of each resistor.

*Answers are at the end of the chapter.

EXAMPLE 4–2   Describe how the resistors on the printed circuit (PC) board in Figure 4–5 are related electrically. Determine the resistance value of each resistor.

FIGURE 4–5

Solution   Resistors R_1 through R_7 are in series with each other. This series combination is connected between pins 1 and 2 on the PC board.

Resistors R_8 through R_{13} are in series with each other. This series combination is connected between pins 3 and 4 on the PC board.

The values of the resistors are $R_1 = 2.2\,\text{k}\Omega$, $R_2 = 3.3\,\text{k}\Omega$, $R_3 = 1.0\,\text{k}\Omega$, $R_4 = 1.2\,\text{k}\Omega$, $R_5 = 3.3\,\text{k}\Omega$, $R_6 = 4.7\,\text{k}\Omega$, $R_7 = 5.6\,\text{k}\Omega$, $R_8 = 12\,\text{k}\Omega$, $R_9 = 68\,\text{k}\Omega$, $R_{10} = 27\,\text{k}\Omega$, $R_{11} = 12\,\text{k}\Omega$, $R_{12} = 82\,\text{k}\Omega$, and $R_{13} = 270\,\text{k}\Omega$.

Related Problem   How is the circuit in Figure 4–5 changed when pin 2 and pin 3 are connected?

**SECTION 4–1
REVIEW**

Answers are at the end of the chapter.

1. How are the resistors connected in a series circuit?
2. How can you identify a series circuit?
3. Complete the schematics for the circuits in each part of Figure 4–6 by connecting the resistors in series in numerical order from *A* to *B*.
4. Now connect each group of series resistors in Figure 4–6 in series.

▶ FIGURE 4–6

(a)   (b)   (c)

4–2   TOTAL SERIES RESISTANCE

The total resistance of a series circuit is equal to the sum of the resistances of each individual resistor.

After completing this section, you should be able to

◆ **Determine total series resistance**

   ◆ Explain why resistance values add when resistors are connected in series

   ◆ Apply the series resistance formula

Series Resistor Values Add

When resistors are connected in series, the resistor values add because each resistor offers opposition to the current in direct proportion to its resistance. A greater number of resistors connected in series creates more opposition to current. More opposition to current implies a higher value of resistance. Thus, for every resistor that is added in series, the total resistance increases.

Figure 4–7 illustrates how series resistances add together to increase the total resistance. Part (a) has a single 10 Ω resistor. Part (b) shows another 10 Ω resistor connected in series with the first one, making a total resistance of 20 Ω. If a third 10 Ω resistor is connected in series with the first two, as shown in part (c), the total resistance becomes 30 Ω.

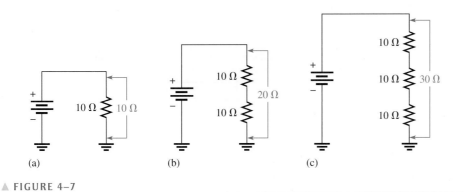

(a)   (b)   (c)

▲ FIGURE 4–7

Total resistance increases with each additional series resistor. The ground symbol used here was introduced in Section 2–6.

Series Resistance Formula

For any number of individual resistors connected in series, the total resistance is the sum of each of the individual values.

$$R_T = R_1 + R_2 + R_3 + \cdots + R_n$$

Equation 4–1

where R_T is the total resistance and R_n is the last resistor in the series string (n can be any positive integer equal to the number of resistors in series). For example, if there are four resistors in series ($n = 4$), the total resistance formula is

$$R_T = R_1 + R_2 + R_3 + R_4$$

If there are six resistors in series ($n = 6$), the total resistance formula is

$$R_T = R_1 + R_2 + R_3 + R_4 + R_5 + R_6$$

To illustrate the calculation of total series resistance, let's determine R_T of the circuit of Figure 4–8, where V_S is the source voltage. This circuit has five resistors in series. To find the total resistance, simply add the values.

$$R_T = 56\ \Omega + 100\ \Omega + 27\ \Omega + 10\ \Omega + 47\ \Omega = 240\ \Omega$$

Note in Figure 4–8 that the order in which the resistances are added does not matter. Also, you can physically change the positions of the resistors in the circuit without affecting the total resistance or the current.

◀ FIGURE 4–8

Example of five resistors in series. V_S stands for source voltage.

EXAMPLE 4–3

Connect the resistors on the protoboard in Figure 4–9 in series, and determine the total resistance, R_T.

▶ FIGURE 4–9

Solution   The resistors are connected as shown in Figure 4–10. Find the total resistance by adding all the values.

$$R_T = R_1 + R_2 + R_3 + R_4 + R_5 = 33\ \Omega + 68\ \Omega + 100\ \Omega + 47\ \Omega + 10\ \Omega = \textbf{258}\ \boldsymbol{\Omega}$$

▶ FIGURE 4–10

(a) Circuit assembly

(b) Schematic

Related Problem   Determine the total resistance in Figure 4–10(a) if the positions of R_2 and R_4 are interchanged.

EXAMPLE 4–4

Calculate the total resistance, R_T, for each circuit in Figure 4–11.

▶ FIGURE 4–11

(a)   (b)

Solution   For circuit (a),

$$R_T = 1.0\ k\Omega + 2.2\ k\Omega + 4.7\ k\Omega + 10\ k\Omega = \textbf{17.9\ k}\boldsymbol{\Omega}$$

For circuit (b),

$$R_T = 4.7\,k\Omega + 10\,k\Omega + 1.0\,k\Omega + 2.2\,k\Omega = \mathbf{17.9\,k\Omega}$$

Notice that the total resistance does not depend on the position of the resistors. Both circuits are identical in terms of total resistance.

Related Problem   What is the total resistance for the following series resistors: $1.0\,k\Omega$, $2.2\,k\Omega$, $3.3\,k\Omega$, and $5.6\,k\Omega$?

EXAMPLE 4–5   Determine the value of R_4 in the circuit of Figure 4–12.

▶ **FIGURE 4–12**

Solution   From the ohmmeter reading, $R_T = 146\,k\Omega$.

$$R_T = R_1 + R_2 + R_3 + R_4$$

Solving for R_4 yields

$$R_4 = R_T - (R_1 + R_2 + R_3) = 146\,k\Omega - (10\,k\Omega + 33\,k\Omega + 47\,k\Omega) = \mathbf{56\,k\Omega}$$

Related Problem   Determine the value of R_4 in Figure 4–12 if the ohmmeter reading is $112\,k\Omega$.

Equal-Value Series Resistors

When a circuit has more than one resistor of the same value in series, there is a shortcut method to obtain the total resistance: Simply multiply the resistance value of the resistors having the same value by the number of equal-value resistors that are in series. This method is essentially the same as adding the values. For example, five $100\,\Omega$ resistors in series have an R_T of $5(100\,\Omega) = 500\,\Omega$. In general, the formula is expressed as

$$R_T = nR$$ Equation 4–2

where n is the number of equal-value resistors and R is the resistance value.

EXAMPLE 4–6

Find the R_T of eight 22 Ω resistors in series.

Solution

Find R_T by adding the values.

$$R_T = 22\ \Omega + 22\ \Omega + 22\ \Omega + 22\ \Omega + 22\ \Omega + 22\ \Omega + 22\ \Omega + 22\ \Omega = \mathbf{176\ \Omega}$$

However, it is much easier to multiply.

$$R_T = 8(22\ \Omega) = \mathbf{176\ \Omega}$$

Related Problem

Find R_T for three 1.0 kΩ and two 680 Ω resistors in series.

**SECTION 4–2
REVIEW**

1. Calculate R_T between points A and B for each circuit in Figure 4–13.
2. The following resistors are in series: one 100 Ω, two 47 Ω, four 12 Ω, and one 330 Ω. What is the total resistance?
3. Suppose that you have one resistor for each of the following values: 1.0 kΩ, 2.7 kΩ, 3.3 kΩ, and 1.8 kΩ. To get a total resistance of 10 kΩ, you need one more resistor. What should its value be?
4. What is the R_T for twelve 47 Ω resistors in series?

▶ FIGURE 4–13

(a)   (b)   (c)

4–3   CURRENT IN A SERIES CIRCUIT

The current is the same through all points in a series circuit. The current through each resistor in a series circuit is the same as the current through all the other resistors that are in series with it.

After completing this section, you should be able to

◆ **Determine the current throughout a series circuit**

   ◆ Show that the current is the same at all points in a series circuit

Figure 4–14 shows three resistors connected in series to a voltage source. *At any point in this circuit, the current into that point must equal the current out of that point,* as illustrated by the current directional arrows. Notice also that the current out of each of the resistors must equal the current in because there is no place where part of the current can branch off and go somewhere else. Therefore, the current in each section of the circuit is the same as the current in all other sections. It has only one path going from the negative (−) side of the source to the positive (+) side.

In Figure 4–15, the battery supplies 1 A of current to the series resistors. There is one ampere of current out of the battery's negative terminal. As shown, one ampere of current is measured at several points in the series circuit.

(a) Pictorial

(b) Schematic

Current entering any point in a series circuit is the same as the current leaving that point.

(a) Pictorial

(b) Schematic

▲ FIGURE 4–15

Current is the same at all points in a series circuit.

SECTION 4–3 REVIEW

1. What statement can you make about the amount of current at any point in a series circuit?

2. In a series circuit with a 10 Ω and a 4.7 Ω resistor in series, there are 2 A through the 10 Ω resistor. How much current is there through the 4.7 resistor?

3. A milliammeter is connected between points *A* and *B* in Figure 4–16. It measures 50 mA. If you move the meter and connect it between points *C* and *D*, how much current will it indicate? Between *E* and *F*?

4. In Figure 4–17, how much current does ammeter 1 indicate? Ammeter 2?

FIGURE 4–16

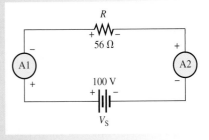

▲ FIGURE 4–17

4–4 APPLICATION OF OHM'S LAW

The basic concepts of series circuits and Ohm's law can be applied to series circuit analysis.

After completing this section, you should be able to

◆ **Apply Ohm's law in series circuits**

  ◆ Find the current in a series circuit

  ◆ Find the voltage across each resistor in series

The following are key points to remember when you analyze series circuits:

1. Current through any of the series resistors is the same as the total current.

2. If you know the total applied voltage and the total resistance, you can determine the total current by Ohm's law.

$$I_T = \frac{V_T}{R_T}$$

3. If you know the voltage drop across one of the series resistors, R_x, you can determine the total current by Ohm's law.

$$I_T = \frac{V_x}{R_x}$$

4. If you know the total current, you can find the voltage drop across any of the series resistors by Ohm's law.

$$V_x = I_T R_x$$

5. The polarity of a voltage drop across a resistor is positive at the end of the resistor that is closest to the positive terminal of the voltage source.

6. The current through a resistor is defined to be in a direction from the negative end of the resistor to the positive end.

7. An open in a series circuit prevents current; and, therefore, there is zero voltage drop across each series resistor. The total voltage appears across the points between which there is an open.

Now let's look at several examples that use Ohm's law for series circuit analysis.

EXAMPLE 4–7

Find the current in the circuit of Figure 4–18.

▶ FIGURE 4–18

Solution   The current is determined by the source voltage and the total resistance. First, calculate the total resistance.

$$R_T = R_1 + R_2 + R_3 + R_4 = 82\,\Omega + 18\,\Omega + 15\,\Omega + 10\,\Omega = 125\,\Omega$$

Next, use Ohm's law to calculate the current.

$$I = \frac{V_S}{R_T} = \frac{25\,\text{V}}{125\,\Omega} = 0.2\,\text{A} = \mathbf{200\,mA}$$

Remember, the same current exists at all points in the circuit. Thus, each resistor has 200 mA through it.

Related Problem   What is the current in the circuit of Figure 4–18 if R_4 is changed to 100 Ω?

 Open Multisim file E04-07 on your CD-ROM. Connect the multimeter and verify the value of current calculated in this example. Change the value of R_4 to 100 Ω and verify the value of current calculated in the related problem.

EXAMPLE 4–8   The current in the circuit of Figure 4–19 is 1 mA. For this amount of current, what must the source voltage V_S be?

▶ FIGURE 4–19

Solution   In order to calculate V_S, first determine R_T.

$$R_T = 1.2\,\text{k}\Omega + 5.6\,\text{k}\Omega + 1.2\,\text{k}\Omega + 1.5\,\text{k}\Omega = 9.5\,\text{k}\Omega$$

Now use Ohm's law to determine V_S.

$$V_S = IR_T = (1\,\text{mA})(9.5\,\text{k}\Omega) = \mathbf{9.5\,V}$$

Related Problem   If the 5.6 kΩ resistor is changed to 3.9 kΩ, what value of V_S is necessary to keep the current at 1 mA?

 Open Multisim file E04-08 on your CD-ROM. Verify that the calculated source voltage establishes the current in Figure 4–19. Verify the value of V_S determined in the related problem.

EXAMPLE 4–9   Calculate the voltage drop across each resistor in Figure 4–20, and find the value of V_S. To what value can V_S be raised if the current is to be limited to 5 mA?

▶ FIGURE 4–20

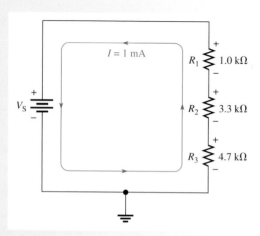

Solution   By Ohm's law, the voltage drop across each resistor is equal to its resistance multiplied by the current through it. Use the Ohm's law formula $V = IR$ to determine the voltage drop across each of the resistors. Keep in mind that there is the same current through each series resistor. The voltage drop across R_1 (designated V_1) is

$$V_1 = IR_1 = (1 \text{ mA})(1.0 \text{ k}\Omega) = \textbf{1 V}$$

The voltage drop across R_2 is

$$V_2 = IR_2 = (1 \text{ mA})(3.3 \text{ k}\Omega) = \textbf{3.3 V}$$

The voltage drop across R_3 is

$$V_3 = IR_3 = (1 \text{ mA})(4.7 \text{ k}\Omega) = \textbf{4.7 V}$$

To calculate the value of V_S, first determine the total resistance.

$$R_T = 1.0 \text{ k}\Omega + 3.3 \text{ k}\Omega + 4.7 \text{ k}\Omega = 9 \text{ k}\Omega$$

The source voltage V_S is equal to the current times the total resistance.

$$V_S = IR_T = (1 \text{ mA})(9 \text{ k}\Omega) = \textbf{9 V}$$

Notice that if you add the voltage drops of the resistors, they total 9 V, which is the same as the source voltage.

V_S can be increased to a maximum value where $I = 5$ mA. Therefore the maximum value of V_S is

$$V_{S(max)} = IR_T = (5 \text{ mA})(9 \text{ k}\Omega) = \textbf{45 V}$$

Related Problem   Repeat the calculations for V_1, V_2, V_3, V_S, and $V_{S(max)}$ if $R_3 = 2.2 \text{ k}\Omega$ and I is maintained at 1 mA.

Open Multisim file E04-09 on your CD-ROM. Using the multimeter, verify that the voltages across the resistors agree with the values calculated in this example.

EXAMPLE 4–10   Some resistors are not color coded with bands but have the values stamped on the resistor body. When the portion of the circuit board shown in Figure 4–21 was assembled, someone mounted the resistors with the labels turned down, and there is no documentation showing the resistor values. Assume that a voltmeter, ammeter, and

▶ FIGURE 4–21

power supply are available, but no ohmmeter. Without removing the resistors from the board, use Ohm's law to determine the resistance of each one.

Solution The resistors are all in series, so the current is the same through each one. Measure the current by connecting a 12 V source (arbitrary value) and an ammeter as shown in Figure 4–22. Measure the voltage across each resistor. Start with the voltmeter across the first resistor (R_1), and then repeat this measurement for the other three resistors. For illustration, the voltage values indicated are assumed to be the measured values.

▲ FIGURE 4–22

The voltages measured across each resistor are indicated beside the resistor.

Determine the resistance of each resistor by substituting the measured values of current and voltage into the Ohm's law formula.

$$R_1 = \frac{V_1}{I} = \frac{2.5\text{ V}}{25\text{ mA}} = \textbf{100 }\Omega$$

$$R_2 = \frac{V_2}{I} = \frac{3\text{ V}}{25\text{ mA}} = \textbf{120 }\Omega$$

$$R_3 = \frac{V_3}{I} = \frac{4.5\text{ V}}{25\text{ mA}} = \textbf{180 }\Omega$$

$$R_4 = \frac{V_4}{I} = \frac{2\text{ V}}{25\text{ mA}} = \textbf{80 }\Omega$$

Related Problem If R_2 is open, what voltage is measured across each resistor?

**SECTION 4–4
REVIEW**

1. A 10 V battery is connected across three 100 Ω resistors in series. What is the current through each resistor?

2. How much voltage is required to produce 5 mA through the circuit of Figure 4–23?

3. How much voltage is dropped across each resistor in Figure 4–23 when the current is 5 mA?

4. Four equal-value resistors are connected in series with a 5 V source. The measured current is 4.63 mA. What is the value of each resistor?

▸ FIGURE 4–23

4–5 VOLTAGE SOURCES IN SERIES

Recall that a voltage source is an energy source that provides a constant voltage to a load. Batteries and power supplies are practical examples of dc voltage sources. When two or more voltage sources are in series, the total voltage is equal to the algebraic sum of the individual source voltages.

After completing this section, you should be able to

◆ **Determine the total effect of voltage sources connected in series**

　◆ Determine the total voltage of series sources with the same polarities

　◆ Determine the total voltage of series sources with opposite polarities

When batteries are placed in a flashlight, they are connected in a **series-aiding** arrangement to produce a larger voltage, as illustrated in Figure 4–24. In this example, three 1.5 V batteries are placed in series to produce a total voltage ($V_{S(tot)}$).

$$V_{S(tot)} = V_{S1} + V_{S2} + V_{S3} = 1.5 \text{ V} + 1.5 \text{ V} + 1.5 \text{ V} = 4.5 \text{ V}$$

(a) Flashlight with series batteries

(b) Schematic of flashlight circuit

▲ FIGURE 4–24

Example of series-aiding voltage sources.

Series voltage sources (batteries in this case) are added when their polarities are in the same direction, or series-aiding, and are subtracted when their polarities are in opposite directions, or **series-opposing**. For example, if one of the batteries in the flashlight is turned around, as indicated in the schematic of Figure 4–25, its voltage subtracts because it has a negative value and reduces the total voltage.

$$V_{S(tot)} = V_{S1} - V_{S2} + V_{S3} = 1.5\,V - 1.5\,V + 1.5\,V = 1.5\,V$$

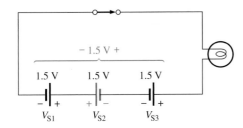

◀ FIGURE 4–25

When batteries are connected in opposite directions, their voltages subtract.

EXAMPLE 4–11

What is the total source voltage ($V_{S(tot)}$) in Figure 4–26?

▶ FIGURE 4–26

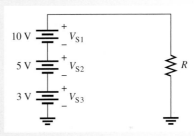

Solution   The polarity of each source is the same (the sources are connected in the same direction in the circuit). Therefore, add the three voltages to get the total.

$$V_{S(tot)} = V_{S1} + V_{S2} + V_{S3} = 10\,V + 5\,V + 3\,V = \textbf{18 V}$$

The three individual sources can be replaced by a single equivalent source of 18 V with its polarity as shown in Figure 4–27.

▶ FIGURE 4–27

Related Problem   If the battery V_{S3} in Figure 4–26 is reversed, what is the total voltage?

Open Multisim file E04-11 on your CD-ROM. Verify the total source voltage. Repeat for the related problem.

EXAMPLE 4–12

Determine $V_{S(tot)}$ in Figure 4–28.

▲ FIGURE 4–28

▲ FIGURE 4–29

Solution

These sources are connected in opposing directions. If you go clockwise around the circuit, you go from plus to minus through V_{S1}, and minus to plus through V_{S2}. The total voltage is the difference of the two source voltages (algebraic sum of oppositely signed values). The total voltage has the same polarity as the larger-value source. Here we will choose V_{S2} to be positive.

$$V_{S(tot)} = V_{S2} - V_{S1} = 25\ V - 15\ V = \mathbf{10\ V}$$

The two sources in Figure 4–28 can be replaced by a 10 V equivalent one with polarity as shown in Figure 4–29.

Related Problem

If an 8 V source in the same direction as V_{S1} is connected in series with the other batteries in Figure 4–28, what is the total voltage?

**SECTION 4–5
REVIEW**

1. How many 12 V batteries must be connected in series to produce 60 V? Draw a schematic that shows the battery connections.

2. Four 1.5 V flashlight batteries are connected in series positive to negative. What is the total voltage across the bulb?

3. The resistive circuit in Figure 4–30 is used to bias a transistor amplifier. Show how to connect the resistors to two 15 V power supplies in order to get 30 V across the series resistors.

4. Determine the total source voltage in each circuit of Figure 4–31.

5. Draw the equivalent single source circuit for each circuit of Figure 4–31.

▲ FIGURE 4–30

(a)

(b)

FIGURE 4–31

4–6 KIRCHHOFF'S VOLTAGE LAW

Kirchhoff's voltage law is a fundamental circuit law that states that the algebraic sum of all the voltages around a single closed path is zero or, in other words, the sum of the voltage drops equals the total source voltage.

After completing this section, you should be able to

◆ **Apply Kirchhoff's voltage law**

  ◆ State Kirchhoff's voltage law

  ◆ Determine the source voltage by adding the voltage drops

  ◆ Determine an unknown voltage drop

In an electric circuit, the voltages across the resistors (voltage drops) *always* have polarities opposite to the source voltage polarity. For example, in Figure 4–32, follow a counterclockwise loop around the circuit. Note that the source polarity is plus-to-minus and each voltage drop is minus-to-plus.

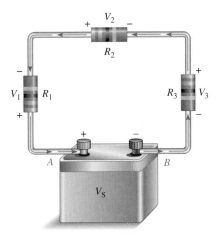

▲ FIGURE 4–32

Illustration of voltage polarities in a closed-loop circuit.

In Figure 4–32, the current is out of the negative side of the source and through the resistors as the arrows indicate. The current is into the negative side of each resistor and out the positive side. As you learned in Chapter 3, when electrons flow through a resistor, they lose energy and are therefore at a lower energy level when they emerge. The lower energy side is less negative (more positive) than the higher energy side. The drop in energy level across a resistor creates a potential difference, or voltage drop, with a minus-to-plus polarity in the direction of the current.

The voltage from point A to point B in the circuit of Figure 4–32 is the source voltage, V_S. Also, the voltage from A to B is the sum of the series resistor voltage drops. Therefore, the source voltage is equal to the sum of the three voltage drops, as stated by **Kirchhoff's voltage law**.

The sum of all the voltage drops around a single closed path in a circuit is equal to the total source voltage in that closed path.

The general concept of Kirchhoff's voltage law is illustrated in Figure 4–33 and expressed by Equation 4–3.

Equation 4–3

$$V_S = V_1 + V_2 + V_3 + \cdots + V_n$$

where the subscript n represents the number of voltage drops.

▶ FIGURE 4–33

Sum of n voltage drops equals the source voltage.

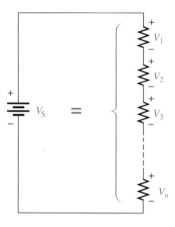

If all the voltage drops around a closed path are added and then this total is subtracted from the source voltage, the result is zero. This result occurs because the sum of the voltage drops always equals the source voltage.

The algebraic sum of all the voltages (both source and drops) around a single closed path is zero.

Therefore, another way of expressing Kirchhoff's voltage law in equation form is as follows:

Equation 4–4

$$V_S - V_1 - V_2 - V_3 - \cdots - V_n = 0$$

You can verify Kirchhoff's voltage law by connecting a circuit and measuring each resistor voltage and the source voltage, as illustrated in Figure 4–34. When the resistor voltages are added together, their sum will equal the source voltage. Any number of resistors can be used.

▲ FIGURE 4–34

Illustration of a verification of Kirchhoff's voltage law.

EXAMPLE 4–13   Determine the source voltage, V_S, in Figure 4–35 where the two voltage drops are given.

▶ FIGURE 4–35

Solution   By Kirchhoff's voltage law (Eq. 4–3), the source voltage (applied voltage) must equal the sum of the voltage drops. Adding the voltage drops gives the value of the source voltage.

$$V_S = 5\,V + 10\,V = \mathbf{15\,V}$$

Related Problem   If V_S is increased to 30 V in Figure 4–35, what are the two voltage drops?

Open Multisim file E04-13 on your CD-ROM. Verify that the voltage drops equal to V_S. Repeat for the related problem.

EXAMPLE 4–14   Determine the unknown voltage drop, V_3, in Figure 4–36.

▶ FIGURE 4–36

Solution   By Kirchhoff's voltage law (Eq. 4–4), the algebraic sum of all the voltages around the circuit is zero (the signs of the voltage drops are opposite the sign of the source).

$$V_S - V_1 - V_2 - V_3 = 0$$

The value of each voltage drop except V_3 is known. Substitute these values into the equation.

$$50\,V - 12\,V - 25\,V - V_3 = 0\,V$$

Next, combine the known values, transpose 13 V to the right side of the equation, and cancel the minus signs.

$$13\,V - V_3 = 0\,V$$
$$-V_3 = -13\,V$$
$$V_3 = \mathbf{13\,V}$$

The voltage drop, V_3, across R_3 is 13 V, and its polarity is as shown in Figure 4–36.

Related Problem   Determine V_3 in Figure 4–36 if the source is changed to 25 V.

  Open Multisim file E04-14 on your CD-ROM. Verify that V_3 agrees with the calculated value. Repeat for the related problem.

EXAMPLE 4–15   Find the value of R_4 in Figure 4–37.

▲ FIGURE 4–37

Solution   In this problem you will use both Ohm's law and Kirchhoff's voltage law. First, use Ohm's law to find the voltage drop across each of the known resistors.

$$V_1 = IR_1 = (200\ \text{mA})(10\ \Omega) = 2\ \text{V}$$
$$V_2 = IR_2 = (200\ \text{mA})(47\ \Omega) = 9.4\ \text{V}$$
$$V_3 = IR_3 = (200\ \text{mA})(100\ \Omega) = 20\ \text{V}$$

Next, use Kirchhoff's voltage law to find V_4, the voltage drop across the unknown resistor.

$$V_S - V_1 - V_2 - V_3 - V_4 = 0\ \text{V}$$
$$100\ \text{V} - 2\ \text{V} - 9.4\ \text{V} - 20\ \text{V} - V_4 = 0\ \text{V}$$
$$68.6\ \text{V} - V_4 = 0\ \text{V}$$
$$V_4 = 68.6\ \text{V}$$

Now that you know V_4, you can use Ohm's law to calculate R_4.

$$R_4 = \frac{V_4}{I} = \frac{68.6\ \text{V}}{200\ \text{mA}} = \textbf{343}\ \boldsymbol{\Omega}$$

R_4 is most likely a 330 Ω standard-value resistor because 343 Ω is within a standard tolerance range (+5%) of 330 Ω.

Related Problem   Determine R_4 in Figure 4–37 for V_S = 150 V and I = 200 mA.

  Open Multisim file E04-15 on your CD-ROM. Verify that the calculated value of R_4 produces the current in Figure 4–37. Repeat for the related problem.

SECTION 4–6
REVIEW

1. State Kirchhoff's voltage law in two ways.

2. A 50 V source is connected to a series resistive circuit. What is the sum of the voltage drops in this circuit?

3. Two equal-value resistors are connected in series across a 10 V battery. What is the voltage drop across each resistor?

4. In a series circuit with a 25 V source, there are three resistors. One voltage drop is 5 V, and the other is 10 V. What is the value of the third voltage drop?

5. The individual voltage drops in a series circuit are 1 V, 3 V, 5 V, 7 V, and 8 V. What is the total voltage applied across the series circuit?

4–7 VOLTAGE DIVIDERS

A series circuit acts as a voltage divider. The voltage divider is an important application of series circuits.

After completing this section, you should be able to

◆ **Use a series circuit as a voltage divider**

　◆ Apply the voltage-divider formula

　◆ Use the potentiometer as an adjustable voltage divider

　◆ Describe some voltage-divider applications

A circuit consisting of a series string of resistors connected to a voltage source acts as a **voltage divider**. Figure 4–38(a) shows a circuit with two resistors in series, although there can be any number. As you already know, there are two voltage drops: one across R_1 and one across R_2. These voltage drops are labeled V_1 and V_2, respectively, as indicated in the schematic. Since each resistor has the same current through it, the voltage drops are proportional to the resistance values. For example, if the value of R_2 is twice that of R_1, then the value of V_2 is twice that of V_1.

The total voltage drop around a single closed path divides among the series resistors in amounts directly proportional to the resistance values. The smallest resistance has the least voltage, and the largest resistance has the most voltage ($V = IR$). For example, in Figure 4–38(b), if V_S is 10 V, R_1 is 50 Ω, and R_2 is 100 Ω, then V_1 is one-third the total voltage, or 3.33 V,

The source voltage is applied between these two terminals. This notation is equivalent to a battery symbol.

(a)

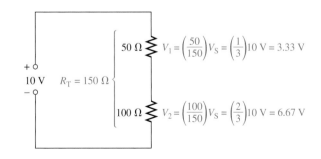

$$V_1 = \left(\frac{50}{150}\right)V_S = \left(\frac{1}{3}\right)10\text{ V} = 3.33\text{ V}$$

$$V_2 = \left(\frac{100}{150}\right)V_S = \left(\frac{2}{3}\right)10\text{ V} = 6.67\text{ V}$$

$R_T = 150\ \Omega$

(b)

▲ **FIGURE 4–38**

Example of a two-resistor voltage divider.

because R_1 is one-third the total resistance. Likewise, V_2 is two-thirds V_S, or 6.67 V, because R_2 is two-thirds the total resistance.

Voltage-Divider Formula

With a few calculations, you can develop a formula for determining how the voltages divide among series resistors. Assume a circuit with n resistors in series as shown in Figure 4–39, where n can be any number.

▶ FIGURE 4–39

Generalized voltage divider with n resistors.

Let V_x represent the voltage drop across any one of the resistors and R_x represent the number of a particular resistor or combination of resistors. By Ohm's law, you can express the voltage drop across R_x as follows:

$$V_x = IR_x$$

The current through the circuit is equal to the source voltage divided by the total resistance $(I = V_S/R_T)$. In the circuit of Figure 4–39, the total resistance is $R_1 + R_2 + R_3 + \cdots + R_n$. By substitution of V_S/R_T for I in the expression for V_x,

$$V_x = \left(\frac{V_S}{R_T}\right)R_x$$

Rearranging the terms you get

Equation 4–5

$$V_x = \left(\frac{R_x}{R_T}\right)V_S$$

Equation 4–5 is the general voltage-divider formula, which can be stated as follows:

> **The voltage drop across any resistor or combination of resistors in a series circuit is equal to the ratio of that resistance value to the total resistance, multiplied by the source voltage.**

EXAMPLE 4–16

Determine V_1 (the voltage across R_1) and V_2 (the voltage across R_2) in the circuit in Figure 4–40.

▶ FIGURE 4–40

Solution To determine V_1, use the voltage-divider formula, $V_x = (R_x/R_T)V_S$, where $x = 1$. The total resistance is

$$R_T = R_1 + R_2 = 82\ \Omega + 68\ \Omega = 150\ \Omega$$

R_1 is 82 Ω and V_S is 10 V. Substitute these values into the voltage-divider formula.

$$V_1 = \left(\frac{R_1}{R_T}\right)V_S = \left(\frac{82\ \Omega}{150\ \Omega}\right)10\ V = \mathbf{5.47\ V}$$

There are two ways to find the value of V_2: Kirchhoff's voltage law or the voltage-divider formula. If you use Kirchhoff's voltage law ($V_S = V_1 + V_2$), substitute the values for V_S and V_1 and solve for V_2.

$$V_2 = V_S - V_1 = 10\ V - 5.47\ V = \mathbf{4.53\ V}$$

To determine V_2, use the voltage-divider formula where $x = 2$.

$$V_2 = \left(\frac{R_2}{R_T}\right)V_S = \left(\frac{68\ \Omega}{150\ \Omega}\right)10\ V = \mathbf{4.53\ V}$$

Related Problem Find the voltage drops across R_1 and R_2 if R_2 is changed to 180 Ω in Figure 4–40.

  Open Multisim file E04-16 on your CD-ROM. Use the multimeter to verify the calculated values of V_1 and V_2. Repeat for the related problem.

EXAMPLE 4–17 Calculate the voltage drop across each resistor in the circuit of Figure 4–41.

▲ FIGURE 4–41

Solution Look at the circuit for a moment and consider the following: The total resistance is 1000 Ω. Ten percent of the total voltage is across R_1 because it is 10% of the total resistance (100 Ω is 10% of 1000 Ω). Likewise, 22% of the total voltage is dropped across R_2 because it is 22% of the total resistance (220 Ω is 22% of 1000 Ω). Finally, R_3 drops 68% of the total voltage (680 Ω is 68% of 1000 Ω).

Because of the convenient values in this problem, it is easy to mentally calculate the voltage drops ($V_1 = 0.10 \times 10\ V = 1\ V$, $V_2 = 0.22 \times 10\ V = 2.2\ V$, and $V_3 = 0.68 \times 10\ V = 6.8\ V$). Such is not always the case, but sometimes a little thinking will produce a result more efficiently.

Although you have already reasoned through this problem, the calculations are

$$V_1 = \left(\frac{R_1}{R_T}\right)V_S = \left(\frac{100\ \Omega}{1000\ \Omega}\right)10\ V = \mathbf{1\ V}$$

$$V_2 = \left(\frac{R_2}{R_T}\right)V_S = \left(\frac{220\ \Omega}{1000\ \Omega}\right)10\ V = \mathbf{2.2\ V}$$

$$V_3 = \left(\frac{R_3}{R_T}\right)V_S = \left(\frac{680\ \Omega}{1000\ \Omega}\right)10\ V = \mathbf{6.8\ V}$$

Notice that the sum of the voltage drops is equal to the source voltage, in accordance with Kirchhoff's voltage law. This check is a good way to verify your results.

Related Problem   If R_1 and R_2 are both changed to 680 Ω in Figure 4–41, what are all the voltage drops?

Open Multisim file E04-17 on your CD-ROM. Verify the values of V_1, V_2, and V_3. Repeat for the related problem.

EXAMPLE 4–18

Determine the voltages between the following points in the circuit of Figure 4–42:

(a) *A* to *B*   **(b)** *A* to *C*   **(c)** *B* to *C*   **(d)** *B* to *D*   **(e)** *C* to *D*

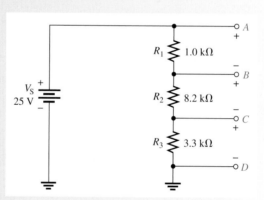

▲ FIGURE 4–42

Solution   First determine R_T.

$$R_T = 1.0\ k\Omega + 8.2\ k\Omega + 3.3\ k\Omega = 12.5\ k\Omega$$

Then apply the voltage-divider formula to obtain each required voltage.

(a) The voltage *A* to *B* is also the voltage drop across R_1.

$$V_{AB} = \left(\frac{R_1}{R_T}\right)V_S = \left(\frac{1.0\ k\Omega}{12.5\ k\Omega}\right)25\ V = \mathbf{2\ V}$$

(b) The voltage from *A* to *C* is the combined voltage drop across both R_1 and R_2. In this case, R_x in the general formula given in Equation 4–5 is $R_1 + R_2$.

$$V_{AC} = \left(\frac{R_1 + R_2}{R_T}\right)V_S = \left(\frac{9.2\ k\Omega}{12.5\ k\Omega}\right)25\ V = \mathbf{18.4\ V}$$

(c) The voltage from B to C is the voltage drop across R_2.

$$V_{BC} = \left(\frac{R_2}{R_T}\right)V_S = \left(\frac{8.2\,k\Omega}{12.5\,k\Omega}\right)25\,V = \mathbf{16.4\,V}$$

(d) The voltage from B to D is the combined voltage drop across both R_2 and R_3. In this case, R_x in the general formula is $R_2 + R_3$.

$$V_{BD} = \left(\frac{R_2 + R_3}{R_T}\right)V_S = \left(\frac{11.5\,k\Omega}{12.5\,k\Omega}\right)25\,V = \mathbf{23\,V}$$

(e) Finally, the voltage from C to D is the voltage drop across R_3.

$$V_{CD} = \left(\frac{R_3}{R_T}\right)V_S = \left(\frac{3.3\,k\Omega}{12.5\,k\Omega}\right)25\,V = \mathbf{6.6\,V}$$

If you connect this voltage divider, you can verify each of the calculated voltages by connecting a voltmeter between the appropriate points in each case.

Related Problem   Determine each of the previously calculated voltages if V_S is doubled.

Open Multisim file E04-18 on your CD-ROM. Verify the values of V_{AB}, V_{AC}, V_{BC}, V_{BD}, and V_{CD}. Repeat for the related problem.

The Potentiometer as an Adjustable Voltage Divider

Recall from Chapter 2 that a potentiometer is a variable resistor with three terminals. A potentiometer connected to a voltage source is shown in Figure 4–43. Notice that the two end terminals are labeled 1 and 2. The adjustable terminal or wiper is labeled 3. The potentiometer acts as a voltage divider, which can be illustrated by separating the total resistance into two parts as shown in Figure 4–43(c). The resistance between terminal 1 and terminal 3 (R_{13}) is one part, and the resistance between terminal 3 and terminal 2 (R_{32}) is the other part. The potentiometer actually is a two-resistor voltage divider that can be manually adjusted.

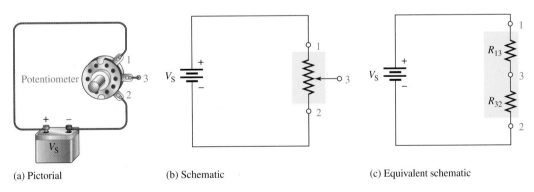

(a) Pictorial   (b) Schematic   (c) Equivalent schematic

▲ **FIGURE 4–43**

The potentiometer used as a voltage divider.

Figure 4–44 shows what happens when the wiper contact (3) is moved. In part (a), the wiper is exactly centered, making the two resistances equal. If you measure the voltage across terminals 3 to 2 as indicated, you have one-half of the total source voltage. When the wiper is moved up from the center position, as in part (b), the resistance between terminals 3 and 2 increases, and the voltage across it increases proportionally. When the wiper is moved down from the center position, as in part (c), the resistance between terminals 3 and 2 decreases, and the voltage decreases proportionally.

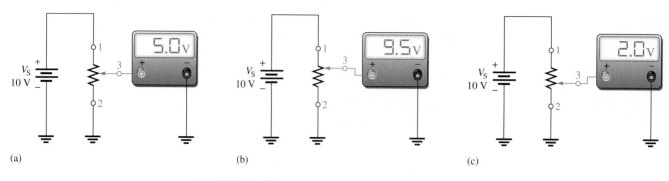

(a)   (b)   (c)

▲ FIGURE 4–44

Adjusting the voltage divider.

Applications

The volume control of a radio receiver is a common application of a potentiometer used as a voltage divider. Since the loudness of the sound is dependent on the amount of voltage associated with the audio signal, you can increase or decrease the volume by adjusting the potentiometer, that is, by turning the knob of the volume control on the set. The block diagram in Figure 4–45 shows how a potentiometer can be used for volume control in a typical receiver.

▶ FIGURE 4–45

A variable voltage divider used for volume control in a radio receiver.

Another application of a voltage divider is illustrated in Figure 4–46, which depicts a potentiometer voltage divider as a level sensor in a storage tank. As shown in part (a), the float moves up as the tank is filled and moves down as the tank empties. The float is mechanically

(a) Storage tank   (b) Detail of level sensor   (c) Schematic of level sensor

▲ FIGURE 4–46

A potentiometer voltage divider used as a level sensor.

linked to the wiper arm of a potentiometer, as shown in part (b). The output voltage varies proportionally with the position of the wiper arm. As the liquid in the tank decreases, the sensor output voltage also decreases. The output voltage goes to the indicator circuitry, which controls a digital readout to show the amount of liquid in the tank. The schematic of this system is shown in part (c).

Still another application for voltage dividers is in setting the dc operating voltage (bias) in transistor amplifiers. Figure 4–47 shows a voltage divider used for this purpose. You will study transistor amplifiers and biasing later, so it is important that you understand the basics of voltage dividers at this point.

These examples are only three out of many possible applications of voltage dividers.

◀ **FIGURE 4–47**

The voltage divider used as a bias circuit for a transistor amplifier.

SECTION 4–7 REVIEW

1. What is a voltage divider?
2. How many resistors can there be in a series voltage-divider circuit?
3. Write the general voltage-divider formula.
4. If two series resistors of equal value are connected across a 20 V source, how much voltage is there across each resistor?
5. A 56 kΩ resistor and an 82 kΩ resistor are connected as a voltage divider. The source voltage is 100 V. Draw the circuit, and determine the voltage across each of the resistors.
6. The circuit of Figure 4–48 is an adjustable voltage divider. If the potentiometer is linear, where would you set the wiper in order to get 5 V from B to A and 5 V from C to B?

FIGURE 4–48

4–8 POWER IN SERIES CIRCUITS

The power dissipated by each individual resistor in a series circuit contributes to the total power in the circuit. The individual powers are additive.

After completing this section, you should be able to

◆ **Determine power in a series circuit**

    ◆ Apply any of the power formulas

The total amount of power in a series resistive circuit is equal to the sum of the powers in each resistor in series.

Equation 4–6

$$P_T = P_1 + P_2 + P_3 + \cdots + P_n$$

where P_T is the total power and P_n is the power in the last resistor in series (n can be any positive integer equal to the number of resistors in series).

The power formulas that you learned in Chapter 3 are, applicable to series circuits. Since each resistor in series has the same current through it, the following formulas are used to calculate the total power:

$$P_T = V_S I$$
$$P_T = I^2 R_T$$
$$P_T = \frac{V_S^2}{R_T}$$

where I is the current through the circuit, V_S is the source voltage across the series circuit, and R_T is the total resistance.

EXAMPLE 4–19

Determine the total amount of power in the series circuit in Figure 4–49.

▶ FIGURE 4–49

Solution   The source voltage is 15 V. The total resistance is

$$R_T = 10\ \Omega + 12\ \Omega + 56\ \Omega + 22\ \Omega = 100\ \Omega$$

The easiest formula to use is $P_T = V_S^2/R_T$ since you know both V_S and R_T.

$$P_T = \frac{V_S^2}{R_T} = \frac{(15\ \text{V})^2}{100\ \Omega} = \frac{225\ \text{V}^2}{100\ \Omega} = 2.25\ \text{W}$$

If you determine the power of each resistor separately and add all these powers, you obtain the same result. Another calculation will illustrate. First, find the current.

$$I = \frac{V_S}{R_T} = \frac{15\ \text{V}}{100\ \Omega} = 150\ \text{mA}$$

Next, calculate the power for each resistor using $P = I^2 R$.

$$P_1 = (150\ \text{mA})^2(10\ \Omega) = 225\ \text{mW}$$
$$P_2 = (150\ \text{mA})^2(12\ \Omega) = 270\ \text{mW}$$
$$P_3 = (150\ \text{mA})^2(56\ \Omega) = 1.26\ \text{W}$$
$$P_4 = (150\ \text{mA})^2(22\ \Omega) = 495\ \text{mW}$$

Now, add these powers to get the total power.

$$P_T = 225\,\text{mW} + 270\,\text{mW} + 1.260\,\text{W} + 495\,\text{mW} = \mathbf{2.25\,W}$$

This result shows that the sum of the individual powers is equal to the total power as determined by the formula $P_T = V_S^2/R_T$.

Related Problem   What is the total power in the circuit of Figure 4–49 if V_S is increased to 30 V?

SECTION 4–8 REVIEW	1. If you know the power in each resistor in a series circuit, how can you find the total power?
	2. The resistors in a series circuit have the following powers: 1 W, 2 W, 5 W, and 8 W. What is the total power in the circuit?
	3. A circuit has a 100 Ω, a 330 Ω, and a 680 Ω resistor in series. There is a current of 1 mA through the circuit. What is the total power?

4–9   VOLTAGE MEASUREMENTS

Voltage is relative. That is, the voltage at one point in a circuit is always measured relative to another point. For example, if we say that there are +100 V at a certain point in a circuit, we mean that the point is 100 V more positive than some reference point in the circuit. This reference point in a circuit is usually called the ground or common point.

After completing this section, you should be able to

- ◆ **Measure voltage with respect to ground**
  - ◆ Determine and identify ground in a circuit
  - ◆ Define the term *reference ground*

The concept of *ground* was introduced in Chapter 2. In most electronic equipment, a large conductive area on a printed circuit board or the metal chassis that houses the assembly is used as the reference point, called the **reference ground** or **common,** as illustrated in Figure 4–50.

Reference ground has a potential of zero volts (0 V) with respect to all other points in the circuit that are referenced to it, as illustrated in Figure 4–51. In part (a), the negative side of the source is grounded, and all voltages indicated are positive with respect to ground. In part (b), the positive side of the source is grounded. The voltages at all other points are therefore negative with respect to ground.

Measuring Voltages with Respect to Ground

When you measure voltages with respect to the reference ground in a circuit, connect one meter lead to ground and the other to the point at which the voltage is to be measured. In a negative-ground circuit, as illustrated in Figure 4–52, the negative meter terminal is connected to the reference ground. The positive terminal of the voltmeter is then connected to the positive voltage point. The meter reads the voltage at point *A* with respect to ground.

▶ FIGURE 4–50

Simple illustration of ground in a circuit.

▶ FIGURE 4–51

Examples of negative and positive grounds. Multiple ground symbols actually represent the same electrical point, so you can think of them as being connected together.

(a) Negative ground

(b) Positive ground

▶ FIGURE 4–52

Measuring a voltage with respect to negative ground.

For a circuit with a positive ground, the positive analog voltmeter lead is connected to reference ground, and the negative lead is connected to the negative voltage point, as indicated in Figure 4–53. Here the meter reads the voltage at point A with respect to ground. When using a digital voltmeter, you can connect it either way because a digital meter can display both positive and negative voltages.

When you must measure voltages at several points in a circuit, you can clip the ground lead to ground at one point in the circuit and leave it there. Then move the other lead from point to point as you measure the voltages. This method is illustrated in Figure 4–54 and in equivalent schematic form in Figure 4–55.

◀ FIGURE 4–53

Measuring a voltage with respect to positive ground.

(a)   (b)   (c)

▲ FIGURE 4–54

Measuring voltages at several points in a circuit with respect to ground.

(a)   (b)   (c)

▲ FIGURE 4–55

Equivalent schematics for Figure 4–54.

Measuring Voltage across an Ungrounded Resistor

Voltage can normally be measured across a resistor, as shown in Figure 4–56, even though neither side of the resistor is connected to ground.

Another method can be used, as illustrated in Figure 4–57. The voltages on each side of the resistor (R_2) are measured with respect to ground. The difference of these two measurements is the voltage drop across the resistor.

$$V_{R2} = V_{AB} = V_A - V_B$$

▶ FIGURE 4–56

Measuring voltage directly across a resistor.

$$V_{R2} = V_{AB} = V_A - V_B$$

▲ FIGURE 4–57

Measuring voltage across R_2 with two separate measurements to ground.

EXAMPLE 4–20

Determine the voltages at each of the indicated points in each circuit of Figure 4–58 with respect to ground. Since each of the four resistors has the same value, 25 V are dropped across each one.

(a)   (b)   (c)

▲ FIGURE 4–58

Solution   For the circuit in Figure 4–58(a), the voltage polarities are as shown. Point E is ground. Single-letter subscripts denote voltage at a point with respect to ground. The voltages with respect to ground are as follows:

$$V_E = 0\,\text{V}, \quad V_D = +25\,\text{V}, \quad V_C = +50\,\text{V}, \quad V_B = +75\,\text{V}, \quad V_A = +100\,\text{V}$$

For the circuit in Figure 4–58(b), the voltage polarities are as shown. Point D is ground. The voltages with respect to ground are as follows:

$$V_E = -25\,\text{V}, \quad V_D = 0\,\text{V}, \quad V_C = +25\,\text{V}, \quad V_B = +50\,\text{V}, \quad V_A = +75\,\text{V}$$

For the circuit in Figure 4–58(c), the voltage polarities are as shown. Point C is ground. The voltages with respect to ground are as follows:

$$V_E = -50\,\text{V}, \quad V_D = -25\,\text{V}, \quad V_C = 0\,\text{V}, \quad V_B = +25\,\text{V}, \quad V_A = +50\,\text{V}$$

Related Problem   If the ground is moved to point A in Figure 4–58(a), what are the voltages at each of the other points with respect to ground?

 Open Multisim file E04-20 on your CD-ROM. For each circuit, verify the values of the voltages at each point with respect to ground. Repeat for the related problem.

SECTION 4–9 REVIEW

1. What is the reference point in a circuit called?
2. Voltages in a circuit are generally referenced to ground.   (True or False)
3. The housing or chassis can be used as reference ground.   (True or False)

4–10 TROUBLESHOOTING

Open components or contacts and shorts between conductors are common problems in all circuits. An open produces an infinite resistance. A short produces a zero resistance.

After completing this section, you should be able to

◆ **Troubleshoot series circuits**

  ◆ Check for an open circuit

  ◆ Check for a short circuit

  ◆ Identify primary causes of opens and shorts

Open Circuit

The most common failure in a series circuit is an **open**. For example, when a resistor or a lamp burns out, it creates an open, causing a break in the current path, as illustrated in Figure 4–59.

An open in a series circuit prevents current.

Troubleshooting an Open   In Chapter 3, you were introduced to the analysis, planning, and measurement (APM) approach to troubleshooting. You also learned about the half-splitting method and saw an example using an ohmmeter. Now, the same principles will be applied using voltage measurements instead of resistance measurements. As you know, voltage measurements are generally the easiest to make because you do not have to disconnect anything.

As a beginning step, prior to analysis, it is a good idea to make a visual check of the faulty circuit. Occasionally, you can find a charred resistor, a broken lamp filament, a loose

(a) A complete series circuit has current.

0 A

Open filament

(b) An open series circuit has no current.

▲ FIGURE 4–59

Current ceases when an open occurs.

wire, or a loose connection this way. However, it is possible (and probably more common) for a resistor or other component to open without showing visible signs of damage. When a visual check reveals nothing, then proceed with the APM approach.

When an open occurs in a series circuit, all of the source voltage appears across the open. The reason for this is that the open condition prevents current through the series circuit. With no current, there can be no voltage drop across any of the other resistors (or other component). Since $IR = (0 \text{ A})R = 0 \text{ V}$, the voltage on each end of a good resistor is the same. Therefore, the voltage applied across a series string also appears across the open component because there are no other voltage drops in the circuit, as illustrated in Figure 4–60. The source voltage will appear across the open resistor in accordance with Kirchhoff's voltage law as follows:

$$V_S = V_1 + V_2 + V_3 + V_4 + V_5 + V_6$$
$$V_4 = V_S - V_1 - V_2 - V_3 - V_5 - V_6$$
$$= 10 \text{ V} - 0 \text{ V} - 0 \text{ V} - 0 \text{ V} - 0 \text{ V} - 0 \text{ V}$$
$$V_4 = V_S = 10 \text{ V}$$

▶ FIGURE 4–60

The source voltage appears across the open series resistor.

HANDS ON TIP

When measuring a resistance, make sure that you do not touch the meter leads or the resistor leads. If you hold both ends of a high-value resistor in your fingers along with the meter probes, the measurement will be inaccurate because your body resistance can affect the measured value. When body resistance is placed in parallel with a high-value resistor, the measured value will be less than the actual value of the resistor.

Example of Half-Splitting Using Voltage Measurements Suppose a circuit has four resistors in series. You have determined by *analyzing* the symptoms (there is voltage but no current) that one of the resistors is open, and you are *planning* to find the open resistor using a voltmeter for *measuring* by the half-splitting method. A sequence of measurements for this particular case is illustrated in Figure 4–61.

Step 1: Measure across R_1 and R_2 (the left half of the circuit). A 0 V reading indicates that neither of these resistors is open.

Step 2: Move meter to measure across R_3 and R_4; the reading is 10 V. This indicates there is an open in the right half of the circuit, so either R_3 or R_4 is the faulty resistor (assume no bad connections).

Step 3: Move the meter to measure across R_3. A measurement of 10 V across R_3 identifies it as the open resistor. If you had measured across R_4, it would have indicated 0 V. This would have also identified R_3 as the faulty component because it would have been the only one left that could have 10 V across it.

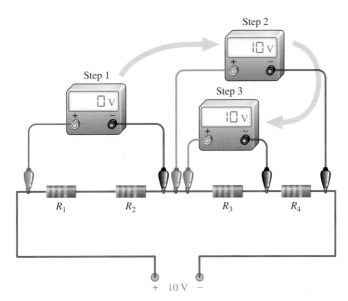

◀ FIGURE 4–61

Troubleshooting a series circuit for an open using half-splitting.

Short Circuit

Sometimes an unwanted short circuit occurs when two conductors touch or a foreign object such as solder or a wire clipping accidentally connects two sections of a circuit together. This situation is particularly common in circuits with a high component density. Three potential causes of short circuits are illustrated on the PC board in Figure 4–62.

When there is a **short**, a portion of the series resistance is bypassed (all of the current goes through the short), thus reducing the total resistance as illustrated in Figure 4–63. Notice that the current increases as a result of the short.

A short in a series circuit causes more current.

◀ FIGURE 4–62

Examples of shorts on a PC board.

◀ FIGURE 4–63

The effect of a short in a series circuit.

(a) Before short

$$I = \frac{100 \text{ V}}{100 \text{ }\Omega} = 1 \text{ A}$$

(b) After short

$$I = \frac{100 \text{ V}}{28 \text{ }\Omega} = 3.57 \text{ A}$$

Troubleshooting a Short A short is generally very difficult to troubleshoot. As in any troubleshooting situation, it is a good idea to make a visual check of the faulty circuit. In the case of a short in the circuit, a wire clipping, solder splash, or touching leads is often found to be the culprit. In terms of component failure, shorts are less common than opens in many types of components. Furthermore, a short in one part of a circuit can cause over-heating in another part due to the higher current caused by the short. As a result two failures, an open and a short, may occur together.

When a short occurs in a series circuit, there is essentially no voltage across the shorted part. A short has zero or near zero resistance, although shorts with significant resistance values can occur from time to time. These are called *resistive shorts.* For purposes of illustration, zero resistance is assumed for all shorts.

In order to troubleshoot a short, measure the voltage across each resistor until you get a reading of 0 V. This is the straightforward approach and does not use half-splitting. In order to apply the half-splitting method, you must know the correct voltage at each point in the circuit and compare it to measured voltages. Example 4–21 illustrates using half-splitting to find a short.

EXAMPLE 4–21

Assume you have determined that there is a short in a circuit with four series resistors because the current is higher than it should be. You know that the voltage at each point in the circuit should be as shown in Figure 4–64 if the circuit is working properly. The voltages are shown relative to the negative terminal of the source. Find the location of the short.

▲ FIGURE 4–64

Series circuit (without a short) with correct voltages marked.

Solution Use the half-splitting method to troubleshoot the short.

Step 1: Measure across R_1 and R_2. The meter shows a reading of 6.67 V, which is higher than the normal voltage (it should be 5 V). Look for a voltage that is lower than normal because a short will make the voltage less across that part of the circuit.

Step 2: Move the meter and measure across R_3 and R_4; the reading of 3.33 V is incorrect and lower than normal (it should be 5 V). This shows that the short is in the right half of the circuit and that either R_3 or R_4 is shorted.

Step 3: Again move the meter and measure across R_3. A reading of 3.3 V across R_3 tells you that R_4 is shorted because it must have 0 V across it. Figure 4–65 illustrates this troubleshooting technique.

▶ FIGURE 4–65

Troubleshooting a series circuit for a short using half-splitting.

Step 2
3.33 V

Step 1
6.67 V

Step 3
3.33 V

R_1 R_2 R_3 R_4

+ 10 V −

Related Problem   Assume that R_1 is shorted in Figure 4–65. What would the Step 1 measurement be?

SECTION 4–10 REVIEW

1. Define *open*.
2. Define *short*.
3. What happens when a series circuit opens?
4. Name two general ways in which an open circuit can occur in practice. How can a short circuit occur?
5. When a resistor fails, it will normally open.   (True or False)
6. The total voltage across a string of series resistors is 24 V. If one of the resistors is open, how much voltage is there across it? How much is there across each of the good resistors?
7. Explain why the voltage measured in Step 1 of Figure 4–65 is higher than normal.

Application Assignment

PUTTING YOUR KNOWLEDGE TO WORK

For this assignment, suppose your supervisor has given you a voltage-divider board to evaluate and modify if necessary. You will use it to obtain five different voltage levels from a 12 V battery that has a 6.5 Ah rating. The voltage divider provides positive reference voltages to an electronic circuit in an analog-to-digital converter. Your job will be to check the circuit to see if it provides the following voltages within a tolerance of ±5% with respect to the negative side of the battery: 10.4 V, 8.0 V, 7.3 V, 6.0 V, and 2.7 V. If the

existing circuit does not provide the specified voltages, you will modify it so that it does. Also, you must make sure that the power ratings of the resistors are adequate for the application and determine how long the battery will last with the voltage divider connected to it.

Step 1: Drawing the Schematic of the Circuit

Use Figure 4–66 to determine the resistor values and draw the schematic of the voltage-divider circuit. All the resistors on the board are 0.25 W.

▲ FIGURE 4–66

Step 2: Determining the Voltages

Determine each output voltage on the existing circuit board when the positive side of the 12 V battery is connected to pin 3 and the negative side is connected to pin 1. Compare the existing output voltages to the following specifications:

Pin 1: negative terminal of 12 V battery

Pin 2: 2.7 V ± 5%

Pin 3: positive terminal of 12 V battery

Pin 4: 10.4 V ± 5%

Pin 5: 8.0 V ± 5%

Pin 6: 7.3 V ± 5%

Pin 7: 6.0 V ± 5%

Step 3: Modifying the Existing Circuit (if necessary)

If the output voltages of the existing circuit are not the same as those stated in the specifications of Step 2, make the necessary changes in the circuit to meet the specifications. Draw a schematic of the modified circuit showing resistor values and adequate power ratings.

Step 4: Determining the Life of the Battery

Find the total current drawn from the 12 V battery when the voltage-divider circuit is connected and determine how many days the 6.5 Ah battery will last.

Step 5: Developing a Test Procedure

Determine how you would test the voltage-divider board and what instruments you would use. Then detail your test procedure in a step-by-step format.

Step 6: Troubleshooting the Circuit

Determine the most likely fault for each of the following cases (voltages are with respect to the negative battery terminal (pin 1 on the circuit board):

1. No voltage at any of the pins on the circuit board

2. 12 V at pins 3 and 4. All other pins have 0 V.

3. 12 V at all pins except 0 V at pin 1

4. 12 V at pin 6 and 0 V at pin 7

5. 3.3 V at pin 2

Multisim Analysis

1. Using Multisim, connect the circuit based on the schematic from Step 1 and verify the output voltages specified in Step 2.

2. Insert faults determined in Step 6 and verify the resulting voltage measurements.

Review

1. What is the total power dissipated by the voltage-divider circuit with a 12 V battery?

2. What are the output voltages from the voltage divider if the positive terminal of a 6 V battery is connected to pin 3 and the negative terminal to pin 1?

3. When the voltage-divider board is connected to the electronic circuit to which it is providing positive reference voltages, which pin on the board should be connected to the ground of the electronic circuit?

SUMMARY

♦ The total series resistance is the sum of all resistors in the series circuit.

♦ The total resistance between any two points in a series circuit is equal to the sum of all resistors connected in series between those two points.

♦ If all of the resistors in a series circuit are of equal value, the total resistance is the number of resistors multiplied by the resistance value of one resistor.

♦ The current is the same at all points in a series circuit.

♦ Voltage sources in series add algebraically.

♦ Kirchhoff's voltage law: The sum of the voltage drops equals the total source voltage.

♦ Kirchhoff's voltage law: the algebraic sum of all the voltages around a closed single path is zero.

♦ The voltage drops in a circuit are always opposite in polarity to the total source voltage.

♦ Current is defined to be out of the negative side of a source and into the positive side.

♦ Current is defined to be into the negative side of each resistor and out of the positive side.

♦ A voltage divider is a series arrangement of resistors connected to a voltage source.

♦ A voltage divider is so named because the voltage drop across any resistor in the series circuit is divided down from the total voltage by an amount proportional to that resistance value in relation to the total resistance.

♦ A potentiometer can be used as an adjustable voltage divider.

♦ The total power in a resistive circuit is the sum of all the individual powers of the resistors making up the series circuit.

♦ All voltages in a circuit are referenced to ground unless otherwise specified.

♦ Ground (common) is zero volts with respect to all points referenced to it in the circuit.

♦ *Negative ground* is the term used when the negative side of the source is grounded.

♦ *Positive ground* is the term used when the positive side of the source is grounded.

♦ The voltage across an open component always equals the source voltage.

♦ The voltage across a shorted component is always 0 V.

KEY TERMS

These key terms are also in the end-of-book glossary.

Kirchhoff's voltage law   A law stating that (1) the sum of the voltage drops around a single closed path equals the source voltage in that loop or (2) the algebraic sum of all the voltages (drops and source) around a single closed path is zero.

Open   A circuit condition in which the current path is interrupted.

Reference ground   The metal chassis that houses the assembly or a large conductive area on a printed circuit board used as the common or reference point; also called common (com).

Series   In an electric circuit, a relationship of components in which the components are connected such that they provide a single current path between two points.

Series-aiding   An arrangement of two or more series voltage sources with polarities in the same direction.

Series-opposing   An arrangement of two series voltage sources with polarities in the opposite direction.

Short   A circuit condition in which there is a zero or abnormally low resistance path between two points: usually an inadvertent condition.

Voltage divider   A circuit consisting of series resistors across which one or more output voltages are taken.

FORMULAS

4–1	$R_T = R_1 + R_2 + R_3 + \cdots + R_n$	Total resistance of n resistors in series
4–2	$R_T = nR$	Total resistance of n equal-value resistors in series
4–3	$V_S = V_1 + V_2 + V_3 + \cdots + V_n$	Kirchhoff's voltage law
4–4	$V_S - V_1 - V_2 - V_3 - \cdots - V_n = 0$	Kirchhoff's voltage law stated another way
4–5	$V_x = \left(\dfrac{R_x}{R_T}\right)V_S$	Voltage-divider formula
4–6	$P_T = P_1 + P_2 + P_3 + \cdots + P_n$	Total power

SELF-TEST

Answers are at the end of the chapter.

1. Five equal-value resistors are connected in series and there is a current of 2 mA into the first resistor. The amount of current out of the second resistor is

   (a) 2 mA   (b) 1 mA   (c) 4 mA   (d) 0.4 mA

2. To measure the current out of the third resistor in a circuit consisting of four series resistors, an ammeter can be placed

   (a) between the third and fourth resistors   (b) between the second and third resistors

   (c) at the positive terminal of the source   (d) at any point in the circuit

3. When a third resistor is connected in series with two series resistors, the total resistance

   (a) remains the same   (b) increases   (c) decreases   (d) increases by one-third

4. When one of four series resistors is removed from a circuit and the circuit reconnected, the current

   (a) decreases by the amount of current through the removed resistor

   (b) decreases by one-fourth   (c) quadruples   (d) increases

5. A series circuit consists of three resistors with values of 100 Ω, 220 Ω, and 330 Ω. The total resistance is

   (a) less than 100 Ω (b) the average of the values   (c) 550 Ω (d) 650 Ω

6. A 9 V battery is connected across a series combination of 68 Ω, 33 Ω, 100 Ω, and 47 Ω resistors. The amount of current is

   (a) 36.3 mA   (b) 27.6 A   (c) 22.3 mA   (d) 363 mA

7. While putting four 1.5 V batteries in a flashlight, you accidentally put one of them in backward. The light will be

   (a) brighter than normal   (b) dimmer than normal   (c) off   (d) the same

8. If you measure all the voltage drops and the source voltage in a series circuit and add them together, taking into consideration the polarities, you will get a result equal to

   (a) the source voltage   (b) the total of the voltage drops

   (c) zero   (d) the total of the source voltage and the voltage drops

9. There are six resistors in a given series circuit and each resistor has 5 V dropped across it. The source voltage is

   (a) 5 V   (b) 30 V

   (c) dependent on the resistor values   (d) dependent on the current

10. A series circuit consists of a 4.7 kΩ, a 5.6 kΩ, and a 10 kΩ resistor. The resistor that has the most voltage across it is

    (a) the 4.7 kΩ (b) the 5.6 kΩ

    (c) the 10 kΩ (d) impossible to determine from the given information

11. Which of the following series combinations dissipates the most power when connected across a 100 V source?

    (a) one 100 Ω resistor   (b) two 100 Ω resistors

    (c) three 100 Ω resistors   (d) four 100 Ω resistors

12. The total power in a certain circuit is 1 W. Each of the five equal-value series resistors making up the circuit dissipates

    (a) 1 W   (b) 5 W   (c) 0.5 W   (d) 0.2 W

13. When you connect an ammeter in a series resistive circuit and turn on the source voltage, the meter reads zero. You should check for

    (a) a broken wire   (b) a shorted resistor

    (c) an open resistor   (d) both (a) and (c)

14. While checking out a series resistive circuit, you find that the current is higher than it should be. You should look for

    (a) an open circuit   (b) a short   (c) a low resistor value   (d) both (b) and (c)

TROUBLESHOOTING: SYMPTOM AND CAUSE

The purpose of these exercises is to help develop thought processes essential to troubleshooting. Answers are at the end of the chapter.

Determine the cause for each set of symptoms. Refer to Figure 4–67.

▶ **FIGURE 4–67**

The meters indicate the correct readings for this circuit.

1. *Symptom:* The ammeter reading is zero, the voltmeter 1 and voltmeter 3 readings are zero, and the voltmeter 2 reading is 10 V.

   Cause:

   (a) R_1 is open.

   (b) R_2 is open.

   (c) R_3 is open.

2. *Symptom:* The ammeter reading is zero, and all the voltmeter readings are zero.

   Cause:

   (a) A resistor is open.

   (b) The voltage source is turned off or faulty.

   (c) One of the resistor values is too high.

3. *Symptom:* The ammeter reading is 2.33 mA, and the voltmeter 2 reading is zero.

   Cause:

   (a) R_1 is shorted.

   (b) The voltage source is set too high.

   (c) R_2 is shorted.

4. *Symptom:* The ammeter reading is zero, voltmeter 1 reads 0 V, voltmeter 2 reads 5 V, and voltmeter 3 reads 5 V.

   Cause:

   (a) R_1 is shorted.

   (b) R_1 and R_2 are open.

   (c) R_2 and R_3 are open.

5. *Symptom:* The ammeter reading is 0.645 mA, the voltmeter 1 reading is too high, and the other two voltmeter readings are too low.

   Cause:

   (a) R_1 has an incorrect value of $10\,k\Omega$.

   (b) R_2 has an incorrect value of $10\,k\Omega$.

   (c) R_3 has an incorrect value of $10\,k\Omega$.

PROBLEMS

Answers to odd-numbered problems are at the end of the book.

BASIC PROBLEMS

SECTION 4–1   **Resistors in Series**

1. Connect each set of resistors in Figure 4–68 in series between points *A* and *B*.

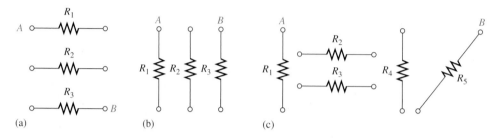

▲ FIGURE 4–68

2. Determine which resistors in Figure 4–69 are in series. Show how to interconnect the pins to put all the resistors in series.

3. Determine the resistance between pins 1 and 8 in the circuit board in Figure 4–69.

4. Determine the resistance between pins 2 and 3 in the circuit board in Figure 4–69.

▶ FIGURE 4–69

SECTION 4–2   **Total Series Resistance**

5. An 82 Ω resistor and a 56 Ω resistor are connected in series. What is the total resistance?

6. Find the total resistance of each group of series resistors shown in Figure 4–70.

(a)

(b)

(c)

(d)

▲ FIGURE 4–70

7. Determine R_T for each circuit in Figure 4–71. Show how to measure R_T with an ohmmeter.

(a) (b) (c)

▲ FIGURE 4–71

8. What is the total resistance of twelve 5.6 kΩ resistors in series?

9. Six 47 Ω resistors, eight 100 Ω resistors, and two 22 Ω resistors are in series. What is the total resistance?

10. The total resistance in Figure 4–72 is 20 kΩ. What is the value of R_5?

▶ FIGURE 4–72

11. Determine the resistance between each of the following sets of pins on the PC board in Figure 4–69.

   (a) pin 1 and pin 8   (b) pin 2 and pin 3

   (c) pin 4 and pin 7   (d) pin 5 and pin 6

12. If all the resistors in Figure 4–69 are connected in series, what is the total resistance?

SECTION 4–3 **Current in a Series Circuit**

13. What is the current through each of four resistors in a series circuit if the source voltage is 12 V and the total resistance is 120 Ω?

14. The current from the source in Figure 4–73 is 5 mA. How much current does each milliammeter in the circuit indicate?

▶ FIGURE 4–73

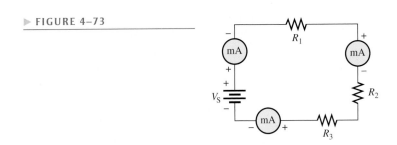

SECTION 4–4 **Application of Ohm's Law**

15. What is the current in each circuit of Figure 4–74? Show how to connect an ammeter in each case.

(a) (b)

16. Determine the voltage across each resistor in Figure 4–74.

17. Three 470 Ω resistors are in series with a 48 V source.

   (a) How much current is there?

   (b) What is the voltage across each resistor?

   (c) What is the minimum power rating of the resistors?

18. Four equal-value resistors are in series with a 5 V source, and a current of 1 mA is measured. What is the value of each resistor?

SECTION 4–5 Voltage Sources in Series

19. A 5 V battery and a 9 V battery are connected in series with their polarities in the same direction. What is the total voltage?

20. Determine the total source voltage in each circuit of Figure 4–75.

(a) (b) (c)

SECTION 4–6 Kirchhoff's Voltage Law

21. The following voltage drops are measured across each of three resistors in series: 5.5 V, 8.2 V, and 12.3 V. What is the value of the source voltage to which these resistors are connected?

22. Five resistors are in series with a 20 V source. The voltage drops across four of the resistors are 1.5 V, 5.5 V, 3 V, and 6 V. How much voltage is across the fifth resistor?

23. Determine the unspecified voltage drop(s) in each circuit of Figure 4–76. Show how to connect a voltmeter to measure each unknown voltage drop.

(a) (b)

SECTION 4–7 Voltage Dividers

24. The total resistance of a series circuit is 500 Ω. What percentage of the total voltage appears across a 22 Ω resistor in the series circuit?

25. Find the voltage between *A* and *B* in each voltage divider of Figure 4–77.

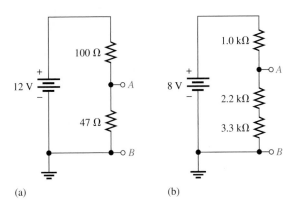

(a)   (b)

▲ FIGURE 4–77

26. Determine the voltage with respect to ground for output *A*, *B*, and *C* in Figure 4–78(a).

27. Determine the minimum and maximum output voltage from the voltage divider in Figure 4–78(b).

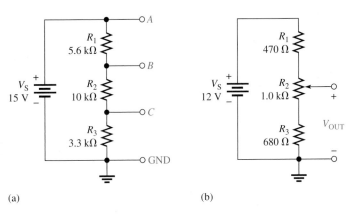

(a)   (b)

▲ FIGURE 4–78

28. What is the voltage across each resistor in Figure 4–79? *R* is the lowest value and all others are multiples of that value as indicated.

▶ FIGURE 4–79

(b) Protoboard with meter leads (yellow and green) and power supply leads (red and black) connected

(a) Meter with leads going to protoboard

▲ FIGURE 4–80

29. What is the voltage across each resistor on the protoboard in Figure 4–80(b)?

SECTION 4–8   Power in Series Circuits

30. Five series resistors each dissipate 50 mW of power. What is the total power?

31. Use the results of Problem 29 to find the total power in Figure 4–80.

SECTION 4–9   Voltage Measurements

32. Determine the voltage at each point with respect to ground in Figure 4–81.

▶ FIGURE 4–81

33. In Figure 4–82, how would you determine the voltage across R_2 by measurement, without connecting a meter directly across the resistor?

34. Determine the voltage at each point with respect to ground in Figure 4–82.

▶ FIGURE 4–82

SECTION 4–10   Troubleshooting

35. By observing the meters in Figure 4–83, determine the types of failures in the circuits and which components have failed.

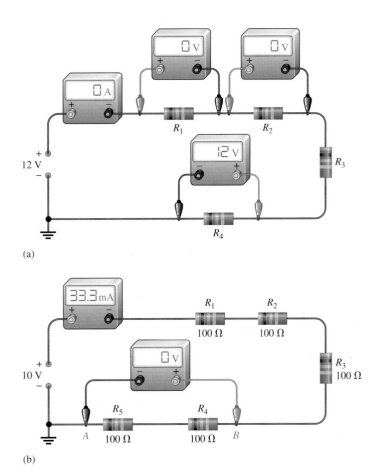

(a)

(b)

▲ FIGURE 4–83

36. Is the multimeter reading in Figure 4–84 correct? If not, what is wrong?

▶ FIGURE 4–84

(a) Meter with leads going to protoboard

(b) Protoboard with meter leads connected

ADVANCED PROBLEMS

37. Determine the unknown resistance (R_3) in the circuit of Figure 4–85.

▶ FIGURE 4–85

38. You have the following resistor values available to you in the lab in unlimited quantities: 10 Ω, 100 Ω, 470 Ω, 560 Ω, 680 Ω, 1.0 kΩ, 2.2 kΩ, and 5.6 kΩ. All of the other standard values are out of stock. A project that you are working on requires an 18 kΩ resistance. What combination of available values can you use to obtain the needed value?

39. Determine the voltage at each point in Figure 4–86 with respect to ground.

▶ FIGURE 4–86

40. Find all the unknown quantities (appearing in color) in Figure 4–87.

▲ FIGURE 4–87

41. There are 250 mA in a series circuit with a total resistance of 1.5 kΩ. The current must be reduced by 25%. Determine how much resistance must be added in order to accomplish this reduction in current.

42. Four ½ W resistors are in series: 47 Ω, 68 Ω, 100 Ω, and 120 Ω. To what maximum value can the current be raised before the power rating of one of the resistors is exceeded? Which resistor will burn out first if the current is increased above the maximum?

43. A certain series circuit is made up of a ⅛ W resistor, a ¼ W resistor, and a ½ W resistor. The total resistance is 2400 Ω. If each of the resistors is operating at its maximum power level, determine the following:

    (a) I **(b)** V_S **(c)** the value of each resistor

44. Using 1.5 V batteries, a switch, and three lamps, devise a circuit to apply 4.5 V across one lamp, two lamps in series, or three lamps in series with a single control switch. Draw the schematic.

45. Develop a variable voltage divider to provide output voltages ranging from a minimum of 10 V to a maximum of 100 V using a 120 V source. The maximum voltage must be at the maximum resistance setting of the potentiometer. The minimum voltage must be at the minimum resistance (zero ohms) setting. The current is to be 10 mA.

46. Using the standard resistor values given in Appendix A, design a voltage divider to provide the following approximate voltages with respect to the negative terminal of a 30 V source: 8.18 V, 14.7 V, and 24.6 V. The current drain on the source must be limited to no more than 1 mA. The number of resistors, their resistance values, and their power ratings must be specified. Draw a schematic showing the circuit with all resistor values indicated.

47. On the double-sided PC board in Figure 4–88, identify each group of series resistors and determine its total resistance. Note that many of the interconnections feed through the board from the top side to the bottom side.

◀ FIGURE 4–88

Top   Bottom

48. What is the total resistance from A to B for each switch position in Figure 4–89?

49. Determine the current measured by the meter in Figure 4–90 for each switch position.

▲ FIGURE 4–89

▲ FIGURE 4–90

50. Determine the current measured by the meter in Figure 4–91 for each position of the ganged switch.

▶ FIGURE 4–91

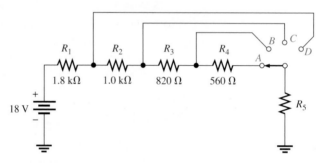

51. Determine the voltage across each resistor in Figure 4–92 for each switch position if the current through R_5 is 6 mA when the switch is in the D position.

▲ FIGURE 4–92

52. Table 4–1 shows the results of resistance measurements on the PC circuit board in Figure 4–88. Are these results correct? If not, identify the possible problems.

▶ TABLE 4–1

BETWEEN PINS	RESISTANCE
1 and 2	∞
1 and 3	∞
1 and 4	4.23 kΩ
1 and 5	∞
1 and 6	∞
2 and 3	23.6 kΩ
2 and 4	∞
2 and 5	∞
2 and 6	∞
3 and 4	∞
3 and 5	∞
3 and 6	∞
4 and 5	∞
4 and 6	∞
5 and 6	19.9 kΩ

53. You measure 15 kΩ between pins 5 and 6 on the PC board in Figure 4–88. Does this indicate a problem? If so, identify it.

54. In checking out the PC board in Figure 4–88, you measure 17.83 kΩ between pins 1 and 2. Also, you measure 13.6 kΩ between pins 2 and 4. Does this indicate a problem on the PC board? If so, identify the fault.

55. The three groups of series resistors on the PC board in Figure 4–88 are connected in series with each other to form a single series circuit by connecting pin 2 to pin 4 and pin 3 to pin 5. A voltage source is connected across pins 1 and 6 and an ammeter is placed in series. As you increase the source voltage, you observe the corresponding increase in current. Suddenly, the current drops to zero and you smell smoke. All resistors are ½ W.

   (a) What has happened?

   (b) Specifically, what must you do to fix the problem?

   (c) At what voltage did the failure occur?

MULTISIM TROUBLESHOOTING PROBLEMS

56. Open file P04-56 on your CD-ROM. Determine if there is a fault and, if so, identify the fault.

57. Open file P04-57 on your CD-ROM. Determine if there is a fault and, if so, identify the fault.

58. Open file P04-58 on your CD-ROM. Determine if there is a fault and, if so, identify the fault.

59. Open file P04-59 on your CD-ROM. Determine if there is a fault and, if so, identify the fault.

60. Open file P04-60 on your CD-ROM. Determine if there is a fault and, if so, identify the fault.

61. Open file P04-61 on your CD-ROM. Determine if there is a fault and, if so, identify the fault.

ANSWERS

SECTION REVIEWS

SECTION 4–1   **Resistors in Series**

   1. Series resistors are connected end-to-end in a "string."

   2. There is a single current path in a series circuit.

   3. See Figure 4–93.

▶ FIGURE 4–93

(a)   (b)   (c)

   4. See Figure 4–94.

▶ FIGURE 4–94

SECTION 4–2 Total Series Resistance

1. (a) $R_T = 33\,\Omega + 100\,\Omega + 10\,\Omega = 143\,\Omega$

(b) $R_T = 39\,\Omega + 56\,\Omega + 10\,\Omega = 105\,\Omega$

(c) $R_T = 820\,\Omega + 2200\,\Omega + 1000\,\Omega = 4020\,\Omega$

2. $R_T = 100\,\Omega + 2(47\,\Omega) + 4(12\,\Omega) + 330\,\Omega = 572\,\Omega$

3. $10\,k\Omega - 8.8\,k\Omega = 1.2\,k\Omega$

4. $R_T = 12(47\,\Omega) = 564\,\Omega$

SECTION 4–3 Current in a Series Circuit

1. The current is the same at all points in a series circuit.

2. There are 2 A through the 4.7 Ω resistor.

3. 50 mA between C and D, 50 mA between E and F

4. Ammeter 1 indicates 1.79 A; Ammeter 2 indicates 1.79 A.

SECTION 4–4 Ohm's Law in Series Circuits

1. $I = 10\,\text{V}/300\,\Omega = 0.033\,\text{A} = 33\,\text{mA}$

2. $V = (5\,\text{mA})(43\,\Omega) = 125\,\text{mV}$

3. $V_1 = (5\,\text{mA})(10\,\Omega) = 50\,\text{mV}$, $V_2 = (5\,\text{mA})(15\,\Omega) = 75\,\text{mV}$, $V_3 = (5\,\text{mA})(18\,\Omega) = 90\,\text{mV}$

4. $R = 1.25\,\text{V}/4.63\,\text{mA} = 270\,\Omega$

SECTION 4–5 Voltage Sources in Series

1. 60 V/12 V = 5; see Figure 4–95.

▲ FIGURE 4–95

2. $V_T = (4)(1.5\,\text{V}) = 6.0\,\text{V}$

3. See Figure 4–96.

▶ FIGURE 4–96

4. (a) $V_{S(\text{tot})} = 100\,\text{V} + 50\,\text{V} - 75\,\text{V} = 75\,\text{V}$

(b) $V_{S(\text{tot})} = 20\,\text{V} + 10\,\text{V} - 10\,\text{V} - 5\,\text{V} = 15\,\text{V}$

5. See Figure 4–97.

▶ FIGURE 4–97

(a) (b)

SECTION 4–6 **Kirchhoff's Voltage Law**

1. Kirchhoff's voltage law states:

    (a) The algebraic sum of the voltages around a closed path is zero.

    (b) The sum of the voltage drops equals the total source voltage.

2. $V_{R(\text{tot})} = V_S = 50\,\text{V}$

3. $V_{R1} = V_{R2} = 10\,\text{V}/2 = 5\,\text{V}$

4. $V_{R3} = 25\,\text{V} - 5\,\text{V} - 10\,\text{V} = 10\,\text{V}$

5. $V_S = 1\,\text{V} + 3\,\text{V} + 5\,\text{V} + 7\,\text{V} + 8\,\text{V} = 24\,\text{V}$

SECTION 4–7 **Voltage Dividers**

1. A voltage divider is a series circuit with two or more resistors in which the voltage taken across any resistor or combination of resistors is proportional to the value of that resistance.

2. Two or more resistors form a voltage divider.

3. $V_x = (R_x/R_T)V_S$ is the general voltage-divider formula.

4. $V_R = 20\,\text{V}/2 = 10\,\text{V}$

5. $V_{56} = (56\,\text{k}\Omega/138\,\text{k}\Omega)100\,\text{V} = 40.6\,\text{V}$, $V_{82} = (82\,\text{k}\Omega/138\,\text{k}\Omega)100\,\text{V} = 59.4\,\text{V}$. See Figure 4–98.

6. Set the potentiometer at the midpoint.

▶ FIGURE 4–98

SECTION 4–8 **Power in Series Circuits**

1. Add the powers in each resistor to get total power.

2. $P_T = 1\,\text{W} + 2\,\text{W} = 5\,\text{W} + 8\,\text{W} = 16\,\text{W}$

3. $P_T = (1\,\text{mA})^2(100\,\Omega + 330\,\Omega + 680\,\Omega) = 1.11\,\text{mW}$

SECTION 4–9 **Voltage Measurements**

1. Ground

2. True

3. True

SECTION 4–10 **Troubleshooting**

1. An open is a break in the current path.

2. A short is a zero resistance path that bypasses a portion of a circuit.

3. Current ceases when a series circuit opens.

4. An open can be created by a component failure or a faulty contact. A short can be created by wire clippings, solder splashes, etc.

5. True

6. 24 V across the open R; 0 V across the other resistors.

7. Because R_4 is shorted, more voltage is dropped across the other resistors than normal. The total voltage is divided across three equal-value resistors.

Application Assignment

1. $P_T = (12\,\text{V})^2/16.6\,\text{k}\Omega = 8.67\,\text{mW}$

2. Pin 2: 1.41 V; Pin 6: 3.65 V; Pin 5: 4.01 V; Pin 4: 5.20 V; Pin 7: 3.11 V

3. Pin 3 connects to ground.

RELATED PROBLEMS FOR EXAMPLES

4–1 **a.** Left end of R_1 to terminal A, right end of R_1 to top end of R_3, bottom end of R_3 to right end of R_5, left end of R_5 to left end of R_2, right end of R_2 to right end of R_4, left end of R_4 to terminal B

   b. $R_1 = 1.0\,\text{k}\Omega$, $R_2 = 33\,\text{k}\Omega$, $R_3 = 39\,\text{k}\Omega$, $R_4 = 470\,\Omega$, $R_5 = 22\,\text{k}\Omega$

4–2 The two series circuits are connected in series, so all the resistors on the board are in series.

4–3 $258\,\Omega$ (No change)

4–4 $12.1\,\text{k}\Omega$

4–5 $22\,\text{k}\Omega$

4–6 $4.36\,\text{k}\Omega$

4–7 $116\,\text{mA}$

4–8 $7.8\,\text{V}$

4–9 $V_1 = 1\,\text{V}, V_2 = 3.3\,\text{V}, V_3 = 2.2\,\text{V}, V_S = 6.5\,\text{V}, V_{S(\text{max})} = 32.5\,\text{V}$

4–10 $V_1 = 0\,\text{V}, V_2 = 12\,\text{V}, V_3 = 0\,\text{V}, V_4 = 0\,\text{V}$

4–11 $12\,\text{V}$

4–12 $2\,\text{V}$

4–13 $10\,\text{V}, 20\,\text{V}$

4–14 $6.5\,\text{V}$

4–15 $593\,\Omega$

4–16 $V_1 = 3.13\,\text{V}; V_2 = 6.87\,\text{V}$

4–17 $V_1 = V_2 = V_3 = 3.33\,\text{V}$

4–18 $V_{AB} = 4\,\text{V}; V_{AC} = 36.8\,\text{V}; V_{BC} = 32.8\,\text{V}; V_{BD} = 46\,\text{V}; V_{CD} = 13.2\,\text{V}$

4–19 $9\,\text{W}$

4–20 $V_A = 0\,\text{V}; V_B = -25\,\text{V}; V_C = -50\,\text{V}; V_D = -75\,\text{V}; V_E = -100\,\text{V}$

4–21 $3.33\,\text{V}$

SELF-TEST

1. (a)   **2.** (d)   **3.** (b)   **4.** (d)   **5.** (d)   **6.** (a)   **7.** (b)
8. (c)   **9.** (b)   **10.** (c)   **11.** (a)   **12.** (d)   **13.** (d)   **14.** (d)

TROUBLESHOOTING: SYMPTOM AND CAUSE

1. (b)

2. (b)

3. (c)

4. (c)

5. (a)

PARALLEL CIRCUITS

5

CHAPTER OBJECTIVES

◆ Identify a parallel resistive circuit
◆ Determine total parallel resistance
◆ Determine the voltage across each parallel branch
◆ Apply Ohm's law in a parallel circuit
◆ Apply Kirchhoff's current law
◆ Use a parallel circuit as a current divider
◆ Determine power in a parallel circuit
◆ Troubleshoot parallel circuits

KEY TERMS

◆ Parallel
◆ Branch
◆ Kirchhoff's current law
◆ Node
◆ Current divider

APPLICATION ASSIGNMENT PREVIEW

In this application, a panel-mounted power supply will be modified by adding a milliammeter to indicate current to a load. Expansion of the meter for multiple current ranges using parallel (shunt) resistors will be demonstrated. The problem with very low-value resistors when a switch is used to select the current ranges will be introduced and the effect of switch contact resistance will be demonstrated. A way of eliminating the contact resistance problem will be presented. Finally, the ammeter circuit will be installed in the power supply. The knowledge of parallel circuits and of basic ammeters that you will acquire in this chapter plus your understanding of Ohm's law and current dividers will be put to good use. After studying this chapter, you should be able to complete the application assignment.

VISIT THE COMPANION WEBSITE

Study aids for this chapter are available at
http://www.prenhall.com/floyd

INTRODUCTION

In this chapter, you will see how Ohm's law is used in parallel circuits; and you will learn Kirchhoff's current law. Also, several applications of parallel circuits, including automotive lighting, residential wiring, and the internal wiring of analog ammeters are presented. You will learn how to determine total parallel resistance and how to troubleshoot for open resistors.

When resistors are connected in parallel and a voltage is applied across the parallel circuit, each resistor provides a separate path for current. The total resistance of a parallel circuit is reduced as more resistors are connected in parallel. The voltage across each of the parallel resistors is equal to the voltage applied across the entire parallel circuit.

5–1   RESISTORS IN PARALLEL

When two or more resistors are individually connected between the same two points, they are in **parallel** with each other. A parallel circuit provides more than one path for current.

After completing this section, you should be able to

◆ **Identify a parallel resistive circuit**

◆ Translate a physical arrangement of parallel resistors into a schematic

Each parallel path in a circuit is called a **branch**. Two resistors connected in parallel are shown in Figure 5–1(a). As shown in part (b), the current out of the source (I_T) divides when it gets to point B. I_1 goes through R_1 and I_2 goes through R_2. The two currents come back together at point A. If additional resistors are connected in parallel with the first two, more current paths are provided, as shown in Figure 5–1(c). All points along the top shown in blue are electrically the same as point A, and all the points along the bottom shown in green are electrically the same as point B.

(a)   (b)   (c)

▲ FIGURE 5–1

Resistors in parallel.

In Figure 5–1, it is obvious that the resistors are connected in parallel. However, in actual circuit diagrams, the parallel relationship often is not as clear. It is important that you learn to recognize parallel circuits regardless of how they may be drawn.

A rule for identifying parallel circuits is as follows:

If there is more than one current path (branch) between two points, and if the voltage between those two points also appears across each of the branches, then there is a parallel circuit between those two points.

Figure 5–2 shows parallel resistors drawn in different ways between two points labeled A and B. Notice that in each case, the current has two paths going from A to B, and the

(a)   (b)   (c)   (d)   (e)

▲ FIGURE 5–2

Examples of circuits with two parallel paths.

voltage across each branch is the same. Although these figures show only two parallel paths, there can be any number of resistors in parallel.

EXAMPLE 5–1

Five resistors are positioned on a protoboard as shown in Figure 5–3. Show the wiring required to connect all the resistors in parallel between *A* and *B*. Draw a schematic and label each of the resistors with its value.

▷ FIGURE 5–3

Solution   Wires are connected as shown in the assembly wiring diagram of Figure 5–4(a). The schematic is shown in Figure 5–4(b) with resistance values from the color bands. Again, note that the schematic does not necessarily have to show the actual physical arrangement of the resistors. The schematic shows how components are connected electrically.

(a) Assembly wiring diagram

(b) Schematic

▲ FIGURE 5–4

*Related Problem**   Would the circuit have to be rewired if R_2 is removed?

*Answers are at the end of the chapter.

EXAMPLE 5–2

Determine the parallel groupings in Figure 5–5 and the value of each resistor.

Solution   Resistors R_1 through R_4 and R_{11} and R_{12} are all in parallel. This parallel combination is connected to pins 1 and 4. Each resistor in this group is 56 kΩ.

FIGURE 5–5

Resistors R_5 through R_{10} are all in parallel. This combination is connected to pins 2 and 3. Each resistor in this group is $100 \, \text{k}\Omega$.

Related Problem   How would you connect all the resistors on the PC board in parallel?

**SECTION 5–1
REVIEW**

Answers are at the end of the chapter.

1. How are the resistors connected in a parallel circuit?
2. How do you identify a parallel circuit?
3. Complete the schematics for the circuits in each part of Figure 5–6 by connecting the resistors in parallel between points A and B.
4. Connect each group of parallel resistors in Figure 5–6 in parallel with each other.

FIGURE 5–6

5–2   TOTAL PARALLEL RESISTANCE

When resistors are connected in parallel, the total resistance of the circuit decreases. The total resistance of a parallel circuit is always less than the value of the smallest resistor. For example, if a 10 Ω resistor and a 100 Ω resistor are connected in parallel, the total resistance is less than 10 Ω.

After completing this section, you should be able to

◆ **Determine total parallel resistance**

  ◆ Explain why resistance decreases as resistors are connected in parallel

  ◆ Apply the parallel-resistance formula

  ◆ Describe two applications of a parallel circuit

As you know, when resistors are connected in parallel, the current has more than one path. The number of current paths is equal to the number of parallel branches.

In Figure 5–7(a), there is only one current path because it is a series circuit. There is a certain amount of current, I_1, through R_1. If resistor R_2 is connected in parallel with R_1, as shown in Figure 5–7(b), there is an additional amount of current, I_2, through R_2. The total current coming from the source has increased with the addition of the parallel branch. Assuming that the source voltage is constant, an increase in the total current from the source means that the total resistance has decreased, in accordance with Ohm's law. Additional resistors connected in parallel will further reduce the resistance and increase the total current.

(a)   (b)

▲ FIGURE 5–7

Connecting resistors in parallel reduces total resistance and increases total current.

Formula for Total Parallel Resistance, R_T

The circuit in Figure 5–8 shows a general case of n resistors in parallel (n can be any number). According to Kirchhoff's current law (Section 5–5), the total current is

$$I_T = I_1 + I_2 + I_3 + \cdots + I_n$$

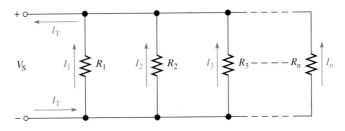

◀ FIGURE 5–8

Circuit with n resistors in parallel.

Since V_S is the voltage across each of the parallel resistors, by Ohm's law, $I_1 = V_S/R_1$, $I_2 = V_S/R_2$, and so on. By substitution into the equation for current,

$$\frac{V_S}{R_T} = \frac{V_S}{R_1} + \frac{V_S}{R_2} + \frac{V_S}{R_3} + \cdots + \frac{V_S}{R_n}$$

The term V_S can be factored out of the right side of the equation and canceled with V_S on the left side, leaving only the reciprocal resistance terms.

$$\frac{\cancel{V_S}}{R_T} = \cancel{V_S}\left(\frac{1}{R_1} + \frac{1}{R_2} + \frac{1}{R_3} + \cdots + \frac{1}{R_n}\right)$$

$$\frac{1}{R_T} = \frac{1}{R_1} + \frac{1}{R_2} + \frac{1}{R_3} + \cdots + \frac{1}{R_n}$$

Recall that the reciprocal of resistance ($1/R$) is called *conductance* and its symbol is G. The unit of conductance is the siemens (S). Since $G = 1/R$, the equation for $1/R_T$ can be expressed in terms of conductance as

$$G_T = G_1 + G_2 + G_3 + \cdots + G_n$$

Solve for R_T by taking the reciprocal of (that is, by inverting) both sides of the equation for $1/R_T$.

Equation 5–1

$$R_T = \frac{1}{\dfrac{1}{R_1} + \dfrac{1}{R_2} + \dfrac{1}{R_3} + \cdots + \dfrac{1}{R_n}}$$

Equation 5–1 shows that to find the total parallel resistance, add all the $1/R$ (or conductance, G) terms and then take the reciprocal of the sum.

$$R_T = \frac{1}{G_T}$$

EXAMPLE 5–3

Calculate the total parallel resistance between points A and B of the circuit in Figure 5–9.

▶ FIGURE 5–9

Solution Use Equation 5–1 to calculate the total resistance when you know the individual resistances. First, find the conductance, which is the reciprocal of the resistance, of each of the three resistors.

$$G_1 = \frac{1}{R_1} = \frac{1}{100\ \Omega} = 10\ \text{mS}$$

$$G_2 = \frac{1}{R_2} = \frac{1}{47\ \Omega} = 21.3\ \text{mS}$$

$$G_3 = \frac{1}{R_3} = \frac{1}{22\ \Omega} = 45.5\ \text{mS}$$

Next, calculate R_T by adding G_1, G_2, and G_3 and taking the reciprocal of the sum.

$$R_T = \frac{1}{G_T} = \frac{1}{G_1 + G_2 + G_3} = \frac{1}{10\,\text{mS} + 21.3\,\text{mS} + 45.5\,\text{mS}} = \frac{1}{76.8\,\text{mS}} = \mathbf{13.0\,\Omega}$$

For a rough accuracy check, notice that the value of R_T (13.0 Ω) is smaller than the smallest value in parallel, which is R_3 (22 Ω), as it should be.

Related Problem If a 33 Ω resistor is connected in parallel in Figure 5–9, what is R_T?

Calculator Tip The parallel-resistance formula is easily solved on a calculator using Equation 5–1. The general procedure is to enter the value of R_1 and then take its reciprocal by pressing the x^{-1} key (x^{-1} is a secondary function on some calculators). The notation x^{-1} means $1/x$. Some calculators use $1/x$ instead of x^{-1}. Next press the $+$ key; then enter the value of R_2 and take its reciprocal. Repeat this procedure until all of the resistor values have been entered and the reciprocal of each has been added. The final step is to press the x^{-1} key to convert $1/R_T$ to R_T. The total parallel resistance is now on the display. The display format may vary, depending on the particular calculator.

EXAMPLE 5–4

Show the steps required for a typical calculator solution of Example 5–3.

Solution
1. Enter 100. Display shows 100.

2. Press the x^{-1} key (or the 2nd then x^{-1} keys).

3. Press the $+$ key.

4. Enter 47.

5. Press the x^{-1} key.

6. Press the $+$ key.

7. Enter 22.

8. Press the x^{-1} key.

9. Press the ENTER key. Display shows $76.7311411992\text{E}^{-3}$.

10. Press the x^{-1} and ENTER keys. Display shows $13.0325182758\text{E}0$.

The number displayed in Step 10 is the total resistance in ohms.

Related Problem Show the additional calculator steps for R_T when a 33 Ω resistor is placed in parallel in the circuit of Example 5–3.

The Case of Two Resistors in Parallel Equation 5–1 is a general formula for finding the total resistance of any number of resistors in parallel. It is often useful to consider only two resistors in parallel because this situation occurs commonly in practice.

Derived from Equation 5–1, the formula for two resistors in parallel is

$$R_T = \frac{R_1 R_2}{R_1 + R_2}$$

Equation 5–2

Equation 5–2 states *the total resistance of two resistors in parallel is equal to the product of the two resistors divided by the sum of the two resistors.* This equation is sometimes referred to as the "product over the sum" formula.

EXAMPLE 5–5

Calculate the total resistance connected to the voltage source of the circuit in Figure 5–10.

▶ FIGURE 5–10

Solution   Use Equation 5–2.

$$R_T = \frac{R_1 R_2}{R_1 + R_2} = \frac{(680 \; \Omega)(330 \; \Omega)}{680 \; \Omega + 330 \; \Omega} = \frac{224{,}000 \; \Omega^2}{1{,}010 \; \Omega} = \mathbf{222 \; \Omega}$$

Related Problem   Find R_T if a 220 Ω resistor replaces R_1 in Figure 5–10.

The Case of Equal-Value Resistors in Parallel   Another special case of parallel circuits is the parallel connection of several resistors having the same value. The following is a shortcut method of calculating R_T when this case occurs:

Equation 5–3

$$R_T = \frac{R}{n}$$

Equation 5–3 says that when any number of resistors (n), all having the same resistance (R), are connected in parallel, R_T is equal to the resistance divided by the number of resistors in parallel.

EXAMPLE 5–6

Find the total resistance between points A and B in Figure 5–11.

▲ FIGURE 5–11

Solution   There are five 100 Ω resistors in parallel. Use Equation 5–3.

$$R_T = \frac{R}{n} = \frac{100 \; \Omega}{5} = \mathbf{20 \; \Omega}$$

Related Problem   Find R_T for three 100 kΩ resistors in parallel.

Notation for Parallel Resistors   Sometimes, for convenience, parallel resistors are designated by two parallel vertical marks. For example, R_1 in parallel with R_2 can be written as $R_1 \parallel R_2$. Also, when several resistors are in parallel with each other, this notation can be used. For example,

$$R_1 \parallel R_2 \parallel R_3 \parallel R_4 \parallel R_5$$

indicates that R_1 through R_5 are all in parallel.

This notation is also used with resistance values. For example,

$$10\,k\Omega \parallel 5\,k\Omega$$

means that a $10\,k\Omega$ resistor is in parallel with a $5\,k\Omega$ resistor.

Applications of a Parallel Circuit

Automotive One advantage of a parallel circuit over a series circuit is that when one branch opens, the other branches are not affected. For example, Figure 5–12 shows a simplified diagram of an automobile lighting system. When one headlight on your car goes out, it does not cause the other lights to go out because they are all in parallel.

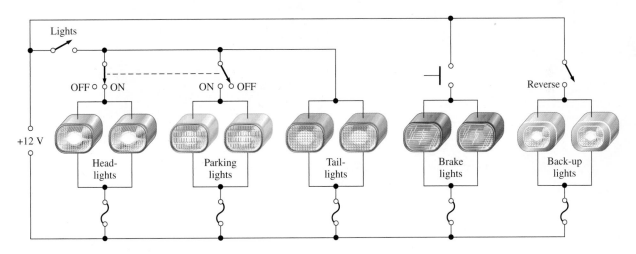

▲ FIGURE 5–12

Simplified diagram of the exterior light system of an automobile.

Notice that the brake lights are switched on independently of the headlights and taillights. They come on only when the driver closes the brake light switch by depressing the brake pedal. When the lights switch is closed, both headlights and both taillights are on. When the headlights are on, the parking lights are off and vice versa. If any one of the lights burns out (opens), there is still current in each of the other lights. The back-up lights are switched on when the reverse gear is engaged.

Residential Another common use of parallel circuits is in residential electrical systems. All the lights and appliances in a home are wired in parallel. Figure 5–13 shows a typical room wiring arrangement with two switch-controlled lights and three wall outlets in parallel.

◀ FIGURE 5–13

Example of parallel circuits in residential wiring.

1. Does the total resistance increase or decrease as more resistors are connected in parallel?

2. The total parallel resistance is always less than what value?

3. Determine R_T (between pin 1 and pin 4) for the circuit in Figure 5–14. Note that pins 1 and 2 are connected and pins 3 and 4 are connected.

▲ FIGURE 5–14

5–3 VOLTAGE IN A PARALLEL CIRCUIT

The voltage across any given branch of a parallel circuit is equal to the voltage across each of the other branches in parallel. As you know, each current path in a parallel circuit is called a branch.

After completing this section, you should be able to

◆ **Determine the voltage across each parallel branch**

  ◆ Explain why the voltage is the same across all parallel resistors

To illustrate voltage in a parallel circuit, let's examine Figure 5–15(a). Points *A*, *B*, *C*, and *D* along the left side of the parallel circuit are electrically the same point because the voltage is the same along this line. You can think of all of these points as being connected by a single wire to the negative terminal of the battery. The points *E*, *F*, *G*, and *H* along the right side of the circuit are all at a voltage equal to that of the positive terminal of the source. Thus, voltage across each parallel resistor is the same, and each is equal to the source voltage. Notice that the parallel circuit in Figure 5–15 resembles a ladder.

Figure 5–15(b) is the same circuit as in part (a), drawn in a slightly different way. Here the left side of each resistor is connected to a single point, which is the negative battery terminal. The right side of each resistor is connected to a single point, which is the positive battery terminal. The resistors are still all in parallel across the source.

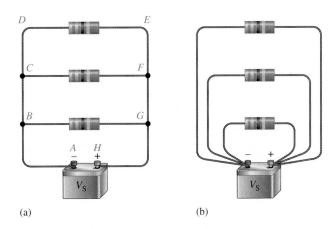

Voltage across parallel branches is the same.

(a)   (b)

In Figure 5–16, a 12 V battery is connected across three parallel resistors. When the voltage is measured across the battery and then across each of the resistors, the readings are the same. As you can see, the same voltage appears across each branch in a parallel circuit.

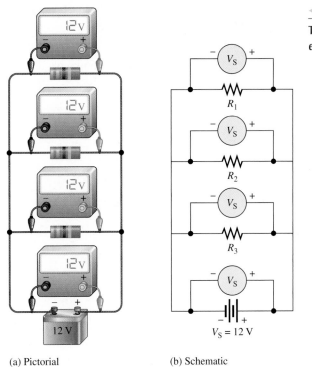

The same voltage appears across each resistor in parallel.

(a) Pictorial   (b) Schematic

EXAMPLE 5–7   Determine the voltage across each resistor in Figure 5–17.

FIGURE 5–17

Solution The five resistors are in parallel; so the voltage across each one is equal to the source voltage, V_S. There is no voltage across the fuse.

$$V_1 = V_2 = V_3 = V_4 = V_5 = V_S = \mathbf{25\ V}$$

Related Problem If R_4 is removed from the circuit, what is the voltage across R_3?

Open Multisim file E05-07 on your CD-ROM. Verify that each resistor voltage equals the source voltage. Repeat for the related problem.

SECTION 5–3 REVIEW

1. A 10 Ω and a 22 Ω resistor are connected in parallel with a 5 V source. What is the voltage across each of the resistors?

2. A voltmeter connected across R_1 in Figure 5–18 measures 118 V. If you move the meter and connect it across R_2, how much voltage will it indicate? What is the source voltage?

3. In Figure 5–19, how much voltage does voltmeter 1 indicate? Voltmeter 2?

4. How are voltages across each branch of a parallel circuit related?

▲ FIGURE 5–18

▲ FIGURE 5–19

5–4 APPLICATION OF OHM'S LAW

Ohm's law can be applied to parallel circuit analysis.

After completing this section, you should be able to

- ◆ **Apply Ohm's law in a parallel circuit**
    - ◆ Find the total current in a parallel circuit
    - ◆ Find each branch current in a parallel circuit
    - ◆ Find the voltage across a parallel circuit
    - ◆ Find the resistance of a parallel circuit

The following examples illustrate how to apply Ohm's law to determine the total current, branch currents, voltage, and resistance in parallel circuits.

EXAMPLE 5–8

Find the total current produced by the battery in Figure 5–20.

▶ FIGURE 5–20

Solution

The battery "sees" a total parallel resistance that determines the amount of current that it produces. First, calculate R_T.

$$R_T = \frac{R_1 R_2}{R_1 + R_2} = \frac{(100\ \Omega)(56\ \Omega)}{100\ \Omega + 56\ \Omega} = \frac{5600\ \Omega^2}{156\ \Omega} = 35.9\ \Omega$$

The battery voltage is 10 V. Use Ohm's law to find I_T.

$$I_T = \frac{V_S}{R_T} = \frac{10\ \text{V}}{35.9\ \Omega} = \textbf{279 mA}$$

Related Problem

Find the currents through R_1 and R_2 in Figure 5–20. Show that the sum of the currents through R_1 and R_2 equals the total current.

Open Multisim file E05-08 on your CD-ROM. Using the multimeter, verify the calculated values of total current and the branch currents.

EXAMPLE 5–9

Determine the current through each resistor in the parallel circuit of Figure 5–21.

▶ FIGURE 5–21

Solution

The voltage across each resistor (branch) is equal to the source voltage. That is, the voltage across R_1 is 20 V, the voltage across R_2 is 20 V, and the voltage across R_3 is 20 V. Determine the current through each resistor as follows:

$$I_1 = \frac{V_S}{R_1} = \frac{20\ \text{V}}{1.0\ \text{k}\Omega} = \textbf{20.0 mA}$$

$$I_2 = \frac{V_S}{R_2} = \frac{20\ \text{V}}{2.2\ \text{k}\Omega} = \textbf{9.09 mA}$$

$$I_3 = \frac{V_S}{R_3} = \frac{20\ \text{V}}{560\ \Omega} = \textbf{35.7 mA}$$

Related Problem   If an additional resistor of 910 Ω is connected in parallel to the circuit in Figure 5–21, determine all the branch circuits.

    Open Multisim file E05-09 on your CD-ROM. Measure the current through each resistor. Connect a 910 Ω resistor in parallel with the other resistors and measure the branch currents. How much does the total current from the source change when the new resistor is added?

EXAMPLE 5–10   Find the voltage across the parallel circuit shown in Figure 5–22.

▶ FIGURE 5–22

Solution   The total current into the parallel circuit is 10 mA. If you know the total resistance, then you can apply Ohm's law to get the voltage. The total resistance is

$$R_T = \cfrac{1}{\cfrac{1}{R_1} + \cfrac{1}{R_2} + \cfrac{1}{R_3}} = \cfrac{1}{\cfrac{1}{220\,\Omega} + \cfrac{1}{560\,\Omega} + \cfrac{1}{1.0\,k\Omega}}$$

$$= \cfrac{1}{4.55\,mS + 1.79\,mS + 1\,mS} = \cfrac{1}{7.34\,mS} = 136\,\Omega$$

Therefore, the source voltage and the voltage across each branch is

$$V_S = I_T R_T = (10\,mA)(136\,\Omega) = \mathbf{1.36\,V}$$

Related Problem   Find the total current if R_3 opens in Figure 5–22. Assume V_S remains the same.

EXAMPLE 5–11   The circuit board in Figure 5–23 has three resistors in parallel. The values of two of the resistors are known from the color bands, but the top resistor is not clearly marked. Determine the value of the unknown resistor without disconnecting it from the circuit board or without using an ohmmeter.

▶ FIGURE 5–23

Solution If you can determine the total resistance of the three resistors in parallel, then you can use the parallel-resistance formula to calculate the unknown resistance. You can use Ohm's law to find the total resistance if you know the voltage and total current.

In Figure 5–24, a 12 V source (arbitrary value) is connected across the resistors and the total current is measured. Using these measured values, find the total resistance.

$$R_T = \frac{V}{I_T} = \frac{12\text{ V}}{24.1\text{ mA}} = 498\ \Omega$$

Find the unknown resistance as follows:

$$\frac{1}{R_T} = \frac{1}{R_1} + \frac{1}{R_2} + \frac{1}{R_3}$$

$$\frac{1}{R_1} = \frac{1}{R_T} - \frac{1}{R_2} - \frac{1}{R_3} = \frac{1}{498\ \Omega} - \frac{1}{1.8\text{ k}\Omega} - \frac{1}{1.0\text{ k}\Omega} = 452\ \mu S$$

$$R_1 = \frac{1}{452\ \mu S} = \mathbf{2.21\text{ k}\Omega}$$

FIGURE 5–24

Related Problem Explain how to determine the value of R_1 using an ohmmeter and without removing R_1 from the circuit.

Open Multisim file E05-11 on your CD-ROM. This is a schematic of the circuit board in Figure 5–24. Connect the circuit as shown and verify the current measurement. Remove R_1 from the circuit and verify its value with the ohmmeter.

SECTION 5–4 REVIEW

1. A 10 V battery is connected across three 68 Ω resistors that are in parallel. What is the total current from the battery?

2. How much voltage is required to produce 20 mA through the circuit of Figure 5–25?

FIGURE 5–25

3. How much current is there through each resistor of Figure 5–25?

4. There are four equal-value resistors in parallel with a 12 V source and 6 mA of current from the source. What is the value of each resistor?

5. A 1.0 kΩ and a 2.2 kΩ resistor are connected in parallel. There is a total of 100 mA through the parallel combination. How much voltage is dropped across the resistors?

5–5 KIRCHHOFF'S CURRENT LAW

Kirchhoff's voltage law deals with voltages in a single closed path. Kirchhoff's current law applies to currents in multiple paths.

After completing this section, you should be able to

◆ **Apply Kirchhoff's current law**

◆ State Kirchhoff's current law

◆ Define *node*

◆ Determine the total current by adding the branch currents

◆ Determine an unknown branch current

Kirchhoff's current law, often abbreviated KCL, can be stated as follows:

The sum of the currents into a node (total current in) is equal to the sum of the currents out of that node (total current out).

A **node** is any point or junction in a circuit where two or more components are connected. In a parallel circuit, a node is a point where the parallel branches come together. For example, in the circuit of Figure 5–26, there are two nodes as indicated, node A and node B. Let's start at the negative terminal of the source and follow the current. The total current I_T from the source is *into* node A. At this point, the current splits up among the three branches as indicated. Each

▷ FIGURE 5–26

Kirchhoff's current law: The current into a node equals the current out of that node.

of the three branch currents (I_1, I_2 and I_3) is *out of* node A. Kirchhoff's current law says that the total current into node A is equal to the total current out of node A; that is,

$$I_T = I_1 + I_2 + I_3$$

Now, following the currents in Figure 5–26 through the three branches, you see that they come back together at node B. Currents I_1, I_2, and I_3 are into node B, and I_T is out of node B. Kirchhoff's current law formula at node B is therefore the same as at node A.

$$I_1 + I_2 + I_3 = I_T$$

Figure 5–27 shows a generalized circuit node where a number of branches are connected at a point in a circuit. Currents $I_{IN(1)}$ through $I_{IN(n)}$ are into the node (n can be any number). Currents $I_{OUT(1)}$ through $I_{OUT(m)}$ are out of the node (m can be any number but not necessarily equal to n).

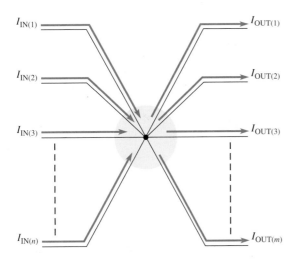

$$I_{IN(1)} + I_{IN(2)} + I_{IN(3)} + \cdots + I_{IN(n)} = I_{OUT(1)} + I_{OUT(2)} + I_{OUT(3)} + \cdots I_{OUT(m)}$$

▲ FIGURE 5–27

Generalized circuit node illustrates Kirchhoff's current law.

By Kirchhoff's current law, the sum of the currents into a node must equal the sum of the currents out of the node. With reference to Figure 5–27, the general formula for Kirchhoff's current law is

$$I_{IN(1)} + I_{IN(2)} + I_{IN(3)} + \cdots + I_{IN(n)} = I_{OUT(1)} + I_{OUT(2)} + I_{OUT(3)} + \cdots + I_{OUT(m)}$$

Equation 5–4

If all of the terms on the right side of Equation 5–4 are brought over to the left side, their signs change to negative, and a zero is left on the right side.

$$I_{IN(1)} + I_{IN(2)} + I_{IN(3)} + \cdots + I_{IN(n)} - I_{OUT(1)} - I_{OUT(2)} - I_{OUT(3)} - \cdots - I_{OUT(m)} = 0$$

Based on this last equation, Kirchhoff's current law can also be stated in this way:

The algebraic sum of all the currents entering and leaving a node is equal to zero.

You can verify Kirchhoff's current law by connecting a circuit and measuring each branch current and the total current from the source, as illustrated in Figure 5–28. *When the branch currents are added together, their sum will equal the total current.* This rule applies for any number of branches.

The following three examples illustrate use of Kirchhoff's current law.

▶ FIGURE 5–28

An illustration of Kirchhoff's current law.

EXAMPLE 5–12

You know the branch currents in the circuit of Figure 5–29. Determine the total current entering node A and the total current leaving node B.

▶ FIGURE 5–29

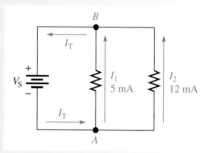

Solution The total current out of node A is the sum of the two branch currents. Therefore, the total current into node A is

$$I_T = I_1 + I_2 = 5\,\text{mA} + 12\,\text{mA} = \mathbf{17\,mA}$$

The total current entering node B is the sum of the two branch currents. Thus, the total current out of node B is

$$I_T = I_1 + I_2 = 5\,\text{mA} + 12\,\text{mA} = \mathbf{17\,mA}$$

Related Problem If a third resistor is connected in parallel to the circuit of Figure 5–29 and its current is 3 mA, what is the total current into node A and out of node B?

Open Multisim file E05-12 on your CD-ROM. Verify that the total current is the sum of the branch currents. Repeat for the related problem.

EXAMPLE 5–13

Determine the current through R_2 in Figure 5–30.

Solution The total current out of node A is $I_T = I_1 + I_2 + I_3$. From Figure 5–30, you know the total current and the branch currents through R_1 and R_3. Solve for I_2.

$$I_2 = I_T - I_1 - I_3 = 100\,\text{mA} - 30\,\text{mA} - 20\,\text{mA} = \mathbf{50\,mA}$$

FIGURE 5–30

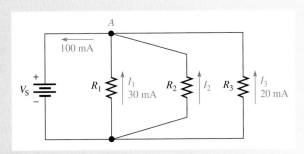

Related Problem   Determine I_T and I_2 if a fourth branch is added to the circuit in Figure 5–30 and it has 12 mA through it.

    Open Multisim file E05-13 on your CD-ROM. Verify the calculated value for I_2. Repeat for the related problem.

EXAMPLE 5–14   Use Kirchhoff's current law to find the current measured by ammeters A3 and A5 in Figure 5–31.

FIGURE 5–31

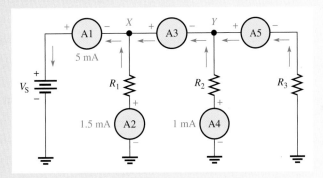

Solution   The total current out of node X is 5 mA. Two currents are into node X: 1.5 mA through resistor R_1 and the current through A3. Kirchhoff's current law at node X is

$$5\,\text{mA} = 1.5\,\text{mA} + I_{A3}$$

Solving for I_{A3} yields

$$I_{A3} = 5\,\text{mA} - 1.5\,\text{mA} = \textbf{3.5\,mA}$$

The total current out of node Y is $I_{A3} = 3.5$ mA. Two currents are into node Y: 1 mA through resistor R_2 and the current through A5 and R_3. Kirchhoff's current law applied to node Y gives

$$3.5\,\text{mA} = 1\,\text{mA} + I_{A5}$$

Solving for I_{A5} yields

$$I_{A5} = 3.5\,\text{mA} - 1\,\text{mA} = \textbf{2.5\,mA}$$

Related Problem   How much current will an ammeter measure when it is placed in the circuit in Figure 5–31 right below R_3? Below the negative battery terminal?

1. State Kirchhoff's current law in two ways.

2. A total current of 2.5 A is into a node and the current out of the node divides into three parallel branches. What is the sum of all three branch currents?

3. In Figure 5–32, 100 mA and 300 mA are into the node. What is the amount of current out of the node?

4. Determine I_1 in the circuit of Figure 5–33.

5. Two branch currents enter a node, and two branch currents leave the same node. One of the currents entering the node is 1 A, and one of the currents leaving the node is 3 A. The total current entering and leaving the node is 8 A. Determine the value of the unknown current entering the node and the value of the unknown current leaving the node.

▲ FIGURE 5–32

▲ FIGURE 5–33

5–6 CURRENT DIVIDERS

A parallel circuit acts as a **current divider** because the current entering the junction of parallel branches "divides" up into several individual branch currents.

After completing this section, you should be able to

- ◆ **Use a parallel circuit as a current divider**
  - ◆ Apply the current-divider formula
  - ◆ Determine an unknown branch current

In a parallel circuit, the total current into the junction of the parallel branches (node) divides among the branches. Thus, a parallel circuit acts as a current divider. This current-divider principle is illustrated in Figure 5–34 for a two-branch parallel circuit in which part of the total current I_T goes through R_1 and part through R_2.

▶ FIGURE 5–34

Total current divides between the two branches.

Since the same voltage is across each of the resistors in parallel, the branch currents are inversely proportional to the values of the resistors. For example, if the value of R_2 is twice that of R_1, then the value of I_2 is one-half that of I_1. In other words,

The total current divides among parallel resistors into currents with values inversely proportional to the resistance values.

The branches with higher resistance have less current, and the branches with lower resistance have more current, in accordance with Ohm's law. If all the branches have the same resistance, the branch currents are all equal.

Figure 5–35 shows specific values to demonstrate how the currents divide according to the branch resistances. Notice that in this case the resistance of the upper branch is one-tenth the resistance of the lower branch, but the upper branch current is ten times the lower branch current.

◀ FIGURE 5–35

The branch with the lowest resistance has the most current, and the branch with the highest resistance has the least current.

Current-Divider Formula

You can develop a formula for determining how currents divide among any number of parallel resistors, as shown in Figure 5–36, where n is the total number of resistors.

◀ FIGURE 5–36

A parallel circuit with n branches.

The current through any one of the parallel resistors is I_x, where x represents the number of a particular resistor (1, 2, 3, and so on). By Ohm's law, you can express the current through any one of the resistors in Figure 5–36 as follows:

$$I_x = \frac{V_S}{R_x}$$

The source voltage, V_S, appears across each of the parallel resistors, and R_x represents any one of the parallel resistors. The total source voltage, V_S, is equal to the total current times the total parallel resistance.

$$V_S = I_T R_T$$

Substituting $I_T R_T$ for V_S in the expression for I_x results in

$$I_x = \frac{I_T R_T}{R_x}$$

Rearranging terms yields

Equation 5–5

$$I_x = \left(\frac{R_T}{R_x}\right) I_T$$

where $x = 1, 2, 3$, etc. Equation 5–5 is the general current-divider formula and applies to a parallel circuit with any number of branches.

The current (I_x) through any branch equals the total parallel resistance (R_T) divided by the resistance (R_x) of that branch, and then multiplied by the total current (I_T) into the junction of parallel branches.

EXAMPLE 5–15

Determine the current through each resistor in the circuit of Figure 5–37.

▶ FIGURE 5–37

Solution First, calculate the total parallel resistance.

$$R_T = \frac{1}{\dfrac{1}{R_1} + \dfrac{1}{R_2} + \dfrac{1}{R_3}} = \frac{1}{\dfrac{1}{680\ \Omega} + \dfrac{1}{330\ \Omega} + \dfrac{1}{220\ \Omega}} = 111\ \Omega$$

The total current is 10 mA. Use Equation 5–5 to calculate each branch current.

$$I_1 = \left(\frac{R_T}{R_1}\right) I_T = \left(\frac{111\ \Omega}{680\ \Omega}\right) 10\ \text{mA} = \mathbf{1.63\ mA}$$

$$I_2 = \left(\frac{R_T}{R_2}\right) I_T = \left(\frac{111\ \Omega}{330\ \Omega}\right) 10\ \text{mA} = \mathbf{3.36\ mA}$$

$$I_3 = \left(\frac{R_T}{R_3}\right) I_T = \left(\frac{111\ \Omega}{220\ \Omega}\right) 10\ \text{mA} = \mathbf{5.05\ mA}$$

Related Problem Determine the current through R_1 and R_2 in Figure 5–37 if R_3 is removed. Assume the source voltage remains the same.

Current-Divider Formulas for Two Branches You already know how to use Ohm's law ($I = V/R$) to determine the current in any parallel branch when you know the voltage and resistance. When you do not know the voltage but you know total current, you can find both of the branch currents (I_1 and I_2) by using the following formulas:

$$I_1 = \left(\frac{R_2}{R_1 + R_2}\right)I_T$$

Equation 5–6

$$I_2 = \left(\frac{R_1}{R_1 + R_2}\right)I_T$$

Equation 5–7

These formulas show that the current in either branch is equal to the opposite branch resistance divided by the sum of the two resistances and then multiplied by the total current.

EXAMPLE 5–16

Find I_1 and I_2 in Figure 5–38.

FIGURE 5–38

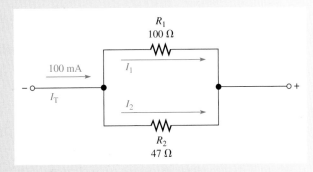

Solution   Use Equation 5–6 to determine I_1.

$$I_1 = \left(\frac{R_2}{R_1 + R_2}\right)I_T = \left(\frac{47\ \Omega}{147\ \Omega}\right)100\ \text{mA} = \textbf{32.0 mA}$$

Use Equation 5–7 to determine I_2.

$$I_2 = \left(\frac{R_1}{R_1 + R_2}\right)I_T = \left(\frac{100\ \Omega}{147\ \Omega}\right)100\ \text{mA} = \textbf{68.0 mA}$$

Related Problem   If $R_1 = 56\ \Omega$ and $R_2 = 82\ \Omega$ in Figure 5–38 and I_T stays the same, what will each branch current be?

**SECTION 5–6
REVIEW**

1. A circuit has the following resistors in parallel with a voltage source: 220 Ω, 100 Ω, 68 Ω, 56 Ω, and 22 Ω. Which resistor has the most current through it? The least current?
2. Determine the current through R_3 in Figure 5–39.
3. Find the currents through each resistor in the circuit of Figure 5–40.

FIGURE 5–39

FIGURE 5–40

5–7   POWER IN PARALLEL CIRCUITS

Total power in a parallel circuit is found by adding up the powers of all the individual resistors, the same as for series circuits.

After completing this section, you should be able to

- ◆ **Determine power in a parallel circuit**

Equation 5–8 states the formula for total power for any number of resistors in parallel.

Equation 5–8

$$P_T = P_1 + P_2 + P_3 + \cdots + P_n$$

where P_T is the total power and P_n is the power in the last resistor in parallel. As you can see, the powers are additive, just as in a series circuit.

The power formulas from Chapter 3 are directly applicable to parallel circuits. The following formulas are used to calculate the total power P_T:

$$P_T = V_S I_T$$
$$P_T = I_T^2 R_T$$
$$P_T = \frac{V_S^2}{R_T}$$

where V_S is the voltage across the parallel circuit, I_T is the total current into the parallel circuit, and R_T is the total resistance of the parallel circuit. Examples 5–17 and 5–18 show how total power can be calculated in a parallel circuit.

EXAMPLE 5–17

Determine the total amount of power in the parallel circuit in Figure 5–41.

▶ FIGURE 5–41

Solution   The total current is 200 mA. The total resistance is

$$R_T = \frac{1}{\dfrac{1}{68\ \Omega} + \dfrac{1}{33\ \Omega} + \dfrac{1}{22\ \Omega}} = 11.1\ \Omega$$

The easiest formula to use is $P_T = I_T^2 R_T$ since you know both I_T and R_T. Thus,

$$P_T = I_T^2 R_T = (200\ \text{mA})^2 (11.1\ \Omega) = \textbf{444 mW}$$

Let's demonstrate that if you determine the power in each resistor and if you add all of these values together, you get the same result. First, find the voltage across each branch of the circuit.

$$V_S = I_T R_T = (200\ \text{mA})(11.1\ \Omega) = 2.22\ \text{V}$$

Remember that the voltage across all branches is the same.

Next, use $P = V_S^2/R$ to calculate the power for each resistor.

$$P_1 = \frac{(2.22 \text{ V})^2}{68 \text{ }\Omega} = 72.5 \text{ mW}$$

$$P_2 = \frac{(2.22 \text{ V})^2}{33 \text{ }\Omega} = 149 \text{ mW}$$

$$P_3 = \frac{(2.22 \text{ V})^2}{22 \text{ }\Omega} = 224 \text{ mW}$$

Now, add these powers to get the total power.

$$P_T = 72.5 \text{ mW} + 149 \text{ mW} + 224 \text{ mW} = \textbf{446 mW}$$

This calculation shows that the sum of the individual powers is equal (approximately) to the total power as determined by one of the power formulas. Rounding to three significant figures accounts for the difference.

Related Problem   Find the total power in Figure 5–41 if the total current is doubled.

EXAMPLE 5–18

The amplifier in one channel of a stereo system as shown in Figure 5–42 drives two parallel speakers. If the maximum voltage* to the speakers is 15 V, how much power must the amplifier be able to deliver to the speakers?

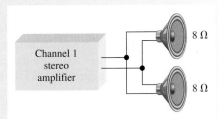

▲ FIGURE 5–42

Solution   The speakers are connected in parallel to the amplifier output, so the voltage across each is the same. The maximum power to each speaker is

$$P_{max} = \frac{V_{max}^2}{R} = \frac{(15 \text{ V})^2}{8 \text{ }\Omega} = 28.1 \text{ W}$$

The total power that the amplifier must be capable of delivering to the speaker system is twice the power in an individual speaker because the total power is the sum of the individual powers.

$$P_{T(max)} = P_{max} + P_{max} = 2P_{max} = 2(28.1 \text{ W}) = \textbf{56.2 W}$$

Related Problem   If the amplifier can produce a maximum of 18 V, what is the maximum total power to the speakers?

---

*Voltage is ac in this case; but power is determined the same for ac voltage as for dc voltage, as you will learn later.

SECTION 5–7 REVIEW	1. If you know the power in each resistor in a parallel circuit, how can you find the total power?
	2. The resistors in a parallel circuit dissipate the following powers: 1 W, 2 W, 5 W, and 8 W. What is the total power in the circuit?
	3. A circuit has a 1.0 kΩ, a 2.7 kΩ, and a 3.9 kΩ resistor in parallel. There is a total current of 1 mA into the parallel circuit. What is the total power?

5–8   TROUBLESHOOTING

Recall that an open circuit is one in which the current path is interrupted and there is no current. In this section, you will see how an open in a parallel branch affects the parallel circuit.

After completing this section, you should be able to

◆ **Troubleshoot parallel circuits**

    ◆ Check for an open in a circuit

Open Branches

If a switch is connected in a branch of a parallel circuit, as shown in Figure 5–43, an open or a closed path can be made by the switch. When the switch is closed, as in Figure 5–43(a), R_1 and R_2 are in parallel. The total resistance is 50 Ω (two 100 Ω resistors in parallel). Current is through both resistors. If the switch is opened, as in Figure 5–43(b), R_1 is effectively removed from the circuit, and the total resistance is 100 Ω. There is still the same voltage across R_2 and the same current through it although the total current from the source is reduced by the amount of the R_1 current.

▶ FIGURE 5–43

When the switch opens, total current decreases and current through R_2 remains unchanged.

(a)   (b)

In general,

When an open occurs in a parallel branch, the total resistance increases, the total current decreases, and the same current continues through each of the remaining parallel paths.

Consider the lamp circuit in Figure 5–44. There are four bulbs in parallel with a 12 V source. In part (a), there is current through each bulb. Now suppose that one of the bulbs burns out, creating an open path as shown in Figure 5–44(b). This light will go out because there is no current through the open path. Notice, however, that current continues through all the other parallel bulbs, and they continue to glow. The open branch does not change the

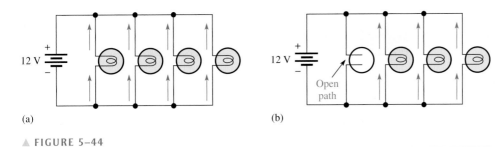

(a)   (b)

▲ FIGURE 5–44

When a lamp filament opens, total current decreases by the amount of current in the lamp that opened. The other branch currents remain unchanged.

voltage across the remaining parallel branches; it remains at 12 V, and the current through each branch remains the same.

You can see that a parallel circuit has an advantage over a series connection in lighting systems because if one or more of the parallel bulbs burn out, the others will stay on. In a series circuit, when one bulb goes out, all of the others go out also because the current path is completely interrupted.

When a resistor in a parallel circuit opens, the open resistor cannot be located by measurement of the voltage across the branches because the same voltage exists across all the branches. Thus, there is no way to tell which resistor is open by simply measuring voltage (the half-splitting method is not applicable). The good resistors will always have the same voltage as the open one, as illustrated in Figure 5–45 (note that the middle resistor is open).

If a visual inspection does not reveal the open resistor, it can be located by resistance or current measurements. In practice, measuring resistance or current is more difficult than measuring voltage because you must disconnect a component to measure the resistance and you must insert an ammeter in series to measure the current. Thus, a wire or a printed circuit connection must usually be cut or disconnected, or one end of a component must be lifted off the circuit board, in order to connect a DMM to measure resistance and current. This procedure, of course, is not required when voltage measurements are made because the meter leads are simply connected across a component.

▲ FIGURE 5–45

All parallel branches (open or not) have the same voltage.

Finding an Open Branch by Current Measurement

In a parallel circuit with a suspected open branch, the total current can be measured to find the open. *When a parallel resistor opens, I_T is always less than its normal value.* Once you know I_T and the voltage across the branches, a few calculations will determine the open resistor when all the resistors are of different values.

Consider the two-branch circuit in Figure 5–46(a). If one of the resistors opens, the total current will equal the current in the good resistor. Ohm's law quickly tells you what the current in each resistor should be.

$$I_1 = \frac{50\,\text{V}}{560\,\Omega} = 89.3\,\text{mA}$$

$$I_2 = \frac{50\,\text{V}}{100\,\Omega} = 500\,\text{mA}$$

$$I_T = I_1 + I_2 = 589.3\,\text{mA}$$

If R_2 is open, the total current is 89.3 mA, as indicated in Figure 5–46(b). If R_1 is open, the total current is 500 mA, as indicated in Figure 5–46(c).

HANDS ON TIP

An alternate way to measure current without having to break a circuit to connect an ammeter is to place, as part of the original circuit, a 1 Ω series resistor in each line through which current is to be measured. This small "sense" resistor will generally not affect the total resistance. By measuring the voltage across the sense resistor, you automatically have the current reading since

$$I = \frac{V}{R} = \frac{V}{1\,\Omega} = V$$

(a) Current with no open branch   (b) Current with R_2 open   (c) Current with R_1 open

▲ FIGURE 5–46

Finding an open path by current measurement.

This procedure can be extended to any number of branches having unequal resistances. If the parallel resistances are all equal, the current in each branch must be checked until a branch is found with no current.

EXAMPLE 5–19

In Figure 5–47, there is a total current of 31.09 mA, and the voltage across the parallel branches is 20 V. Is there an open resistor, and if so, which one is it?

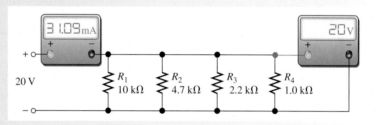

▲ FIGURE 5–47

Solution   Calculate the current in each branch.

$$I_1 = \frac{V}{R_1} = \frac{20\,\text{V}}{10\,\text{k}\Omega} = 2\,\text{mA}$$

$$I_2 = \frac{V}{R_2} = \frac{20\,\text{V}}{4.7\,\text{k}\Omega} = 4.26\,\text{mA}$$

$$I_3 = \frac{V}{R_3} = \frac{20\,\text{V}}{2.2\,\text{k}\Omega} = 9.09\,\text{mA}$$

$$I_4 = \frac{V}{R_4} = \frac{20\,\text{V}}{1.0\,\text{k}\Omega} = 20\,\text{mA}$$

The total current should be

$$I_T = I_1 + I_2 + I_3 + I_4 = 2\,\text{mA} + 4.26\,\text{mA} + 9.09\,\text{mA} + 20\,\text{mA} = 35.35\,\text{mA}$$

The actual measured current is 31.09 mA, as stated, which is 4.26 mA less than normal, indicating that the branch with 4.26 mA is open. Thus, **R_2 must be open.**

Related Problem   What is the total current measured in Figure 5–47 if R_4 and not R_2 is open?

Open Multisim file E05-19 on your CD-ROM. Measure the total current and the current in each resistor. There are no faults in the circuit.

Finding an Open Branch by Resistance Measurement

If the parallel circuit to be checked can be disconnected from its voltage source and from any other circuit to which it may be connected, a measurement of the total resistance can be used to locate an open branch.

Recall that conductance, G, is the reciprocal of resistance ($1/R$) and its unit is the siemens (S). The total conductance of a parallel circuit is the sum of the conductances of all the resistors.

$$G_T = G_1 + G_2 + G_3 + \cdots + G_n$$

To locate an open branch, do the following steps:

1. Calculate what the total conductance should be using the individual resistor values.

$$G_{T(calc)} = \frac{1}{R_1} + \frac{1}{R_2} + \frac{1}{R_3} + \cdots + \frac{1}{R_n}$$

2. Measure the total resistance and calculate the total measured conductance.

$$G_{T(meas)} = \frac{1}{R_{T(meas)}}$$

3. Subtract the measured total conductance (Step 2) from the calculated total conductance (Step 1). The result is the conductance of the open branch, and the resistance is obtained by taking its reciprocal ($R = 1/G$).

$$R_{open} = \frac{1}{G_{T(calc)} - G_{T(meas)}}$$

EXAMPLE 5–20

Your ohmmeter measures 402 Ω between pin 1 and pin 4 in Figure 5–48. Check the printed circuit board between these two pins for open branches.

▲ FIGURE 5–48

Solution The circuit between pin 1 and pin 4 is checked as follows:

1. Calculate what the total conductance should be using the individual resistor values.

$$G_{T(calc)} = \frac{1}{R_1} + \frac{1}{R_2} + \frac{1}{R_3} + \frac{1}{R_4} + \frac{1}{R_{11}} + \frac{1}{R_{12}}$$

$$= \frac{1}{1.0\,k\Omega} + \frac{1}{1.8\,k\Omega} + \frac{1}{2.2\,k\Omega} + \frac{1}{2.7\,k\Omega} + \frac{1}{3.3\,k\Omega} + \frac{1}{3.9\,k\Omega}$$

$$= 2.94\,mS$$

2. Calculate the total measured conductance.

$$G_{T(meas)} = \frac{1}{402\,\Omega} = 2.49\,mS$$

3. Subtract the measured total conductance (Step 2) from the calculated total conductance (Step 1). The result is the conductance of the open branch and the resistance is obtained by taking its reciprocal.

$$G_{open} = G_{T(calc)} - G_{T(meas)} = 2.94\,mS - 2.49\,mS = 0.45\,mS$$

$$R_{open} = \frac{1}{G_{open}} = \frac{1}{0.45\,mS} = 2.2\,k\Omega$$

Resistor R_3 **is open** and must be replaced.

Related Problem Your ohmmeter indicates 9.6 kΩ between pin 2 and pin 3 on the PC board in Figure 5–48. Determine if this is correct and, if not, which resistor is open.

Shorted Branches

When a branch in a parallel circuit shorts, the current increases to an excessive value, usually causing the resistor to burn open or a fuse or circuit breaker to blow. This results in a difficult troubleshooting problem because it is hard to isolate the shorted branch.

A pulser and a current tracer are tools often used to find shorts in a circuit. They are not restricted to use in digital circuits but can be effective in any type of circuit. The pulser is a pen-shaped tool that applies pulses to a selected point in a circuit, causing pulses of current through the shorted path. The current tracer is also a pen-shaped tool that senses pulses of current. By following the current with the tracer, the current path can be identified.

**SECTION 5–8
REVIEW**

1. If a parallel branch opens, what changes can be detected in the circuit's voltage and the currents, assuming that the parallel circuit is across a constant voltage source?
2. What happens to the total resistance if one branch opens?
3. If several light bulbs are connected in parallel and one of the bulbs opens (burns out), will the others continue to glow?
4. There is one ampere of current in each branch of a parallel circuit. If one branch opens, what is the current in each of the remaining branches?
5. A three-branch circuit normally has the following branch currents: 1 mA, 2.5 mA, and 1.2 mA. If the total current measures 3.5 mA, which branch is open?

Application Assignment

PUTTING YOUR KNOWLEDGE TO WORK

In this application, a dc power supply is modified by adding a 3-range ammeter to indicate current to the load. Parallel resistances can be used to extend the range of an ammeter. These parallel resistors, called *shunts,* bypass current around the meter movement, allowing for the meter to effectively measure higher currents than the maximum current for which the meter movement is designed. A multiple-range analog meter circuit is based on resistance placed in parallel with the meter movement to achieve the specified full-scale deflection of the needle.

General Theory of Operation

Parallel circuits are an important part of the operation of this type of ammeter because they allow the user to select various ranges in order to measure many different current values.

The mechanism in an analog ammeter that causes the pointer to move in proportion to the current is called the *meter movement,* which is based on a magnetic principle that you will learn in Chapter 7. Right now, all you need to know is that a meter movement has a certain resistance and a maximum current. This maximum current, called the *full-scale deflection current,* causes the pointer to go all the way to the end of the scale. For example, a certain meter movement has a 50 Ω resistance and a full-scale deflection current of 1 mA. A meter with this particular movement can measure currents of 1 mA or less. Currents greater than 1 mA will cause the pointer to "peg" (or stop) at full scale. Figure 5–49 illustrates a 1 mA meter.

Figure 5–50 shows a simple ammeter with a resistor in parallel with the meter movement; this resistor is called a *shunt resistor.* Its purpose is to bypass any current in excess of 1 mA around the

(a) Half-scale deflection   (b) Full-scale deflection   (c) "Pegged"

▲ **FIGURE 5–49**

A 1 mA meter.

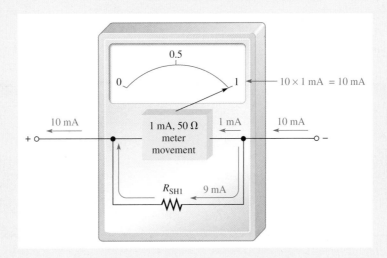

▲ **FIGURE 5–50**

A 10 mA meter.

meter movement to extend the range of currents that can be measured. The figure specifically shows 9 mA through the shunt resistor and 1 mA through the meter movement. Thus, up to 10 mA can be measured. To find the actual current value, simply multiply the reading on the scale by 10.

A practical ammeter has a range switch that permits the selection of several full-scale current settings. In each switch position, a certain amount of current is bypassed through a parallel resistor as determined by the resistance value. In our example, the current through the movement is never greater than 1 mA.

Figure 5–51 illustrates a meter with three ranges: 1 mA, 10 mA, and 100 mA. When the range switch is in the 1 mA position, all of the current coming into the meter goes through the meter movement. In the 10 mA setting, up to 9 mA goes through R_{SH1} and up to 1 mA through the movement. In the 100 mA setting, up to 99 mA goes through R_{SH2} and the movement can still have only 1 mA for full-scale.

For example, in Figure 5–51, if 50 mA of current are being measured, the needle points to the 0.5 mark on the scale; you must multiply 0.5 by 100 to find the current value. In this situation, 0.5 mA is through the movement (half-scale deflection), and 49.5 mA are through R_{SH2}.

The Power Supply

A rack-mounted power supply is shown in Figure 5–52. The voltmeter indicates the output voltage, which can be adjusted from 0 V to 10 V using the voltage control. The power supply is capable of providing up to 2 A to a load. A basic block diagram of the power supply is shown in Figure 5–53. It consists of a rectifier circuit that converts ac voltage from the wall outlet to dc voltage and a regulator circuit that keeps the output voltage at a constant value.

It is required that the power supply be modified by adding an ammeter with three switch-selected current ranges of 25 mA,

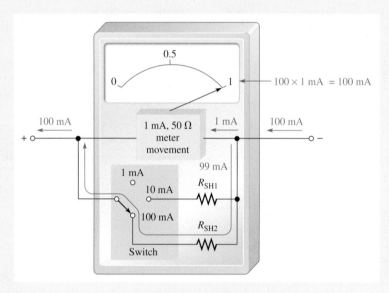

▲ FIGURE 5–51

A milliammeter with three ranges.

▲ FIGURE 5–52

Front panel view of a rack-mounted power supply.

▲ FIGURE 5–53

Basic block diagram of the dc power supply.

250 mA, and 2.5 A. To accomplish this, two shunt resistances are used that can each be switched into a parallel connection with the meter movement. This approach works fine as long as the required values of the shunt resistors are not too small. However, there are problems at very low values of shunt resistance and you will see why next.

The Shunt Circuit

An ammeter is selected that has a full-scale deflection of 25 mA and a resistance of 6 Ω*. Two shunt resistors must be added— one for 250 mA and one for 2.5 A full-scale deflections. The internal meter movement provides the 25 mA range. This is shown in Figure 5–54. The range selection is provided by a 1-pole, 3-position rotary switch with a contact resistance of 50 mΩ. Contact resistance of switches can be from less than 20 mΩ to about 100 mΩ. The contact resistance of a given switch can vary with temperature, current, and usage and, therefore, cannot be relied upon to remain within a reasonable tolerance of the specified value. Also, the switch is a make-before-break type, which

means that contact with the previous position is not broken until contact with the new position is made.

The shunt resistance value for the 2.5 A range is determined as follows where the voltage across the meter movement is

$$V_M = I_M R_M = (25\,\text{mA})(6\,\Omega) = 150\,\text{mV}$$

The current through the shunt resistor for full-scale deflection is

$$I_{SH2} = I_{FULL\,SCALE} - I_M = 2.5\,\text{A} - 25\,\text{mA} = 2.475\,\text{A}$$

The total shunt resistance is

$$R_{SH2(tot)} = \frac{V_M}{I_{SH2}} = \frac{150\,\text{mV}}{2.475\,\text{A}} = 60.6\,\text{m}\Omega$$

Low-ohm precision resistors are generally available in values from 1 mΩ to 10 Ω or greater from various manufacturers.

Notice in Figure 5–54 that the contact resistance, R_{CONT}, of the switch appears in series with R_{SH2}. Since the total shunt resistance must be 60.6 mΩ, the value of the shunt resistor R_{SH2} is

$$R_{SH2} = R_{SH2(tot)} - R_{CONT} = 60.6\,\text{m}\Omega - 50\,\text{m}\Omega = 10.6\,\text{m}\Omega$$

◀ FIGURE 5–54

Ammeter modified to provide three current ranges.

*See the Simpson model 1227 milliammeter at www.simpsonelectric.com

Although this value, or one close to it, may be available, the problem in this case is that the switch contact resistance is almost twice that of R_{SH2} and any variation in it would create a significant inaccuracy in the meter. As you can see, this approach is not acceptable for these particular requirements.

Another Approach

A variation of the standard shunt resistance circuit is shown in Figure 5–55. The shunt resistor, R_{SH}, is connected in parallel for the two higher current range settings and disconnected for the 25 mA setting using a 2-pole, 3-position switch. This circuit avoids dependency on the switch contact resistance by using resistor values that are large enough to make it insignificant. The disadvantages of this meter circuit are that it requires a more complex switch and the voltage drops from input to output are greater than in the previous shunt circuit.

For the 250 mA range, the current through the meter movement for full-scale deflection is 25 mA. The voltage across the meter movement is 150 mV

$$I_{SH} = 250\,\text{mA} - 25\,\text{mA} = 225\,\text{mA}$$

$$R_{SH} = \frac{150\,\text{mV}}{225\,\text{mA}} = 0.67\,\Omega = 670\,\text{m}\Omega$$

This value of R_{SH} is more than thirteen times the expected switch contact resistance of 50 mΩ, thus minimizing the effect of the contact resistance.

For the 2.5 A range, the current through the meter movement for full-scale deflection is still 25 mA. This is also the current through R_1.

$$I_{SH} = 2.5\,\text{A} - 25\,\text{mA} = 2.475\,\text{A}$$

The voltage across the meter circuit from A to B is

$$V_{AB} = I_{SH}R_{SH} = (2.475\,\text{A})(670\,\text{m}\Omega) = 1.66\,\text{V}$$

Applying Kirchhoff's voltage law and Ohm's law to find R_1,

$$V_{R1} + V_M = V_{AB}$$

$$V_{R1} = V_{AB} - V_M = 1.66\,\text{V} - 150\,\text{mV} = 1.51\,\text{V}$$

$$R_1 = \frac{V_{R1}}{I_M} = \frac{1.51\,\text{V}}{25\,\text{mA}} = 60.4\,\Omega$$

This value is much greater than the contact resistance of the switch, thus making the effect of R_{CONT} negligible.

◆ Determine the maximum power dissipated by R_{SH} in Figure 5–55 for each range setting.

◆ How much voltage is there from A to B in Figure 5–55 when the switch is set to the 2.5 A range and the current is 1 A?

◆ The meter indicates 250 mA. How much does the voltage across the meter circuit from A to B change when the switch is moved from the 250 mA position to the 2.5 A position?

◆ Assume the meter movement has a resistance of 4 Ω instead of 6 Ω. Specify any changes necessary in the circuit of Figure 5–55.

Implementing the Power Supply Modification

Once the proper values are obtained, the resistors are placed on a board which is then mounted in the power supply. The resistors and the range switch are connected to the power supply as shown in Figure 5–56. The ammeter circuit is connected between the rectifier circuit in the power supply and the regulator circuit in order to reduce the impact of the voltage drop across the meter circuit on the output voltage. The regulator maintains, within certain limits, a constant dc output voltage even though its input voltage coming from the meter circuit may change.

▲ FIGURE 5–55

Meter circuit redesigned to eliminate or minimize the effect of switch contact resistance. The switch is a 2-pole, 3-position make-before-break rotary type.

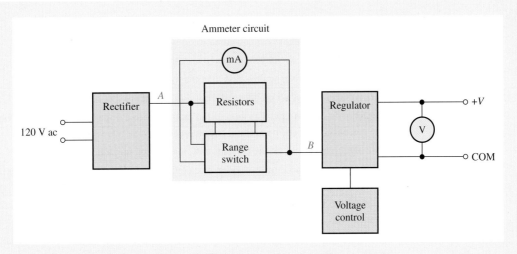

▲ FIGURE 5–56

Block diagram of dc power supply with 3-range milliammeter.

▲ FIGURE 5–57

The power supply with the addition of the milliammeter and the current range selection switch.

Figure 5–57 shows the modified power supply front panel with the rotary range switch and milliammeter installed. The red portion of the scale indicates excess current for the 2.5 A range since the power supply has a maximum current of 2 A for safe operation.

Review

1. When the meter in Figure 5–55 is set to the 250 mA range, which resistance has the most current through it?

2. Determine the total resistance from A to B of the meter circuit in Figure 5–55 for each of the three current ranges.

3. Explain why the circuit in Figure 5–55 was used instead of the one in Figure 5–54.

4. If the ammeter pointer is at 15 and the range switch is set to 250 mA, what is the current?

5. How much current is indicated by the ammeter in Figure 5–58 for each of the three range switch settings in Figure 5–55?

▲ FIGURE 5–58

SUMMARY

- Resistors in parallel are connected between two nodes in a circuit.
- A parallel circuit provides more than one path for current.
- The total parallel resistance is less than the lowest-value parallel resistor.
- The voltages across all branches of a parallel circuit are the same.
- Kirchhoff's current law: The sum of the currents into a node (total current in) equals the sum of the currents out of the node (total current out).

  The algebraic sum of all the currents entering and leaving a node is zero.
- A parallel circuit is a current divider, so called because the total current entering a node divides up into each of the branches connected to the node.
- If all of the branches of a parallel circuit have equal resistance, the currents through all of the branches are equal.
- The total power in a parallel-resistive circuit is the sum of all of the individual powers of the resistors making up the parallel circuit.
- The total power for a parallel circuit can be calculated with the power formulas using values of total current, total resistance, or total voltage.
- If one of the branches of a parallel circuit opens, the total resistance increases, and therefore the total current decreases.
- If a branch of a parallel circuit opens, there is still the same current through the remaining branches.

KEY TERMS

These key terms are also in the end-of-book glossary.

Branch One current path in a parallel circuit.

Current divider A parallel circuit in which the currents divide inversely proportional to the parallel branch resistances.

Kirchhoff's current law A law stating that the total current into a node equals the total current out of the node. Equivalently, it can be stated that the algebraic sum of all the currents entering and leaving a node is zero.

Node A point or junction in a circuit at which two or more components are connected.

Parallel The relationship in electric circuits in which two or more current paths are connected between two separate nodes.

FORMULAS

5–1 $R_T = \dfrac{1}{\dfrac{1}{R_1} + \dfrac{1}{R_2} + \dfrac{1}{R_3} + \cdots + \dfrac{1}{R_n}}$ Total parallel resistance

5–2 $R_T = \dfrac{R_1 R_2}{R_1 + R_2}$ Special case for two resistors in parallel

5–3 $R_T = \dfrac{R}{n}$ Special case for n equal-value resistors in parallel

5–4 $I_{IN(1)} + I_{IN(2)} + I_{IN(3)} + \cdots + I_{IN(n)}$ $= I_{OUT(1)} + I_{OUT(2)} + I_{OUT(3)} + \cdots + I_{OUT(m)}$ Kirchhoff's current law

5–5 $I_x = \left(\dfrac{R_T}{R_x} \right) I_T$ General current-divider formula

5–6 $I_1 = \left(\dfrac{R_2}{R_1 + R_2} \right) I_T$ Two-branch current-divider formula

5–7 $I_2 = \left(\dfrac{R_1}{R_1 + R_2} \right) I_T$ Two-branch current-divider formula

5–8 $P_T = P_1 + P_2 + P_3 + \cdots + P_n$ Total power

SELF-TEST   **Answers are at the end of the chapter.**

1. In a parallel circuit, each resistor has
   - **(a)** the same current
   - **(b)** the same voltage
   - **(c)** the same power
   - **(d)** all of the above

2. When a 1.2 kΩ resistor and a 100 Ω resistor are connected in parallel, the total resistance is
   - **(a)** greater than 1.2 kΩ
   - **(b)** greater than 100 Ω but less than 1.2 kΩ
   - **(c)** less than 100 Ω but greater than 90 Ω
   - **(d)** less than 90 Ω

3. A 330 Ω resistor, a 270 Ω resistor, and a 68 Ω resistor are all in parallel. The total resistance is approximately
   - **(a)** 668 Ω
   - **(b)** 47 Ω
   - **(c)** 68 Ω
   - **(d)** 22 Ω

4. Eight resistors are in parallel. The two lowest-value resistors are both 1.0 kΩ. The total resistance
   - **(a)** cannot be determined
   - **(b)** is greater than 1.0 kΩ
   - **(c)** is less than 1.0 kΩ
   - **(d)** is less than 500 Ω

5. When an additional resistor is connected across an existing parallel circuit, the total resistance
   - **(a)** decreases
   - **(b)** increases
   - **(c)** remains the same
   - **(d)** increases by the value of the added resistor

6. If one of the resistors in a parallel circuit is removed, the total resistance
   - **(a)** decreases by the value of the removed resistor
   - **(b)** remains the same
   - **(c)** increases
   - **(d)** doubles

7. The currents into a node are along two paths. One current is 5 A and the other is 3 A. The total current out of the node is
   - **(a)** 2 A
   - **(b)** unknown
   - **(c)** 8 A
   - **(d)** the larger of the two

8. The following resistors are in parallel across a voltage source: 390 Ω, 560 Ω, and 820 Ω. The resistor with the least current is
   - **(a)** 390 Ω
   - **(b)** 560 Ω
   - **(c)** 820 Ω
   - **(d)** impossible to determine without knowing the voltage

9. A sudden decrease in the total current into a parallel circuit may indicate
   - **(a)** a short
   - **(b)** an open resistor
   - **(c)** a drop in source voltage
   - **(d)** either (b) or (c)

10. In a four-branch parallel circuit, there are 10 mA of current in each branch. If one of the branches opens, the current in each of the other three branches is
    - **(a)** 13.33 mA
    - **(b)** 10 mA
    - **(c)** 0 A
    - **(d)** 30 mA

11. In a certain three-branch parallel circuit, R_1 has 10 mA through it, R_2 has 15 mA through it, and R_3 has 20 mA through it. After measuring a total current of 35 mA, you can say that
    - **(a)** R_1 is open
    - **(b)** R_2 is open
    - **(c)** R_3 is open
    - **(d)** the circuit is operating properly

12. If there are a total of 100 mA into a parallel circuit consisting of three branches and two of the branch currents are 40 mA and 20 mA, the third branch current is
    - **(a)** 60 mA
    - **(b)** 20 mA
    - **(c)** 160 mA
    - **(d)** 40 mA

13. A complete short develops across one of five parallel resistors on a PC board. The most likely result is
    - **(a)** the smallest-value resistor will burn out
    - **(b)** one or more of the other resistors will burn out
    - **(c)** the fuse in the power supply will blow
    - **(d)** the resistance values will be altered

14. The power dissipation in each of four parallel branches is 1 mW. The total power dissipation is
    - **(a)** 1 mW
    - **(b)** 4 mW
    - **(c)** 0.25 mW
    - **(d)** 16 mW

TROUBLESHOOTING: SYMPTOM AND CAUSE

The purpose of these exercises is to help develop thought processes essential to troubleshooting. Answers are at the end of the chapter.

Determine the cause for each set of symptoms. Refer to Figure 5–59.

▶ FIGURE 5–59

The meters indicate the correct readings for this circuit.

1. *Symptom:* The ammeter and voltmeter readings are zero.

   Cause:

   (a) R_1 is open.

   (b) The voltage source is turned off or faulty.

   (c) R_3 is open.

2. *Symptom:* The ammeter reading is 16.7 mA, and the voltmeter reading is 6 V.

   Cause:

   (a) R_1 is open.

   (b) R_2 is open.

   (c) R_3 is open.

3. *Symptom:* The ammeter reading is 28.9 mA, and the voltmeter reading is 6 V.

   Cause:

   (a) R_1 is open.

   (b) R_2 is open.

   (c) R_3 is open.

4. *Symptom:* The ammeter reading is 24.2 mA, and the voltmeter reading is 6 V.

   Cause:

   (a) R_1 is open.

   (b) R_2 is open.

   (c) R_3 is open.

5. *Symptom:* The ammeter reading is 34.9 mA, and the voltmeter reading is 0 V.

   Cause:

   (a) A resistor is shorted.

   (b) The voltmeter is faulty.

   (c) The voltage source is turned off or faulty.

PROBLEMS

Answers to odd-numbered problems are at the end of the book.

BASIC PROBLEMS

SECTION 5–1   **Resistors in Parallel**

1. Connect the resistors in Figure 5–60 in parallel across the battery.

2. Determine whether or not all the resistors in Figure 5–61 are connected in parallel on the printed circuit board. Draw the schematic including resistor values.

▲ FIGURE 5–60

▲ FIGURE 5–61

SECTION 5–2 Total Parallel Resistance

3. Determine the total resistance between pins 1 and 2 in Figure 5–61.

4. The following resistors are connected in parallel: $1.0 \text{ M}\Omega$, $2.2 \text{ M}\Omega$, $4.7 \text{ M}\Omega$, $12 \text{ M}\Omega$, and $22 \text{ M}\Omega$. Determine the total resistance.

5. Find the total resistance between nodes A and B for each group of parallel resistors in Figure 5–62.

▶ FIGURE 5–62

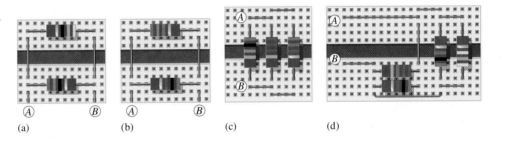

(a)   (b)   (c)   (d)

6. Calculate R_T for each circuit in Figure 5–63.

▶ FIGURE 5–63

(a)   (b)   (c)

7. What is the total resistance of eleven $22 \text{ k}\Omega$ resistors in parallel?

8. Five 15Ω, ten 100Ω, and two 10Ω resistors are all connected in parallel. What is the total resistance?

SECTION 5–3 Voltage in a Parallel Circuit

9. Determine the voltage across and the current through each parallel resistor if the total voltage is 12 V and the total resistance is 600Ω. There are four resistors, all of equal value.

▷ FIGURE 5–64

10. The source voltage in Figure 5–64 is 100 V. How much voltage does each of the three meters read?

SECTION 5–4 Application of Ohm's Law

11. What is the total current, I_T, in each circuit of Figure 5–65?

▷ FIGURE 5–65

(a)

(b)

12. Three 33 Ω resistors are connected in parallel with a 110 V source. What is the current from the source?

13. Which circuit of Figure 5–66 has more total current?

▷ FIGURE 5–66

(a)

(b)

14. Four equal-value resistors are connected in parallel. Five volts are applied across the parallel circuit, and 2.5 mA are measured from the source. What is the value of each resistor?

SECTION 5–5 Kirchhoff's Current Law

15. The following currents are measured in the same direction in a three-branch parallel circuit: 250 mA, 300 mA, and 800 mA. What is the value of the current into the node to which these three branches are connected?

16. There is a total of 500 mA of current into five parallel resistors. The currents through four of the resistors are 50 mA, 150 mA, 25 mA, and 100 mA. What is the current through the fifth resistor?

17. How much current is through R_2 and R_3 in Figure 5–67 if R_2 and R_3 have the same resistance? Show how to connect ammeters to measure these currents.

▷ FIGURE 5–67

SECTION 5–6 Current Dividers

18. A 10 kΩ resistor and a 15 kΩ resistor are in parallel with a voltage source. Which resistor has the highest current?

19. How much branch current should each meter in Figure 5–68 indicate?

▶ **FIGURE 5–68**

20. Using the current-divider formula, determine the current in each branch of the circuits of Figure 5–69.

▶ **FIGURE 5–69**

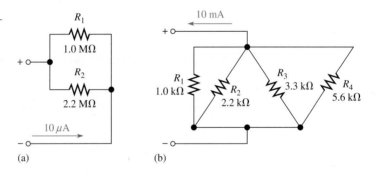

(a)   (b)

SECTION 5–7 Power in Parallel Circuits

21. Five parallel resistors each handle 40 mW. What is the total power?

22. Determine the total power in each circuit of Figure 5–69.

23. Six light bulbs are connected in parallel across 110 V. Each bulb is rated at 75 W. How much current is through each bulb, and what is the total current?

SECTION 5–8 Troubleshooting

24. If one of the bulbs burns out in Problem 23, how much current will be through each of the remaining bulbs? What will be the total current?

25. In Figure 5–70, the current and voltage measurements are indicated. Has a resistor opened, and, if so, which one?

▶ **FIGURE 5–70**

26. What is wrong with the circuit in Figure 5–71?

▶ FIGURE 5–71

25 V

27. Find the open resistor in Figure 5–72.

▶ FIGURE 5–72

28. Determine if there is a resistor open in Figure 5–73. If so, identify it.

▶ FIGURE 5–73

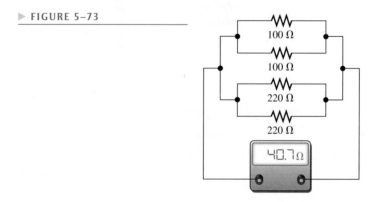

ADVANCED PROBLEMS

29. In the circuit of Figure 5–74, determine resistances R_2, R_3, and R_4.

▶ FIGURE 5–74

30. The total resistance of a parallel circuit is 25 Ω. If the total current is 100 mA, how much current is through a 220 Ω resistor that makes up part of the parallel circuit?

31. What is the current through each resistor in Figure 5–75? R is the lowest-value resistor, and all others are multiples of that value as indicated.

▶ FIGURE 5–75

32. A certain parallel circuit consists of only ½ W resistors each having the same resistance. The total resistance is 1 kΩ, and the total current is 50 mA. If each resistor is operating at one-half its maximum power level, determine the following:

   (a) the number of resistors   (b) the value of each resistor

   (c) the current in each branch   (d) the applied voltage

33. Find the values of the unspecified quantities (shown in color) in each circuit of Figure 5–76.

(a)

(b)

(c)

▲ FIGURE 5–76

34. What is the total resistance between terminal A and ground in Figure 5–77 for the following conditions?

   (a) SW1 and SW2 open   (b) SW1 closed, SW2 open

   (c) SW1 open, SW2 closed   (d) SW1 and SW2 closed

▶ FIGURE 5–77

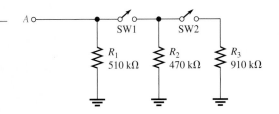

35. What value of R_2 in Figure 5–78 will cause excessive current?

▶ FIGURE 5–78

36. Determine the total current from the source and the current through each resistor for each switch position in Figure 5–79.

▲ FIGURE 5–79

37. The electrical circuit in a room has a ceiling lamp that draws 1.25 A and four wall outlets. Two table lamps that each draw 0.833 A are plugged into two outlets, and a TV set that draws 1 A is connected to the third outlet. When all of these items are in use, how much current is in the main line serving the room? If the main line is protected by a 5 A circuit breaker, how much current can be drawn from the fourth outlet? Draw a schematic of this wiring.

38. The total resistance of a parallel circuit is 25 Ω. What is the current through a 220 Ω resistor that makes up part of the parallel circuit if the total current is 100 mA?

39. Identify which groups of resistors are in parallel on the double-sided PC board in Figure 5–80. Determine the total resistance of each group.

▲ FIGURE 5–80

40. If the total resistance in Figure 5–81 is 200 Ω, what is the value of R_2?

▶ FIGURE 5–81

41. Determine the unknown resistances in Figure 5–82.

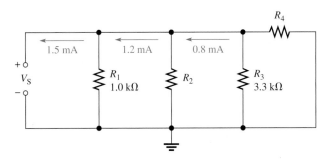

▲ FIGURE 5–82

42. There is a total of 250 mA into a parallel circuit with a total resistance of 1.5 kΩ. The current must be increased by 25%. Determine how much resistance to add in parallel to accomplish this increase in current.

43. Draw the schematic for the setup in Figure 5–83 and determine what is wrong with the circuit if 25 V are applied across the red and black leads.

(a) Meter with yellow lead going to protoboard and red lead going to the positive terminal of the 25 V power supply.

(b) Protoboard with leads connected. Yellow lead is from meter and gray lead is from 25 V power supply ground. The red meter lead goes to +25 V.

▲ FIGURE 5–83

▶ FIGURE 5–84

44. Develop a test procedure to check the circuit in Figure 5–84 to make sure that there are no open components. You must do this test without removing any component from the board. List the procedure in a detailed step-by-step format.

45. A certain parallel circuit consists of five ½ W resistors with the following values: 1.8 kΩ, 2.2 kΩ, 3.3 kΩ, 3.9 kΩ and 4.7 kΩ. As you slowly increase the voltage across the parallel circuit, the total current slowly increases. Suddenly, the total current drops to a lower value.

(a) Excluding a power supply failure, what happened?

(b) What is the maximum voltage you should have applied?

(c) Specifically, what must be done to repair the fault?

46. For the circuit board shown in Figure 5–85, determine the resistance between the following pins if there is a short between pins 2 and 4.

(a) pins 1 and 2   (b) pins 2 and 3   (c) pins 3 and 4   (d) pins 1 and 4

▲ FIGURE 5–85

47. For the circuit board shown in Figure 5–85, determine the resistance between the following pins if there is a short between pins 3 and 4.

(a) pins 1 and 2   (b) pins 2 and 3   (c) pins 2 and 4   (d) pins 1 and 4

MULTISIM TROUBLESHOOTING PROBLEMS

48. Open file P05-48 on your CD-ROM. Using current measurements, determine if there is a fault in the circuit. If so, identify the fault.

49. Open file P05-49 on your CD-ROM. Using current measurements, determine if there is a fault in the circuit. If so, identify the fault.

50. Open file P05-50 on your CD-ROM. Using resistance measurements, determine if there is a fault in the circuit. If so, identify the fault.

51. Open file P05-51 on your CD-ROM. Measure the total resistance of each circuit and compare to the calculated values.

ANSWERS

SECTION REVIEWS

SECTION 5–1 **Resistors in Parallel**

1. Parallel resistors are connected between the same two points.

2. A parallel circuit has more than one current path between two given points.

3. See Figure 5–86.

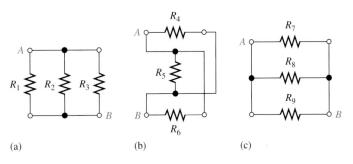

(a) (b) (c)

▲ FIGURE 5–86

4. See Figure 5–87.

▲ FIGURE 5–87

SECTION 5–2 **Total Parallel Resistance**

1. As more resistors are connected in parallel, the total resistance decreases.

2. R_T is always less than the smallest resistance value.

3. $R_T = 2.2\,\text{k}\Omega/12 = 183\,\Omega$

SECTION 5–3 **Voltage in a Parallel Circuit**

   1. 5 V
   2. $V_{R2} = 118\,\text{V}; V_S = 118\,\text{V}$
   3. $V_{R1} = 50\,\text{V}; V_{R2} = 50\,\text{V}$
   4. Voltage is the same across all parallel branches.

SECTION 5–4 **Application Ohm's Law**

   1. $I_T = 10\,\text{V}/(68\,\Omega/3) = 441\,\text{mA}$
   2. $V_S = 20\,\text{mA}(680\,\Omega \parallel 330\,\Omega) = 4.44\,\text{V}$
   3. $I_1 = 4.44\,\text{V}/680\,\Omega = 6.53\,\text{mA}; I_2 = 4.44\,\text{V}/330\,\Omega = 13.5\,\text{mA}$
   4. $R_T = 4(12\,\text{V}/6\,\text{mA}) = 8\,\text{k}\Omega$
   5. $V = (1.0\,\text{k}\Omega \parallel 2.2\,\text{k}\Omega)100\,\text{mA} = 68.8\,\text{V}$

SECTION 5–5 **Kirchhoff's Current Law**

   1. Kirchhoff's current law: The algebraic sum of all currents at a node is zero; The sum of the currents entering a node equals the sum of all the currents leaving that node.
   2. $I_1 + I_2 + I_3 = 2.5\,\text{A}$
   3. $100\,\text{mA} + 300\,\text{mA} = 400\,\text{mA}$
   4. $I_1 = 5\,\mu\text{A} - 2\,\mu\text{A} = 3\mu\text{A}$
   5. $8\,\text{A} - 1\,\text{A} = 7\,\text{A}$ entering, $8\,\text{A} - 3\,\text{A} = 5\,\text{A}$ leaving

SECTION 5–6 **Current Dividers**

   1. The $22\,\Omega$ has most current; the $220\,\Omega$ has least current.
   2. $I_3 = (R_T/R_3)4\,\text{mA} = (113.6\,\Omega/470\,\Omega)4\,\text{mA} = 967\,\mu\text{A}$
   3. $I_2 = (R_T/680\,\Omega)10\,\text{mA} = 3.27\,\text{mA}; I_1 = (R_T/330\,\Omega)10\,\text{mA} = 6.73\,\text{mA}$

SECTION 5–7 **Power in Parallel Circuits**

   1. Add the powers in each resistor to get P_T.
   2. $P_T = 1\,\text{W} + 2\,\text{W} + 5\,\text{W} + 8\,\text{W} = 16\,\text{W}$
   3. $P_T = (1\,\text{mA})^2 R_T = 615\,\mu\text{W}$

SECTION 5–8 **Troubleshooting**

   1. When a parallel branch opens, there is no change in voltage and the total current decreases.
   2. When the total resistance is greater than it should be, a branch is open.
   3. Yes, all other bulbs continue to glow.
   4. The current in each nonopen branch remains 1 A.
   5. $1\,\text{mA} + 2.5\,\text{mA} = 3.5\,\text{mA}$; therefore, the 1.2 mA branch is open.

Application Assignment

   1. R_{SH} has the most current.
   2. 25 mA range: $R_{AB} = R_M = 6\,\Omega$

      250 mA range: $R_{AB} = R_M \parallel R_{SH} = 6\,\Omega \parallel 670\,\text{m}\Omega = 603\,\text{m}\Omega$

      2.5 A range: $R_{AB} = (R_1 + R_M) \parallel R_{SH} = (60.4\,\Omega + 6\,\Omega) \parallel 670\,\text{m}\Omega = 66.4\,\Omega \parallel 670\,\text{m}\Omega = 663\,\text{m}\Omega$
   3. To eliminate effect of contact resistance
   4. 150 mA
   5. 25 mA range: 7.5 mA; 250 mA range: 75 mA; 2.5 A range: 0.75 A

RELATED PROBLEMS FOR EXAMPLES

5–1 No rewiring is necessary.

5–2 Connect pin 1 to pin 2 and pin 3 to pin 4.

5–3 $9.34\,\Omega$

5–4 Replace Step 9 with "Press the $+$ key."
Display shows $100^{-1} + 47^{-1} + 22^{-1} +$.
Replace Step 10 with "Enter 33."
Display shows $100^{-1} + 47^{-1} + 22^{-1} + 33$.
Step 11: Press the x^{-1} key.
Display shows $100^{-1} + 47^{-1} + 22^{-1} + 33^{-1}$.
Step 12: Press the ENTER key. Display shows $107.034171502\mathrm{E}^{-3}$.
Step 13: Press the x^{-1} and ENTER keys. Display shows $9.34281067406\mathrm{E}0$.

5–5 $132\,\Omega$

5–6 $33.3\,\mathrm{k}\Omega$

5–7 $25\,\mathrm{V}$

5–8 $I_1 = 100\,\mathrm{mA}; I_2 = 179\,\mathrm{mA}; 100\,\mathrm{mA} + 179\,\mathrm{mA} = 279\,\mathrm{mA}$

5–9 $I_1 = 20.0\,\mathrm{mA}; I_2 = 9.09\,\mathrm{mA}; I_3 = 35.7\,\mathrm{mA}; I_4 = 22.0\,\mathrm{mA}$

5–10 $8.62\,\mathrm{mA}$

5–11 Use an ohmmeter to measure R_T and then calculate R_1 using the parallel-resistance formula.

5–12 $20\,\mathrm{mA}$

5–13 $I_\mathrm{T} = 112\,\mathrm{mA}; I_2 = 50\,\mathrm{mA}$

5–14 $2.5\,\mathrm{mA}; 5\,\mathrm{mA}$

5–15 $I_1 = 1.63\,\mathrm{mA}; I_2 = 3.35\,\mathrm{mA}$

5–16 $I_1 = 59.4\,\mathrm{mA}; I_2 = 40.6\,\mathrm{mA}$

5–17 $1.78\,\mathrm{W}$

5–18 $81\,\mathrm{W}$

5–19 $15.4\,\mathrm{mA}$

5–20 Not correct; $R_{10}\,(68\,\mathrm{k}\Omega)$ is open.

SELF-TEST

1. (b)   **2.** (c)   **3.** (b)   **4.** (d)   **5.** (a)   **6.** (c)   **7.** (c)
8. (c)   **9.** (d)   **10.** (b)   **11.** (a)   **12.** (d)   **13.** (c)   **14.** (b)

TROUBLESHOOTING: SYMPTOM AND CAUSE

1. (b)

2. (c)

3. (a)

4. (b)

5. (b)

6

SERIES-PARALLEL CIRCUITS

CHAPTER OBJECTIVES

  Identify series-parallel relationships

  Analyze series-parallel circuits

  Analyze loaded voltage dividers

  Determine the loading effect of a voltmeter on a circuit

  Analyze and apply a Wheatstone bridge

◆ Apply Thevenin's theorem to simplify a circuit for analysis

◆ Apply the maximum power transfer theorem

◆ Apply the superposition theorem to circuit analysis

◆ Troubleshoot series-parallel circuits

KEY TERMS

◆ Loading
◆ Load current
◆ Bleeder current
◆ Wheatstone bridge
◆ Balanced bridge

◆ Unbalanced bridge
◆ Thevenin's theorem
◆ Terminal equivalency
◆ Maximum power transfer
◆ Superposition

APPLICATION ASSIGNMENT PREVIEW

Your application assignment in this chapter is to evaluate a voltage-divider circuit board used in a portable power supply by applying your knowledge of loaded voltage dividers gained in this chapter as well as skills developed in previous chapters. The voltage divider in this application is designed to provide reference voltages to three different instruments that act as loads on the circuit. You will also troubleshoot the circuit board for various common faults. After studying this chapter, you should be able to complete the application assignment.

VISIT THE COMPANION WEBSITE

Study aids for this chapter are available at
http://www.prenhall.com/floyd

INTRODUCTION

Various combinations of both series and parallel resistors are often found in electronic circuits. In this chapter, examples of such series-parallel arrangements are examined and analyzed. An important circuit called the *Wheatstone bridge* is introduced, and you will learn how complex circuits can be simplified using Thevenin's theorem. The maximum power transfer theorem, used in applications where it is important for a given circuit to provide maximum power to a load, is discussed. Also, circuits with more than one voltage source are analyzed in simple steps using the superposition theorem. Troubleshooting series-parallel circuits for shorts and opens is also covered.

6–1 IDENTIFYING SERIES-PARALLEL RELATIONSHIPS

A series-parallel circuit consists of combinations of both series and parallel current paths. It is important to be able to identify how the components in a circuit are arranged in terms of their series and parallel relationships.

After completing this section, you should be able to

◆ **Identify series-parallel relationships**

  ◆ Recognize how each resistor in a given circuit is related to the other resistors

  ◆ Determine series and parallel relationships on a PC board

Figure 6–1(a) shows an example of a simple series-parallel combination of resistors. Notice that the resistance from point A to point B is R_1. The resistance from point B to point C is R_2 and R_3 in parallel ($R_2 \parallel R_3$). The total resistance from point A to point C is R_1 in series with the parallel combination of R_2 and R_3, as indicated in Figure 6–1(b).

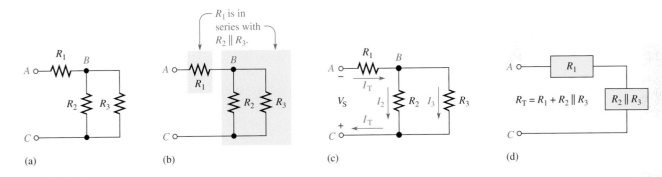

(a)   (b)   (c)   (d)

▲ FIGURE 6–1

A simple series-parallel resistive circuit.

When the circuit in Figure 6–1 is connected to a voltage source as shown in part (c) the total current through R_1 divides at point B into the two parallel paths. These two branch currents then recombine. The total current is into the positive source terminal as shown. The resistor relationships are shown in block form in part (d).

Now, to further illustrate series-parallel relationships, let's increase the complexity of the circuit in Figure 6–1(a) step-by-step.

1. In Figure 6–2(a), R_4 is connected in series with R_1. The resistance between points A and B is now $R_1 + R_4$. This series combination is in series with the parallel combination of R_2 and R_3, as illustrated in Figure 6–2(b). Part (c) shows the resistor relationships in block form.

(a)   (b)   (c)

▲ FIGURE 6–2

R_4 is added to the circuit in series with R_1.

2. In Figure 6–3(a), R_5 is connected in series with R_2. The series combination of R_2 and R_5 is in parallel with R_3. This entire series-parallel combination is in series with the $R_1 + R_4$ combination, as illustrated in Figure 6–3(b). The block diagram is shown in part (c).

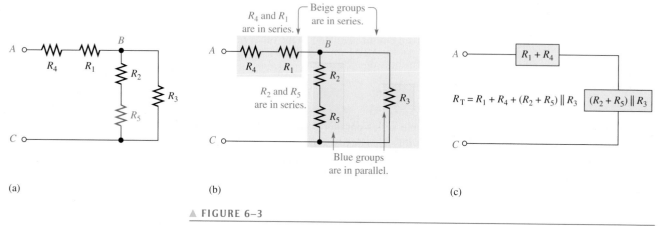

(a)　　　　　　　　　　　　(b)　　　　　　　　　　　　(c)

▲ **FIGURE 6–3**

R_5 is added to the circuit in series with R_2.

3. In Figure 6–4(a), R_6 is connected in parallel with the series combination of R_1 and R_4. The series-parallel combination of R_1, R_4, and R_6 is in series with the series-parallel combination of R_2, R_3, and R_5, as indicated in Figure 6–4(b). The block diagram is shown in part (c).

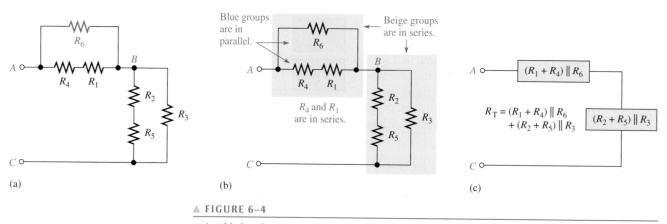

(a)　　　　　　　　　　　　(b)　　　　　　　　　　　　(c)

▲ **FIGURE 6–4**

R_6 is added to the circuit in parallel with the series combination of R_1 and R_4.

EXAMPLE 6–1

Identify the series-parallel relationships in Figure 6–5.

Solution   Starting at the negative terminal of the source, follow the current paths.

1. All the current produced by the source must go through R_1, which is in series with the rest of the circuit.

2. The total current takes two paths when it gets to node A. Part of it is through R_2, and part of it is through R_3.

▲ FIGURE 6–5   ▲ FIGURE 6–6

3. Resistors R_2 and R_3 are in parallel with each other, and this parallel combination is in series with R_1.

4. At node B, the currents through R_2 and R_3 come together again into a single path. Thus, the total current is through R_4.

5. Resistor R_4 is in series with both R_1 and the parallel combination of R_2 and R_3.

The currents are shown in Figure 6–6, where I_T is the total current. In summary, R_1 and R_4 are in series with the parallel combination of R_2 and R_3.

$$R_1 + R_4 + R_2 \| R_3$$

Related Problem* If another resistor, R_5, is connected from node A to the positive side of the source in Figure 6–6, what is its relationship to the other resistors?

*Answers are at the end of the chapter.

EXAMPLE 6–2   Describe the series-parallel combination between terminals A and D in Figure 6–7.

▶ FIGURE 6–7

Solution   Between nodes B and C, there are two parallel paths.

1. The lower path consists of R_4.

2. The upper path consists of a series combination of R_2 and R_3.

This parallel combination is in series with both R_1 and R_5. In summary, R_1 and R_5 are in series with the parallel combination of R_4 and $(R_2 + R_3)$.

$$R_1 + R_5 + R_4 \| (R_2 + R_3)$$

Related Problem   If a resistor is connected from node C to node D in Figure 6–7, describe its relationship in the circuit.

EXAMPLE 6–3

Describe the total resistance between each pair of terminals in Figure 6–8.

▶ FIGURE 6–8

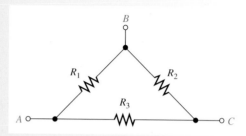

Solution   **1.** From *A* to *B*: R_1 is in parallel with the series combination of R_2 and R_3.

2. From *A* to *C*: R_3 is in parallel with the series combination of R_1 and R_2.

3. From *B* to *C*: R_2 is in parallel with the series combination of R_1 and R_3.

Related Problem   In Figure 6–8, describe the total resistance between each terminal and an added ground if a new resistor, R_4, is connected from terminal *C* to ground. None of the existing resistors connect directly to the ground.

When connecting a circuit on a protoboard from a schematic, it is easier to check the circuit if the resistors and connections on the protoboard are oriented so that they approximately match the way the schematic is drawn. In some cases, it is difficult to see the series-parallel relationships on a schematic because of the way in which it is drawn. In such a situation, it helps to redraw the diagram so that the relationships become clear.

EXAMPLE 6–4

Identify the series-parallel relationships in Figure 6–9.

▲ FIGURE 6–9   ▲ FIGURE 6–10

Solution   The circuit schematic is redrawn in Figure 6–10 to better illustrate the series-parallel relationships. Now you can see that R_2 and R_3 are in parallel with each other and also that R_4 and R_5 are in parallel with each other. Both parallel combinations are in series with each other and with R_1.

$$R_1 + R_2 \| R_3 + R_4 \| R_5$$

Related Problem   If a resistor is connected from the bottom end of R_3 to the top end of R_5 in Figure 6–10, what effect does it have on the circuit? Explain.

Usually, the physical arrangement of components on a PC or protoboard bears no resemblance to the actual electrical relationships. By tracing out the circuit and rearranging the components on paper into a recognizable form, you can determine the series-parallel relationships.

EXAMPLE 6–5

Determine the relationships of the resistors on the PC board in Figure 6–11.

▶ **FIGURE 6–11**

Solution

In Figure 6–12(a), the schematic is drawn approximately in the same arrangement as that of the resistors on the board. In part (b), the resistors are reoriented so that the series-parallel relationships are more obvious.

Resistors R_1 and R_4 are in series, $R_1 + R_4$ is in parallel with R_2; R_5 and R_6 are in parallel, and this combination is in series with R_3.

The $R_3, R_5,$ and R_6 series-parallel combination is in parallel with both R_2 and the $R_1 + R_4$ combination. This entire series-parallel combination is in series with R_7.

Figure 6–12(c) illustrates these relationships. Summarizing in equation form,

$$R_{AB} = (R_5 \parallel R_6 + R_3) \parallel R_2 \parallel (R_1 + R_4) + R_7$$

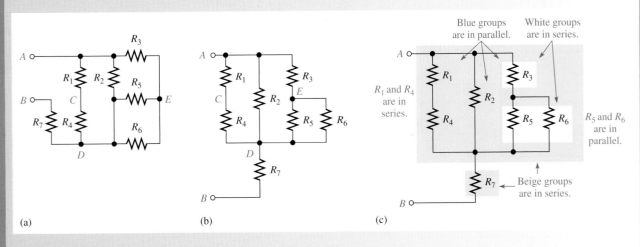

▲ **FIGURE 6–12**

Related Problem

What happens if there is an open connection between R_1 and R_4 on the printed circuit board in Figure 6–11?

SECTION 6–1
REVIEW
Answers are at the end of the chapter.

1. A certain series-parallel circuit is described as follows: R_1 and R_2 are in parallel. This parallel combination is in series with another parallel combination of R_3 and R_4. Draw the circuit.

2. In the circuit of Figure 6–13, describe the series-parallel relationships of the resistors.

3. Which resistors are in parallel in Figure 6–14?

▲ FIGURE 6–13

▲ FIGURE 6–14

4. Identify the parallel resistors in Figure 6–15.

5. Are the parallel combinations in Figure 6–15 in series?

▷ FIGURE 6–15

6–2 ANALYSIS OF SERIES-PARALLEL RESISTIVE CIRCUITS

The analysis of series-parallel circuits can be approached in many ways, depending on what information you need and what circuit values you know. The examples in this section do not represent an exhaustive coverage, but they give you an idea of how to approach series-parallel circuit analysis.

After completing this section, you should be able to

◆ **Analyze series-parallel circuits**

  ◆ Determine total resistance

  ◆ Determine all the currents

  ◆ Determine all the voltage drops

If you know Ohm's law, Kirchhoff's laws, the voltage-divider formula, and the current-divider formula, and if you know how to apply these laws, you can solve most resistive circuit analysis problems. The ability to recognize series and parallel combinations is, of course, essential. There is no standard "cookbook" approach that can be applied to all situations. Logical thought is the most powerful tool you can apply to problem solving.

Total Resistance

In Chapter 4, you learned how to determine total series resistance. In Chapter 5, you learned how to determine total parallel resistance. To find the total resistance (R_T) of a series-parallel combination, first identify the series and parallel relationships, and then apply what you have previously learned. The following two examples illustrate the general approach.

EXAMPLE 6–6

Determine R_T between terminals A and B of the circuit in Figure 6–16.

▶ FIGURE 6–16

Solution Resistors R_2 and R_3 are in parallel, and this parallel combination is in series with R_1. First find the parallel resistance of R_2 and R_3. Since R_2 and R_3 are equal in value, divide the value by 2.

$$R_{2\|3} = \frac{R}{n} = \frac{100\ \Omega}{2} = 50\ \Omega$$

Now, since R_1 is in series with $R_{2\|3}$, add their values.

$$R_T = R_1 + R_{2\|3} = 10\ \Omega + 50\ \Omega = \mathbf{60\ \Omega}$$

Related Problem Determine R_T in Figure 6–16 if R_3 is changed to 82 Ω.

Open Multisim file E06-06 on your CD-ROM. Using the multimeter, verify the calculated value of total resistance. Change R_1 to 18 Ω, R_2 to 82 Ω, and R_3 to 82 Ω and measure the total resistance.

EXAMPLE 6–7

Find R_T of the circuit in Figure 6–17.

▶ FIGURE 6–17

Solution **1.** In the upper branch between nodes A and B, R_2 is in series with R_3. The series combination is designated R_{2+3} and is equal to $R_2 + R_3$.

$$R_{2+3} = R_2 + R_3 = 47\ \Omega + 47\ \Omega = 94\ \Omega$$

2. In the lower branch, R_4 and R_5 are in parallel with each other. This parallel combination is designated $R_{4\|5}$.

$$R_{4\|5} = \frac{R_4 R_5}{R_4 + R_5} = \frac{(68\ \Omega)(39\ \Omega)}{68\ \Omega + 39\ \Omega} = 24.8\ \Omega$$

3. Also in the lower branch, the parallel combination of R_4 and R_5 is in series with R_6. This series-parallel combination is designated $R_{4\|5+6}$.

$$R_{4\|5+6} = R_6 + R_{4\|5} = 75\ \Omega + 24.8\ \Omega = 99.8\ \Omega$$

Figure 6–18 shows the original circuit in a simplified equivalent form.

▶ FIGURE 6–18

4. Now you can find the resistance between nodes A and B. It is R_{2+3} in parallel with $R_{4\|5+6}$. Calculate the equivalent resistance as follows:

$$R_{AB} = \frac{1}{\dfrac{1}{R_{2+3}} + \dfrac{1}{R_{4\|5+6}}} = \frac{1}{\dfrac{1}{94\ \Omega} + \dfrac{1}{99.8\ \Omega}} = 48.4\ \Omega$$

5. Finally, the total circuit resistance is R_1 in series with R_{AB}.

$$R_T = R_1 + R_{AB} = 100\ \Omega + 48.4\ \Omega = \mathbf{148.4\ \Omega}$$

Related Problem Determine R_T if a 68 Ω resistor is connected to the circuit in Figure 6–17 from node A to node B.

 Open Multisim file E06-07 on your CD-ROM. Verify the total calculated resistance. Remove R_5 from the circuit and measure the total resistance. Then check your measured value by calculating the total resistance.

Total Current

Once you know the total resistance and the source voltage, you can apply Ohm's law to find the total current in a circuit. Total current is the source voltage divided by the total resistance.

$$I_T = \frac{V_S}{R_T}$$

For example, let's find the total current in the circuit of Example 6–7 (Figure 6–17). Assume that the source voltage is 30 V. The calculation is

$$I_T = \frac{V_S}{R_T} = \frac{30\ V}{148.4\ \Omega} = 202\ mA$$

Branch Currents

Using the current-divider formula, Kirchhoff's current law, Ohm's law, or combinations of these, you can find the current in any branch of a series-parallel circuit. In some cases, it may take repeated application of the formula to find a given current.

EXAMPLE 6–8

Determine the current through R_4 in Figure 6–19 if $V_S = 50$ V.

▶ FIGURE 6–19

Solution   First, find the current (I_2) into node B. Once you know this current, you can use the current-divider formula to find I_4, the current through R_4.

Notice that there are two main branches in the circuit. The left-most branch consists of only R_1. The right-most branch has R_2 in series with the parallel combination of R_3 and R_4. The voltage across both of these main branches is the same and equal to 50 V. Calculate the equivalent resistance ($R_{2+3\|4}$) of the right-most main branch and then apply Ohm's law; I_2 is the total current through this main branch. Thus,

$$R_{2+3\|4} = R_2 + \frac{R_3 R_4}{R_3 + R_4} = 330\ \Omega + \frac{(330\ \Omega)(560\ \Omega)}{890\ \Omega} = 538\ \Omega$$

$$I_2 = \frac{V_S}{R_{2+3\|4}} = \frac{50\ V}{538\ \Omega} = 93\ mA$$

Use the two-resistor current-divider formula to calculate I_4.

$$I_4 = \left(\frac{R_3}{R_3 + R_4}\right)I_2 = \left(\frac{330\ \Omega}{890\ \Omega}\right)93\ mA = \mathbf{34.5\ mA}$$

Related Problem   Find I_1, I_3, and I_T in Figure 6–19.

Open Multisim file E06-08 on your CD-ROM. Measure the current in each resistor. Compare the measurements with the calculated values.

Voltage Relationships

The circuit in Figure 6–20 illustrates voltage relationships in a series-parallel circuit. Voltmeters are connected to measure each of the resistor voltages, and the readings are indicated.

Some general observations about Figure 6–20 are as follows:

1. V_{R1} and V_{R2} are equal because R_1 and R_2 are in parallel. (Recall that voltages across parallel branches are the same.) V_{R1} and V_{R2} are the same as the voltage from A to B.

2. V_{R3} is equal to $V_{R4} + V_{R5}$ because R_3 is in parallel with the series combination of R_4 and R_5. (V_{R3} is the same as the voltage from B to C.)

▶ FIGURE 6–20

Illustration of voltage relationships.

3. V_{R4} is about one-third of the voltage from B to C because R_4 is about one-third of the resistance $R_4 + R_5$ (by the voltage-divider principle).

4. V_{R5} is about two-thirds of the voltage from B to C because R_5 is about two-thirds of $R_4 + R_5$.

5. $V_{R1} + V_{R3}$ equals V_S because, by Kirchhoff's voltage law, the sum of the voltage drops around a single closed path must equal the source voltage.

Example 6–9 will verify the meter readings in Figure 6–20.

EXAMPLE 6–9

Verify that the voltmeter readings in Figure 6–20 are correct. The circuit is redrawn as a schematic in Figure 6–21.

FIGURE 6–21

Solution   The resistance from A to B is the parallel combination of R_1 and R_2.

$$R_{AB} = \frac{R_1 R_2}{R_1 + R_2} = \frac{(1.0\,\text{k}\Omega)(2.2\,\text{k}\Omega)}{3.2\,\text{k}\Omega} = 688\,\Omega$$

The resistance from B to C is R_3 in parallel with the series combination of R_4 and R_5.

$$R_4 + R_5 = 330 \, \Omega + 680 \, \Omega = 1010 \, \Omega = 1.01 \, \text{k}\Omega$$

$$R_{BC} = \frac{R_3(R_4 + R_5)}{R_3 + R_4 + R_5} = \frac{(1.8 \, \text{k}\Omega)(1.01 \, \text{k}\Omega)}{2.81 \, \text{k}\Omega} = 647 \, \Omega$$

The resistance from A to B is in series with the resistance from B to C, so the total circuit resistance is

$$R_T = R_{AB} + R_{BC} = 688 \, \Omega + 647 \, \Omega = 1335 \, \Omega$$

Use the voltage-divider principle to calculate the voltages.

$$V_{AB} = \left(\frac{R_{AB}}{R_T}\right)V_S = \left(\frac{688 \, \Omega}{1335 \, \Omega}\right)10 \, \text{V} = 5.15 \, \text{V}$$

$$V_{BC} = \left(\frac{R_{BC}}{R_T}\right)V_S = \left(\frac{647 \, \Omega}{1335 \, \Omega}\right)10 \, \text{V} = 4.85 \, \text{V}$$

$$V_{R1} = V_{R2} = V_{AB} = \mathbf{5.15 \, V}$$

$$V_{R3} = V_{BC} = \mathbf{4.85 \, V}$$

$$V_{R4} = \left(\frac{R_4}{R_4 + R_5}\right)V_{BC} = \left(\frac{330 \, \Omega}{1010 \, \Omega}\right)4.85 \, \text{V} = \mathbf{1.58 \, V}$$

$$V_{R5} = \left(\frac{R_5}{R_4 + R_5}\right)V_{BC} = \left(\frac{680 \, \Omega}{1010 \, \Omega}\right)4.85 \, \text{V} = \mathbf{3.27 \, V}$$

Related Problem   Determine each voltage drop in Figure 6–21 if the source voltage is doubled.

 Open Multisim file E06-09 on your CD-ROM. Measure the voltage across each resistor and compare to the calculated values. Verify by measurement that each voltage drop doubles if the source voltage is doubled and is halved if the source voltage is halved.

EXAMPLE 6–10   Determine the voltage drop across each resistor in Figure 6–22.

▶ **FIGURE 6–22**

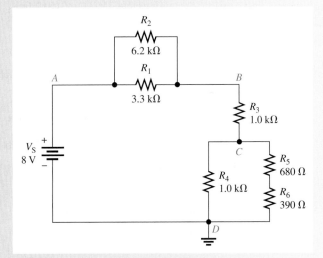

Solution   Because you know the total voltage, you can solve this problem using the voltage-divider formula.

Step 1: Reduce each parallel combination to an equivalent resistance. Since R_1 and R_2 are in parallel between nodes A and B, combine their values.

$$R_{AB} = \frac{R_1 R_2}{R_1 + R_2} + \frac{(3.3\,\text{k}\Omega)(6.2\,\text{k}\Omega)}{9.5\,\text{k}\Omega} = 2.15\,\text{k}\Omega$$

Since R_4 is in parallel with the R_5 and R_6 series combination (R_{5+6}) between nodes C and D, combine these values.

$$R_{CD} = \frac{R_4(R_{5+6})}{R_4 + R_{5+6}} + \frac{(1.0\,\text{k}\Omega)(1.07\,\text{k}\Omega)}{2.07\,\text{k}\Omega} = 517\,\Omega$$

Step 2: Draw the equivalent circuit as shown in Figure 6–23. The total circuit resistance is

$$R_T = R_{AB} + R_3 + R_{CD} = 2.15\,\text{k}\Omega + 1.0\,\text{k}\Omega + 517\,\Omega = 3.67\,\text{k}\Omega$$

▶ FIGURE 6–23

Step 3: Apply the voltage-divider formula to solve for the voltages in the equivalent circuit.

$$V_{AB} = \left(\frac{R_{AB}}{R_T}\right)V_S = \left(\frac{2.15\,\text{k}\Omega}{3.67\,\text{k}\Omega}\right)8\,\text{V} = 4.69\,\text{V}$$

$$V_{BC} = \left(\frac{R_3}{R_T}\right)V_S = \left(\frac{1.0\,\text{k}\Omega}{3.67\,\text{k}\Omega}\right)8\,\text{V} = 2.18\,\text{V}$$

$$V_{CD} = \left(\frac{R_{CD}}{R_T}\right)V_S = \left(\frac{517\,\Omega}{3.67\,\text{k}\Omega}\right)8\,\text{V} = 1.13\,\text{V}$$

Refer to Figure 6–22. V_{AB} equals the voltage across both R_1 and R_2.

$$V_{R1} = V_{R2} = V_{AB} = \textbf{4.69\,V}$$

V_{BC} is the voltage across R_3.

$$V_{R3} = V_{BC} = \textbf{2.18\,V}$$

V_{CD} is the voltage across R_4 and also across the series combination of R_5 and R_6.

$$V_{R4} = V_{CD} = \textbf{1.13\,V}$$

Step 4: Apply the voltage-divider formula to the series combination of R_5 and R_6 to get V_{R5} and V_{R6}.

$$V_{R5} = \left(\frac{R_5}{R_5 + R_6}\right)V_{CD} = \left(\frac{680\,\Omega}{1070\,\Omega}\right)1.13\,\text{V} = \textbf{718\,mV}$$

$$V_{R6} = \left(\frac{R_6}{R_5 + R_6}\right)V_{CD} = \left(\frac{390\,\Omega}{1070\,\Omega}\right)1.13\,\text{V} = \textbf{412\,mV}$$

Related Problem Determine the current and power in each resistor in Figure 6–22.

Open Multisim file E06-10 on your CD-ROM. Measure the voltage across each resistor and compare to the calculated values. If R_4 is increased to 2.2 kΩ, specify which voltage drops increase and which ones decrease. Verify this by measurement.

SECTION 6–2 REVIEW

1. Find the total resistance between A and B in the circuit of Figure 6–24.
2. Find the current through R_3 in Figure 6–24.
3. Find V_{R2} in Figure 6–24.
4. Determine R_T and I_T in Figure 6–25.

▲ FIGURE 6–24   ▲ FIGURE 6–25

6–3 VOLTAGE DIVIDERS WITH RESISTIVE LOADS

Voltage dividers were introduced in Chapter 4. In this section, you will learn how resistive loads affect the operation of voltage-divider circuits.

After completing this section, you should be able to

◆ **Analyze loaded voltage dividers**

  ◆ Determine the effect of a resistive load on a voltage-divider circuit

  ◆ Define *bleeder current*

The voltage divider in Figure 6–26(a) produces an output voltage (V_{OUT}) of 5 V because the input is 10 V and the two resistors are of equal value. This voltage is the unloaded output voltage. When a load resistor, R_L, is connected from the output to ground as shown in Figure 6–26(b), the output voltage is reduced by an amount that depends on the value of R_L. This effect is called **loading**. The load resistor is in parallel with R_2, reducing the resistance from node A to ground and, as a result, also reducing the voltage across the parallel combination. This is one effect of loading a voltage divider. Another effect of a load is that more current is drawn from the source because the total resistance of the circuit is reduced.

The larger R_L is, compared to R_2, the less the output voltage is reduced from its unloaded value, as illustrated in Figure 6–27. When two resistors are connected in parallel and one of the resistors is much greater than the other, the total resistance is close to the value of the smaller resistance.

▶ FIGURE 6–26

A voltage divider with both unloaded and loaded outputs.

(a) Unloaded

(b) Loaded

(a) No load

(b) R_L not significantly greater than R_2

(c) R_L much greater than R_2

▲ FIGURE 6–27

The effect of a load resistor.

EXAMPLE 6–11

(a) Determine the unloaded output voltage of the voltage divider in Figure 6–28.

(b) Find the loaded output voltages of the voltage divider in Figure 6–28 for the following two values of load resistance: $R_L = 10\,\text{k}\Omega$ and $R_L = 100\,\text{k}\Omega$.

▶ FIGURE 6–28

Solution   (a) The unloaded output voltage is

$$V_{OUT(unloaded)} = \left(\frac{R_2}{R_1 + R_2}\right)V_S = \left(\frac{10\,\text{k}\Omega}{14.7\,\text{k}\Omega}\right)5\,\text{V} = \mathbf{3.40\ V}$$

(b) With the 10 kΩ load resistor connected, R_L is in parallel with R_2, which gives

$$R_2 \parallel R_L = \frac{R_2 R_L}{R_2 + R_L} = \frac{(10\,\text{k}\Omega)(10\,\text{k}\Omega)}{20\,\text{k}\Omega} = 5.0\,\text{k}\Omega$$

The equivalent circuit is shown in Figure 6–29(a). The loaded output voltage is

$$V_{OUT(loaded)} = \left(\frac{R_2 \parallel R_L}{R_1 + R_2 \parallel R_L}\right)V_S = \left(\frac{5.0\,\text{k}\Omega}{9.7\,\text{k}\Omega}\right)5\,\text{V} = \mathbf{2.58\ V}$$

FIGURE 6–29

(a) $R_L = 10 \text{ k}\Omega$ (b) $R_L = 100 \text{ k}\Omega$

With the $100 \text{ k}\Omega$ load, the resistance from output to ground is

$$R_2 \parallel R_L = \frac{R_2 R_L}{R_2 + R_L} = \frac{(10 \text{ k}\Omega)(100 \text{ k}\Omega)}{110 \text{ k}\Omega} = 9.1 \text{ k}\Omega$$

The equivalent circuit is shown in Figure 6–29(b). The loaded output voltage is

$$V_{\text{OUT(loaded)}} = \left(\frac{R_2 \parallel R_L}{R_1 + R_2 \parallel R_L} \right) V_S = \left(\frac{9.1 \text{ k}\Omega}{13.8 \text{ k}\Omega} \right) 5 \text{ V} = \mathbf{3.30 \text{ V}}$$

For the smaller value of R_L, the reduction in V_{OUT} is

$$3.40 \text{ V} - 2.58 \text{ V} = 0.82 \text{ V}$$

For the larger value of R_L, the reduction in V_{OUT} is

$$3.40 \text{ V} - 3.30 \text{ V} = 0.10 \text{ V}$$

This illustrates the loading effect of R_L on the voltage divider.

Related Problem   Determine V_{OUT} in Figure 6–28 for a $1.0 \text{ M}\Omega$ load resistance.

Open Multisim file E06-11 on your CD-ROM. Measure the voltage at the output terminal with respect to ground. Connect a $10 \text{ k}\Omega$ load resistor from the output to ground and measure the output voltage. Change the load resistor to $100 \text{ k}\Omega$ and measure the output voltage. Do these measurements agree closely with the calculated values?

Load Current and Bleeder Current

In a multiple-tap loaded voltage-divider circuit, the total current drawn from the source consists of currents through the load resistors, called **load currents**, and the divider resistors. Figure 6–30 shows a voltage divider with two voltage outputs or taps. Notice that the

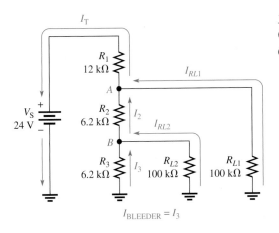

◀ FIGURE 6–30

Currents in a two-tap loaded voltage divider.

total current, I_T, is through R_1. The total current is composed of the two branch currents, I_{RL1} and I_2. The current I_2 is composed of two additional branch currents, I_{RL2} and I_3. Current I_3 is called the **bleeder current**, which is the current left after the total load current is subtracted from the total current in the circuit.

Equation 6–1

$$I_{BLEEDER} = I_T - I_{RL1} - I_{RL2}$$

EXAMPLE 6–12

Determine the load currents I_{RL1} and I_{RL2} and the bleeder current I_3 in the two-tap loaded voltage divider in Figure 6–30.

Solution

The equivalent resistance from node A to ground is the 100 kΩ load resistor R_{L1} in parallel with the combination of R_2 in series with the parallel combination of R_3 and R_{L2}. Determine the resistance values first. R_3 in parallel with R_{L2} is designated R_B. The resulting equivalent circuit is shown in Figure 6–31(a).

$$R_B = \frac{R_3 R_{L2}}{R_3 + R_{L2}} = \frac{(6.2\ \text{k}\Omega)(100\ \text{k}\Omega)}{106.2\ \text{k}\Omega} = 5.84\ \text{k}\Omega$$

R_2 in series with R_B is designated R_{2+B}. The resulting equivalent circuit is shown in Figure 6–31(b).

$$R_{2+B} = R_2 + R_B = 6.2\ \text{k}\Omega + 5.84\ \text{k}\Omega = 12.0\ \text{k}\Omega$$

R_{L1} in parallel with R_{2+B} is designated R_A. The resulting equivalent circuit is shown in Figure 6–31(c).

$$R_A = \frac{R_{L1} R_{2+B}}{R_{L1} + R_{2+B}} = \frac{(100\ \text{k}\Omega)(12.0\ \text{k}\Omega)}{112\ \text{k}\Omega} = 10.7\ \text{k}\Omega$$

R_A is the total resistance from node A to ground. The total resistance for the circuit is

$$R_T = R_A + R_1 = 10.7\ \text{k}\Omega + 12\ \text{k}\Omega = 22.7\ \text{k}\Omega$$

(a)   (b)   (c)

▲ **FIGURE 6–31**

Determine the voltage across R_{L1} as follows, using the equivalent circuit in Figure 6–31(c):

$$V_{RL1} = V_A = \left(\frac{R_A}{R_T}\right)V_S = \left(\frac{10.7\ \text{k}\Omega}{22.7\ \text{k}\Omega}\right)24\ \text{V} = 11.3\ \text{V}$$

The load current through R_{L1} is

$$I_{RL1} = \frac{V_{RL1}}{R_{L1}} = \left(\frac{11.3 \text{ V}}{100 \text{ k}\Omega}\right) = \mathbf{113 \ \mu A}$$

Determine the voltage at node B by using the equivalent circuit in Figure 6–31(a) and the voltage at node A.

$$V_B = \left(\frac{R_B}{R_{2+B}}\right)V_A = \left(\frac{5.84 \text{ k}\Omega}{12.0 \text{ k}\Omega}\right)11.3 \text{ V} = 5.50 \text{ V}$$

The load current through R_{L2} is

$$I_{RL2} = \frac{V_{RL2}}{R_{L2}} = \frac{V_B}{R_{L2}} = \frac{5.50 \text{ V}}{100 \text{ k}\Omega} = \mathbf{55 \ \mu A}$$

The bleeder current is

$$I_3 = \frac{V_B}{R_3} = \frac{5.50 \text{ V}}{6.2 \text{ k}\Omega} = \mathbf{887 \ \mu A}$$

Related Problem   How can the bleeder current in Figure 6–30 be reduced without affecting the load currents?

 Open Multisim file E06-12 on your CD-ROM. Measure the voltage across and the current through each load resistor, R_{L1} and R_{L2}.

Bipolar Voltage Dividers

An example of a voltage divider that produces both positive and negative voltages from a single source is shown in Figure 6–32. Notice that neither the positive nor the negative terminal of the source is connected to reference ground or common. The voltages at nodes A and B are positive with respect to ground, and the voltages at nodes C and D are negative with respect to ground.

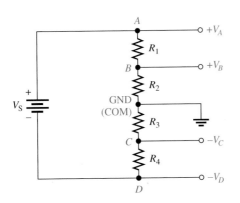

◀ **FIGURE 6–32**

A bipolar voltage divider. The positive and negative voltages are with respect to reference ground.

SECTION 6–3 REVIEW

1. A load resistor is connected to an output on a voltage divider. What effect does the load resistor have on the output voltage?

2. A larger-value load resistor will cause the output voltage of a voltage divider to change less than a small-value one will.   (True or False)

3. For the voltage divider in Figure 6–33, determine the unloaded output voltage. Also determine the output voltage with a 10 MΩ load resistor connected from the output to ground.

FIGURE 6–33

R_1 56 kΩ

30 V

R_2 100 kΩ   Output

6–4   LOADING EFFECT OF A VOLTMETER

As you have learned, voltmeters must be connected in parallel with a resistor in order to measure the voltage across the resistor. Because of its internal resistance, a voltmeter, or any other measuring instrument for that matter, puts a load on the circuit and will affect, to a certain extent, the voltage that is being measured. Until now, we have ignored the loading effect because the internal resistance of a voltmeter is very high, and normally it has negligible effect on the circuit that is being measured. However, if the internal resistance of the voltmeter is not sufficiently greater than the circuit resistance across which it is connected, the loading effect will cause the measured voltage to be less than its actual value.

After completing this section, you should be able to

◆ **Determine the loading effect of a voltmeter on a circuit**

  ◆ Explain why a voltmeter can load a circuit

  ◆ Discuss the internal resistance of a voltmeter

When a voltmeter is connected to a circuit as shown, for example, in Figure 6–34(a), its internal resistance appears in parallel with R_3, as shown in part (b). The resistance from A to B is altered by the loading effect of the voltmeter's internal resistance, R_M, and is equal to $R_3 \| R_M$, as indicated in part (c).

If R_M is much greater than R_3, the resistance from A to B changes very little, and the meter reading is very close to the actual voltage. If R_M is not sufficiently greater than R_3, the resistance from A to B is reduced significantly, and the voltage across R_3 is altered by the loading effect of the meter. A good rule of thumb is that *if the meter resistance is at least ten times greater than the resistance across which it is connected, the loading effect can be neglected (measurement error is less than 10%).*

The basic categories of voltmeters are the electromagnetic (needle-type) analog voltmeter, whose internal resistance is determined by its **sensitivity factor,** and the digital voltmeter, whose internal resistance is typically at least 10 MΩ. The digital voltmeter presents fewer loading problems than the electromagnetic type because its internal resistance is much higher.

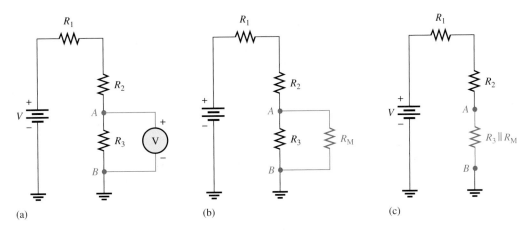

▲ FIGURE 6–34

The loading effect of a voltmeter.

EXAMPLE 6–13

How much does the digital voltmeter affect the voltage being measured for each circuit indicated in Figure 6–35? Assume the meter has an input resistance (R_M) of 10 MΩ.

▶ FIGURE 6–35

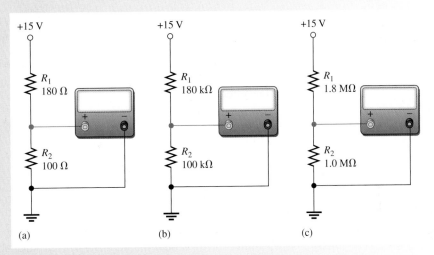

Solution   To show the small differences more clearly, the results are expressed in more than three significant digits in this example.

(a) Refer to Figure 6–35(a). The unloaded voltage across R_2 in the voltage-divider circuit is

$$V_{R2} = \left(\frac{R_2}{R_1 + R_2}\right)V_S = \left(\frac{100\ \Omega}{280\ \Omega}\right)15\ V = 5.357\ V$$

The meter's resistance in parallel with R_2 is

$$R_2 \parallel R_M = \left(\frac{R_2 R_M}{R_2 + R_M}\right) = \frac{(100\ \Omega)(10\ M\Omega)}{10.0001\ M\Omega} = 99.999\ \Omega$$

The voltage actually measured by the meter is

$$V_{R2} = \left(\frac{R_2 \parallel R_M}{R_1 + R_2 \parallel R_M}\right)V_S = \left(\frac{99.999\ \Omega}{279.999\ \Omega}\right)15\ V = 5.357\ V$$

The voltmeter has no measurable loading effect.

(b) Refer to Figure 6–35(b).

$$V_{R2} = \left(\frac{R_2}{R_1 + R_2}\right)V_S = \left(\frac{100\,k\Omega}{280\,k\Omega}\right)15\,V = 5.357\,V$$

$$R_2 \| R_M = \frac{R_2 R_M}{R_2 + R_M} = \frac{(100\,k\Omega)(10\,M\Omega)}{10.1\,M\Omega} = 99.01\,k\Omega$$

The voltage actually measured by the meter is

$$V_{R2} = \left(\frac{R_2 \| R_M}{R_1 + R_2 \| R_M}\right)V_S = \left(\frac{99.01\,k\Omega}{279.01\,k\Omega}\right)15\,V = 5.323\,V$$

The loading effect of the voltmeter reduces the voltage by a very small amount.

(c) Refer to Figure 6–35(c).

$$V_{R2} = \left(\frac{R_2}{R_1 + R_2}\right)V_S = \left(\frac{1.0\,M\Omega}{2.8\,M\Omega}\right)15\,V = 5.357\,V$$

$$R_2 \| R_M = \frac{R_2 R_M}{R_2 + R_M} = \frac{(1.0\,M\Omega)(10\,M\Omega)}{11\,M\Omega} = 909.09\,k\Omega$$

The voltage actually measured is

$$V_{R2} = \left(\frac{R_2 \| R_M}{R_1 + R_2 \| R_M}\right)V_S = \left(\frac{909.09\,k\Omega}{2.709\,M\Omega}\right)15\,V = 5.034\,V$$

The loading effect of the voltmeter reduces the voltage by a noticeable amount. As you can see, the higher the resistance across which a voltage is measured, the more the loading effect.

Related Problem Calculate the voltage across R_2 in Figure 6–35(c) if the meter resistance is 20 MΩ.

**SECTION 6–4
REVIEW**

1. Explain why a voltmeter can potentially load a circuit.
2. If a voltmeter with a 10 MΩ internal resistance is measuring the voltage across a 1.0 kΩ resistor, should you normally be concerned about the loading effect?
3. If a voltmeter with a 10 MΩ resistance is measuring the voltage across a 3.3 MΩ resistor, should you be concerned about the loading effect?

6–5 THE WHEATSTONE BRIDGE

The Wheatstone bridge circuit can be used to precisely measure resistance. However, the bridge is most commonly used in conjunction with transducers to measure physical quantities such as strain, temperature, and pressure. **Transducers** are devices that sense a change in a physical parameter and convert that change into an electrical quantity such as a change in resistance. For example, a strain gauge exhibits a change in resistance when it is exposed to mechanical factors such as force, pressure, or displacement. A thermistor exhibits a change in its resistance when it is exposed to a change in temperature. The Wheatstone bridge can be operated in a balanced or an unbalanced condition. The condition of operation depends on the type of application.

After completing this section, you should be able to

◆ **Analyze and apply a Wheatstone bridge**

  ◆ Determine when a bridge is balanced

  ◆ Determine an unknown resistance with a balanced bridge

  ◆ Determine when a bridge is unbalanced

  ◆ Discuss measurements using an unbalanced bridge

A **Wheatstone bridge** circuit is shown in its most common "diamond" configuration in Figure 6–36(a). It consists of four resistors and a dc voltage source connected across the top and bottom points of the "diamond." The output voltage is taken across the left and right points of the "diamond" between A and B. In part (b), the circuit is drawn in a slightly different way to more clearly show its series-parallel configuration.

(a)   (b)

◀ **FIGURE 6–36**

Wheatstone bridge.

The Balanced Wheatstone Bridge

The Wheatstone bridge in Figure 6–36 is in the **balanced bridge** condition when the output voltage (V_{OUT}) between terminals A and B is equal to zero.

$$V_{OUT} = 0 \text{ V}$$

When the bridge is balanced, the voltages across R_1 and R_2 are equal ($V_1 = V_2$) and the voltages across R_3 and R_4 are equal ($V_3 = V_4$). Therefore, the voltage ratios can be written as

$$\frac{V_1}{V_3} = \frac{V_2}{V_4}$$

Substituting IR for V by Ohm's law gives

$$\frac{I_1R_1}{I_3R_3} = \frac{I_2R_2}{I_4R_4}$$

Since $I_1 = I_3$ and $I_2 = I_4$, all the current terms cancel, leaving the resistor ratios.

$$\frac{R_1}{R_3} = \frac{R_2}{R_4}$$

Solving for R_1 results in the following formula:

$$R_1 = R_3\left(\frac{R_2}{R_4}\right)$$

This formula allows you to find the value of resistor R_1 in terms of the other resistor values when the bridge is balanced. You can also find the value of any other resistor in a similar way.

Using the Balanced Wheatstone Bridge to Find an Unknown Resistance: Assume that R_1 in Figure 6–36 has an unknown value, which we call R_X. Resistors R_2 and R_4 have fixed values so that their ratio, R_2/R_4, also has a fixed value. Since R_X can be any value, R_3 must be adjusted to make $R_1/R_3 = R_2/R_4$ in order to create a balanced condition. Therefore, R_3 is a variable resistor, which we will call R_V. When R_X is placed in the bridge, R_V is adjusted until the bridge is balanced as indicated by a zero output voltage. Then, the unknown resistance is found as

Equation 6–2
$$R_X = R_V\left(\frac{R_2}{R_4}\right)$$

The ratio R_2/R_4 is the scale factor.

An older type of measuring instrument called a galvanometer can be connected between the output terminals A and B to detect a balanced condition. The galvanometer is essentially a very sensitive ammeter that senses current in either direction. It differs from a regular ammeter in that the midscale point is zero. In modern instruments, an amplifier connected across the bridge output indicates a balanced condition when its output is 0 V.

From Equation 6–2, the value of R_V at balance multiplied by the scale factor R_2/R_4 is the actual resistance value of R_X. If $R_2/R_4 = 1$, then $R_X = R_V$, if $R_2/R_4 = 0.5$, then $R_X = 0.5R_V$, and so on. In a practical bridge circuit, the position of the R_V adjustment can be calibrated to indicate the actual value of R_X on a scale or with some other method of display.

EXAMPLE 6–14

Determine the value of R_X in the balanced bridge shown in Figure 6–37. The bridge is balanced ($V_{OUT} = 0$ V) when R_V is set at 1200 Ω.

▶ FIGURE 6–37

Solution The scale factor is

$$\frac{R_2}{R_4} = \frac{150\ \Omega}{100\ \Omega} = 1.5$$

The unknown resistance is

$$R_X = R_V\left(\frac{R_2}{R_4}\right) = (1200\ \Omega)(1.5) = \mathbf{1800\ \Omega}$$

Related Problem If R_V must be adjusted to 2.2 kΩ to balance the bridge in Figure 6–37, what is R_X?

The Unbalanced Wheatstone Bridge

An **unbalanced bridge** condition occurs when V_{OUT} is not equal to zero. The unbalanced bridge is used to measure several types of physical quantities such as mechanical strain, temperature, or pressure. This can be done by connecting a transducer in one leg of the bridge, as shown in Figure 6–38. The resistance of the transducer changes proportionally to the changes in the parameter that it is measuring. If the bridge is balanced at a known point, then the amount of deviation from the balanced condition, as indicated by the output voltage, indicates the amount of change in the parameter being measured. Therefore, the value of the parameter being measured can be determined by the amount that the bridge is unbalanced.

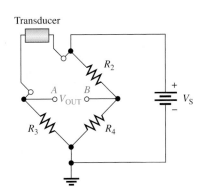

◀ FIGURE 6–38

A bridge circuit for measuring a physical parameter using a transducer.

A Bridge Circuit for Measuring Temperature If temperature is to be measured, the transducer can be a thermistor, which is a temperature-sensitive resistor. The thermistor resistance changes in a predictable way as the temperature changes. A change in temperature causes a change in thermistor resistance, which causes a corresponding change in the output voltage of the bridge as it becomes unbalanced. The output voltage is proportional to the temperature; therefore, either a voltmeter connected across the output can be calibrated to show the temperature or the output voltage can be amplified and converted to digital form to drive a readout display of the temperature.

A bridge circuit used to measure temperature is designed so that it is balanced at a reference temperature and becomes unbalanced at a measured temperature. For example, let's say the bridge is to be balanced at 25°C. A thermistor will have a known value of resistance at 25°C.

EXAMPLE 6–15

Determine the output voltage of the temperature-measuring bridge circuit in Figure 6–39 if the thermistor is exposed to a temperature of 50°C and its resistance at 25°C is 1.0 kΩ. Assume the resistance of the thermistor decreases to 900 Ω at 50°C.

▶ FIGURE 6–39

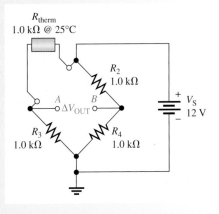

Solution   Apply the voltage-divider formula to the left side of the bridge at 50°C.

$$V_A = \left(\frac{R_3}{R_3 + R_{\text{therm}}}\right)V_S = \left(\frac{1 \text{ k}\Omega}{1 \text{ k}\Omega + 900 \text{ }\Omega}\right)12 \text{ V} = 6.32 \text{ V}$$

Apply the voltage-divider formula to the right side of the bridge.

$$V_B = \left(\frac{R_4}{R_2 + R_4}\right)V_S = \left(\frac{1 \text{ k}\Omega}{2 \text{ k}\Omega}\right)12 \text{ V} = 6.00 \text{ V}$$

The output voltage at 50°C is the difference between V_A and V_B.

$$V_{\text{OUT}} = V_A - V_B = 6.32 \text{ V} - 6.00 \text{ V} = \mathbf{0.32 \text{ V}}$$

Node *A* is positive with respect to node *B*.

Related Problem   If the temperature is increased to 60°C, causing the thermistor resistance in Figure 6–39 to decrease to 850 Ω, what is V_{OUT}?

Other Unbalanced Wheatstone Bridge Applications   A Wheatstone bridge with a strain gauge can be used to measure certain forces. A **strain gauge** is a device that exhibits a change in resistance when it is compressed or stretched by the application of an external force. As the resistance of the strain gauge changes, the previously balanced bridge becomes unbalanced. This unbalance causes the output voltage to change from zero, and this change can be measured to determine the amount of strain. In strain gauges, the resistance change is extremely small. This tiny change unbalances a Wheatstone bridge because of its high sensitivity. For example, Wheatstone bridges with strain gauges are commonly used in weight scales.

Some resistive transducers have extremely small resistance changes, and these changes are difficult to measure accurately with a direct measurement. In particular, strain gauges are one of the most useful resistive transducers that convert the stretching or compression of a fine wire into a change in resistance. When strain causes the wire in the gauge to stretch, the resistance increases a small amount and when it compresses, the resistance of the wire decreases.

Strain gauges are used in many types of scales, from those that are used for weighing small parts to those for weighing huge trucks. Typically, the gauges are mounted on a special block of aluminum that deforms when a weight is on the scale. The strain gauges are extremely delicate and must be mounted properly, so the entire assembly is generally prepared as a single unit called a load cell. A wide variety of load cells with different shapes and sizes are available from manufacturers depending on the application. A typical S-shaped load cell for a weighing application that has four strain gauges is illustrated in Figure 6–40(a). The gauges are mounted so that two of the gauges stretch (tension) when a load is placed on the scale and two of the gauges compress.

Load cells are usually connected to a Wheatstone bridge as shown in Figure 6–40(b) with strain gauges (SG) in tension (*T*) and compression (*C*) in opposite diagonal legs as shown. The output of the bridge is normally digitized and converted to a reading for a display or sent to a computer for processing. The major advantage of the Wheatstone bridge circuit is that it is capable of accurately measuring very small differences in resistance. The use of four active transducers increases the sensitivity of the measurement and makes the bridge the ideal circuit for instrumentation. The Wheatstone bridge circuit has the added benefit of compensating for temperature variations and wire resistance of connecting wires that would otherwise contribute to inaccuracies.

Applied force

Strain gauges (SG)

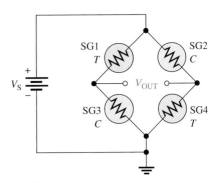

(a) A typical load cell with four active strain gauges
(two compression and two tension)

(b) Wheatstone bridge

In addition to scales, strain gauges are used with Wheatstone bridges in other types of measurements including pressure measurements, displacement and acceleration measurements to name a few. In pressure measurements, the strain gauges are bonded to a flexible diaphragm that stretches when pressure is applied to the transducer. The amount of flexing is related to the pressure, which again converts to a very small resistance change.

SECTION 6–5 REVIEW	1. Draw a basic Wheatstone bridge circuit.
	2. Under what condition is a bridge balanced?
	3. What is the unknown resistance in Figure 6–37 when $R_V = 3.3\,k\Omega$, $R_2 = 10\,k\Omega$, and $R_4 = 2.2\,k\Omega$?
	4. How is a Wheatstone bridge used in the unbalanced condition?

6–6 THEVENIN'S THEOREM

Thevenin's theorem provides a method for simplifying a circuit to a standard equivalent form. In many cases, this theorem can be used to simplify the analysis of series-parallel circuits. Another method for simplifying a circuit to an equivalent form is Norton's theorem, which is covered in Appendix C.

After completing this section, you should be able to

◆ **Apply Thevenin's theorem to simplify a circuit for analysis**

  ◆ Describe the form of a Thevenin equivalent circuit

  ◆ Obtain the Thevenin equivalent voltage source

  ◆ Obtain the Thevenin equivalent resistance

  ◆ Explain terminal equivalency in the context of Thevenin's theorem

  ◆ Thevenize a portion of a circuit

  ◆ Thevenize a Wheatstone bridge

▲ FIGURE 6–41

The general form of a Thevenin equivalent circuit is a voltage source in series with a resistance.

The Thevenin equivalent form of any two-terminal resistive circuit consists of an equivalent voltage source (V_{TH}) and an equivalent resistance (R_{TH}), arranged as shown in Figure 6–41. The values of the equivalent voltage and resistance depend on the values in the original circuit. Any two-terminal resistive circuit can be simplified to a Thevenin equivalent regardless of its complexity.

The equivalent voltage, V_{TH}, is one part of the complete Thevenin equivalent circuit. The other part is R_{TH}.

The Thevenin equivalent voltage (V_{TH}) is the open circuit (no-load) voltage between two specified output terminals in a circuit.

Any component connected between these two terminals effectively "sees" V_{TH} in series with R_{TH}. As defined by **Thevenin's theorem**,

The Thevenin equivalent resistance (R_{TH}) is the total resistance appearing between two specified output terminals in a circuit with all sources replaced by their internal resistances (which for an ideal voltage source is zero).

Although a Thevenin equivalent circuit is not of the same form as the original circuit, it acts the same in terms of the output voltage and current. Consider the following demonstration as illustrated in Figure 6–42. A resistive circuit of any complexity is placed in a box with only the output terminals exposed. The Thevenin equivalent of that circuit is placed in an identical box with, again, only the output terminals exposed. Identical load resistors are connected across the output terminals of each box. Next, a voltmeter and an ammeter are connected to measure the voltage and current for each load as shown in the figure. The measured values will be identical (neglecting tolerance variations), and you will not be able to determine which box contains the original circuit and which contains the Thevenin equivalent of the original circuit. That is, in terms of what you can observe by electrical measurement, both circuits appear to be the same. This condition is sometimes known as **terminal equivalency** because both circuits look the same from the "viewpoint" of the two output terminals.

▷ FIGURE 6–42

Which box contains the original circuit and which contains the Thevenin equivalent circuit? You cannot tell by observing the meters because the circuits have terminal equivalency.

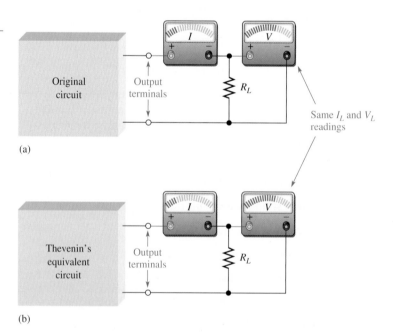

(a)

(b)

To find the Thevenin equivalent of any circuit, you must determine the equivalent voltage, V_{TH}, and the equivalent resistance, R_{TH}. For example, the Thevenin equivalent for the circuit between output terminals A and B is developed in Figure 6–43.

(a) Finding V_{TH}

$$V_{TH} = V_{R2} = \left(\frac{R_2}{R_1 + R_2}\right)V_S$$

(b) Finding R_{TH}

$$R_{TH} = R_3 + R_1 \| R_2$$

(c) Thevenin equivalent circuit

▲ FIGURE 6–43

Example of the simplification of a circuit by Thevenin's theorem.

In Figure 6–43(a), the voltage across the designated terminals A and B is the Thevenin equivalent voltage. In this particular circuit, the voltage from A to B is the same as the voltage across R_2 because there is no current through R_3 and, therefore, no voltage drop across it. V_{TH} is expressed as follows for this particular example:

$$V_{TH} = \left(\frac{R_2}{R_1 + R_2}\right)V_S$$

In Figure 6–43(b), the resistance between terminals A and B with the source replaced by a short to represent its zero internal resistance is the Thevenin equivalent resistance. In this particular circuit, the resistance from A to B is R_3 in series with the parallel combination of R_1 and R_2. Therefore, R_{TH} is expressed as follows:

$$R_{TH} = R_3 + \frac{R_1 R_2}{R_1 + R_2}$$

The Thevenin equivalent circuit is shown in Figure 6–43(c).

EXAMPLE 6–16

Find the Thevenin equivalent circuit between the output terminals A and B of the circuit in Figure 6–44. If there were a load resistance connected across terminals A and B, it would first have to be removed.

▶ FIGURE 6–44

Solution   Since there is no voltage drop across R_4, V_{AB}, equals the voltage across $R_2 + R_3$ and $V_{TH} = V_{AB}$, as shown in Figure 6–45(a). Use the voltage-divider principle to find V_{TH}.

$$V_{TH} = \left(\frac{R_2 + R_3}{R_1 + R_2 + R_3} \right) V_S = \left(\frac{69\ \Omega}{169\ \Omega} \right) 10\ V = \mathbf{4.08\ V}$$

(a) The voltage from A to B is V_{TH} and equals V_{2+3}.

(b) Looking from terminals A and B, R_4 appears in series with the combination of R_1 in parallel with ($R_2 + R_3$).

(c) Thevenin equivalent circuit

▲ FIGURE 6–45

To find R_{TH}, first replace the source with a short to simulate a zero internal resistance. Then R_1 appears in parallel with $R_2 + R_3$, and R_4 is in series with the series-parallel combination of R_1, R_2, and R_3 as indicated in Figure 6–45(b).

$$R_{TH} = R_4 + \frac{R_1(R_2 + R_3)}{R_1 + R_2 + R_3} = 100\ \Omega + \frac{(100\ \Omega)(69\ \Omega)}{169\ \Omega} = \mathbf{141\ \Omega}$$

The resulting Thevenin equivalent circuit is shown in Figure 6–45(c).

Related Problem   Determine V_{TH} and R_{TH} if a 56 Ω resistor is connected in parallel across R_2 and R_3 in Figure 6–44.

Thevenin Equivalency Depends on the Viewpoint

The Thevenin equivalent for any circuit depends on the location of the two output terminals from which the circuit is "viewed." In Figure 6–44, you viewed the circuit from between the two terminals labeled A and B. Any given circuit can have more than one Thevenin equivalent, depending on how the output terminals are designated. For example, if you view the circuit in Figure 6–46 from between terminals A and C, you obtain a completely different result than if you view it from between terminals A and B or from between terminals B and C.

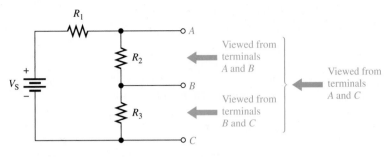

▲ FIGURE 6–46

Thevenin's equivalent depends on the output terminals from which the circuit is viewed.

In Figure 6–47(a), when viewed from between terminals A and C, V_{TH} is the voltage across $R_2 + R_3$ and can be expressed using the voltage-divider formula as

$$V_{TH(AC)} = \left(\frac{R_2 + R_3}{R_1 + R_2 + R_3}\right)V_S$$

Also, as shown in Figure 6–47(b), the resistance between terminals A and C is $R_2 + R_3$ in parallel with R_1 (the source is replaced by a short) and can be expressed as

$$R_{TH(AC)} = R_1 \parallel (R_2 + R_3) = \frac{R_1(R_2 + R_3)}{R_1 + R_2 + R_3}$$

The resulting Thevenin equivalent circuit is shown in Figure 6–47(c).

When viewed from between terminals B and C as indicated in Figure 6–47(d), $V_{TH(BC)}$ is the voltage across R_3 and can be expressed as

$$V_{TH(BC)} = \left(\frac{R_3}{R_1 + R_2 + R_3}\right)V_S$$

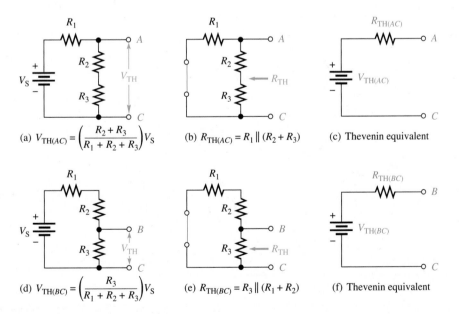

(a) $V_{TH(AC)} = \left(\dfrac{R_2 + R_3}{R_1 + R_2 + R_3}\right)V_S$

(b) $R_{TH(AC)} = R_1 \parallel (R_2 + R_3)$

(c) Thevenin equivalent

(d) $V_{TH(BC)} = \left(\dfrac{R_3}{R_1 + R_2 + R_3}\right)V_S$

(e) $R_{TH(BC)} = R_3 \parallel (R_1 + R_2)$

(f) Thevenin equivalent

▲ FIGURE 6–47

Example of a circuit thevenized from two different sets of terminals. Parts (a), (b), and (c) illustrate one set of terminals and parts (d), (e), and (f) illustrate another set of terminals. (The V_{TH} and R_{TH} values are different for each case.)

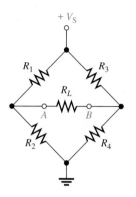

A Wheatstone bridge with a load resistor connected between the output terminals is not a straight-forward series-parallel circuit.

As shown in Figure 6–47(e), the resistance between terminals B and C is R_3 in parallel with the series combination of R_1 and R_2.

$$R_{TH(BC)} = R_3 \| (R_1 + R_2) = \frac{R_3(R_1 + R_2)}{R_1 + R_2 + R_3}$$

The resulting Thevenin equivalent is shown in Figure 6–47(f).

Thevenizing a Bridge Circuit

The usefulness of Thevenin's theorem can be illustrated when it is applied to a Wheatstone bridge circuit. For example, consider the case when a load resistor is connected to the output terminals of a Wheatstone bridge, as shown in Figure 6–48. The bridge circuit is difficult to analyze because it is not a straightforward series-parallel arrangement when a resistance, such as the very small resistance of a galvanometer, is connected between the output terminals A and B. There are no resistors that are in series or in parallel with another resistor.

Using Thevenin's theorem, you can simplify the bridge circuit to an equivalent circuit viewed from the load resistor as shown step-by-step in Figure 6–49. Study carefully the steps in this figure. Once the equivalent circuit for the bridge is found, the voltage and current for any value of load resistor can easily be determined by Ohm's law.

(a) Remove R_L to create an open circuit between the output terminals A and B.

(b) Redraw (if you wish).

(c) Find V_{TH}:
$$V_{TH} = V_A - V_B = \left(\frac{R_3}{R_1 + R_3}\right)V_S - \left(\frac{R_4}{R_2 + R_4}\right)V_S$$

(d) Replace V_S with a short to represent its zero internal resistance. *Note*: The red lines represent the same electrical point as the red lines in Part (e).

(e) Redraw (if you wish) and find R_{TH}:
$$R_{TH} = R_1 \| R_3 + R_2 \| R_4$$

(f) Thevenin's equivalent circuit (beige block) with R_L reconnected

▲ FIGURE 6–49

Simplifying a Wheatstone bridge with Thevenin's theorem.

EXAMPLE 6–17

Determine the voltage and current for the load resistor, R_L, in the bridge circuit of Figure 6–50.

▶ FIGURE 6–50

Solution

Step 1: Remove R_L to create an open circuit between A and B.

Step 2: To thevenize the bridge as viewed from between terminals A and B, as was shown in Figure 6–49, first determine V_{TH}.

$$V_{TH} = V_A - V_B = \left(\frac{R_3}{R_1 + R_3}\right)V_S - \left(\frac{R_4}{R_2 + R_4}\right)V_S$$

$$= \left(\frac{680\,\Omega}{1010\,\Omega}\right)24\,V - \left(\frac{560\,\Omega}{1240\,\Omega}\right)24\,V = 16.16\,V - 10.84\,V = 5.32\,V$$

Step 3: Determine R_{TH}.

$$R_{TH} = \frac{R_1 R_3}{R_1 + R_3} + \frac{R_2 R_4}{R_2 + R_4}$$

$$= \frac{(330\,\Omega)(680\,\Omega)}{1010\,\Omega} + \frac{(680\,\Omega)(560\,\Omega)}{1240\,\Omega} = 222\,\Omega + 307\,\Omega = 529\,\Omega$$

Step 4: Place V_{TH} and R_{TH} in series to form the Thevenin equivalent circuit.

Step 5: Connect the load resistor from terminals A to B of the equivalent circuit, and determine the load voltage and current as illustrated in Figure 6–51.

$$V_L = \left(\frac{R_L}{R_L + R_{TH}}\right)V_{TH} = \left(\frac{1.0\,k\Omega}{1.529\,k\Omega}\right)5.32\,V = \mathbf{3.48\,V}$$

$$I_L = \frac{V_L}{R_L} = \frac{3.48\,V}{1.0\,k\Omega} = \mathbf{3.48\,mA}$$

▶ FIGURE 6–51

Thevenin's equivalent for the Wheatstone bridge

Related Problem   Calculate I_L for $R_1 = 2.2\,k\Omega$, $R_2 = 3.9\,k\Omega$, $R_3 = 3.3\,k\Omega$, and $R_4 = 2.7\,k\Omega$ in Figure 6–50.

Open Multisim file E06-17 on your CD-ROM. Determine the voltage and current for R_L using a multimeter. Change the resistor values to those specified in the related problem and measure the voltage and current for R_L.

HANDS ON TIP

The Thevenin resistance of a circuit can be measured by connecting a variable resistance on the output of the circuit and adjusting the resistance until the output voltage of the circuit is one-half of its open circuit value. Now, if you remove the variable resistance and measure it, the value equals the Thevenin equivalent resistance of the circuit.

Summary of Thevenin's Theorem

Remember, the Thevenin equivalent circuit for any resistive circuit is *always* an equivalent voltage source in series with an equivalent resistance regardless of the original circuit that it replaces. The significance of Thevenin's theorem is that the equivalent circuit can replace the original circuit as far as any external load is concerned. Any load resistor connected between the terminals of a Thevenin equivalent circuit will have the same current through it and the same voltage across it as if it were connected to the terminals of the original circuit.

A summary of steps for applying Thevenin's theorem is as follows:

Step 1: Open the two terminals (remove any load) between which you want to find the Thevenin equivalent circuit.

Step 2: Determine the voltage (V_{TH}) across the two open terminals.

Step 3: Determine the resistance (R_{TH}) between the two terminals with all sources replaced by their internal resistance. (An ideal voltage source is replaced by a short.)

Step 4: Connect V_{TH} and R_{TH} in series to produce the complete Thevenin equivalent for the original circuit.

Step 5: Replace the load removed in Step 1 across the terminals of the Thevenin equivalent circuit. You can now calculate the load current and load voltage using only Ohm's law, and they have the same value as the load current and load voltage in the original circuit.

Two additional theorems are sometimes used in circuit analysis. One of these is Norton's theorem, which is similar to Thevenin's theorem except that it deals with current sources instead of voltage sources. The other is Millman's theorem, which deals with parallel voltage sources. See Appendix C for a coverage of Norton's theorem and Millman's theorem.

SECTION 6–6
REVIEW

1. What are the two components of a Thevenin equivalent circuit?
2. Draw the general from of a Thevenin equivalent circuit.
3. Define V_{TH}.
4. Define R_{TH}.
5. For the original circuit in Figure 6–52, determine the Thevenin equivalent circuit as viewed from the output terminals *A* and *B*.

FIGURE 6–52

6–7   THE MAXIMUM POWER TRANSFER THEOREM

The maximum power transfer theorem is important when you need to know the value of the load at which the most power is delivered from the source.

After completing this section, you should be able to

◆ **Apply the maximum power transfer theorem**

  ◆ State the theorem

  ◆ Determine the value of load resistance for which maximum power is transferred from a given circuit

The **maximum power transfer** theorem is stated as follows:

For a given source voltage, maximum power is transferred from a source to a load when the load resistance is equal to the internal source resistance.

The source resistance, R_S, of a circuit is the equivalent resistance as viewed from the output terminals using Thevenin's theorem. A Thevenin equivalent circuit with its output resistance and load is shown in Figure 6–53. When $R_L = R_S$, the maximum power possible is transferred from the voltage source to R_L for a given value of V_S.

Practical applications of the maximum power transfer theorem include audio systems such as stereo, radio, and public address. In these systems the resistance of the speaker is the load. The circuit that drives the speaker is a power amplifier. The systems are typically optimized for maximum power to the speakers. Thus, the resistance of the speaker must equal the internal source resistance of the amplifier.

Example 6–18 shows that maximum power occurs when $R_L = R_S$.

Source

▲ FIGURE 6–53

Maximum power is transferred to the load when $R_L = R_S$.

EXAMPLE 6–18

The source in Figure 6–54 has an internal resistance of 75 Ω. Determine the load power for each of the following values of the variable load resistance:

(a) 0 Ω   **(b)** 25 Ω   **(c)** 50 Ω   **(d)** 75 Ω   **(e)** 100 Ω   **(f)** 125 Ω

Draw a graph showing the load power versus the load resistance.

▶ FIGURE 6–54

Solution   Use Ohm's law ($I = V/R$) and the power formula ($P = I^2R$) to find the load power, P_L, for each value of load resistance.

(a) For $R_L = 0\,\Omega$,

$$I = \frac{V_S}{R_S + R_L} = \frac{10\ \text{V}}{75\ \Omega + 0\ \Omega} = 133\ \text{mA}$$

$$P_L = I^2R_L = (133\ \text{mA})^2(0\ \Omega) = 0\ \text{mW}$$

(b) For $R_L = 25\,\Omega$,

$$I = \frac{V_S}{R_S + R_L} = \frac{10\,V}{75\,\Omega + 25\,\Omega} = 100\,mA$$
$$P_L = I^2 R_L = (100\,mA)^2(25\,\Omega) = \mathbf{250\,mW}$$

(c) For $R_L = 50\,\Omega$,

$$I = \frac{V_S}{R_S + R_L} = \frac{10\,V}{125\,\Omega} = 80\,mA$$
$$P_L = I^2 R_L = (80\,mA)^2(50\,\Omega) = \mathbf{320\,mW}$$

(d) For $R_L = 75\,\Omega$,

$$I = \frac{V_S}{R_S + R_L} = \frac{10\,V}{150\,\Omega} = 66.7\,mA$$
$$P_L = I^2 R_L = (66.7\,mA)^2(75\,\Omega) = \mathbf{334\,mW}$$

(e) For $R_L = 100\,\Omega$,

$$I = \frac{V_S}{R_S + R_L} = \frac{10\,V}{175\,\Omega} = 57.1\,mA$$
$$P_L = I^2 R_L = (57.1\,mA)^2(100\,\Omega) = \mathbf{326\,mW}$$

(f) For $R_L = 125\,\Omega$,

$$I = \frac{V_S}{R_S + R_L} = \frac{10\,V}{200\,\Omega} = 50\,mA$$
$$P_L = I^2 R_L = (50\,mA)^2(125\,\Omega) = \mathbf{313\,mW}$$

Notice that the load power is greatest when $R_L = R_S = 75\,\Omega$, which is the same as the internal source resistance. When the load resistance is less than or greater than this value, the power drops off, as the curve in Figure 6–55 graphically illustrates.

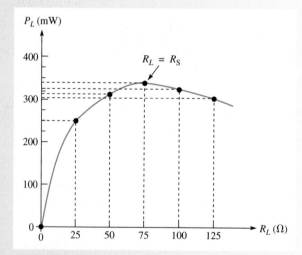

▲ **FIGURE 6–55**

Curve showing that the load power is maximum when $R_L = R_S$.

Related Problem   If the source resistance in Figure 6–54 is 600 Ω, what is the maximum power that can be delivered to a load?

**SECTION 6–7
REVIEW**

1. State the maximum power transfer theorem.
2. When is maximum power delivered from a source to a load?
3. A given circuit has an internal source resistance of 50 Ω. What will be the value of the load to which the maximum power is delivered?

6–8 THE SUPERPOSITION THEOREM

Some circuits require more than one voltage or current source. For example, most amplifiers operate with two voltage sources: an ac and a dc source. Additionally, some amplifiers require both a positive and a negative dc voltage source for proper operation. When multiple sources are used in a circuit, the superposition theorem provides a method for analysis.

After completing this section, you should be able to

◆ **Apply the superposition theorem to circuit analysis**

   ◆ State the superposition theorem

   ◆ List the steps in applying the theorem

The **superposition** theorem is a way to determine currents in a circuit with multiple sources by leaving one source at a time and replacing the other sources by their internal resistances. Recall that the ideal voltage source has a zero internal resistance and the ideal current source has infinite internal resistance. All sources will be treated as ideal in order to simplify the coverage.

A general statement of the superposition theorem is as follows:

The current in any given branch of a multiple-source linear circuit can be found by determining the currents in that particular branch produced by each source acting alone, with all other sources replaced by their internal resistances. The total current in the branch is the algebraic sum of the individual source currents in that branch.

The steps in applying the superposition theorem are as follows:

Step 1: Leave one voltage (or current) source at a time in the circuit and replace each of the other voltage (or current) sources with its internal resistance. For ideal sources, a short represents zero internal resistance and an open represents infinite internal resistance.

Step 2: Determine the particular current (or voltage) that you want to find just as if there were only one source in the circuit. This is a component of the total current or voltage that you are looking for.

Step 3: Take the next source in the circuit and repeat Steps 1 and 2 for each source.

Step 4: To find the actual current in a given branch, add or subtract the component currents due to each individual source. If the currents are in the same direction, add them. If the currents are in opposite directions, subtract them with the direction of the resulting current the same as the larger of the individual currents. Once you find the current, you can determine the voltage using Ohm's law.

The approach to superposition is illustrated in Figure 6–56 for a series-parallel circuit with two ideal voltage sources. Study the steps in this figure.

(a) Problem: Find I_2.

(b) Replace V_{S2} with zero resistance (short).

(c) Find R_T and I_T looking from V_{S1}:
$$R_{T(S1)} = R_1 + R_2 \| R_3$$
$$I_{T(S1)} = V_{S1}/R_{T(S1)}$$

(d) Find I_2 due to V_{S1}:
$$I_{2(S1)} = \left(\frac{R_3}{R_2 + R_3}\right) I_{T(S1)}$$

(e) Replace V_{S1} with zero resistance (short).

(f) Find R_T and I_T looking from V_{S2}:
$$R_{T(S2)} = R_3 + R_1 \| R_2$$
$$I_{T(S2)} = V_{S2}/R_{T(S2)}$$

(g) Find I_2 due to V_{S2}:
$$I_{2(S2)} = \left(\frac{R_1}{R_1 + R_2}\right) I_{T(S2)}$$

(h) Restore the original sources. Add $I_{2(S1)}$ and $I_{2(S2)}$ to get the actual I_2 (they are in same direction):
$$I_2 = I_{2(S1)} + I_{2(S2)}$$

▲ FIGURE 6–56

Illustration of the superposition theorem.

EXAMPLE 6–19

Use the superposition theorem to find the current through R_2 and the voltage across it in Figure 6–57.

▲ FIGURE 6–57

Solution **Step 1:** Replace V_{S2} with a short to represent its zero internal resistance and find the current through R_2 due to voltage source V_{S1}, as shown in Figure 6–58. To find I_2, use the current-divider formula. Looking from V_{S1},

$$R_{T(S1)} = R_1 + \frac{R_3}{2} = 100 \ \Omega + 50 \ \Omega = 150 \ \Omega$$

$$I_{T(S1)} = \frac{V_{S1}}{R_{T(S1)}} = \frac{10 \text{ V}}{150 \ \Omega} = 66.7 \text{ mA}$$

▲ FIGURE 6–58

The component of the total current through R_2 due to V_{S1} is

$$I_{2(S1)} = \left(\frac{R_3}{R_2 + R_3}\right)I_{T(S1)} = \left(\frac{100\,\Omega}{200\,\Omega}\right)66.7\,\text{mA} = 33.3\,\text{mA}$$

Note that this current is upward through R_2.

Step 2: Find the current through R_2 due to voltage source V_{S2} by replacing V_{S1} with a short, as shown in Figure 6–59. Looking from V_{S2},

$$R_{T(S2)} = R_3 + \frac{R_1}{2} = 100\,\Omega + 50\,\Omega = 150\,\Omega$$

$$I_{T(S2)} = \frac{V_{S2}}{R_{T(S2)}} = \frac{5\,\text{V}}{150\,\Omega} = 33.3\,\text{mA}$$

The component of the total current through R_2 due to V_{S2} is

$$I_{2(S2)} = \left(\frac{R_1}{R_1 + R_2}\right)I_{T(S2)} = \left(\frac{100\,\Omega}{200\,\Omega}\right)33.3\,\text{mA} = 16.7\,\text{mA}$$

Note that this current is upward through R_2.

▲ FIGURE 6–59

Step 3: Both component currents are upward through R_2, so they have the same algebraic sign. Therefore, add the values to get the total current through R_2.

$$I_{2(\text{tot})} = I_{2(S1)} + I_{2(S2)} = 33.3\,\text{mA} + 16.7\,\text{mA} = \mathbf{50\,mA}$$

The voltage across R_2 is

$$V_{R2} = I_{2(\text{tot})}R_2 = (50\,\text{mA})(100\,\Omega) = \mathbf{5\,V}$$

Related Problem   Determine the total current through R_2 if the polarity of V_{S2} in Figure 6–57 is reversed.

EXAMPLE 6–20   Find the total current through and voltage across R_3 in Figure 6–60.

▶ FIGURE 6–60

Solution   **Step 1:** Find the current through R_3 due to source V_{S1} by replacing source V_{S2} with a short to represent its zero internal resistance, as shown in Figure 6–61. Looking from V_{S1},

$$R_{T(S1)} = R_1 + \frac{R_2 R_3}{R_2 + R_3} = 1.0\,k\Omega + \frac{(1.0\,k\Omega)(2.2\,k\Omega)}{3.2\,k\Omega} = 1.69\,k\Omega$$

$$I_{T(S1)} = \frac{V_{S1}}{R_{T(S1)}} = \frac{20\,V}{1.69\,k\Omega} = 11.8\,mA$$

Now apply the current-divider formula to get the current through R_3 due to source V_{S1}.

$$I_{3(S1)} = \left(\frac{R_2}{R_2 + R_3}\right) I_{T(S1)} = \left(\frac{1.0\,k\Omega}{3.2\,k\Omega}\right) 11.8\,mA = 3.69\,mA$$

Notice that this current is upward through R_3.

▶ FIGURE 6–61

Step 2: Find the current through R_3 due to source V_{S2} by replacing source V_{S1} with a short, as shown in Figure 6–62. Looking from V_{S2},

$$R_{T(S2)} = R_2 + \frac{R_1 R_3}{R_1 + R_3} = 1.0\,k\Omega + \frac{(1.0\,k\Omega)(2.2\,k\Omega)}{3.2\,k\Omega} = 1.69\,k\Omega$$

$$I_{T(S2)} = \frac{V_{S2}}{R_{T(S2)}} = \frac{15\,V}{1.69\,k\Omega} = 8.88\,mA$$

▶ FIGURE 6–62

Now apply the current-divider formula to find the current through R_3 due to source V_{S2}.

$$I_{3(S2)} = \left(\frac{R_1}{R_1 + R_3}\right)I_{T(S2)} = \left(\frac{1.0\,\text{k}\Omega}{3.2\,\text{k}\Omega}\right)8.88\,\text{mA} = 2.78\,\text{mA}$$

Notice that this current is downward through R_3.

Step 3: Calculate the total current through R_3 and the voltage across it.

$$I_{3(\text{tot})} = I_{3(S1)} - I_{3(S2)} = 3.69\,\text{mA} - 2.78\,\text{mA} = 0.91\,\text{mA} = \textbf{910}\,\boldsymbol{\mu}\textbf{A}$$
$$V_{R3} = I_{3(\text{tot})}R_3 = (910\,\mu\text{A})(2.2\,\text{k}\Omega) \cong \textbf{2 V}$$

The current is upward through R_3.

Related Problem   Find the total current through R_3 in Figure 6–60 if V_{S1} is changed to 12 V and its polarity reversed.

Although regulated dc power supplies are close to ideal voltage sources, many ac sources are not. For example, function generators generally have 50 Ω or 600 Ω of internal resistance, which appears as a resistance in series with an ideal source. Also, batteries can look ideal when they are fresh, but as they age, the internal resistance increases. When applying the superposition theorem, it is important to recognize when a source is not ideal and replace it with its equivalent internal resistance.

Current sources are not as common as voltage sources and are also not always ideal. If a current source is not ideal, as in the case of transistors, it should be replaced by its equivalent internal resistance when the superposition theorem is applied.

SECTION 6–8 REVIEW

1. State the superposition theorem.
2. Why is the superposition theorem useful for analysis of multiple-source linear circuits?
3. Why is a voltage source shorted when the superposition theorem is applied?
4. If, as a result of applying the superposition theorem, two component currents are in opposing directions through a branch of a circuit, in which direction is the net current?

5. Using the superposition theorem, find the current through R_1 in Figure 6–63.

FIGURE 6–63

6–9 TROUBLESHOOTING

Troubleshooting is the process of identifying and locating a failure or problem in a circuit. Some troubleshooting techniques and the application of logical thought have already been discussed in relation to both series circuits and parallel circuits. A basic premise of troubleshooting is that you must know what to look for before you can successfully troubleshoot a circuit.

After completing this section, you should be able to

◆ **Troubleshoot series-parallel circuits**

  ◆ Determine the effects of an open in a circuit

  ◆ Determine the effects of a short in a circuit

  ◆ Locate opens and shorts

Opens and shorts are typical problems that occur in electric circuits. As mentioned in Chapter 4, if a resistor burns out, it will normally produce an open. Bad solder connections, broken wires, and poor contacts can also be causes of open paths. Pieces of foreign material, such as solder splashes, broken insulation on wires, and so on, can often lead to shorts in a circuit. A short is considered to be a zero resistance path between two points.

In addition to complete opens or shorts, partial opens or partial shorts can develop in a circuit. A partial open would be a much higher than normal resistance, but not infinitely large. A partial short would be a much lower than normal resistance, but not zero.

The following three examples illustrate troubleshooting series-parallel circuits.

EXAMPLE 6–21

From the indicated voltmeter reading in Figure 6–64, determine if there is a fault by applying the APM approach. If there is a fault, identify it as either a short or an open.

FIGURE 6–64

Solution   **Step 1:** Analysis

Determine what the voltmeter should be indicating as follows. Since R_2 and R_3 are in parallel, their combined resistance is

$$R_{2\|3} = \frac{R_2 R_3}{R_2 + R_3} = \frac{(4.7\,\text{k}\Omega)(10\,\text{k}\Omega)}{14.7\,\text{k}\Omega} = 3.20\,\text{k}\Omega$$

Determine the voltage across the parallel combination by the voltage-divider formula.

$$V_{2\|3} = \left(\frac{R_{2\|3}}{R_1 + R_{2\|3}}\right)V_S = \left(\frac{3.2\,\text{k}\Omega}{18.2\,\text{k}\Omega}\right)24\,\text{V} = 4.22\,\text{V}$$

This calculation shows that 4.22 V is the voltage reading that you should get on the meter. However, the meter reads 9.6 V across $R_{2\|3}$. This value is incorrect, and, because it is higher than it should be, either R_2 or R_3 is probably open. Why? Because if either of these two resistors is open, the resistance across which the meter is connected is larger than expected. A higher resistance will drop a higher voltage in this circuit.

Step 2: Planning

Start trying to find the open resistor by assuming that R_2 is open. If it is, the voltage across R_3 is

$$V_3 = \left(\frac{R_3}{R_1 + R_3}\right)V_S = \left(\frac{10\,\text{k}\Omega}{25\,\text{k}\Omega}\right)24\,\text{V} = 9.6\,\text{V}$$

Since the measured voltage is also 9.6 V, this calculation shows that R_2 is probably open.

Step 3: Measurement

Disconnect power and remove R_2. Measure its resistance to verify it is open. If it is not, inspect the wiring, solder, or connections around R_2, looking for the open.

Related Problem   What would be the voltmeter reading if R_3 were open in Figure 6–64? If R_1 were open?

 Open Multisim file E06-21 on your CD-ROM. Determine if a fault exists in the circuit and, if so, isolate the fault to a single component.

EXAMPLE 6–22   Suppose that you measure 24 V with the voltmeter in Figure 6–65. Determine if there is a fault, and, if there is, identify it.

FIGURE 6–65

Solution **Step 1:** Analysis

There is no voltage drop across R_1 because both sides of the resistor are at +24 V. Either there is no current through R_1 from the source, which tells you that R_2 is open in the circuit, or R_1 is shorted.

Step 2: Planning

The most probable failure is an open R_2. If it is open, then there will be no current from the source. To verify this, measure across R_2 with the voltmeter. If R_2 is open, the meter will indicate 24 V. The right side of R_2 will be at zero volts because there is no current through any of the other resistors to cause a voltage drop across them.

Step 3: Measurement

The measurement to verify that R_2 is open is shown in Figure 6–66.

FIGURE 6–66

Related Problem What would be the voltage across an open R_5 in Figure 6–65 assuming no other faults?

Open Multisim file E06-22 on your CD-ROM. Determine if a fault exists in the circuit and, if so, isolate the fault to a single component.

EXAMPLE 6–23

The two voltmeters in Figure 6–67 indicate the voltages shown. Apply logical thought and your knowledge of circuit operation to determine if there are any opens or shorts in the circuit and, if so, where they are located.

▲ FIGURE 6–67

Solution   **Step 1:** Determine if the voltmeter readings are correct. R_1, R_2, and R_3 act as a voltage divider. Calculate the voltage (V_A) across R_3 as follows:

$$V_A = \left(\frac{R_3}{R_1 + R_2 + R_3}\right)V_S = \left(\frac{3.3\,\text{k}\Omega}{21.6\,\text{k}\Omega}\right)24\,\text{V} = 3.67\,\text{V}$$

The voltmeter A reading is correct. This indicates that R_1, R_2, and R_3 are connected and are not faulty.

Step 2: See if the voltmeter B reading is correct. $R_6 + R_7$ is in parallel with R_5. The series-parallel combination of R_5, R_6, and R_7 is in series with R_4. Calculate the resistance of the R_5, R_6, and R_7 combination as follows:

$$R_{5\|(6+7)} = \frac{R_5(R_6 + R_7)}{R_5 + R_6 + R_7} = \frac{(10\,\text{k}\Omega)(17.2\,\text{k}\Omega)}{27.2\,\text{k}\Omega} = 6.32\,\text{k}\Omega$$

$R_{5\|(6+7)}$ and R_4 form a voltage divider, and voltmeter B is measuring the voltage across $R_{5\|(6+7)}$. Is it correct? Check as follows:

$$V_B = \left(\frac{R_{5\|(6+7)}}{R_4 + R_{5\|(6+7)}}\right)V_S = \left(\frac{6.32\,\text{k}\Omega}{11\,\text{k}\Omega}\right)24\,\text{V} = 13.8\,\text{V}$$

Thus, the actual measured voltage (6.65 V) at this point is incorrect. Some logical thinking will help to isolate the problem.

Step 3: R_4 is not open, because if it were, the meter would read 0 V. If there were a short across it, the meter would read 24 V. Since the actual voltage is much less than it should be, $R_{5\|(6+7)}$ must be less than the calculated value of 6.32 kΩ. The most likely problem is a short across R_7. If there is a short from the top of R_7 to ground, R_6 is effectively in parallel with R_5. In this case,

$$R_5 \| R_6 = \frac{R_5 R_6}{R_5 + R_6} = \frac{(10\,\text{k}\Omega)(2.2\,\text{k}\Omega)}{12.2\,\text{k}\Omega} = 1.80\,\text{k}\Omega$$

Then V_B is

$$V_B = \left(\frac{1.80\,\text{k}\Omega}{6.5\,\text{k}\Omega}\right)24\,\text{V} = 6.65\,\text{V}$$

This value for V_B agrees with the voltmeter B reading. So there is a short across R_7. If this were an actual circuit, you would try to find the physical cause of the short.

Related Problem   If the only fault in Figure 6–67 is that R_2 is shorted, what will voltmeter A read? What will voltmeter B read?

Open Multisim file E06-23 on your CD-ROM. Determine if a fault exists in the circuit and, if so, isolate the fault to a single component.

SECTION 6–9 REVIEW

1. Name two types of common circuit faults.

2. For the following faults in Figure 6–68, determine what voltage would be measured at node *A*:
   (a) no faults   (b) R_1 open
   (c) short across R_5 (d) R_3 and R_4 open
   (e) R_2 open

► FIGURE 6–68

3. In Figure 6–69, one of the resistors in the circuit is open. Based on the meter reading, determine which is the open resistor.

► FIGURE 6–69

Application Assignment

PUTTING YOUR KNOWLEDGE TO WORK

A voltage divider with three output voltages has been designed and constructed on a PC board. The voltage divider is to be used as part of a portable power supply unit for supplying up to three different reference voltages to measuring instruments in the field. The power supply unit contains a battery pack combined with a voltage regulator that produces a constant +12 V to the voltage-divider circuit board. In this assignment, you will apply your knowledge of loaded voltage dividers, Kirchhoff's laws, and Ohm's law to determine the operating parameters of the voltage divider in terms of voltages and currents for all possible load configurations. You will also troubleshoot the circuit for various malfunctions.

▲ FIGURE 6–70

Voltage-divider circuit board.

Step 1: The Schematic

Draw the schematic and label the resistor values for the circuit board in Figure 6–70.

Step 2: Connecting the 12 V Power Supply

Specify how to connect a 12 V power supply to the circuit board so that all resistors are in series and pin 2 has the highest output voltage.

Step 3: Determining the Unloaded Output Voltages

Calculate each of the output voltages with no loads connected. Add these voltage values to a copy of the table in Figure 6–71.

10 MΩ Load	$V_{OUT\,(2)}$	$V_{OUT\,(3)}$	$V_{OUT\,(4)}$	% Deviation	$I_{LOAD\,(2)}$	$I_{LOAD\,(3)}$	$I_{LOAD\,(4)}$
None							
Pin 2 to ground							
Pin 3 to ground							
Pin 4 to ground							
Pin 2 to ground				2			
Pin 3 to ground				3			
Pin 2 to ground				2			
Pin 4 to ground				4			
Pin 3 to ground				3			
Pin 4 to ground				4			
Pin 2 to ground				2			
Pin 3 to ground				3			
Pin 4 to ground				4			

▲ FIGURE 6–71

Table of operating parameters for the power supply voltage divider.

Step 4: Determining the Loaded Output Voltages

The instruments to be connected to the voltage divider each have a 10 MΩ input resistance. This means that when an instrument is connected to a voltage-divider output there is effectively a 10 MΩ resistor from that output to ground (negative side of source). Calculate the output voltage across each load for each of the following load combinations and add these voltage values to a copy of the table in Figure 6–71.

1. A 10 MΩ load connected from pin 2 to ground.

2. A 10 MΩ load connected from pin 3 to ground.

3. A 10 MΩ load connected from pin 4 to ground.

4. A 10 MΩ load connected from pin 2 to ground and another 10 MΩ load from pin 3 to ground.

5. A 10 MΩ load connected from pin 2 to ground and another 10 MΩ load from pin 4 to ground.

6. A 10 MΩ load connected from pin 3 to ground and another 10 MΩ load from pin 4 to ground.

7. A 10 MΩ load connected from pin 2, to ground, another 10 MΩ load from pin 3 to ground, and a third 10 MΩ load from pin 4 to ground.

Step 5: Determining the Percent Deviation of the Output Voltages

Calculate how much each loaded output voltage deviates from its unloaded value for each of the load configurations listed in Step 4 and express as a percentage using the following formula:

$$\text{Percent deviation} = \left(\frac{V_{OUT(unloaded)} - V_{OUT(loaded)}}{V_{OUT(unloaded)}} \right) 100\%$$

Add the values to the table in Figure 6–71.

Step 6: Determining the Load Currents

Calculate the current to each 10 MΩ load for each of the load configurations listed in Step 4. Add these values to the table in Figure 6–71. Specify a minimum value for the fuse.

Step 7: Troubleshooting the Circuit Board

The voltage-divider circuit board is connected to a 12 V power supply and to the three instruments to which it provides reference voltages, as shown in Figure 6–72. Voltages at each of the numbered test points are measured with a voltmeter in each of eight different cases. For each case, determine the problem indicated by the voltage measurements.

The following voltmeter readings are taken at test points 1 through 6 with respect to ground. The readings are in volts.

	Test points (volts)					
Case	1	2	3	4	5	6
1	0	0	0	0	0	0
2	12	0	0	0	0	0
3	12	0	0	0	0	12
4	12	11.6	0	0	0	12
5	12	11.3	10.9	0	0	12
6	12	11	10.3	10	0	12
7	12	5.9	0	0	0	12
8	12	7.8	3.8	0	0	12

▲ FIGURE 6–72

Multisim Analysis and Troubleshooting

1. Using Multisim, connect the circuit shown by the schematic from Step 1 and verify the unloaded output voltages determined in Step 3.

2. Measure the load currents calculated in Step 6.

3. Verify the faults determined in Step 7 for each case by inserting the fault in the circuit and checking the voltage measurements at each point.

Review

1. If the portable unit covered in this section is to supply reference voltages to all three instruments, how many days can a 100 mAh battery be used before recharging?

2. Can ⅛ W resistors be used on the voltage-divider board?

3. If ⅛ W resistors are used, will an output shorted to ground cause any of the resistors to overheat due to excessive power?

SUMMARY

◆ A series-parallel circuit is a combination of both series current paths and parallel current paths.

◆ To determine total resistance in a series-parallel circuit, identify the series and parallel relationships, and then apply the formulas for series resistance and parallel resistance from Chapters 4 and 5.

◆ To find the total current, divide the total voltage by the total resistance.

◆ To determine branch currents, apply the current-divider formula, Kirchhoff's current law, or Ohm's law. Consider each circuit problem individually to determine the most appropriate method.

◆ To determine voltage drops across any portion of a series-parallel circuit, use the voltage-divider formula, Kirchhoff's voltage law, or Ohm's law. Consider each circuit problem individually to determine the most appropriate method.

◆ When a load resistor is connected across a voltage-divider output, the output voltage decreases.

◆ The load resistor should be large compared to the resistance across which it is connected, in order that the loading effect may be minimized. A *10-times* value is sometimes used as a rule of thumb, but the value depends on the accuracy required for the output voltage.

◆ To find any current or voltage in a circuit with two or more voltage sources, take the sources one at a time using the superposition theorem.

◆ A balanced Wheatstone bridge can be used to measure an unknown resistance.

◆ A bridge is balanced when the output voltage is zero. The balanced condition produces zero current through a load connected across the output terminals of the bridge.

◆ An unbalanced Wheatstone bridge can be used to measure physical quantities using transducers.

◆ Any two-terminal resistive circuit, no matter how complex, can be replaced by its Thevenin equivalent.

◆ The Thevenin equivalent circuit is made up of an equivalent resistance (R_{TH}) in series with an equivalent voltage source (V_{TH}).

◆ The maximum power transfer theorem states that maximum power is transferred from a source to a load when $R_S = R_L$.

◆ Opens and shorts in circuits are typical faults.

◆ Resistors normally open when they burn out.

KEY TERMS

Key terms and other bold terms in the chapter are defined in the end-of-book glossary.

Balanced bridge   A bridge circuit that is in the balanced state as indicated by zero volts across the bridge.

Bleeder current   The current left after the total load current is subtracted from the total current into the circuit.

Load current   The output current of a circuit supplied to a load.

Loading   The effect on a circuit when an element that draws current from the circuit is connected across the output terminals.

Maximum power transfer   The condition, when the load resistance equals the source resistance, under which maximum power is transferred from source to load.

Superposition   A method for analyzing circuits with two or more sources by examining the effects of each source by itself and then combining the effects.

Terminal equivalency   A condition that occurs when two circuits produce the same load voltage and load current where the same value of load resistance is connected to either circuit.

Thevenin's theorem   A circuit theorem that provides for reducing any two-terminal resistive circuit to a single equivalent voltage source in series with an equivalent resistance.

Unbalanced bridge   A bridge circuit that is in the unbalanced state as indicated by a voltage across the bridge proportional to the amount of deviation from the balanced state.

Wheatstone bridge   A 4-legged type of bridge circuit with which an unknown resistance can be accurately measured using the balanced state of the bridge. Deviations in resistance can be measured using the unbalanced state.

FORMULAS

6–1 $I_{BLEEDER} = I_T - I_{RL1} - I_{RL2}$ Bleeder current

6–2 $R_X = R_V \left(\dfrac{R_2}{R_4} \right)$ Unknown resistance in a Wheatstone bridge

SELF-TEST

Answers are at the end of the chapter.

1. Which of the following statements are true concerning Figure 6–73?

    (a) R_1 and R_2 are in series with $R_3, R_4,$ and R_5.

    (b) R_1 and R_2 are in series.

    (c) $R_3, R_4,$ and R_5 are in parallel.

    (d) The series combination of R_1 and R_2 is in parallel with the series combination of $R_3, R_4,$ and R_5.

    (e) answers (b) and (d)

▶ FIGURE 6–73

2. The total resistance of Figure 6–73 can be found with which of the following formulas?

    (a) $R_1 + R_2 + R_3 \parallel R_4 \parallel R_5$ (b) $R_1 \parallel R_2 + R_3 \parallel R_4 \parallel R_5$

    (c) $(R_1 + R_2) \parallel (R_3 + R_4 + R_5)$ (d) none of these answers

3. If all of the resistors in Figure 6–73 have the same value, when voltage is applied across terminals A and B, the current is

    (a) greatest in R_5 (b) greatest in $R_3, R_4,$ and R_5

    (c) greatest in R_1 and R_2 (d) the same in all the resistors

4. Two $1.0\,k\Omega$ resistors are in series and this series combination is in parallel with a $2.2\,k\Omega$ resistor. The voltage across one of the $1.0\,k\Omega$ resistors is 6 V. The voltage across the $2.2\,k\Omega$ resistor is

    (a) 6 V   (b) 3 V   (c) 12 V   (d) 13.2 V

5. The parallel combination of a $330\,\Omega$ resistor and a $470\,\Omega$ resistor is in series with the parallel combination of four $1.0\,k\Omega$ resistors. A 100 V source is connected across the circuit. The resistor with the most current has a value of

    (a) $1.0\,k\Omega$ (b) $330\,\Omega$ (c) $470\,\Omega$

6. In the circuit described in Question 5, the resistor(s) with the most voltage has a value of

    (a) $1.0\,k\Omega$ (b) $470\,\Omega$ (c) $330\,\Omega$

7. In the circuit described in Question 5, the percentage of the total current through any single $1.0\,k\Omega$ resistor is

    (a) 100%   (b) 25%   (c) 50%   (d) 31.25%

8. The output of a certain voltage divider is 9 V with no load. When a load is connected, the output voltage

    (a) increases   (b) decreases   (c) remains the same   (d) becomes zero

9. A certain voltage divider consists of two $10\,k\Omega$ resistors in series. Which of the following load resistors will have the most effect on the output voltage?

    (a) $1.0\,M\Omega$ (b) $20\,k\Omega$ (c) $100\,k\Omega$ (d) $10\,k\Omega$

10. When a load resistance is connected to the output of a voltage-divider circuit, the current drawn from the source

    (a) decreases   (b) increases   (c) remains the same   (d) is cut off

11. The output voltage of a balanced Wheatstone bridge is

    (a) equal to the source voltage

    (b) equal to zero

    (c) dependent on all of the resistor values in the bridge

    (d) dependent on the value of the unknown resistor

12. The primary method of analyzing a circuit with two or more voltage sources is usually

    (a) Thevenin's theorem   (b) Ohm's law   (c) superposition   (d) Kirchhoff's law

13. In a certain two-source circuit, one source acting alone produces 10 mA through a given branch. The other source acting alone produces 8 mA in the opposite direction through the same branch. With both sources, the total current through the branch is

(a) 10 mA (b) 8 mA (c) 18 mA (d) 2 mA

14. A Thevenin equivalent circuit consists of

(a) a voltage source in series with a resistance

(b) a voltage source in parallel with a resistance

(c) a current source in parallel with a resistance

(d) two voltage sources and a resistance

15. A voltage source with an internal source resistance of 300 Ω transfers maximum power to a

(a) 150 Ω load (b) 50 Ω load (c) 300 Ω load (d) 600 Ω load

16. You are measuring the voltage at a given point in a circuit that has very high resistance values and the measured voltage is a little lower than it should be. This is possibly because of

(a) one or more of the resistance values being off

(b) the loading effect of the voltmeter

(c) the source voltage is too low

(d) all of these answers

TROUBLESHOOTING: SYMPTOM AND CAUSE

The purpose of these exercises is to help develop thought processes essential to troubleshooting. Answers are at the end of the chapter.

Determine the cause for each set of symptoms. Refer to Figure 6–74.

▲ FIGURE 6–74

The meters indicate the correct readings for this circuit.

1. *Symptom:* The ammeter reading is too low, and the voltmeter reading is 5.45 V.

Cause:

(a) R_1 is open.

(b) R_2 is open.

(c) R_3 is open.

2. *Symptom:* The ammeter reading is 1 mA, and the voltmeter reading is 0 V.

Cause:

(a) There is a short across R_1.

(b) There is a short across R_2.

(c) R_3 is open.

3. *Symptom:* The ammeter reading is near zero, and the voltmeter reading is 12 V.

Cause:

(a) R_1 is open.

(b) R_2 is open.

(c) Both R_2 and R_3 are open.

4. *Symptom:* The ammeter reading is 444 μA, and the voltmeter reading is 6.67 V.

Cause:

(a) R_1 is shorted.

(b) R_2 is open.

(c) R_3 is open.

5. *Symptom:* The ammeter reading is 2 mA, and the voltmeter reading is 12 V.

Cause:

(a) R_1 is shorted.

(b) R_2 is shorted.

(c) Both R_2 and R_3 are open.

PROBLEMS

Answers to odd-numbered problems are at the end of the book.

BASIC PROBLEMS

SECTION 6–1 Identifying Series-Parallel Relationships

1. Identify the series and parallel relationships in Figure 6–75 as seen from the source terminals.

▶ FIGURE 6–75

2. Visualize and draw the following series-parallel combinations:

(a) R_1 in series with the parallel combination of R_2 and R_3.

(b) R_1 in parallel with the series combination of R_2 and R_3.

(c) R_1 in parallel with a branch containing R_2 in series with a parallel combination of four other resistors

3. Visualize and draw the following series-parallel circuits:

(a) a parallel combination of three branches, each containing two series resistors

(b) a series combination of three parallel circuits, each containing two parallel resistors

4. In each circuit of Figure 6–76 identify the series and parallel relationships of the resistors viewed from the source.

▶ FIGURE 6–76

(a)

(b)

SECTION 6–2   **Analysis of Series-Parallel Resistive Circuits**

5. A certain circuit is composed of two parallel resistors. The total resistance is 667 Ω. One of the resistors is 1.0 kΩ. What is the other resistor?

6. For the circuit in Figure 6–77, determine the total resistance between A and B.

7. Determine the total resistance for each circuit in Figure 6–76.

8. Determine the current through each resistor in Figure 6–75; then calculate each voltage drop.

9. Determine the current through each resistor in both circuits of Figure 6–76; then calculate each voltage drop.

10. In Figure 6–78, find the following:

　　(a) total resistance between terminals A and B

　　(b) total current drawn from a 6 V source connected from A to B

　　(c) current through R_5

　　(d) voltage across R_2

11. In Figure 6–78, determine the current through R_2 for $V_{AB} = 6$ V.

12. In Figure 6–78, determine the current through R_4 for $V_{AB} = 6$ V.

▲ FIGURE 6–77

▲ FIGURE 6–78

SECTION 6–3   **Voltage Dividers with Resistive Loads**

13. A voltage divider consists of two 56 kΩ resistors and a 15 V source. Calculate the unloaded output voltage taken across one of the 56 kΩ resistors. What will the output voltage be if a load resistor of 1.0 MΩ is connected across the output?

14. A 12 V battery output is divided down to obtain two output voltages. Three 3.3 kΩ resistors are used to provide the two outputs with only one output at a time loaded with 10 kΩ. Determine the output voltages in both cases.

15. Which will cause a smaller decrease in output voltage for a given voltage divider, a 10 kΩ load or a 56 kΩ load?

16. In Figure 6–79, determine the current drain on the battery with no load on the output terminals. With a 10 kΩ load, what is the current from the battery?

▶ FIGURE 6–79

SECTION 6-4 **Loading Effect of a Voltmeter**

17. Across which one of the following resistances will a voltmeter with a 10 MΩ internal resistance present the minimum load on a circuit?

    (a) 100 kΩ   **(b)** 1.2 MΩ   **(c)** 22 kΩ   **(d)** 8.2 MΩ

18. A certain voltage divider consists of three 1.0 MΩ resistors connected in series to a 100 V source. Determine the voltage across one of the resistors measured by a 10 MΩ voltmeter.

19. What is the difference between the measured and the actual unloaded voltage in Problem 18?

20. By what percentage does the voltmeter in Problem 18 alter the voltage which it measures?

SECTION 6-5 **The Wheatstone Bridge**

21. A resistor of unknown value is connected to a Wheatstone bridge circuit. The bridge parameters for a balanced condition are set as follows: $R_V = 18$ kΩ and $R_2/R_4 = 0.02$. What is R_X?

22. A bridge network is shown in Figure 6-80. To what value must R_V be set in order to balance the bridge?

23. Determine the value of R_X in the balanced bridge in Figure 6-81.

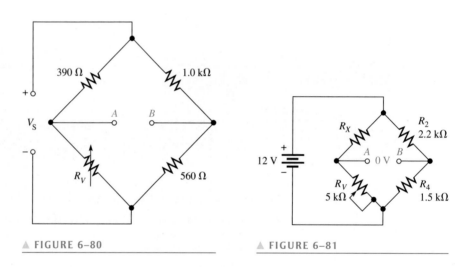

▲ FIGURE 6-80   ▲ FIGURE 6-81

24. Determine the output voltage of the unbalanced bridge in Figure 6-82 for a temperature of 65°C. The thermistor has a nominal resistance of 1 kΩ at 25°C and a positive temperature coefficient. Assume that its resistance changes 5 Ω for each C° change in temperature.

▶ FIGURE 6-82

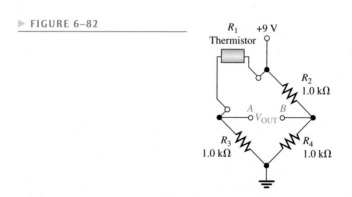

SECTION 6–6 Thevenin's Theorem

25. Reduce the circuit in Figure 6–83 to its Thevenin equivalent as viewed from terminals *A* and *B*.

▶ FIGURE 6–83

26. For each circuit in Figure 6–84, determine the Thevenin equivalent as seen from terminals *A* and *B*.

(a)   (b)   (c)

▲ FIGURE 6–84

27. Determine the voltage and current for R_L in Figure 6–85.

▶ FIGURE 6–85

SECTION 6–7 The Maximum Power Transfer Theorem

28. Determine the value of a load resistor connected between terminals *A* and *B* in Figure 6–83 for maximum power transfer to the load resistor.

29. A certain Thevenin equivalent circuit has a V_{TH} = 5.5 V and an R_{TH} = 75 Ω. To what value of load resistor will maximum power be transferred?

30. Determine the value of R_L in Figure 6–84(a) for which R_L dissipates maximum power.

SECTION 6–8 **The Superposition Theorem**

31. In Figure 6–86, use the superposition theorem to find the current in R_3.

32. In Figure 6–86, what is the current through R_2?

▶ FIGURE 6–86

SECTION 6–9 **Troubleshooting**

33. Is the voltmeter reading in Figure 6–87 correct? If not, what is the problem?

(a) Meter with leads going to protoboard

(b) Protoboard with meter leads and red and black leads from a 12 V dc power supply connected

▲ FIGURE 6–87

34. If R_2 in Figure 6–88 opens, what voltages will be read at points A, B, and C?

▲ FIGURE 6–88

35. Check the meter readings in Figure 6–89 and locate any fault that may exist.

▲ FIGURE 6–89

36. Determine the voltage you would expect to measure across each resistor in Figure 6–88 for each of the following faults. Assume the faults are independent of each other.

(a) R_1 open

(b) R_3 open

(c) R_4 open

(d) R_5 open

(e) point C shorted to ground

37. Determine the voltage you would expect to measure across each resistor in Figure 6–89 for each of the following faults:

(a) R_1 open
(b) R_2 open
(c) R_3 open
(d) a short across R_4

ADVANCED PROBLEMS

38. In each circuit of Figure 6–90, identify the series and parallel relationships of the resistors viewed from the source.

(a)   (b)

▲ FIGURE 6–90

39. Draw the schematic of the PC board layout in Figure 6–91 showing resistor values and identify the series-parallel relationships. Which resistors, if any, can be removed with no effect on R_T?

A   B

▲ FIGURE 6–91

40. For the circuit shown in Figure 6–92, calculate the following:

    (a) total resistance across the source

    (b) total current from the source

    (c) current through the 910 Ω resistor

    (d) voltage from point A to point B

▶ FIGURE 6–92

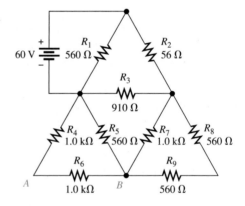

41. Determine the total resistance and the voltage at points A, B, and C in the circuit of Figure 6–93.

▲ FIGURE 6–93

42. Determine the total resistance between terminals *A* and *B* of the circuit in Figure 6–94. Also calculate the current in each branch with 10 V between *A* and *B*.

43. What is the voltage across each resistor in Figure 6–94? There are 10 V between *A* and *B*.

▶ FIGURE 6–94

44. Determine the voltage, V_{AB}, in Figure 6–95.

▶ FIGURE 6–95

45. Find the value of R_2 in Figure 6–96.

▶ FIGURE 6–96

46. Determine the total resistance and the voltage at points *A*, *B*, and *C* in the circuit of Figure 6–97.

▶ FIGURE 6–97

47. Develop a voltage divider to provide a 6 V output with no load and a minimum of 5.5 V across a 1.0 kΩ load. The source voltage is 24 V, and the unloaded current is not to exceed 100 mA.

48. Determine the resistance values for a voltage divider that must meet the following specifications: The current under an unloaded condition is not to exceed 5 mA. The source voltage is to be 10 V. A 5 V output and a 2.5 V output are required. Draw the circuit. Determine the effect on the output voltages if a 1.0 kΩ load is connected to each output.

49. Using the superposition theorem, calculate the current in the right-most branch of Figure 6–98.

▲ FIGURE 6–98

50. Find the current through R_L in Figure 6–99.

▲ FIGURE 6–99

51. Using Thevenin's theorem, find the voltage across R_4 in Figure 6–100.

▲ FIGURE 6–100

52. Determine V_{OUT} for the circuit in Figure 6–101 for the following conditions:

    (a) Switch SW2 connected to +12 V and the rest to ground

    (b) Switch SW1 connected to +12 V and the rest to ground

▶ FIGURE 6–101

53. Develop a schematic for the double-sided PC board in Figure 6–102 and label the resistor values.

▲ FIGURE 6–102

54. Lay out a PC board for the circuit in Figure 6–90(b). The battery is to be connected external to the board.

55. The voltage divider in Figure 6–103 has a switched load. Determine the voltage at each tap (V_1, V_2, and V_3) for each position of the switch.

▶ FIGURE 6–103

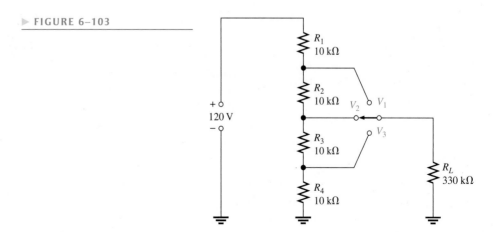

56. Figure 6–104 shows a dc biasing arrangement for a field-effect transistor amplifier. Biasing is a common method for setting up certain dc voltage levels required for proper amplifier operation. Although you may not be familiar with transistor amplifiers at this point, the dc voltages and currents in the circuit can be determined using methods that you already know.

   (a) Find V_G and V_S with respect to ground

   (b) Determine I_1, I_2, I_D, and I_S

   (c) Find V_{DS} and V_{DG}

▶ FIGURE 6–104

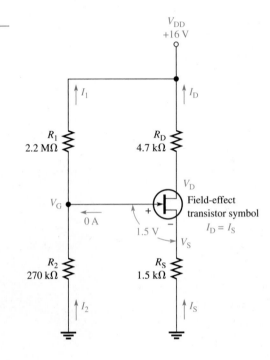

57. Look at the voltmeters in Figure 6–105 and determine if there is a fault in the circuit. If there is a fault, identify it.

58. Are the voltmeter readings in Figure 6–106 correct?

▲ FIGURE 6–105

▲ FIGURE 6–106

59. There is one fault in Figure 6–107. Based on the voltmeter indications, determine what the fault is.

▶ FIGURE 6–107

60. Look at the voltmeters in Figure 6–108 and determine if there is a fault in the circuit. If there is a fault, identify it.

61. Determine the voltmeter readings in Figure 6–108 if the 4.7 kΩ resistor opens.

▶ FIGURE 6–108

MULTISIM TROUBLESHOOTING PROBLEMS

62. Open file P06-62 and determine if there is a fault in the circuit. If so, identify the fault.

63. Open file P06-63 and determine if there is a fault in the circuit. If so, identify the fault.

64. Open file P06-64 and determine if there is a fault in the circuit. If so, identify the fault.

65. Open file P06-65 and determine if there is a fault in the circuit. If so, identify the fault.

66. Open file P06-66 and determine if there is a fault in the circuit. If so, identify the fault.

67. Open file P06-67 and determine if there is a fault in the circuit. If so, identify the fault.

68. Open file P06-68 and determine if there is a fault in the circuit. If so, identify the fault.

69. Open file P06-69 and determine if there is a fault in the circuit. If so, identify the fault.

ANSWERS

SECTION REVIEWS

SECTION 6–1 Identifying Series-Parallel Relationships

1. See Figure 6–109.

▶ FIGURE 6–109

2. R_1 and R_2 are in series with the parallel combination of R_3 and R_4.

3. All resistors are in parallel.

4. R_1 and R_2 are in parallel; R_3 and R_4 are in parallel.

5. Yes, the two parallel combinations are in series with each other.

SECTION 6–2   Analysis of Series-Parallel Circuits

1. $R_T = R_1 + R_4 + R_2 \parallel R_3 = 599\ \Omega$

2. $I_3 = 11.2\ \text{mA}$

3. $V_{R2} = I_2 R_2 = 3.7\ \text{V}$

4. $R_T = 89\ \Omega; I_T = 11.2\ \text{mA}$

SECTION 6–3   Voltage Dividers with Resistive Loads

1. The load resistor decreases the output voltage.

2. True

3. $V_{\text{OUT(unloaded)}} = 19.23\ \text{V},\ V_{\text{OUT(loaded)}} = 19.16\ \text{V}$

SECTION 6–4   Loading Effect of a Voltmeter

1. A voltmeter loads a circuit because the internal resistance of the meter appears in parallel with the circuit resistance across which it is connected, reducing the resistance between those two points of the circuit and drawing current from the circuit.

2. No, because the meter resistance is much larger than $1.0\ \text{k}\Omega$.

3. Yes.

SECTION 6–5   The Wheatstone Bridge

1. See Figure 6–110.

▶ FIGURE 6–110

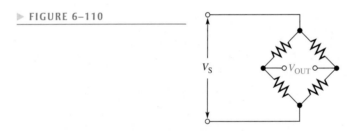

2. A bridge is balanced when the output voltage is zero.

3. $R_X = 15\ \text{k}\Omega$

4. An unbalanced bridge is used to measure transducer-sensed quantities.

SECTION 6–6   Thevenin's Theorem

1. A Thevenin equivalent circuit consists of V_{TH} and R_{TH}.

2. See Figure 6–111.

▶ FIGURE 6–111

3. V_{TH} is the open circuit voltage between two points in a circuit.

4. R_{TH} is the resistance as viewed from two terminals in a circuit, with all sources replaced by their internal resistances.

5. See Figure 6–112.

◆ FIGURE 6–112

SECTION 6–7 **Maximum Power Transfer Theorem**

1. The maximum power transfer theorem states that maximum power is transferred from a source to a load when the load resistance is equal to the internal source resistance.

2. Maximum power is delivered to a load when $R_L = R_S$.

3. $R_L = R_S = 50\,\Omega$

SECTION 6–8 **The Superposition Theorem**

1. The total current in any branch of a multiple-source linear circuit is equal to the algebraic sum of the currents due to the individual sources acting alone, with the other sources replaced by their internal resistances.

2. The superposition method allows each source to be treated independently.

3. A short simulates the zero internal resistance of an ideal voltage source.

4. The net current is in the direction of the larger current.

5. $I_{R1} = 6.67\,\text{mA}$

SECTION 6–9 **Troubleshooting**

1. Opens and short are two common faults.

2. **(a)** 62.8 V   **(b)** 62.8 V   **(c)** 62 V   **(d)** 100 V   **(e)** 0 V

3. The $10\,\text{k}\Omega$ resistor is open.

Application Assignment

1. The battery will last 413 days.

2. Yes, ⅛ W resistors can be used.

3. No, none of the resistors will overheat.

RELATED PROBLEMS FOR EXAMPLES

6–1   The added resistor would be in parallel with the combination of R_4 in series with R_2 and R_3 in parallel.

6–2   The added resistor is in parallel with R_5.

6–3   A to gnd: $R_T = R_3 \parallel (R_1 + R_2) + R_4$

B to gnd: $R_T = R_2 \parallel (R_1 + R_3) + R_4$

C to gnd: $R_T = R_4$

6–4   None. The new resistor will be shorted by the existing connection between those points.

6–5 R_1 and R_4 are effectively removed from the circuit.

6–6   55.1 Ω

6–7   128.3 Ω

6–8 $I_1 = 89.3$ mA; $I_3 = 58.5$ mA; $I_T = 182.3$ mA

6–9 $V_1 = V_2 = 10.3$ V; $V_3 = 9.70$ V; $V_4 = 3.16$ V; $V_5 = 6.54$ V

6–10 $I_1 = 1.42$ mA, $P_1 = 6.67$ mW; $I_2 = 756\,\mu$A, $P_2 = 3.55$ mW;

  $I_3 = 2.18$ mA, $P_3 = 4.75$ mW; $I_4 = 1.13$ mA, $P_4 = 1.28$ mW;

  $I_5 = 1.06$ mA, $P_5 = 758\,\mu$W; $I_6 = 1.06$ mA, $P_6 = 435\,\mu$W

6–11 3.39 V

6–12 Increase the values of R_1, R_2, and R_3 proportionally.

6–13 5.19 V

6–14 3.3 kΩ

6–15 0.49 V

6–16 2.36 V; 124 Ω

6–17 1.17 mA

6–18 41.7 mW

6–19 16.6 mA

6–20 5 mA

6–21 5.73 V, 0 V

6–22 9.46 V

6–23 $V_A = 12$ V; $V_B = 13.8$ V

SELF-TEST

1. (e)   **2.** (c)   **3.** (c)   **4.** (c)   **5.** (b)   **6.** (a)   **7.** (b)

8. (b)   **9.** (d)   **10.** (b)   **11.** (b)   **12.** (c)   **13.** (d)   **14.** (a)

15. (c)   **16.** (d)

TROUBLESHOOTING: SYMPTOM AND CAUSE

1. (c)

2. (b)

3. (c)

4. (b)

5. (a)

MAGNETISM AND ELECTROMAGNETISM

7

CHAPTER OBJECTIVES

◆ Explain the principles of the magnetic field

◆ Explain the principles of electromagnetism

◆ Describe the principle of operation for several types of electromagnetic devices

◆ Explain magnetic hysteresis

◆ Discuss the principle of electromagnetic induction

◆ Describe some applications of electromagnetic induction

KEY TERMS

◆ Magnetic field
◆ Lines of force
◆ Magnetic flux
◆ Weber (Wb)
◆ Tesla (T)
◆ Gauss
◆ Electromagnetism
◆ Electromagnetic field
◆ Permeability
◆ Reluctance ($\mathcal{R}$)
◆ Magnetomotive force (mmf)
◆ Ampere-turn (At)

◆ Solenoid
◆ Relay
◆ Speaker
◆ Magnetic field intensity
◆ Hysteresis
◆ Retentivity
◆ Induced voltage (v_{ind})
◆ Induced current (i_{ind})
◆ Electromagnetic induction
◆ Faraday's law
◆ Lenz's law

APPLICATION ASSIGNMENT PREVIEW

For the application assignment, you will apply what you learn in this chapter about relays and other devices to a simple burglar alarm system. You will determine how to connect the components to form a complete system and specify a check-out procedure to make sure the system is working properly. After studying this chapter, you should be able to complete the application assignment.

VISIT THE COMPANION WEBSITE

Study aids for this chapter are available at http://www.prenhall.com/floyd

INTRODUCTION

This chapter departs from the previous six chapters and introduces two new concepts: magnetism and electromagnetism. The operation of many types of electrical devices is based partially on magnetic or electromagnetic principles. Electromagnetic induction is important in an electrical component called an inductor or coil (covered in Chapter 11).

Two types of magnets are the permanent magnet and the electromagnet. The permanent magnet maintains a constant magnetic field between its two poles with no external excitation. The electromagnet produces a magnetic field only when there is current through it. The electromagnet is basically a coil of wire wound around a magnetic core material.

7–1 The Magnetic Field

A permanent magnet has a magnetic field surrounding it. The **magnetic field** consists of **lines of force** that radiate from the north pole (N) to the south pole (S) and back to the north pole through the magnetic material.

After completing this section, you should be able to

◆ **Explain the principles of the magnetic field**

   ◆ Define *magnetic flux*

   ◆ Define *magnetic flux density*

   ◆ Discuss how materials are magnetized

   ◆ Explain how a magnetic switch works

BIOGRAPHY

Wilhelm
Eduard
Weber
1804–1891

Weber was a German physicist who worked closely with Gauss, whose biography appears later. Independently, he established a system of absolute electrical units and also performed work that was crucial to the later development of the electromagnetic theory of light. The unit of magnetic flux is named in his honor. (Photo credit: Courtesy of the Smithsonian Institution. Photo No. 52,604.)

A permanent magnet, such as the bar magnet shown in Figure 7–1, has a magnetic field surrounding it that consists of lines of force, or flux lines, from the north pole (N) to the south pole (S). All magnetic fields originate from charges in motion, and most often the charges in motion are electrons. For clarity, only a few lines of force are shown in the figure. Imagine, however, that many lines surround the magnet in three dimensions. The lines shrink to the smallest possible size and blend together, although they do not touch. This effectively forms a continuous magnetic field surrounding the magnet.

▶ FIGURE 7–1

Magnetic lines of force around a bar magnet.

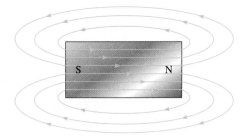

Blue lines represent only a few of the many magnetic lines of force in the magnetic field.

When unlike poles of two permanent magnets are placed close together, their magnetic fields produce an attractive force, as indicated in Figure 7–2(a). When two like poles are brought close together, they repel each other, as shown in part (b).

When a nonmagnetic material such as paper, glass, wood, or plastic is placed in a magnetic field, the lines of force are unaltered, as shown in Figure 7–3(a). However, when a magnetic material such as iron is placed in the magnetic field, the lines of force tend to change course and pass through the iron rather than through the surrounding air. They do so because the iron provides a magnetic path that is more easily established than that of air. Figure 7–3(b) illustrates this principle. The fact that magnetic lines of force follow a path through iron or other materials is a consideration in the design of shields that prevent stray magnetic fields from affecting sensitive circuits.

Magnetic Flux (ϕ)

The group of force lines going from the north pole to the south pole of a magnet is called the **magnetic flux**, symbolized by ϕ (the lowercase Greek letter phi). The number of lines of force in a magnetic field determines the value of the flux. The more lines of force, the greater the flux and the stronger the magnetic field.

(a) Unlike poles attract.

(b) Like poles repel.

▲ FIGURE 7–2

Magnetic attraction and repulsion.

Soft iron

Glass

(a)   (b)

▲ FIGURE 7–3

Effect of (a) nonmagnetic and (b) magnetic materials on a magnetic field.

BIOGRAPHY

Nikola Tesla
1856–1943

Tesla was born in Croatia (then Austria-Hungary). He was an electrical engineer who invented the ac induction motor, polyphase ac systems, the Tesla coil transformer, wireless communications, and fluorescent lights. He worked for Edison when he first came to the U.S. in 1884 and later for Westinghouse. The SI unit of magnetic flux density is named in his honor. (Photo credit: Courtesy of the Nikola Tesla Museum, Belgrade, Yugoslavia.)

The unit of magnetic flux is the **weber (Wb)**. One weber equals 10^8 lines. The weber is a very large unit; thus, in most practical situations, the microweber (μ Wb) is used. One microweber equals 100 lines of magnetic flux.

Magnetic Flux Density (*B*)

The **magnetic flux density** is the amount of flux per unit area perpendicular to the magnetic field. Its symbol is *B*, and its unit is the **tesla (T)**. One tesla equals one weber per square meter (Wb/m^2). The following formula expresses the flux density:

$$B = \frac{\phi}{A}$$

Equation 7–1

where ϕ is the flux in webers (Wb) and *A* is the cross-sectional area in square meters (m^2) of the magnetic field.

EXAMPLE 7–1

Compare the flux and the flux density in the two magnetic cores shown in Figure 7–4. The diagram represents the cross section of a magnetized material. Assume that each dot represents 100 lines or 1 μWb.

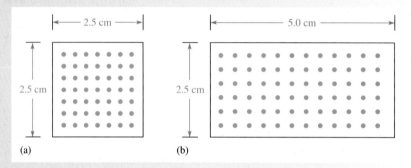

▲ FIGURE 7–4

Solution The flux is simply the number of lines. In Figure 7–4(a) there are 49 dots. Each represents 1 μWb, so the flux is 49 μWb. In Figure 7–4(b) there are 72 dots, so the flux is 72 μWb.

To calculate the flux density, first calculate the area in m². For Figure 7–4(a) the area is

$$A = l \times w = 0.025 \, \text{m} \times 0.025 \, \text{m} = 6.25 \times 10^{-4} \, \text{m}^2$$

For Figure 7–4(b) the area is

$$A = l \times w = 0.025 \, \text{m} \times 0.050 \, \text{m} = 1.25 \times 10^{-3} \, \text{m}^2$$

Use Equation 7–1 to calculate the flux density. For Figure 7–4(a) the flux density is

$$B = \frac{\phi}{A} = \frac{49 \, \mu\text{Wb}}{6.25 \times 10^{-4} \, \text{m}^2} = 78.4 \times 10^{-3} \, \text{Wb/m}^2 = 78.4 \times 10^{-3} \, \text{T}$$

For Figure 7–4(b) the flux density is

$$B = \frac{\phi}{A} = \frac{72 \, \mu\text{Wb}}{1.25 \times 10^{-3} \, \text{m}^2} = 57.6 \times 10^{-3} \, \text{Wb/m}^2 = 57.6 \times 10^{-3} \, \text{T}$$

The data in Table 7–1 compares the two cores. Note that the core with the largest flux does not necessarily have the highest flux density.

TABLE 7–1

	FLUX (Wb)	AREA (m²)	FLUX DENSITY (T)
Figure 7–4(a):	49 μWb	$6.25 \times 10^{-4} \, \text{m}^2$	$78.4 \times 10^{-3} \, \text{T}$
Figure 7–4(b):	72 μWb	$1.25 \times 10^{-3} \, \text{m}^2$	$57.6 \times 10^{-3} \, \text{T}$

*Related Problem** What is the flux density if the same flux shown in Figure 7–4(a) is in a core that is 5.0 cm × 5.0 cm?

*Answers are at the end of the chapter.

EXAMPLE 7–2

If the flux density in a certain magnetic material is 0.23 T and the area of the material is 0.38 in.^{2}, what is the flux through the material?

Solution First, 0.38 in.^{2} must be converted to square meters. 39.37 in. = 1 m; therefore,

$$A = 0.38 \text{ in.}^2[1 \text{ m}^2/(39.37 \text{ in.})^2] = 245 \times 10^{-6} \text{ m}^2$$

The flux through the material is

$$\phi = BA = (0.23 \text{ T})(245 \times 10^{-6} \text{ m}^2) = 56.4 \ \mu\text{Wb}$$

Related Problem Calculate B if $A = 0.05$ in.^{2} and $\phi = 1000 \ \mu$Wb.

The Gauss Although the tesla (T) is the SI unit for flux density, another unit called the **gauss (G)** from the CGS (centimeter-gram-second) system, is occasionally used (10^4 gauss = 1 T). In fact, the instrument used to measure flux density is the gaussmeter. The gauss is a convenient unit for small magnetic fields, such as the earth's field, which ranges from 0.3 G to 0.6 G, depending on location.

How Materials Become Magnetized

Ferromagnetic materials such as iron, nickel, and cobalt become magnetized when placed in the magnetic field of a magnet. We have all seen a permanent magnet pick up paper clips, nails, or iron filings. In these cases, the object becomes magnetized (that is, it actually becomes a magnet itself) under the influence of the permanent magnetic field and becomes attracted to the magnet. When removed from the magnetic field, the object tends to lose its magnetism.

Ferromagnetic materials have minute magnetic domains created within their atomic structure by the orbital motion and spin of electrons. These domains can be viewed as very small bar magnets with north and south poles. When the material is not exposed to an external magnetic field, the magnetic domains are randomly oriented, as shown in Figure 7–5(a). When the material is placed in a magnetic field, the domains align themselves, as shown in part (b). Thus, the object itself effectively becomes a magnet.

BIOGRAPHY

Karl Friedrich Gauss 1777–1855

Gauss, a German mathematician, disproved many 18th century mathematical theories. Later, he worked closely with Weber on a worldwide system of stations for systematic observations of terrestrial magnetism. The most important result of their work in electromagnetism was the later development of telegraphy by others. The CGS unit of magnetic flux density is named in his honor. (Credit: Illustration by Steven S. Nau.)

(a) The magnetic domains (N ◁ S) are randomly oriented in the unmagnetized material.

(b) The magnetic domains become aligned when the material is magnetized.

▲ FIGURE 7–5

Ferromagnetic domains in (a) an unmagnetized and (b) a magnetized material.

Applications Permanent magnets are used in switches such as the normally closed (NC) switch. When a magnet is near the switch mechanism, as shown in Figure 7–6(a), the metallic arm is held in its NC position. When the magnet is moved away, the spring pulls the arm up, breaking the contact as shown in part (b).

Switches of this type are commonly used in perimeter alarm systems to detect entry into a building through windows or doors. As Figure 7–7 shows, several openings can be protected by magnetic switches wired to a common transmitter. When any one of the switches opens, the transmitter is activated and sends a signal to a central receiver and alarm unit.

▶ FIGURE 7–6

Operation of a magnetic switch.

(a) Contact is closed when magnet is near.

(b) Contact opens when magnet is moved away.

▶ FIGURE 7–7

Connection of a typical perimeter alarm system.

SECTION 7–1 REVIEW Answers are at the end of the chapter.	1. When the north poles of two magnets are placed close together, do they repel or attract each other? 2. What is magnetic flux? 3. What is the flux density when $\phi = 4.5 \, \mu$Wb and $A = 5 \times 10^{-3}$ m^2?

7–2 Electromagnetism

Electromagnetism is the production of a magnetic field by current in a conductor.

After completing this section, you should be able to

- ◆ **Explain the principles of electromagnetism**
  - ◆ Determine the direction of the magnetic lines of force
  - ◆ Define *permeability*
  - ◆ Define *reluctance*
  - ◆ Define *magnetomotive force*
  - ◆ Describe a basic electromagnet

Current produces a magnetic field, called an **electromagnetic field**, around a conductor, as illustrated in Figure 7–8. The invisible lines of force of the magnetic field form a concentric circular pattern around the conductor and are continuous along its length. The direction of the lines of force surrounding a conductor for the given current direction is as indicated. The lines of force are in a clockwise direction. When current is reversed, the magnetic field lines are in a counterclockwise direction.

Magnetic lines of force
are continuous along conductor

▲ FIGURE 7–8

Magnetic field around a current-carrying conductor. The red arrows indicate the direction of electron (− to +) current.

Although the magnetic field cannot be seen, it is capable of producing visible effects. For example, if a current-carrying wire is inserted through a sheet of paper in a perpendicular direction, iron filings placed on the surface of the paper arrange themselves along the magnetic lines of force in concentric rings, as illustrated in Figure 7–9(a). Part (b) of the figure illustrates that the needle of a compass placed in the electromagnetic field will point in the direction of the lines of force. The field is stronger closer to the conductor and becomes weaker with increasing distance from the conductor.

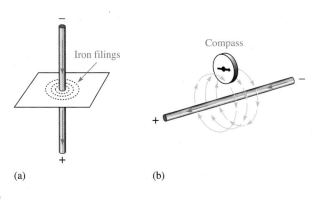

Iron filings

Compass

(a)   (b)

▲ FIGURE 7–9

Visible effects of an electromagnetic field.

Left-Hand Rule   An aid to remembering the direction of the lines of force is illustrated in Figure 7–10. Imagine that you are grasping the conductor with your left hand, with your thumb pointing in the direction of current. Your fingers indicate the direction of the magnetic lines of force.

Illustration of left-hand rule. The left hand rule is used for electron flow current (− to +).

Electromagnetic Properties

Several important properties related to electromagnetic fields are now discussed.

Permeability (μ) The ease with which a magnetic field can be established in a given material is measured by the **permeability** of that material. The higher the permeability, the more easily a magnetic field can be established. The symbol of permeability is μ (the Greek letter mu).

A material's permeability depends on its type. The permeability of a vacuum (μ_0) is 4×10^{-7} Wb/At·m (webers/ampere-turn·meter) and is used as a reference. Ferromagnetic materials typically have permeabilities hundreds of times larger than that of a vacuum, indicating that a magnetic field can be set up with relative ease in these materials. Ferromagnetic materials include iron, steel, nickel, cobalt, and their alloys.

The *relative permeability* (μ_r) of a material is the ratio of its absolute permeability (μ) to the permeability of a vacuum (μ_0). Because it is a ratio of permeabilities, μ_r has no units. Typical magnetic materials, such as iron, have a relative permeability of a few hundred. Highly permeable materials can have a relative permeability as high as 100,000.

Equation 7–2

$$\mu_r = \frac{\mu}{\mu_0}$$

Reluctance $(\mathcal{R})$ The opposition to the establishment of a magnetic field in a material is called **reluctance** $(\mathcal{R})$. The value of reluctance is directly proportional to the length (l) of the magnetic path, and inversely proportional to the permeability (μ) and to the cross-sectional area (A) of the material, as expressed by the following equation:

Equation 7–3

$$\mathcal{R} = \frac{l}{\mu A}$$

Reluctance in magnetic circuits is analogous to resistance in electric circuits. The unit of reluctance can be derived using l in meters, A (area) in square meters, and μ in Wb/At·m as follows:

$$\mathcal{R} = \frac{l}{\mu A} = \frac{\cancel{m}}{(\text{Wb/At}\cdot\cancel{m})(\cancel{m^2})} = \frac{\text{At}}{\text{Wb}}$$

At/Wb is ampere-turns/weber.

Equation 7–3 is similar to Equation 2–6 for determining wire resistance. Recall Equation 2–6 is

$$R = \frac{\rho l}{A}$$

The reciprocal of resistivity (ρ) is conductivity (σ). By substituting $1/\sigma$ for ρ, Equation 2–6 can be written as

$$R = \frac{l}{\sigma A}$$

Compare this last equation for wire resistance with Equation 7–3. The length (l) and the area (A) have the same meaning in both equations. The conductivity (σ) in electrical circuits is analogous to permeability (μ) in magnetic circuits. Also, resistance (R) in electric circuits is analogous to reluctance ($\mathcal{R}$) in magnetic circuits; both are oppositions. Typically, the reluctance of a magnetic circuit is 50,000 At/Wb or more, depending on the size and type of material.

EXAMPLE 7–3

Calculate the reluctance of a torus (a doughnut-shaped core) made of low-carbon steel. The inner radius of the torus is 1.75 cm and the outer radius of the torus is 2.25 cm. Assume the permeability of low-carbon steel is 2×10^{-4} Wb/At·m.

Solution

You must convert centimeters to meters before you calculate the area and length. From the dimensions given, the thickness (diameter) is 0.5 cm = 0.005 m. Thus, the cross-sectional area is

$$A = \pi r^2 = \pi (0.0025)^2 = 1.96 \times 10^{-5}\,\text{m}^2$$

The length is equal to the circumference of the torus measured at the average radius of 2.0 cm or 0.020 m.

$$l = C = 2\pi r = 2\pi(0.020\,\text{m}) = 0.125\,\text{m}$$

Substituting values into Equation 7–3,

$$\mathcal{R} = \frac{l}{\mu A} = \frac{0.125\,\text{m}}{(2 \times 10^{-4}\,\text{Wb/At·m})(1.96 \times 10^{-5}\,\text{m}^2)} = \mathbf{31.9 \times 10^6\,At/Wb}$$

Related Problem

What happens to the reluctance if cast steel with a permeability of 5×10^{-4} Wb/At·m is substituted for the cast iron core?

EXAMPLE 7–4

Mild steel has a relative permeability of 800. Calculate the reluctance of a mild steel core that has a length of 10 cm, and has a cross section of 1.0 cm × 1.2 cm.

Solution

First, determine the permeability of mild steel.

$$\mu = \mu_0 \mu_r = (4\pi \times 10^{-7}\,\text{Wb/At·m})(800) = 1.00 \times 10^{-3}\,\text{Wb/At·m}$$

Next, convert the length to meters and the area to square meters.

$$l = 10\,\text{cm} = 0.10\,\text{m}$$
$$A = 0.010\,\text{m} \times 0.012\,\text{m} = 1.2 \times 10^{-4}\,\text{m}^2$$

Substituting values into Equation 7–3,

$$\mathcal{R} = \frac{l}{\mu A} = \frac{0.10\,\text{m}}{(1.00 \times 10^{-3}\,\text{Wb/At·m})(1.2 \times 10^{-4}\,\text{m}^2)} = \mathbf{8.33 \times 10^5\,At/Wb}$$

Related Problem

What happens to the reluctance if the core is made from 78 Permalloy with a relative permeability of 4000?

Magnetomotive Force (mmf)   As you have learned, current in a conductor produces a magnetic field. The cause of a magnetic field is called the **magnetomotive force (mmf)**. Magnetomotive force is something of a misnomer because in a physics sense it is not really a force, rather a direct result of the movement of charge (current). The unit of mmf, the ampere-turn (At), is established on the basis of the current in a coil of wire. The formula for mmf is

Equation 7–4

$$F_m = NI$$

where F_m is the magnetomotive force, N is the number of turns of wire, and I is the current in amperes.

Figure 7–11 illustrates that a number of turns of wire carrying a current around a magnetic material creates a force that sets up flux lines through the magnetic path. The amount of flux depends on the magnitude of the mmf and on the reluctance of the material, as expressed by the following equation:

Equation 7–5

$$\phi = \frac{F_m}{\mathcal{R}}$$

Equation 7–5 is known as the *Ohm's law for electromagnetic circuits* because the flux (ϕ) is analogous to current, the mmf (F_m) is analogous to voltage, and the reluctance ($\mathcal{R}$) is analogous to resistance.

▶ FIGURE 7–11

A basic electromagnetic circuit.

How much flux is established in the magnetic path of Figure 7–12 if the reluctance of the material is 2.8×10^5 At/Wb?

EXAMPLE 7–5

▶ FIGURE 7–12

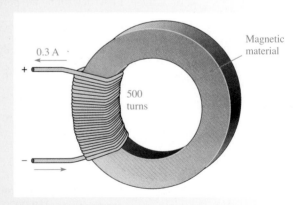

Solution

$$\phi = \frac{F_m}{\mathcal{R}} = \frac{NI}{\mathcal{R}} = \frac{(500 \text{ t})(0.3 \text{ A})}{2.8 \times 10^5 \text{At/Wb}} = 5.36 \times 10^{-4} \text{ Wb} = \mathbf{536 \ \mu Wb}$$

Related Problem How much flux is established in the magnetic path of Figure 7–12 if the reluctance is 7.5×10^3 At/Wb, the number of turns is 300, and the current is 0.18 A?

EXAMPLE 7–6

There is 0.1 ampere of current through a coil with 400 turns.

(a) What is the mmf?

(b) What is the reluctance of the circuit if the flux is 250 μWb?

Solution   **(a)** $N = 400$ and $I = 0.1$ A

$$F_m = NI = (400\,\text{t})(0.1\,\text{A}) = \mathbf{40\,At}$$

(b) $\mathcal{R} = \dfrac{F_m}{\phi} = \dfrac{40\,\text{At}}{250\,\mu\text{Wb}} = \mathbf{1.60 \times 10^5\,At/Wb}$

Related Problem   Rework the example for $I = 85$ mA, $N = 500$, and $\phi = 500\,\mu$Wb.

The Electromagnet

An electromagnet is based on the properties that you have just learned. A basic electromagnet is simply a coil of wire wound around a core material that can be easily magnetized.

The shape of the electromagnet can be designed for various applications. For example, Figure 7–13 shows a U-shaped magnetic core. When the coil of wire is connected to a battery and there is current, as shown in part (a), a magnetic field is established as indicated. If the current is reversed, as shown in part (b), the direction of the magnetic field is also reversed. The closer the north and south poles are brought together, the smaller the air gap between them becomes, and the easier it becomes to establish a magnetic field because the reluctance is reduced.

(a)   (b)

◀ FIGURE 7–13

Reversing the current in the coil causes the electromagnetic field to reverse.

SECTION 7–2 REVIEW

1. Explain the difference between magnetism and electromagnetism.
2. What happens to the magnetic field in an electromagnet when the current through the coil is reversed?
3. State Ohm's law for electromagnetic circuits.
4. Compare each quantity in Question 3 to its electrical counterpart.

7–3 ELECTROMAGNETIC DEVICES

Many types of useful devices such as tape recorders, electric motors, speakers, solenoids, and relays are based on electromagnetism. The transformer is another important example and will be covered in Chapter 14.

After completing this section, you should be able to

◆ **Describe the principle of operation for several types of electromagnetic devices**

   ◆ Discuss how a solenoid and a solenoid valve work

   ◆ Discuss how a relay works

   ◆ Discuss how a speaker works

   ◆ Discuss the basic analog meter movement

   ◆ Explain a magnetic disk and tape read/write operation

   ◆ Explain the concept of the magneto-optical disk

The Solenoid

The **solenoid** is a type of electromagnetic device that has a movable iron core called a *plunger*. The movement of this iron core depends on both an electromagnetic field and a mechanical spring force. The basic structure of a solenoid is shown in Figure 7–14. It consists of a cylindrical coil of wire wound around a nonmagnetic hollow form. A stationary iron core is fixed in position at the end of the shaft, and a sliding iron core is attached to the stationary core with a spring.

(a) Solenoid

(b) Basic construction

(c) Cutaway view

▲ FIGURE 7–14

Basic solenoid structure.

In the at-rest (or unenergized) state, the plunger is extended as shown in Figure 7–15(a). The solenoid is energized by current through the coil, as shown in part (b). The current sets up an electromagnetic field that magnetizes both iron cores as indicated. The south pole of the stationary core attracts the north pole of the movable core, which causes it to slide inward, thus retracting the plunger and compressing the spring. As long as there is coil current, the plunger remains retracted by the attractive force of the magnetic fields. When the current is cut off, the magnetic fields collapse; and the force of the compressed spring pushes the plunger back out. The solenoid is used for applications such as opening and closing valves and automobile door locks.

(a) Unenergized (no voltage or current)– plunger extended

(b) Energized – plunger retracted

▲ FIGURE 7–15

Basic solenoid operation.

Solenoid Valves   In industrial controls, **solenoid valves** are widely used to control the flow of air, water, steam, oils, refrigerants, and other fluids. Solenoid valves are used in both pneumatic (air) and hydraulic (oil) systems, common in machine controls. Solenoid valves are also common in the aerospace and medical fields. Solenoid valves can either move a plunger to open or close a port or can rotate a blocking flap a fixed amount.

A solenoid valve consists of two functional units: a solenoid coil that provides the magnetic field to provide the required movement to open or close the valve and a valve body, which is isolated from the coil assembly via a leakproof seal and includes a pipe and butterfly valve. Figure 7–16 shows a cutaway of one type of solenoid valve. When the solenoid is energized, the butterfly valve is turned to open a normally closed (NC) valve or to close a normally open (NO) valve.

Solenoid valves are available with a wide variety of configurations including normally open or normally closed valves. They are rated for different types of fluids (for example, gas or water), pressures, number of pathways, sizes, and more. The same valve may control more than one line and may have more than one solenoid to move.

▲ FIGURE 7–16

A basic solenoid valve structure.

The Relay

Relays differ from solenoids in that the electromagnetic action is used to open or close electrical contacts rather than to provide mechanical movement. Figure 7–17 shows the basic operation of an armature-type relay with one normally open (NO) contact and one normally closed (NC) contact (single pole–double throw). When there is no coil current, the armature is held against the upper contact by the spring, thus providing continuity from terminal 1 to terminal 2, as shown in Figure 7–17(a). When energized with coil current, the armature is pulled down by the attractive force of the electromagnetic field and makes connection with the lower contact to provide continuity from terminal 1 to terminal 3, as shown in Figure 7–17(b).

◀ FIGURE 7–17

Basic structure of a single-pole–double-throw armature relay.

(a) Unenergized: continuity from terminal 1
   to terminal 2

(b) Energized: continuity from terminal 1
   to terminal 3

A typical armature relay and its schematic symbol are shown in Figure 7–18.

▶ FIGURE 7–18

A typical armature relay.

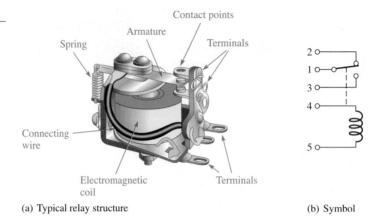

(a) Typical relay structure   (b) Symbol

Another widely used type of relay is the *reed relay,* which is shown in Figure 7–19. The reed relay, like the armature relay, uses an electromagnetic coil. The contacts are thin reeds of magnetic material and are usually located inside the coil. When there is no coil current, the reeds are in the open position as shown in Figure 7–19(b). When there is current through the coil, the reeds make contact because they are magnetized and attract each other as shown in part (c).

▶ FIGURE 7–19

Basic structure of a reed relay.

(a)   (b) Unenergized   (c) Energized

Reed relays are faster, are more reliable, and produce less contact arcing than armature relays. However, they have less current-handling capability than armature relays and are more susceptible to mechanical shock.

The Speaker

A **speaker** is an electromagnetic device that converts electrical signals to sound waves. Permanent-magnet speakers are commonly used in stereos, radios, and TVs, and their operation is based on the principle of electromagnetism. A typical speaker is constructed with a permanent magnet and an electromagnet, as shown in Figure 7–20(a). The cone of the speaker consists of a paper-like flexible diaphragm to which is attached a hollow cylinder with a coil around it, forming an electromagnet. One of the poles of the permanent magnet is positioned within the cylindrical coil. When there is current through the coil in one direction, the interaction of the permanent magnetic field with the electromagnetic field causes the cone to move to the right, as indicated in Figure 7–20(b).

(a) Basic speaker construction

(b) Coil current producing movement of cone to the right

(c) Coil current producing movement of cone to the left

▲ FIGURE 7–20

Basic speaker operation with movement exaggerated to illustrate the principle.

Current through the coil in the other direction causes the cone to move to the left, as shown in Figure 7–20(c).

The movement of the coil cylinder causes the flexible diaphragm also to move in or out, depending on the direction of the coil current. The amount of coil current determines the intensity of the magnetic field, which controls the amount that the diaphragm moves.

As shown in Figure 7–21, when an audio signal voltage (voice or music) is applied to the speaker coil, the current varies proportionally in both direction and amount. In response, the diaphragm will vibrate in and out by varying amounts and at varying rates. Vibration in the diaphragm causes the air that is in contact with it to vibrate in the same manner. These air vibrations move through the air as sound waves.

(a) Speaker

(b) How the speaker produces sound

▲ FIGURE 7–21

The speaker converts audio signal voltages into sound waves.

Meter Movement

The d'Arsonval meter movement is the most common type used in analog multimeters. In this type of meter movement, the pointer is deflected in proportion to the amount of current

The basic d'Arsonval meter movement.

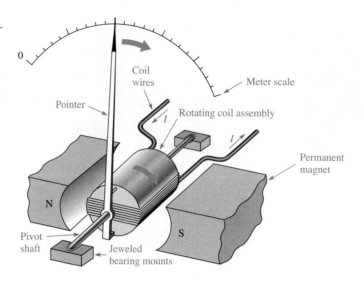

through a coil. Figure 7–22 shows a basic d'Arsonval meter movement. It consists of a coil of wire wound on a bearing-mounted assembly that is placed between the poles of a permanent magnet. A pointer is attached to the moving assembly. With no current through the coil, a spring mechanism keeps the pointer at its left-most (zero) position. When there is current through the coil, electromagnetic forces act on the coil, causing a rotation to the right. The amount of rotation depends on the amount of current.

Figure 7–23 illustrates how the interaction of magnetic fields produces rotation of the coil assembly. Current is inward at the "cross" and outward at the "dot" in the single winding shown. The inward current produces a counterclockwise electromagnetic field that reinforces the permanent magnetic field below it. The result is an upward force on the left side of the coil as shown. A downward force is developed on the right side of the coil, where the current is outward. These forces produce a clockwise rotation of the coil assembly and are opposed by a spring mechanism. The indicated forces and the spring force are balanced at the value of the current. When current is removed, the spring force returns the pointer to its zero position.

▶ FIGURE 7–23

When the electromagnetic field interacts with the permanent magnetic field, forces are exerted on the rotating coil assembly, causing it to move clockwise and thus deflecting the pointer.

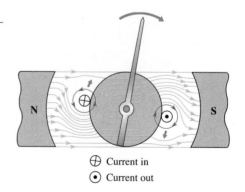

⊕ Current in
⊙ Current out

Magnetic Disk and Tape Read/Write Head

A simplified diagram of a magnetic disk or tape surface read/write operation is shown in Figure 7–24. A data bit (1 or 0) is written on the magnetic surface by the magnetization

(a) The magnetic flux from the write head follows the low reluctance path through the moving magnetic surface.

(b) When read head passes over magnetized spot, an induced voltage appears at the output.

▲ **FIGURE 7–24**

Read/write function on a magnetic surface.

of a small segment of the surface as it moves by the write head. The direction of the magnetic flux lines is controlled by the direction of the current pulse in the winding, as shown in Figure 7–24(a) for the case of a positive pulse. At the air gap in the write head, the magnetic flux takes a path through the surface of the storage device. This magnetizes a small spot on the surface in the direction of the field. A magnetized spot of one polarity represents a binary 1, and one of the opposite polarity represents a binary 0. Once a spot on the surface is magnetized, it remains until written over with an opposite magnetic field.

When the magnetic surface passes a read head, the magnetized spots produce magnetic fields in the read head, which induce voltage pulses in the winding. The polarity of these pulses depends on the direction of the magnetized spot and indicates whether the stored bit is a 1 or a 0. This process is illustrated in Figure 7–24(b). Often the read and write heads are combined into a single unit.

The Magneto-Optical Disk

The magneto-optical disk uses an electromagnet and laser beams to read and write (record) data on a magnetic surface. Magneto-optical disks are formatted in tracks and sectors similar to magnetic floppy disks and hard disks. However, because of the ability of a laser beam to be precisely directed to an extremely small spot, magneto-optical disks are capable of storing much more data than standard magnetic hard disks.

Figure 7–25(a) illustrates a small cross-sectional area of a disk before recording, with an electromagnet positioned below it. Tiny magnetic particles, represented by the arrows, are all magnetized in the same direction.

Writing (recording) on the disk is accomplished by applying an external magnetic field opposite to the direction of the magnetic particles as indicated in Figure 7–25(b) and then directing a high-power laser beam to heat the disk at a precise spot where a binary 1 is to be stored. The disk material, a magneto-optic alloy, is highly resistant to magnetization at room temperature; but at the spot where the laser beam heats the material, the inherent direction of magnetism is reversed by the external magnetic field produced by the electromagnet. At points where binary 0s are to be stored, the laser beam is not applied and the inherent upward direction of the magnetic particle remains.

As illustrated in Figure 7–25(c), reading data from the disk is accomplished by turning off the external magnetic field and directing a low-power laser beam at a spot where a bit is to be read. Basically, if a binary 1 is stored at the spot (reversed magnetization),

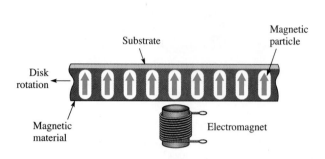

(a) Small cross-section of unrecorded disk

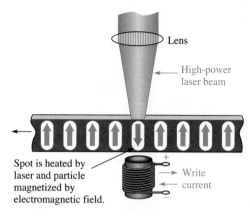

(b) Writing: A high-power laser beam heats the spot, causing the magnetic particle to align with the electromagnetic field.

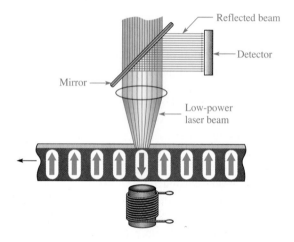

(c) Reading: A low-power laser beam reflects off of the reversed-polarity magnetic particle and its polarization shifts. If the particle is not reversed, the polarization of the reflected beam is unchanged.

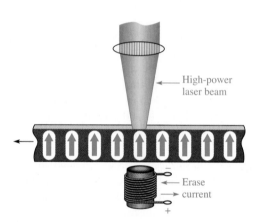

(d) Erasing: The electromagnetic field is reversed as the high-power laser beam heats the spot, causing the magnetic particle to be restored to the original polarity.

▲ FIGURE 7–25

Basic concept of the magneto-optical disk.

the low-power laser beam is reflected and its polarization is shifted; but if a binary 0 is stored, the polarization of the reflected laser beam is unchanged. A detector senses the difference in the polarity of the reflected laser beam to determine if the bit being read is a 1 or a 0.

Figure 7–25(d) shows that the disk is erased by restoring the original magnetic direction of each particle by reversing the external magnetic field and applying the high-power laser beam.

SECTION 7–3 REVIEW

1. Explain the difference between a solenoid and a relay.
2. What is the movable part of a solenoid called?
3. What is the movable part of a relay called?
4. Upon what basic principle is the d'Arsonval meter movement based?

7–4   MAGNETIC HYSTERESIS

When a magnetizing force is applied to a material, the magnetic flux density in the material changes in a certain way.

After completing this section, you should be able to

◆ **Explain magnetic hysteresis**

  ◆ State the formula for magnetic field intensity

  ◆ Discuss a hysteresis curve

  ◆ Define *retentivity*

Magnetic Field Intensity (H)

The **magnetic field intensity** (also called *magnetizing force*) in a material is defined to be the magnetomotive force (F_m) per unit length (l) of the material, as expressed by the following equation. The unit of magnetic field intensity (H) is ampere-turns per meter (At/m).

$$H = \frac{F_m}{l}$$

Equation 7–6

where $F_m = NI$. Note that the magnetic field intensity (H) depends on the number of turns (N) of the coil of wire, the current (I) through the coil, and the length (l) of the material. It does not depend on the type of material.

Since $\phi = F_m/\mathcal{R}$, as $F_m\mathcal{R}$ increases, the flux increases. Also, the magnetic field intensity (H) increases. Recall that the flux density (B) is the flux per unit cross-sectional area ($B = \phi/A$), so B is also proportional to H. The curve showing how these two quantities (B and H) are related is called the *B-H* curve, or the hysteresis curve. The parameters that influence both B and H are illustrated in Figure 7–26.

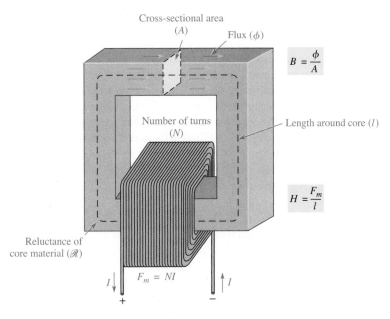

◀ FIGURE 7–26

Parameters that determine the magnetic field intensity (H) and the flux density (B).

The Hysteresis Curve and Retentivity

Hysteresis is a characteristic of a magnetic material whereby a change in magnetization lags the application of the magnetic field intensity. The magnetic field intensity (H) can be readily increased or decreased by varying the current through the coil of wire, and it can be reversed by reversing the voltage polarity across the coil.

Figure 7–27 illustrates the development of the hysteresis curve. Let's start by assuming a magnetic core is unmagnetized so that $B = 0$. As the magnetic field intensity (H) is increased from zero, the flux density (B) increases proportionally as indicated by the curve in Figure 7–27(a). When H reaches a certain value, the value of B begins to level off. As H continues to increase, B reaches a saturation value (B_{sat}) when H reaches a value (H_{sat}), as illustrated in Figure 7–27(b). Once saturation is reached, a further increase in H will not increase B.

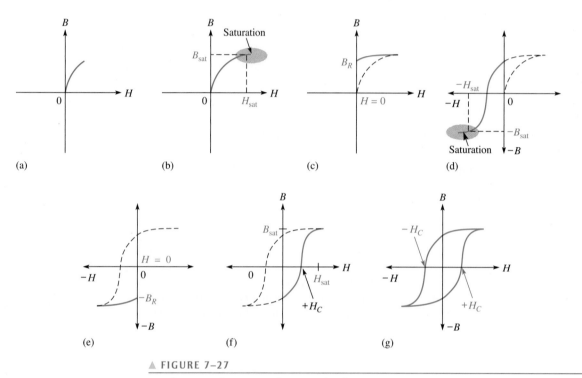

▲ FIGURE 7–27

Development of a magnetic hysteresis (B-H) curve.

Now, if H is decreased to zero, B will fall back along a different path to a residual value (B_R), as shown in Figure 7–27(c). This indicates that the material continues to be magnetized even when the magnetic field intensity is removed ($H = 0$). The ability of a material, once magnetized, to maintain a magnetized state without magnetic field intensity is called **retentivity**. The retentivity of a material is indicated by the ratio of B_R to B_{sat}.

Reversal of the magnetic field intensity is represented by negative values of H on the curve and is achieved by reversing the current in the coil of wire. An increase in H in the negative direction causes saturation to occur at a value ($-H_{sat}$) where the flux density is at its maximum negative value, as indicated in Figure 7–27(d).

When the magnetic field intensity is removed ($H = 0$), the flux density goes to its negative residual value ($-B_R$), as shown in Figure 7–27(e). From the $-B_R$ value, the flux density follows the curve indicated in part (f) back to its maximum positive value when the magnetic field intensity equals H_{sat} in the positive direction.

The complete B-H curve is shown in Figure 7–27(g) and is called the *hysteresis curve*. The magnetic field intensity required to make the flux density zero is called the *coercive force, H_C*.

Materials with a low retentivity do not retain a magnetic field very well while those with high retentivities exhibit values of B_R very close to the saturation value of B. Depending on the application, retentivity in a magnetic material can be an advantage or a disadvantage. In permanent magnets and memory cores, for example, high retentivity is required. In ac motors, retentivity is undesirable because the residual magnetic field must be overcome each time the current reverses, thus wasting energy.

SECTION 7–4 REVIEW	1. For a given wirewound core, how does an increase in current through the coil affect the flux density?
	2. Define *retentivity*.

7–5 ELECTROMAGNETIC INDUCTION

When there is relative motion between a conductor and a magnetic field, a voltage is produced across the conductor. This principle is known as electromagnetic induction, and the resulting voltage is an induced voltage. The principle of electromagnetic induction is what makes transformers, electrical generators, electrical motors, and many other devices possible.

After completing this section, you should be able to

- ◆ **Discuss the principle of electromagnetic induction**
  - ◆ Explain how voltage is induced in a conductor in a magnetic field
  - ◆ Determine polarity of an induced voltage
  - ◆ Discuss forces on a conductor in a magnetic field
  - ◆ State Faraday's law
  - ◆ State Lenz's law

Relative Motion

When a conductor is moved across a magnetic field, there is a relative motion between the conductor and the magnetic field. Likewise, when a magnetic field is moved past a stationary conductor, there is also relative motion. In either case, this relative motion results in an **induced voltage** (v_{ind}) across the conductor, as Figure 7–28 indicates. The lowercase v stands for instantaneous voltage. The amount of the induced voltage depends on the rate at which the conductor and the magnetic field move with respect to each other: The faster the relative motion, the greater the induced voltage.

(a) Conductor moving downward

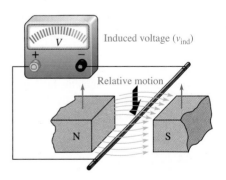

(b) Magnetic field moving upward

◀ **FIGURE 7–28**

Relative motion between a conductor and a magnetic field.

Polarity of the Induced Voltage

If the conductor in Figure 7–28 is moved first one way and then another in the magnetic field, a reversal of the polarity of the induced voltage will be observed. When the relative motion of the conductor is downward, a voltage is induced with the polarity indicated in Figure 7–29(a). When the relative motion of the conductor is upward, the polarity is as indicated in part (b) of the figure.

▶ FIGURE 7–29

Polarity of induced voltage depends on direction of motion of the conductor relative to the magnetic field.

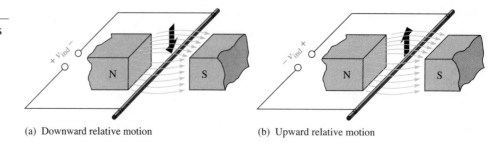

(a) Downward relative motion   (b) Upward relative motion

BIOGRAPHY

Michael Faraday 1791–1867

Faraday was an English physicist and chemist who is best remembered for his contribution to the understanding of electromagnetism. He discovered that electricity could be produced by moving a magnet inside a coil of wire, and he was able to build the first electric motor. He later built the first electromagnetic generator and transformer. The statement of the principles of electromagnetic induction is known today as Faraday's law. Also, the unit of capacitance, the *farad,* is named after him. (Photo credit: Library of Congress.)

Induced Current

When a load resistor is connected to the conductor in Figure 7–29, the voltage induced by the relative motion between the conductor and the magnetic field will cause a current in the load, as shown in Figure 7–30. This current is called the **induced current** (i_{ind}). The lowercase i stands for instantaneous current.

▶ FIGURE 7–30

Induced current (i_{ind}) in a load as the conductor moves through the magnetic field.

The action of producing a voltage and a current in a load by moving a conductor across a magnetic field is the basis for electrical generators. A single conductor will have a small induced current, so practical generators use coils with many turns. Also, the existence of a conductor in a moving magnetic field is fundamental to the concept of inductance in an electric circuit.

Forces on a Current-Carrying Conductor in a Magnetic Field (Motor Action)

Figure 7–31(a) shows current inward through a wire in a magnetic field. The electromagnetic field set up by the current interacts with the permanent magnetic field; as a result, the permanent lines of force above the wire tend to be deflected down under the wire because they are opposite in direction to the electromagnetic lines of force. Therefore, the flux density above is reduced, and the magnetic field is weakened. The flux density below the conductor is increased, and the magnetic field is strengthened. An upward force on the conductor results, and the conductor tends to move toward the weaker magnetic field. Figure 7–31(b) shows the

▶ FIGURE 7–31

Forces on a current-carrying conductor in a magnetic field.

(a) Upward force: weak field above, strong field below.

(b) Downward force: strong field above, weak field below

⊕ Current in
⊙ Current out

current outward, resulting in a force on the conductor in the downward direction. These upward and downward forces on a conductor are the basis for electric motors.

Faraday's Law

Michael Faraday discovered the principle of **electromagnetic induction** in 1831. He found that moving a magnet through a coil of wire induced a voltage across the coil; he also found that when a complete path was provided, the induced voltage caused an induced current, as you have learned. Faraday's two observations are stated as follows:

1. The amount of voltage induced in a coil is directly proportional to the rate of change of the magnetic field with respect to the coil.

2. The amount of voltage induced in a coil is directly proportional to the number of turns of wire in the coil.

Faraday's first observation is demonstrated in Figure 7–32, where a bar magnet is moved through a coil, thus creating a changing magnetic field. In part (a) of the figure, the magnet is moved at a certain rate, and a certain induced voltage is produced as indicated. In part (b), the magnet is moved at a faster rate through the coil, creating a greater induced voltage.

(a) As the magnet moves slowly to the right, its magnetic field is changing with respect to coil, and a voltage is induced.

(b) As the magnet moves more rapidly to the right, its magnetic field is changing more rapidly with respect to coil, and a greater voltage is induced.

▲ FIGURE 7–32

A demonstration of Faraday's first observation: The amount of induced voltage is directly proportional to the rate of change of the magnetic field with respect to the coil.

Faraday's second observation is demonstrated in Figure 7–33. In part (a), the magnet is moved through the coil and a voltage is induced as shown. In part (b), the magnet is moved at the same rate through a coil that has a greater number of turns. The greater number of turns creates a greater induced voltage.

(a) Magnet moves through a coil and induces a voltage.

(b) Magnet moves at same rate through a coil with more turns (loops) and induces a greater voltage.

▲ FIGURE 7–33

A demonstration of Faraday's second observation: The amount of induced voltage is directly proportional to the number of turns in the coil.

BIOGRAPHY

Heinrich
F. E. Lenz
1804–1865

Lenz was born in Estonia (then Russia) and became a professor at the University of St. Petersburg. He carried out many experiments following Faraday's lead and formulated the principle of electromagnetism, which defines the polarity of induced voltage in a coil. The statement of this principle is named in his honor. (Photo credit: AIP Emilio Segré Visual Archives, E. Scott Barr Collection.)

Faraday's law is stated as follows:

The voltage induced across a coil of wire equals the number of turns in the coil times the rate of change of the magnetic flux.

Lenz's Law

You have learned that a changing magnetic field induces a voltage in a coil that is directly proportional to the rate of change of the magnetic field and the number of turns in the coil. **Lenz's law** defines the polarity or direction of the induced voltage.

When the current through a coil changes, the polarity of the induced voltage created by the changing magnetic field is such that it always opposes the change in current that caused it.

**SECTION 7–5
REVIEW**

1. What is the induced voltage across a stationary conductor in a stationary magnetic field?
2. When the rate at which a conductor is moved through a magnetic field is increased, does the induced voltage increase, decrease, or remain the same?
3. When there is current through a conductor in a magnetic field, what happens?

7–6 APPLICATIONS OF ELECTROMAGNETIC INDUCTION

Two representative applications of electromagnetic induction are an automotive crankshaft position sensor and a dc generator.

After completing this section, you should be able to

◆ **Describe some applications of electromagnetic induction**

  ◆ Explain how a crankshaft position sensor works
  ◆ Explain how a dc generator works

Automotive Crankshaft Position Sensor

A type of automotive engine sensor detects the crankshaft position directly using electromagnetic induction. The electronic engine controller in many automobiles uses the position of the crankshaft to set ignition timing and, sometimes, to adjust the fuel control system. Figure 7–34 shows the basic concept. A steel disk is attached to the engine's crankshaft by an extension rod; the protruding tabs on the disk represent specific crankshaft positions.

A crankshaft position sensor that produces a voltage when a tab passes through the air gap of the magnet.

As illustrated in Figure 7–34, as the disk rotates with the crankshaft, the tabs periodically pass through the air gap of the permanent magnet. Since steel has a much lower reluctance than does air (a magnetic field can be established in steel much more easily than in air), the magnetic flux suddenly increases as a tab comes into the air gap, causing a momentary voltage to be induced across the coil. This process is illustrated in Figure 7–35. The electronic engine control circuit uses the induced voltage as an indicator of the crankshaft position.

As the tab passes through the air gap of the magnet, the coil senses a change in the magnetic field, and a voltage is induced.

(a) There is no changing magnetic field, so there is no induced voltage.

(b) Insertion of the steel tab reduces the reluctance of the air gap, causing the magnetic flux to momentarily increase and thus inducing a momentary voltage.

DC Generator

Figure 7–36 shows a greatly simplified dc generator consisting of a single loop of wire that rotates in a permanent magnetic field. Notice that each end of the loop is connected to a split-ring arrangement. This conductive metal ring is called a *commutator*. As the wire loop

A basic dc generator.

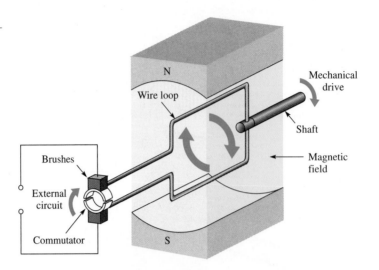

rotates in the magnetic field, the split commutator ring also rotates. Each half of the split ring rubs against the fixed contacts, called *brushes,* and connects the wire to an external circuit.

Driven by an external mechanical force, the loop of wire rotates through the magnetic field and cuts through the flux lines at varying angles, as illustrated in Figure 7–37. At position *A* in its rotation, the loop is effectively moving parallel with the magnetic field. Therefore, at this instant, the rate at which it is cutting through the magnetic flux lines is zero. As the loop moves from position *A* to position *B*, it cuts through the flux lines at an increasing rate. At position *B*, it is moving effectively perpendicular to the magnetic field and thus is cutting through a maximum number of lines. As the loop rotates from position *B* to position *C*, the rate at which it cuts the flux lines decreases to minimum (zero) at *C*. From position *C* to position *D*, the rate at which the loop cuts the flux lines increases to a maximum at *D* and then back to a minimum again at *A*.

▶ FIGURE 7–37

End view of loop of wire cutting through the magnetic field.

As you have learned, when a wire moves through a magnetic field, a voltage is induced, and by Faraday's law, the amount of induced voltage is proportional to the number of loops (turns) in the wire and the rate at which it is moving with respect to the magnetic field. The angle at which the wire moves with respect to the magnetic flux lines determines the amount of induced voltage because the rate at which the wire cuts through the flux lines depends on the angle of motion.

Figure 7–38 illustrates how a voltage is induced in the external circuit as a single loop of wire rotates in the magnetic field. Assume that the loop is in its instantaneous horizontal position, so the induced voltage is zero. As the loop continues in its rotation, the induced

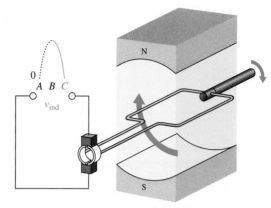

(a) Position *B*: Loop is moving perpendicular to flux lines, and voltage is maximum.

(b) Position *C*: Loop is moving parallel with flux lines, and voltage is zero.

(c) Position *D*: Loop is moving perpendicular to flux lines, and voltage is maximum.

(d) Position *A*: Loop is moving parallel with flux lines, and voltage is zero.

▲ FIGURE 7–38

Basic operation of a dc generator.

voltage builds up to a maximum at position *B*, as shown in part (a) of the figure. Then, as the loop continues from *B* to *C*, the voltage decreases to zero at *C*, as shown in part (b).

During the second half of the revolution, shown in Figure 7–38(c) and (d), the brushes switch to opposite commutator sections, so the polarity of the voltage remains the same across the output. Thus, as the loop rotates from position *C* to *D* and then back to *A*, the voltage increases from zero at *C* to a maximum at *D* and back to zero at *A*.

Figure 7–39 shows how the induced voltage varies as a wire loop in a dc generator goes through several rotations (three in this case). This voltage is a dc voltage because its

◀ FIGURE 7–39

Induced voltage over three rotations of a wire loop in a dc generator.

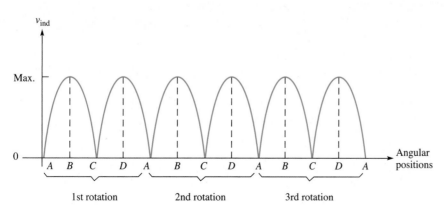

polarity does not change. However, the voltage is pulsating between zero and its maximum value.

When more wire loops are added, the voltages induced across each loop are combined across the output. Since the voltages are offset from each other, they do not reach their maximum or zero values at the same time. A smoother dc voltage results, as shown in Figure 7–40 for two loops. The variations can be further smoothed out by filters to achieve a nearly constant dc voltage. (Filters are discussed later in Chapter 13.)

▶ FIGURE 7–40

The induced voltage for a two-loop generator. There is much less variation in the induced voltage.

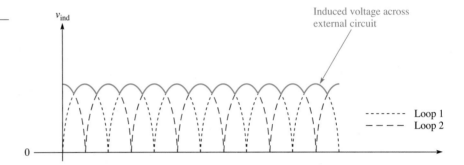

Induced voltage across external circuit

v_{ind}

0

- - - - - - - Loop 1
- - - - Loop 2

DC Motors

In principle, the basic construction of a dc motor is the same as the dc generator except that a dc source is connected to the commutator circuit, producing current through the wire loop. The loop rotates due to the attraction and repulsion of the electromagnetic field set up by the loop current and the static magnetic field. This is called *motor action*. Just as in the dc generator, the commutator serves as a switch to reverse the direction of current in the loop and produce continuous rotation. In the generator, external mechanical energy is used to rotate the loop to produce an induced voltage. In the motor, external electrical energy is used to rotate the loop to produce a mechanical rotation.

| SECTION 7–6 REVIEW | 1. If the steel disk in the crankshaft position sensor has stopped with a tab in the magnet's air gap, what is the induced voltage? |
| | 2. What happens to the induced voltage if the loop in the basic dc generator suddenly begins rotating at a faster speed? |

Application Assignment

PUTTING YOUR KNOWLEDGE TO WORK

The relay is a common type of electromagnetic device that is used in many types of control applications. With a relay, a lower voltage, such as from a battery, can be used to switch a much higher voltage, such as the 110 V from an ac outlet. In this application, you will see how a relay can be used in a basic burglar alarm system.

The schematic in Figure 7–41 shows a simplified intrusion alarm system that uses a relay to turn on an audible alarm (siren) and lights. The system operates from a 9 V battery so that even if power to the house is off, the audible alarm will still work.

The magnetic detection switches are normally open (NO) switches that are parallel connected and located in the windows and doors. The relay is a triple-pole–double-throw device that operates with a coil voltage of 9 V dc and draws approximately 50 mA. When an intrusion occurs, one of the switches closes and allows current from the battery through the relay coil, which energizes the relay and causes the three sets of normally open

Simplified burglar alarm system.

Triple-pole–double-throw relay.

Housing   Pin arrangement (top view)   Schematic

contacts to close. Closure of contact *A* turns on the audible alarm, which draws 2 A from the battery. Closure of contact *C* turns on a light circuit in the house. Closure of contact *B* latches the relay and keeps it energized even if the intruder closes the door or window through which entry was made. If not for contact *B* in parallel with the detection switches, the alarm and lights would go off as soon as the window or door was shut behind the intruder.

The relay contacts are not physically remote in relation to the coil as the schematic indicates. The schematic is drawn this way for functional clarity. The entire triple-pole–double-throw relay is housed in the package shown in Figure 7–42. Also shown are the pin diagram and internal schematic for the relay.

Step 1: Connecting the System

Develop a connection diagram and point-to-point wire list for interconnecting the components in Figure 7–43 to create the alarm system shown in the schematic of Figure 7–41. The connection points on the components are indicated by letters.

Step 2: Testing the System

Develop a step-by-step procedure to check out the completely wired burglar alarm system.

Review

1. How many magnetic detection switches in Figure 7–41 must be closed to activate the system?

2. What is the purpose of each of the three relay contacts?

▶ FIGURE 7–43

Array of burglar alarm components.

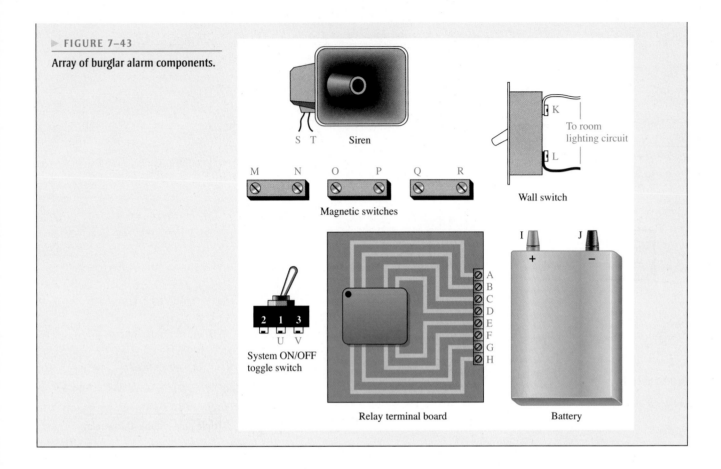

SUMMARY

◆ Unlike magnetic poles attract each other, and like poles repel each other.

◆ Materials that can be magnetized are called *ferromagnetic*.

◆ When there is current through a conductor, it produces an electromagnetic field around the conductor.

◆ You can use the left-hand rule to establish the direction of the electromagnetic lines of force around a conductor.

◆ An electromagnet is basically a coil of wire around a magnetic core.

◆ When a conductor moves within a magnetic field, or when a magnetic field moves relative to a conductor, a voltage is induced across the conductor.

◆ The faster the relative motion between a conductor and a magnetic field, the greater is the induced voltage.

◆ Table 7–2 summarizes the magnetic quantities and SI units.

▶ TABLE 7–2

SYMBOL	QUANTITY	SI UNIT
B	Magnetic flux density	Tesla (T)
ϕ	Flux	Weber (Wb)
μ	Permeability	Webers/ampere-turn·meter (Wb/At·m)
$\mathcal{R}$	Reluctance	Ampere-turns/weber (At/Wb)
F_m	Magnetomotive force (mmf)	Ampere-turn (At)
H	Magnetic field intensity	Ampere-turns/meter (At/m)

KEY TERMS

Key terms and other bold terms in the chapter are defined in the end-of-book glossary.

Ampere-turn (At)   The SI unit of magnetomotive force (mmf).

Electromagnetic field   A formation of a group of magnetic lines of force surrounding a conductor created by electrical current in the conductor.

Electromagnetic induction   The phenomenon or process by which a voltage is produced in a conductor when there is relative motion between the conductor and a magnetic or electromagnetic field.

Electromagnetism   The production of a magnetic field by current in a conductor.

Faraday's law   A law stating that the voltage induced across a coil of wire equals the number of turns in the coil times the rate of change of the magnetic flux.

Gauss   A CGS unit of flux density.

Hysteresis   A characteristic of a magnetic material whereby a change in magnetization lags the application of the magnetic field intensity.

Induced current (i_{ind})   A current induced in a conductor as a result of a changing magnetic field.

Induced voltage (v_{ind})   Voltage produced as a result of a changing magnetic field.

Lenz's law   A physical law that states when the current through a coil changes, the polarity of the induced voltage created by the changing magnetic field is such that it always opposes the change in current that caused it. The current cannot change instantaneously.

Lines of force   Magnetic flux lines in a magnetic field radiating from the north pole to the south pole.

Magnetic field   A force field radiating from the north pole to the south pole of a magnet.

Magnetic flux   The lines of force between the north and south poles of a permanent magnet or an electromagnet.

Magnetic field intensity   The amount of mmf per unit length of magnetic material.

Magnetomotive force (mmf)   The cause of a magnetic field, measured in ampere-turns.

Permeability   The measure of ease with which a magnetic field can be established in a material.

Relay   An electromagnetically controlled mechanical device in which electrical contacts are opened or closed by a magnetizing current.

Reluctance ($\mathcal{R}$)   The opposition to the establishment of a magnetic field in a material.

Retentivity   The ability of a material, once magnetized, to maintain a magnetized state without the presence of a magnetizing force.

Solenoid   An electromagnetically controlled device in which the mechanical movement of a shaft or plunger is activated by a magnetizing current.

Speaker   An electromagnetic device that converts electrical signals to sound waves.

Tesla (T)   The unit of flux density.

Weber (Wb)   The SI unit of magnetic flux, which represents 10^8 lines.

FORMULAS

7–1	$B = \dfrac{\phi}{A}$	Magnetic flux density	
7–2	$\mu_r = \dfrac{\mu}{\mu_0}$	Relative permeability	
7–3	$\mathcal{R} = \dfrac{l}{\mu A}$	Reluctance	
7–4	$F_m = NI$	Magnetomotive force	
7–5	$\phi = \dfrac{F_m}{\mathcal{R}}$	Magnetic flux	
7–6	$H = \dfrac{F_m}{l}$	Magnetic field intensity	

SELF-TEST

Answers are at the end of the chapter.

1. When the south poles of two bar magnets are brought close together, there will be
   (a) a force of attraction   (b) a force of repulsion
   (c) an upward force   (d) no force

2. A magnetic field is made up of
   (a) positive and negative charges   (b) magnetic domains
   (c) flux lines   (d) magnetic poles

3. The direction of a magnetic field is from
   (a) north pole to south pole   (b) south pole to north pole
   (c) inside to outside the magnet   (d) front to back

4. Reluctance in a magnetic circuit is analogous to
   (a) voltage in an electric circuit   (b) current in an electric circuit
   (c) power in an electric circuit   (d) resistance in an electric circuit

5. The unit of magnetic flux is the
   (a) tesla   (b) weber   (c) gauss   (d) ampere-turn

6. The unit of magnetomotive force is the
   (a) tesla   (b) weber   (c) ampere-turn   (d) electron-volt

7. The unit of magnetic flux density is the
   (a) tesla   (b) weber   (c) ampere-turn
   (d) gauss   (e) answer (a) or (d)

8. The electromagnetic activation of a movable shaft is the basis for
   (a) relays   (b) circuit breakers
   (c) magnetic switches   (d) solenoids

9. When there is current through a wire placed in a magnetic field,
   (a) the wire will overheat   (b) the wire will become magnetized
   (c) a force is exerted on the wire   (d) the magnetic field will be cancelled

10. A coil of wire is placed in a changing magnetic field. If the number of turns in the coil is increased, the voltage induced across the coil will
    (a) remain unchanged   (b) decrease
    (c) increase   (d) be excessive

11. If a conductor is moved back and forth at a constant rate in a constant magnetic field, the voltage induced in the conductor will
    (a) remain constant   (b) reverse polarity
    (c) be reduced   (d) be increased

12. In the crankshaft position sensor in Figure 7–34, the induced voltage across the coils is caused by
    (a) current in the coil
    (b) rotation of the disk
    (c) a tab passing through the magnetic field
    (d) acceleration of the disk's rotational speed

PROBLEMS

Answers to odd-numbered problems are at the end of the book.

BASIC PROBLEMS

SECTION 7–1   The Magnetic Field

1. The cross-sectional area of a magnetic field is increased, but the flux remains the same. Does the flux density increase or decrease?

2. In a certain magnetic field the cross-sectional area is 0.5 m² and the flux is 1500 μWb. What is the flux density?

3. What is the flux in a magnetic material when the flux density is 2500×10^{-6} T and the cross-sectional area is 150 cm²?

4. At a given location, the earth's magnetic field is 0.6 G (gauss). Express this flux density in tesla.

5. A very strong permanent magnet has a field of 100,000 μT. Express this flux density in gauss.

SECTION 7–2   Electromagnetism

6. What happens to the compass needle in Figure 7–9 when the current through the conductor is reversed?

7. What is the relative permeability of a ferromagnetic material whose absolute permeability is 750×10^{-6} Wb/At·m?

8. Determine the reluctance of a material with a length of 0.28 m and a cross-sectional area of 0.08 m² if the absolute permeability is 150×10^{-7} Wb/At·m.

9. What is the magnetomotive force in a 500 turn coil of wire with 3 A through it?

SECTION 7–3   Electromagnetic Devices

10. Typically, when a solenoid is activated, is the plunger extended or retracted?

11. (a) What force moves the plunger when a solenoid is activated?

    (b) What force causes the plunger to return to its at-rest position?

12. Explain the sequence of events in the circuit of Figure 7–44 starting when switch 1 (SW1) is closed.

▶ FIGURE 7–44

13. What causes the pointer in a d'Arsonval meter movement to deflect when there is current through the coil?

SECTION 7–4   Magnetic Hysteresis

14. What is the magnetizing force in Problem 9 if the length of the core is 0.2 m?

15. How can the flux density in Figure 7–45 be changed without altering the physical characteristics of the core?

▶ FIGURE 7–45

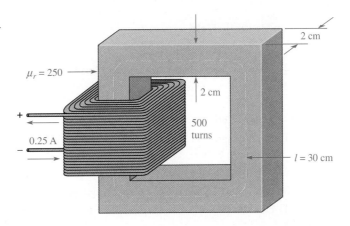

16. In Figure 7–45, determine the following if the winding has 100 turns:

    (a) H (b) ϕ (c) B

17. Determine from the hysteresis curves in Figure 7–46 which material has the most retentivity.

▶ FIGURE 7–46

SECTION 7–5   Electromagnetic Induction

18. According to Faraday's law, what happens to the induced voltage across a given coil if the rate of change of magnetic flux doubles?

19. The voltage induced across a certain coil is 100 mV. A 100 Ω resistor is connected to the coil terminals. What is the induced current?

SECTION 7–6   Applications of Electromagnetic Induction

20. In Figure 7–34, why is there no induced voltage when the steel disk is not rotating?

21. Explain the purpose of the commutator and brushes in Figure 7–36.

ADVANCED PROBLEMS

22. A basic one-loop dc generator is rotated at 60 rps. How many times each second does the dc output voltage peak (reach a maximum)?

23. Assume that another loop of wire, 90° from the first loop, is added to the dc generator in Problem 22. Make a graph of voltage versus time to show how the output voltage appears. Let the maximum voltage be 10 V.

MULTISIM TROUBLESHOOTING PROBLEMS

24. Open file P07-24 and determine if there is a fault in the circuit. If so, identify the fault.

25. Open file P07-25 and determine if there is a fault in the circuit. If so, identify the fault.

ANSWERS

SECTION REVIEWS

SECTION 7–1   The Magnetic Field

1. The north poles repel.

2. Magnetic flux is the group of lines of force that make up a magnetic field.

3. $B = \phi/A = 900\,\mu$T

SECTION 7–2   Electromagnetism

1. Electromagnetism is produced by current through a conductor. An electromagnetic field exists only when there is current. A magnetic field exists independently of current.

2. The direction of the magnetic field also reverses when the current is reversed.

3. Flux equals magnetomotive force divided by reluctance.

4. Flux is analogous to current, mmf is analogous to voltage, and reluctance is analogous to resistance.

SECTION 7–3 **Electromagnetic Devices**

1. A solenoid provides mechanical movement of a shaft. A relay provides an electrical contact closure.

2. The movable part of a solenoid is the plunger.

3. The movable part of a relay is the armature.

4. The d'Arsonval meter movement is based on the interaction of magnetic fields.

SECTION 7–4 **Magnetic Hysteresis**

1. In a wirewound core, an increase in current increases the flux density.

2. Retentivity is the ability of a material to remain magnetized after removal of the magnetizing force.

SECTION 7–5 **Electromagnetic Induction**

1. The induced voltage is zero.

2. The induced voltage increases.

3. A force is exerted on the current-carrying conductor in a magnetic field.

SECTION 7–6 **Applications of Electromagnetic Induction**

1. The induced voltage is zero.

2. The induced voltage increases.

Application Assignment

1. One or more magnetic detection switches must be closed.

2. Contact A activates the audible alarm, contact B latches the relay, contact C turns on house lights.

RELATED PROBLEMS FOR EXAMPLES

7–1 19.6×10^{-3} T

7–2 31.0 T

7–3 The reluctance is reduced to 12.8×10^6 At/Wb.

7–4 Reluctance is 165.7×10^3 At/Wb

7–5 7.2 mWb

7–6 $F_m = 42.5$ At; $\mathcal{R} = 8.5 \times 10^4$ At/Wb

SELF-TEST

1. (b)	**2.** (c)	**3.** (a)	**4.** (d)	**5.** (b)	**6.** (c)
7. (e)	**8.** (d)	**9.** (c)	**10.** (c)	**11.** (b)	**12.** (c)

AC CIRCUITS

PART 2

INTRODUCTION TO ALTERNATING CURRENT AND VOLTAGE

8

CHAPTER OBJECTIVES

◆ Identify a sinusoidal waveform and measure its characteristics

◆ Describe how sine waves are generated

◆ Determine the voltage and current values of sine waves

◆ Describe angular relationships of sine waves

◆ Mathematically analyze a sinusoidal waveform

◆ Apply the basic circuit laws to resistive ac circuits

◆ Determine total voltages that have both ac and dc components

◆ Identify the characteristics of basic nonsinusoidal waveforms

◆ Use the oscilloscope to measure waveforms

KEY TERMS

◆ Sine wave
◆ Waveform
◆ Cycle
◆ Period (T)
◆ Frequency (f)
◆ Hertz (Hz)
◆ Amplitude
◆ Oscillator
◆ Function generator
◆ Instantaneous value
◆ Peak value
◆ Peak-to-peak value
◆ rms value
◆ Average value

◆ Degree
◆ Radian
◆ Phase
◆ Pulse
◆ Pulse width (t_W)
◆ Rise time (t_r)
◆ Fall time (t_f)
◆ Periodic
◆ Duty cycle
◆ Ramp
◆ Fundamental frequency
◆ Harmonics
◆ Oscilloscope

APPLICATION ASSIGNMENT PREVIEW

As an electronics technician working for a company that designs and manufactures laboratory instruments, you have been assigned to the testing of a new function generator that produces various types of time-varying voltages with adjustable parameters. You will analyze measurements and record the limits of operation of a prototype model. After studying this chapter, you should be able to complete the application assignment.

VISIT THE COMPANION WEBSITE

Study aids for this chapter are available at http://www.prenhall.com/floyd

INTRODUCTION

This chapter provides an introduction to alternating current (ac) circuits. Alternating voltages and currents fluctuate with time and periodically change polarity and direction according to certain patterns called *waveforms*. Particular emphasis is given to the sinusoidal waveform (sine wave) because of its basic importance in ac circuits. Other types of waveforms are also introduced, including pulse, triangular, and sawtooth. The use of an oscilloscope for displaying and measuring waveforms is discussed.

8–1 THE SINUSOIDAL WAVEFORM

The sinusoidal waveform or **sine wave** is the fundamental type of alternating current (ac) and alternating voltage. It is also referred to as a sinusoidal wave, or, simply, sinusoid. The electrical service provided by the power companies is in the form of sinusoidal voltage and current. In addition, other types of repetitive **waveforms** are composites of many individual sine waves called harmonics.

After completing this section, you should be able to

♦ **Identify a sinusoidal waveform and measure its characteristics**

    ♦ Define and determine the period

    ♦ Define and determine the frequency

    ♦ Relate the period and the frequency

▲ FIGURE 8–1

Symbol for a sinusoidal voltage source.

Sine waves, or sinusoids, are produced by two types of sources: rotating electrical machines (ac generators) or electronic oscillator circuits, which are used in instruments commonly known as electronic signal generators. Figure 8–1 shows the symbol used to represent a source of sinusoidal voltage.

Figure 8–2 is a graph that shows the general shape of a sine wave, which can be either an alternating current or an alternating voltage. Voltage (or current) is displayed on the vertical axis, and time (*t*) is displayed on the horizontal axis. Notice how the voltage (or current) varies with time. Starting at zero, the voltage (or current) increases to a positive maximum (peak), returns to zero, and then increases to a negative maximum (peak) before returning again to zero, thus completing one full cycle.

▶ FIGURE 8–2

Graph of one cycle of a sine wave.

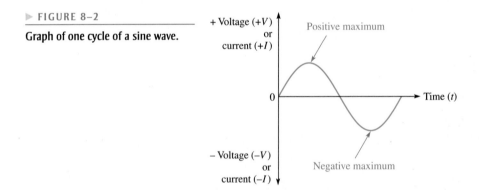

Polarity of a Sine Wave

As mentioned, a sine wave changes polarity at its zero value; that is, it alternates between positive and negative values. When a sinusoidal voltage source (V_s) is applied to a resistive circuit, as in Figure 8–3, an alternating sinusoidal current results. When the voltage changes polarity, the current correspondingly changes direction as indicated.

During the positive alternation of the source voltage V_s, the current is in the direction shown in Figure 8–3(a). During a negative alternation of the source voltage, the current is in the opposite direction, as shown in Figure 8–3(b). The combined positive and negative alternations make up one **cycle** of a sine wave.

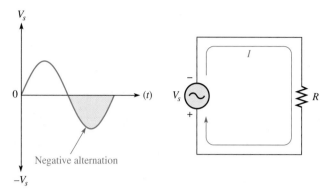

(a) During a positive alternation of the voltage, current is in the direction shown.

(b) During a negative alternation of the voltage, current reverses direction, as shown.

▲ FIGURE 8–3

Alternating current and voltage.

Period of a Sine Wave

A sine wave varies with time (*t*) in a definable manner.

> **The time required for a given sine wave to complete one full cycle is called the period (*T*).**

Figure 8–4(a) illustrates the period of a sine wave. Typically, a sine wave continues to repeat itself in identical cycles, as shown in Figure 8–4(b). Since all cycles of a repetitive sine wave are the same, the period is always a fixed value for a given sine wave. The period of a sine wave can be measured from a zero crossing to the next corresponding zero crossing, as indicated in Figure 8–4(a). The period can also be measured from any peak in a given cycle to the corresponding peak in the next cycle.

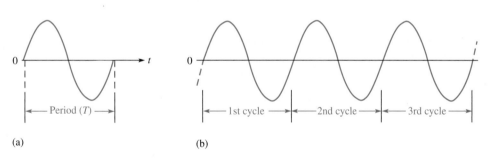

(a)

(b)

◀ FIGURE 8–4

The period of a given sine wave is the same for each cycle.

EXAMPLE 8–1   What is the period of the sine wave in Figure 8–5?

▶ FIGURE 8–5

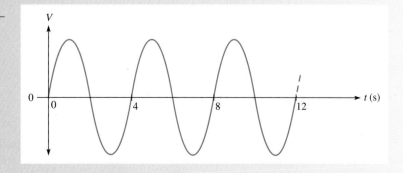

Solution   As shown in Figure 8–5, it takes twelve seconds (12 s) to complete three cycles. Therefore, to complete one cycle it takes four seconds (4 s), which is the period.

$$T = \mathbf{4\,s}$$

*Related Problem**   What is the period if a given sine wave goes through five cycles in 12 s?

*Answers are at the end of the chapter.

EXAMPLE 8–2   Show three possible ways to measure the period of the sine wave in Figure 8–6. How many cycles are shown?

▶ FIGURE 8–6

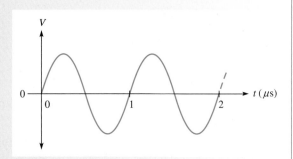

Solution   **Method 1.** The period can be measured from one zero crossing to the corresponding zero crossing in the next cycle (the slope must be the same at the corresponding zero crossings).

Method 2. The period can be measured from the positive peak in one cycle to the positive peak in the next cycle.

Method 3. The period can be measured from the negative peak in one cycle to the negative peak in the next cycle.

These measurements are indicated in Figure 8–7, where **two cycles** of the sine wave are shown. Keep in mind that you obtain the same value for the period no matter which corresponding peaks or corresponding zero crossings on the waveform you use.

◀ FIGURE 8–7

Measurement of the period of a sine wave.

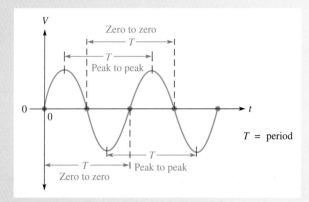

Related Problem   If a positive peak occurs at 1 ms and the next positive peak occurs at 2.5 ms, what is the period?

Frequency of a Sine Wave

Frequency is the number of cycles that a sine wave completes in one second.

The more cycles completed in one second, the higher the frequency. Frequency (f) is measured in units of **hertz (Hz)**. One hertz is equivalent to one cycle per second; for example, 60 Hz is 60 cycles per second. Figure 8–8 shows two sine waves. The sine wave in part (a) completes two full cycles in one second. The one in part (b) completes four cycles in one second. Therefore, the sine wave in part (b) has twice the frequency of the one in part (a).

BIOGRAPHY

Heinrich
Rudolf Hertz
1857–1894

Hertz, a German physicist, was the first to broadcast and receive electromagnetic (radio) waves. He produced electromagnetic waves in the laboratory and measured their parameters. Hertz also proved that the nature of the reflection and refraction of electromagnetic waves was the same as that of light. The unit of frequency is named in his honor. (Photo credit: Deutsches Museum, courtesy AIP Emilio Segre Visual Archives, Physics Today Collection.)

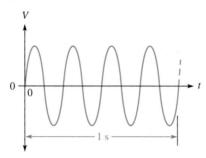

(a) Lower frequency: fewer cycles per second   (b) Higher frequency: more cycles per second

▲ FIGURE 8–8

Illustration of frequency.

Relationship of Frequency and Period

The formulas for the relationship between frequency and period are

$$f = \frac{1}{T}$$

Equation 8–1

$$T = \frac{1}{f}$$

Equation 8–2

There is a reciprocal relationship between f and T. Knowing one, you can calculate the other with the x^{-1} or $1/x$ key on your calculator. (On some calculators, the reciprocal key is a secondary function.) This inverse relationship indicates that a sine wave with a longer period goes through fewer cycles in one second than one with a shorter period.

EXAMPLE 8–3   Which sine wave in Figure 8–9 has the higher frequency? Determine the frequency and the period of both waveforms.

FIGURE 8–9

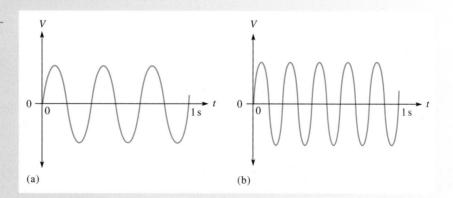

(a)   (b)

Solution   The sine wave in Figure 8–9(b) has the higher frequency because it completes more cycles in 1 s than does the one in part (a).

In Figure 8–9(a), three cycles are completed in 1 s. Therefore,

$$f = \textbf{3 Hz}$$

One cycle takes 0.333 s (one-third second), so the period is

$$T = 0.333 \text{ s} = \textbf{333 ms}$$

In Figure 8–9(b), five cycles are completed in 1 s. Therefore,

$$f = \textbf{5 Hz}$$

One cycle takes 0.2 s (one-fifth second), so the period is

$$T = 0.2 \text{ s} = \textbf{200 ms}$$

Related Problem   If the time interval between consecutive negative peaks of a given sine wave is 50 μs, what is the frequency?

EXAMPLE 8–4   The period of a certain sine wave is 10 ms. What is the frequency?

Solution   Use Equation 8–1.

$$f = \frac{1}{T} = \frac{1}{10 \text{ ms}} = \frac{1}{10 \times 10^{-3} \text{ s}} = \textbf{100 Hz}$$

Related Problem   A certain sine wave goes through four cycles in 20 ms. What is the frequency?

EXAMPLE 8–5   The frequency of a sine wave is 60 Hz. What is the period?

Solution   Use Equation 8–2.

$$T = \frac{1}{f} = \frac{1}{60 \text{ Hz}} = \textbf{16.7 ms}$$

Related Problem   If $f = 1$ kHz, what is T?

SECTION 8–1 REVIEW
Answers are at the end of the chapter.

1. Describe one cycle of a sine wave.
2. At what point does a sine wave change polarity?
3. How many maximum points does a sine wave have during one cycle?
4. How is the period of a sine wave measured?
5. Define *frequency*, and state its unit.
6. Determine f when $T = 5 \mu$s.
7. Determine T when $f = 120$ Hz.

8–2 SINUSOIDAL VOLTAGE SOURCES

As mentioned in the last section, two basic methods of generating sinusoidal voltages are electromagnetic and electronic. Sine waves are produced electromagnetically by ac generators and electronically by oscillator circuits.

After completing this section, you should be able to

◆ **Describe how sine waves are generated**

　◆ Discuss the basic operation of an ac generator

　◆ Discuss factors that affect frequency in ac generators

　◆ Discuss factors that affect voltage in ac generators

AC Generator

Figure 8–10 is a cutaway view of an electromechanical ac generator. To illustrate the basic operation, Figure 8–11 shows a greatly simplified ac generator consisting of a single loop of wire in a permanent magnetic field. Notice that each end of the wire loop is connected to a separate solid conductive ring called a *slip ring*. A mechanical drive, such as a motor, turns the shaft to which the wire loop is connected. As the wire loop rotates in the magnetic field, the slip rings also rotate and rub against the brushes that connect the wire to an external load. Compare this generator to the basic dc generator in Figure 7–36, and note the difference in the ring and brush arrangements.

◀ FIGURE 8–10

The electromechanical ac generator, cutaway view (courtesy of General Electric).

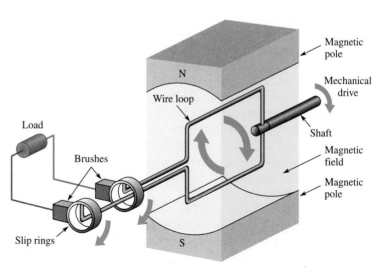

◀ FIGURE 8–11

Basic ac generator operation.

As you learned in Chapter 7, when a conductor moves through a magnetic field, a voltage is induced. Figure 8–12 illustrates how a sinusoidal voltage is produced by the basic ac generator as the wire loop rotates through the magnetic field. An oscilloscope is used to display the voltage waveform.

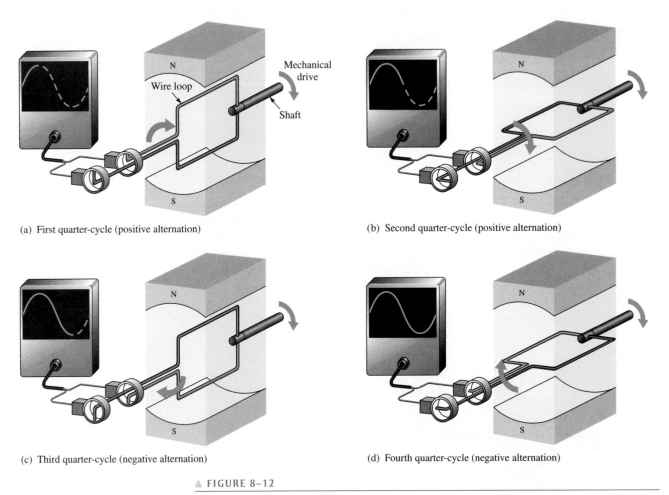

(a) First quarter-cycle (positive alternation)

(b) Second quarter-cycle (positive alternation)

(c) Third quarter-cycle (negative alternation)

(d) Fourth quarter-cycle (negative alternation)

▲ FIGURE 8–12

One revolution of the wire loop generates one cycle of the sinusoidal voltage.

To begin, Figure 8–12(a) shows the wire loop rotating through the first quarter of a revolution. It goes from an instantaneous horizontal position, where the induced voltage is zero, to an instantaneous vertical position, where the induced voltage is maximum. At the horizontal position, the loop is instantaneously moving parallel with the flux lines, which exist between the north (N) and south (S) poles of the magnet; thus, no lines are being cut and the voltage is zero. As the wire loop rotates through the first quarter-cycle, it cuts through the flux lines at an increasing rate until it is instantaneously moving perpendicular to the flux lines at the vertical position and cutting through them at a maximum rate. Thus, the induced voltage increases from zero to a peak during the quarter-cycle. As shown on the display in part (a), this part of the rotation produces the first quarter of the sine wave cycle as the voltage builds up from zero to its positive maximum.

Figure 8–12(b) shows the wire loop completing the first half of a revolution. During this part of the rotation, the voltage decreases from its positive maximum back to zero.

During the second half of the revolution, illustrated in Figure 8–12(c) and 8-12(d), the wire loop is cutting through the magnetic field in the opposite direction, so the voltage produced has a polarity opposite to that produced during the first half of the revolution. After one complete revolution of the loop, one full cycle of the sinusoidal voltage has been produced. As the wire loop continues to rotate, repetitive cycles of the sine wave are generated.

Frequency You have seen that one revolution of the conductor through the magnetic field in the basic ac generator (also called an *alternator*) produces one cycle of induced sinusoidal voltage. It is obvious that the rate at which the conductor is rotated determines the time for completion of one cycle. For example, if the conductor completes 60 revolutions in one second (rps), the period of the resulting sine wave is 1/60 s, corresponding to a frequency of 60 Hz. The faster the conductor rotates, the higher the resulting frequency of the induced voltage, as illustrated in Figure 8–13.

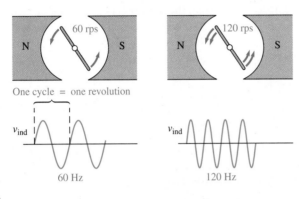

▲ FIGURE 8–13

Frequency is directly proportional to the rate of rotation of the wire loop in an ac generator.

Another way of achieving a higher frequency is to increase the number of magnetic poles. In the previous discussion, two magnetic poles were used to illustrate the ac generator principle. During one revolution, the conductor passes under a north pole and a south pole, thus producing one cycle of a sine wave. When four magnetic poles are used instead of two, as shown in Figure 8–14, one cycle is generated during one-half of a revolution. This doubles the frequency for the same rate of rotation.

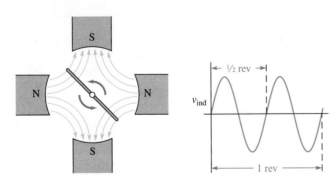

▲ FIGURE 8–14

Four poles achieve twice the frequency of two poles for the same rps.

An expression for frequency in terms of the number of pole pairs and the number of revolutions per second (rps) is

$$f = (\text{number of pole pairs})(\text{rps})$$

Equation 8–3

EXAMPLE 8–6

A four-pole generator has a rotation speed of 100 rps. Determine the frequency of the output voltage.

Solution

$$f = \text{(number of pole pairs)(rps)} = 2(100 \text{ rps}) = \mathbf{200\ Hz}$$

Related Problem

If the frequency of the output of a four-pole generator is 60 Hz, what is the rps?

Voltage Amplitude   The amount of voltage induced in a conductor depends on the number of turns (N) and the rate of change with respect to the magnetic field. Therefore, when the speed of rotation of the conductor is increased, not only does the frequency of the induced voltage increase—so also does the **amplitude**, which is its maximum value. Since the frequency value normally is fixed, the most practical method of increasing the amount or amplitude of induced voltage is to increase the number of wire loops.

Electronic Signal Generators

The signal generator is an instrument that electronically produces sine waves for use in testing or controlling electronic circuits and systems. There are a variety of signal generators, ranging from special-purpose instruments that produce only one type of waveform in a limited frequency range to programmable instruments that produce a wide range of frequencies and a variety of waveforms. All signal generators consist basically of an **oscillator**, which is an electronic circuit that produces sinusoidal voltages or other types of waveforms whose amplitude and frequency can be adjusted.

Function Generators and Arbitrary Waveform Generators   The **function generator** provides pulse waveforms as well as sine waves and triangular waves. Typical function generators are shown in Figure 8–15(a). The arbitrary waveform generator can be used to generate standard signals like sine waves, triangular waves, and pulses as well as signals with various shapes and characteristics. Waveforms can be defined by mathematical or graphical input. A typical arbitrary waveform generator is shown in Figure 8–15(b).

(a) Examples of function generators

(b) A typical arbitrary waveform generator

▲ FIGURE 8–15

Typical signal generators. Copyright © Tektronix, Inc. Reproduced by permission.

SECTION 8–2 REVIEW

1. List two types of sine wave sources.
2. How are sine waves generated electromagnetically?
3. Upon what is the frequency of a mechanical generator's output voltage dependent?
4. Upon what is the amplitude of a mechanical generator's output voltage dependent?

8–3 VOLTAGE AND CURRENT VALUES OF SINE WAVES

Five ways to express and measure the value of a sine wave in terms of its voltage or its current magnitude are instantaneous, peak, peak-to-peak, rms, and average values.

After completing this section, you should be able to

◆ **Determine the voltage and current values of sine waves**

    ◆ Find the instantaneous value at any point

    ◆ Find the peak value

    ◆ Find the peak-to-peak value

    ◆ Define *rms* and find the rms value

    ◆ Explain why the average value of an alternating sine wave is always zero over a complete cycle

    ◆ Find the half-cycle average value

Instantaneous Value

Figure 8–16 illustrates that at any point in time on a sine wave, the voltage (or current) has an **instantaneous value**. This instantaneous value is different at different points along the curve. Instantaneous values are positive during the positive alternation and negative during the negative alternation. Instantaneous values of voltage and current are symbolized by lowercase v and i, respectively. The curve in part (a) shows voltage only, but it applies equally for current when v's are replaced with i's. An example of instantaneous values is shown in part (b), where the instantaneous voltage is 3.1 V at 1 μs, 7.07 V at 2.5 μs, 10 V at 5 μs, 0 V at 10 μs, −3.1 V at 11 μs, and so on.

(a)

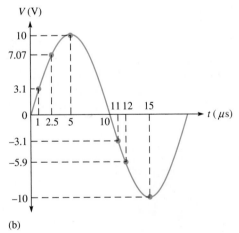

(b)

◀ FIGURE 8–16

Example of instantaneous values of a sinusoidal voltage.

Peak Value

The **peak value** of a sine wave is the value of voltage (or current) at the positive or the negative maximum (peaks) with respect to zero. Since positive and negative peak values are equal in **magnitude,** a sine wave is characterized by a single peak value, as is illustrated in Figure 8–17. For a given sine wave, the peak value is constant and is represented by V_p or I_p. In the figure, the peak value is 8 V.

▶ FIGURE 8–17

Peak values.

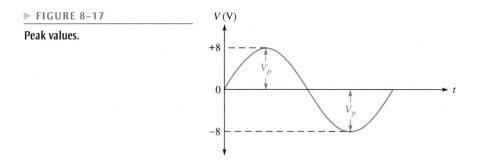

Peak-to-Peak Value

The **peak-to-peak value** of a sine wave, as illustrated in Figure 8–18, is the voltage (or current) from the positive peak to the negative peak. It is always twice the peak value as expressed by the following equations. Peak-to-peak values are represented by V_{pp} or I_{pp}.

Equation 8–4

$$V_{pp} = 2V_p$$

Equation 8–5

$$I_{pp} = 2I_p$$

In Figure 8–18, the peak-to-peak value is 16 V.

▶ FIGURE 8–18

Peak-to-peak value.

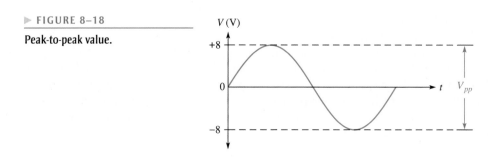

RMS Value

The term *rms* stands for *root mean square*. Most ac voltmeters display the rms voltage. The 110 V at your wall outlet is an rms value. The **rms value**, also referred to as the **effective value,** of a sinusoidal voltage is actually a measure of the heating effect of the sine wave. For example, when a resistor is connected across an ac (sinusoidal) voltage source, as shown in Figure 8–19(a), a certain amount of heat is generated by the power in the resistor.

▲ FIGURE 8–19

When the same amount of heat is being produced by the resistor in both setups, the sinusoidal voltage has an rms value equal to the dc voltage.

Figure 8–19(b) shows the same resistor connected across a dc voltage source. The value of the ac voltage can be adjusted so that the resistor gives off the same amount of heat as it does when connected to the dc source.

The rms value of a sinusoidal voltage is equal to the dc voltage that produces the same amount of heat in a resistance as does the sinusoidal voltage.

You can convert the peak value of a sine wave to the corresponding rms value by using the following relationships for either voltage or current:

$$V_{rms} = 0.707V_p$$

Equation 8–6

$$I_{rms} = 0.707I_p$$

Equation 8–7

Using these formulas, you can also determine the peak value if you know the rms value.

$$V_p = \frac{V_{rms}}{0.707}$$

$$V_p = 1.414V_{rms}$$

Equation 8–8

Similarly,

$$I_p = 1.414I_{rms}$$

Equation 8–9

To find the peak-to-peak value, simply double the peak value.

$$V_{pp} = 2.828V_{rms}$$

Equation 8–10

and

$$I_{pp} = 2.828I_{rms}$$

Equation 8–11

Average Value

The average value of a sine wave when taken over one complete cycle is always zero because the positive values (above the zero crossing) offset the negative values (below the zero crossing).

To be useful for comparison purposes and in determining the average value of a rectified voltage such as found in power supplies, the **average value** of a sine wave is defined over a half-cycle rather than over a full cycle. The average value is expressed in terms of the peak value as follows for both voltage and current sine waves:

$$V_{avg} = 0.637V_p$$

Equation 8–12

$$I_{avg} = 0.637I_p$$

Equation 8–13

The half-cycle average value of a voltage sine wave is illustrated in Figure 8–20.

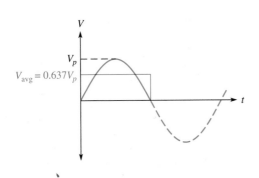

◀ FIGURE 8–20

Half-cycle average value.

EXAMPLE 8–7

Determine V_p, V_{pp}, V_{rms}, and the half-cycle V_{avg} for the sine wave in Figure 8–21.

▶ FIGURE 8–21

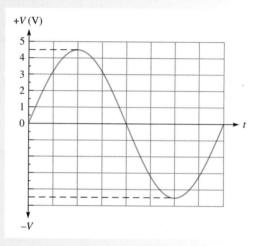

Solution As taken directly from the graph, $V_p = $ **4.5 V**. From this value, calculate the other values.

$$V_{pp} = 2V_p = 2(4.5 \text{ V}) = \mathbf{9\ V}$$
$$V_{rms} = 0.707V_p = 0.707(4.5 \text{ V}) = \mathbf{3.18\ V}$$
$$V_{avg} = 0.637V_p = 0.637(4.5 \text{ V}) = \mathbf{2.87\ V}$$

Related Problem If $V_p = 25$ V, determine V_{pp}, V_{rms}, and V_{avg} for a sine wave.

SECTION 8–3 REVIEW

1. Determine V_{pp} in each case when
   (a) $V_p = 1$ V   (b) $V_{rms} = 1.414$ V   (c) $V_{avg} = 3$ V
2. Determine V_{rms} in each case when
   (a) $V_p = 2.5$ V   (b) $V_{pp} = 10$ V   (c) $V_{avg} = 1.5$ V
3. Determine the half-cycle V_{avg} in each case when
   (a) $V_p = 10$ V   (b) $V_{rms} = 2.3$ V   (c) $V_{pp} = 60$ V

8–4 ANGULAR MEASUREMENT OF A SINE WAVE

As you have seen, sine waves can be measured along the horizontal axis on a time basis; however, since the time for completion of one full cycle or any portion of a cycle is frequency-dependent, it is often useful to specify points on the sine wave in terms of an angular measurement expressed in degrees or radians. Angular measurement is independent of frequency.

After completing this section, you should be able to

◆ **Describe angular relationships of sine waves**

  ◆ Show how to measure a sine wave in terms of angles

  ◆ Define *radian*

  ◆ Convert radians to degrees

  ◆ Determine the phase of a sine wave

As previously discussed, sinusoidal voltage can be produced electromagnetically by rotating electromechanical machines. As the windings on the rotor of the ac generator go through a full 360° of rotation, the resulting output is one full cycle of a sine wave. Thus, the angular measurement of a sine wave can be related to the angular rotation of a generator, as shown in Figure 8–22.

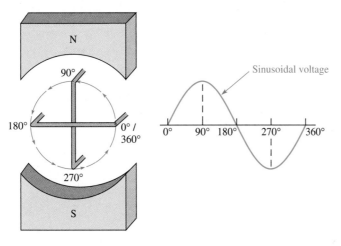

▲ FIGURE 8–22

Relationship of a sine wave to the rotational motion in an ac generator.

Angular Measurement

A **degree** is an angular measurement corresponding to 1/360 of a circle or a complete revolution. A **radian** (rad) is the angle formed when the distance along the circumference of a circle is equal to the radius of the circle. One radian is equivalent to 57.3°, as illustrated in Figure 8–23. In a 360° revolution, there are 2π radians.

> **The Greek letter π (pi) represents the ratio of the circumference of any circle to its diameter and has a constant value of approximately 3.1416.**

Scientific calculators have a π function so that the actual numerical value does not have to be entered.

Table 8–1 lists several values of degrees and the corresponding radian values. These angular measurements are illustrated in Figure 8–24.

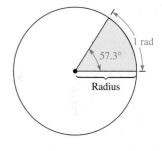

▲ FIGURE 8–23

Angular measurement showing relationship of the radian to degrees.

▼ TABLE 8–1

DEGREES (°)	RADIANS (RAD)
0	0
45	$\pi/4$
90	$\pi/2$
135	$3\pi/4$
180	π
225	$5\pi/4$
270	$3\pi/2$
315	$7\pi/4$
360	2π

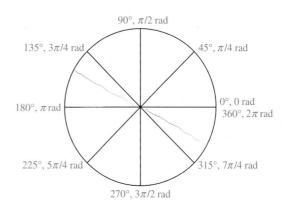

▲ FIGURE 8–24

Angular measurements starting at 0° and going counterclockwise.

Radian/Degree Conversion

Degrees can be converted to radians using Equation 8–14.

Equation 8–14

$$\text{rad} = \left(\frac{\pi \text{ rad}}{180°}\right) \times \text{degrees}$$

Similarly, radians can be converted to degrees with Equation 8–15.

Equation 8–15

$$\text{degrees} = \left(\frac{180°}{\pi \text{ rad}}\right) \times \text{rad}$$

EXAMPLE 8–8

(a) Convert 60° to radians.   (b) Convert $\pi/6$ radian to degrees.

Solution   (a) $\text{Rad} = \left(\dfrac{\pi \text{ rad}}{180°}\right)60° = \dfrac{\pi}{3}\,\textbf{rad}$

(b) $\text{Degrees} = \left(\dfrac{180°}{\pi \text{ rad}}\right)\left(\dfrac{\pi}{6}\text{rad}\right) = \textbf{30°}$

Related Problem   (a) Convert 15° to radians.   (b) Convert $5\pi/8$ radians to degrees.

Sine Wave Angles

The angular measurement of a sine wave is based on 360° or 2π rad for a complete cycle. A half-cycle is 180° or π rad; a quarter-cycle is 90° or $\pi/2$ rad; and so on. Figure 8–25(a) shows angles in degrees over a full cycle of a sine wave; part (b) shows the same points in radians.

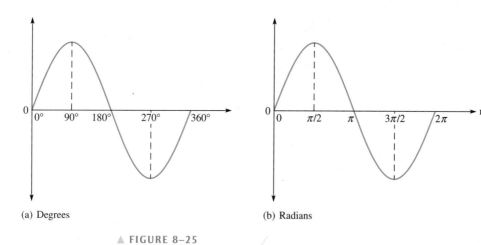

(a) Degrees   (b) Radians

▲ FIGURE 8–25

Sine wave angles.

Phase of a Sine Wave

The **phase** of a sine wave is an angular measurement that specifies the position of that sine wave relative to a reference. Figure 8–26 shows one cycle of a sine wave to be used as the reference. Note that the first positive-going crossing of the horizontal axis (zero crossing) is at 0° (0 rad), and the positive peak is at 90° ($\pi/2$ rad). The negative-going zero crossing is at 180° (π rad), and the negative peak is at 270° ($3\pi/2$ rad). The cycle is completed at 360° (2π rad). When the sine wave is shifted left or right with respect to this reference, there is a phase shift.

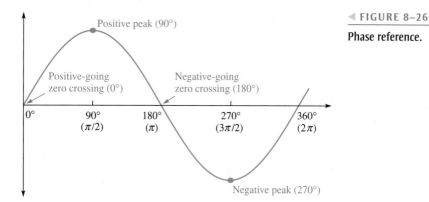

Figure 8–27 illustrates phase shifts of a sine wave. In part (a), sine wave *B* is shifted to the right by 90° (*π*/2 rad) with respect to sine wave *A*. Thus, there is a phase angle of 90° between sine wave *A* and sine wave *B*. In terms of time, the positive peak of sine wave *B* occurs later than the positive peak of sine wave *A* because time increases to the right along the horizontal axis. In this case, sine wave *B* is said to **lag** sine wave *A* by 90° or *π*/2 radians. In other words, sine wave *A* leads sine wave *B* by 90°.

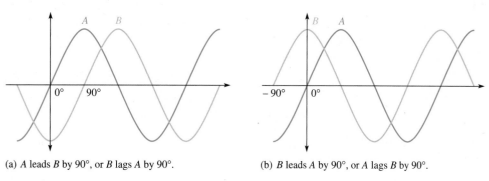

(a) *A* leads *B* by 90°, or *B* lags *A* by 90°.　　　　(b) *B* leads *A* by 90°, or *A* lags *B* by 90°.

▲ FIGURE 8–27

Illustration of a phase shift.

In Figure 8–27(b), sine wave *B* is shown shifted left by 90° with respect to sine wave *A*. Thus, again there is a phase angle of 90° between sine wave *A* and sine wave *B*. In this case, the positive peak of sine wave *B* occurs earlier in time than that of sine wave *A*; therefore, sine wave *B* is said to **lead** sine wave *A* by 90°. In both cases there is a 90° phase angle between the two waveforms.

EXAMPLE 8–9　　　　What are the phase angles between sine waves *A* and *B* in Figure 8–28(a) and 8–28(b)?

FIGURE 8–28

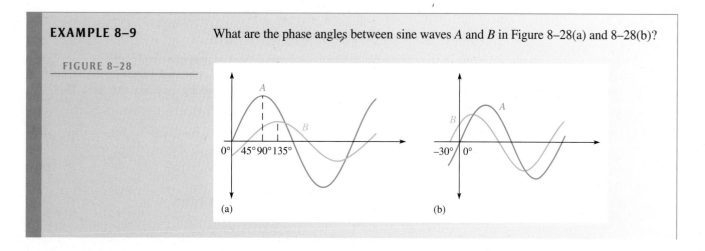

Solution   In Figure 8–28(a), the zero crossing of sine wave *A* is at 0°, and the corresponding zero crossing of sine wave *B* is at 45°. There is a **45°** phase angle between the two waveforms with sine wave *A* leading.

In Figure 8–28(b) the zero crossing of sine wave *B* is at −30°, and the corresponding zero crossing of sine wave *A* is at 0°. There is a **30°** phase angle between the two waveforms with sine wave *B* leading.

Related Problem   If the positive-going zero crossing of one sine wave is at 15° relative to the 0° reference and that of the second sine wave is at 23° relative to the 0° reference, what is the phase angle between the sine waves?

When you measure the phase shift between two waveforms on an oscilloscope, you should align the waveforms vertically and make them appear to have the same amplitude. This is done by taking one of the channels out of vertical calibration and adjusting the corresponding waveform until its apparent amplitude equals that of the other waveform. This procedure eliminates the error caused if both waveforms are not measured at their exact center.

**SECTION 8–4
REVIEW**

1. When the positive-going zero crossing of a sine wave occurs at 0°, at what angle does each of the following points occur?
   (a) positive peak   **(b)** negative-going zero crossing
   (c) negative peak   **(d)** end of first complete cycle
2. A half cycle is completed in _____ degrees, or _____ radians.
3. A full cycle is completed in _____ degrees, or _____ radians.
4. Determine the phase angle between the sine waves *B* and *C* in Figure 8–29.

▶ FIGURE 8–29

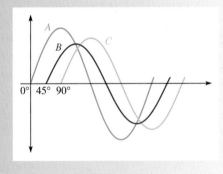

8–5   THE SINE WAVE FORMULA

A sine wave can be graphically represented by voltage or current values on the vertical axis and by angular measurement (degrees or radians) along the horizontal axis. This graph can be expressed mathematically, as you will see.

After completing this section, you should be able to

◆ **Mathematically analyze a sinusoidal waveform**

   ◆ State the sine wave formula

   ◆ Find instantaneous values using the sine wave formula

A generalized graph of one cycle of a sine wave is shown in Figure 8–30. The sine wave amplitude, A, is the maximum value of the voltage or current on the vertical axis; angular values run along the horizontal axis. The variable y is an instantaneous value representing either voltage or current at a given angle, θ. The symbol θ is the Greek letter *theta*.

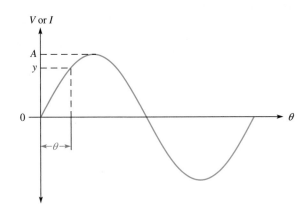

◀ FIGURE 8–30

One cycle of a generic sine wave showing amplitude and phase.

All electrical sine waves follow a specific mathematical formula. The general expression for the sine wave curve in Figure 8–30 is

$$y = A \sin \theta$$

Equation 8–16

This formula states that any point on the sine wave, represented by an instantaneous value y, is equal to the maximum value A times the sine (sin) of the angle θ at that point. For example, a certain voltage sine wave has a peak value of 10 V. The instantaneous voltage at a point 60° along the horizontal axis can be calculated as follows, where $y = v$ and $A = V_p$:

$$v = V_p \sin \theta = (10 \text{ V})\sin 60° = (10 \text{ V})0.866 = 8.66 \text{ V}$$

Figure 8–31 shows this particular instantaneous value on the curve. You can find the sine of any angle on most calculators by first entering the value of the angle and then pressing the SIN key. The calculator must be in the degree mode.

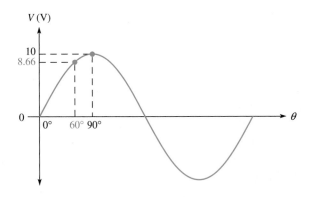

◀ FIGURE 8–31

Illustration of the instantaneous value of a voltage sine wave at $\theta = 60°$.

Derivation of the Sine Wave Formula

As you move along the horizontal axis of a sine wave, the angle increases and the magnitude (height along the y axis) varies. At any given instant, the magnitude of a sine wave can be described by the values of the phase angle and the amplitude (maximum height) and can, therefore, be represented as a **phasor** quantity. A phasor quantity is one that has both magnitude and direction (phase angle). A phasor is represented graphically as an arrow that rotates around a fixed point. The length of a sine wave phasor is the peak value (amplitude), and its angular position as it rotates is the phase angle. One full cycle of a sine wave can be viewed as the rotation of a phasor through 360°.

Figure 8–32 illustrates a phasor rotating counterclockwise through a complete revolution of 360°. If the tip of the phasor is projected over to a graph with the phase angles running along the horizontal axis, a sine wave is "traced out," as shown in the figure. At each angular position of the phasor, there is a corresponding magnitude value. As you can see, at 90° and at 270°, the amplitude of the sine wave is maximum and equal to the length of the phasor. At 0° and at 180°, the sine wave is equal to zero because the phasor lies horizontally at these points.

▶ FIGURE 8–32

Sine wave represented by a rotating phasor.

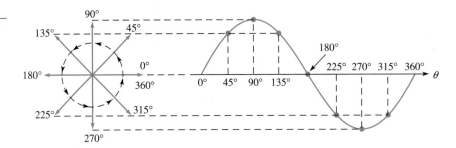

Let's examine, a phasor representation at one specific angle. Figure 8–33 shows the voltage phasor at an angular position of 45° and the corresponding point on the sine wave. The instantaneous value, v, of the sine wave at this point is related to both the position (angle) and the length (amplitude) of the phasor. The vertical distance from the phasor tip down to the horizontal axis represents the instantaneous value of the sine wave at that point.

▶ FIGURE 8–33

Right triangle derivation of sine wave formula, $v = V_p \sin \theta$.

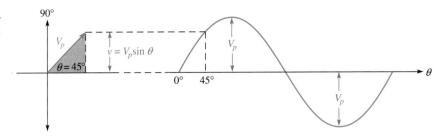

Notice that when a vertical line is drawn from the phasor tip down to the horizontal axis, a **right triangle** is formed, as shown in Figure 8–33. The length of the phasor is the **hypotenuse** of the triangle, and the vertical projection is the opposite side. From trigonometry, *the opposite side of a right triangle is equal to the hypotenuse times the sine of the angle θ.* In this case, the length of the phasor is the peak value of the voltage sine wave, V_p. Thus, the opposite side of the triangle, which is the instantaneous value, can be expressed as

Equation 8–17
$$v = V_p \sin \theta$$

This formula also applies to a current sine wave.

Equation 8–18
$$i = I_p \sin \theta$$

Expressions for Phase-Shifted Sine Waves

When a sine wave is shifted to the right of the reference (lags) by a certain angle, ϕ, (Greek letter phi) as illustrated in Figure 8–34(a), the general expression is

Equation 8–19
$$y = A \sin(\theta - \phi)$$

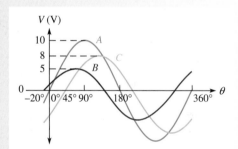

(a) $y = A \sin(\theta - \phi)$ (b) $y = A \sin(\theta + \phi)$

▲ FIGURE 8–34

Shifted sine waves.

where y represents instantaneous voltage or current, and A represents the peak value (amplitude). When a sine wave is shifted to the left of the reference (leads) by a certain angle, ϕ, as shown in Figure 8–34(b), the general expression is

$$y = A \sin(\theta + \phi)$$ Equation 8–20

EXAMPLE 8–10

Determine the instantaneous value at 90° on the horizontal axis for each voltage sine wave in Figure 8–35.

▶ FIGURE 8–35

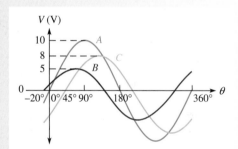

Solution   Sine wave A is the reference. Sine wave B is shifted left 20° with respect to A, so B leads. Sine wave C is shifted right 45° with respect to A, so C lags.

$$v_A = V_p\sin \theta = (10 \text{ V})\sin 90° = \textbf{10 V}$$
$$v_B = V_p\sin(\theta + \phi_B) = (5 \text{ V})\sin(90° + 20°) = (5 \text{ V})\sin 110° = \textbf{4.70 V}$$
$$v_C = V_p\sin(\theta - \phi_C) = (8 \text{ V})\sin(90° - 45°) = (8 \text{ V})\sin 45° = \textbf{5.66 V}$$

Related Problem   A sine wave has a peak value of 20 V. What is the instantaneous value at +65° from the 0° reference?

SECTION 8–5 REVIEW

1. Determine the sine of the following angles:
   (a) 30°   (b) 60°   (c) 90°
2. Calculate the instantaneous value at 120° for the sine wave in Figure 8–31.
3. Determine the instantaneous value at 45° on a voltage sine wave that leads the zero reference by 10° ($V_p = 10$ V).

8–6   ANALYSIS OF AC CIRCUITS

When a time-varying ac voltage such as a sinusoidal voltage is applied to a circuit, the circuit laws and power formulas that you studied earlier still apply. Ohm's law, Kirchhoff's laws and the power formulas apply to ac circuits in the same way that they apply to dc circuits.

After completing this section, you should be able to

♦ **Apply the basic circuit laws to resistive ac circuits**

  ♦ Apply Ohm's law to resistive circuits with ac sources

  ♦ Apply Kirchhoff's voltage law and current law to resistive circuits with ac sources

  ♦ Determine power in resistive ac circuits

If a sinusoidal voltage is applied across a resistor, as shown in Figure 8–36, there is a sinusoidal current. The current is zero when the voltage is zero and is maximum when the voltage is maximum. When the voltage changes polarity, the current reverses direction. As a result, the voltage and current are said to be in phase, with each other.

When you use Ohm's law in ac circuits, remember that both the voltage and the current must be expressed consistently, that is, both as peak values, both as rms values, both as average values, and so on.

▶ **FIGURE 8–36**

A sinusoidal voltage produces a sinusoidal current.

Sine wave generator

Kirchhoff's voltage and current laws apply to ac circuits as well as to dc circuits. Figure 8–37 illustrates Kirchhoff's voltage law in a resistive circuit that has a sinusoidal voltage source. As you can see, the source voltage is the sum of all the voltage drops across the resistors, just as in a dc circuit.

▶ **FIGURE 8–37**

Illustration of Kirchhoff's voltage law in an ac circuit.

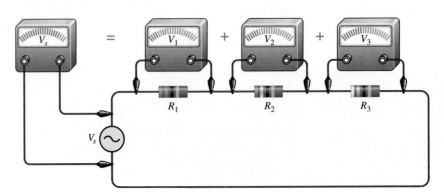

Power in resistive ac circuits is determined the same as for dc circuits except that you must use rms values of current and voltage. Recall that the rms value of a sine wave voltage is equivalent to a dc voltage of the same value in terms of its heating effect. The general power formulas are restated for a resistive ac circuit as

$$P = V_{rms}I_{rms}$$

$$P = \frac{V_{rms}^2}{R}$$

$$P = I_{rms}^2 R$$

EXAMPLE 8–11

Determine the rms voltage across each resistor and the rms current in Figure 8–38. The source voltage is given as an rms value. Also, determine the total power.

▶ FIGURE 8–38

Solution   The total resistance of the circuit is

$$R_{tot} = R_1 + R_2 = 1.0\,k\Omega + 560\,\Omega = 1.56\,k\Omega$$

Use Ohm's law to find the rms current.

$$I_{rms} = \frac{V_{s(rms)}}{R_{tot}} = \frac{110\,V}{1.56\,k\Omega} = \textbf{70.5\,mA}$$

The rms voltage drop across each resistor is

$$V_{1(rms)} = I_{rms}R_1 = (70.5\,mA)(1.0\,k\Omega) = \textbf{70.5\,V}$$

$$V_{2(rms)} = I_{rms}R_2 = (70.5\,mA)(560\,\Omega) = \textbf{39.5\,V}$$

The total power is

$$P_{tot} = I_{rms}^2 R_{tot} = (70.5\,mA)^2(1.56\,k\Omega) = \textbf{7.75\,W}$$

Related Problem   Repeat this example for a source voltage of 10 V peak.

Open Multisim file E08-11 on your CD-ROM. Measure the rms voltage across each resistor and compare to the calculated values. Change the source voltage to a peak value of 10 V, measure each resistor voltage, and compare to your calculated values.

EXAMPLE 8–12

All values in Figure 8–39 are given in rms.

(a) Find the unknown peak voltage drop in Figure 8–39(a).

(b) Find the total rms current in Figure 8–39(b).

(c) Find the total power in Figure 8–39(b).

FIGURE 8–39

Solution **(a)** Use Kirchhoff's voltage law to find V_3.

$$V_s = V_1 + V_2 + V_3$$

$$V_{3(rms)} = V_{s(rms)} - V_{1(rms)} - V_{2(rms)} = 24\,V - 12\,V - 8\,V = 4\,V$$

Convert rms to peak.

$$V_{3(p)} = 1.414V_{3(rms)} = 1.414(4\,V) = \textbf{5.66 V}$$

(b) Use Kirchhoff's current law to find I_{tot}.

$$I_{tot(rms)} = I_{1(rms)} + I_{2(rms)} = 10\,mA + 3\,mA = \textbf{13 mA}$$

(c) $P_{tot} = V_{rms}I_{rms} = (24\,V)(13\,mA) = \textbf{312 mW}$

Related Problem A series circuit has the following voltage drops: $V_{1(rms)} = 3.50\,V$, $V_{2(p)} = 4.25\,V$, $V_{3(avg)} = 1.70\,V$. Determine the peak-to-peak source voltage.

**SECTION 8–6
REVIEW**

1. A sinusoidal voltage with a half-cycle average value of 12.5 V is applied to a circuit with a resistance of 330 Ω. What is the peak current in the circuit?

2. The peak voltage drops in a series resistive circuit are 6.2 V, 11.3 V, and 7.8 V. What is the rms value of the source voltage?

8–7 SUPERIMPOSED DC AND AC VOLTAGES

In many practical circuits, you will find both dc and ac voltages combined. An example of this is in amplifier circuits where ac signal voltages are superimposed on dc operating voltages.

After completing this section, you should be able to

◆ **Determine total voltages that have both ac and dc components**

Figure 8–40 shows a dc source and an ac source in series. These two voltages will add algebraically to produce an ac voltage "riding" on a dc level, as measured across the resistor.

If V_{DC} is greater than the peak value of the sinusoidal voltage, the combined ac and dc voltage is a sine wave that never reverses polarity and is therefore nonalternating. That is,

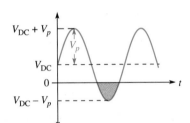

▶ FIGURE 8–40

Superimposed dc and ac voltages.

the sine wave is riding on a dc level, as shown in Figure 8–41(a). If V_{DC} is less than the peak value of the sine wave, the sine wave will be negative during a portion of its lower half-cycle, as illustrated in Figure 8–41(b), and is therefore alternating. In either case, the sine wave will reach a maximum voltage equal to $V_{DC} + V_p$, and it will reach a minimum voltage equal to $V_{DC} - V_p$.

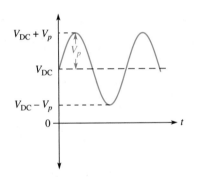

(a) $V_{DC} > V_p$. The sine wave never goes negative.

(b) $V_{DC} < V_p$. The sine wave reverses polarity during a portion of its cycle.

▶ FIGURE 8–41

Sine waves with dc levels.

EXAMPLE 8–13

Determine the maximum and minimum voltages across the resistor in each circuit of Figure 8–42 and show the resulting waveforms.

FIGURE 8–42

(a)

(b)

Solution   In Figure 8–42(a), the maximum voltage across R is

$$V_{max} = V_{DC} + V_p = 12\,V + 10\,V = \textbf{22 V}$$

The minimum voltage across R is

$$V_{min} = V_{DC} - V_p = 12\,V - 10\,V = \textbf{2 V}$$

Therefore, $V_{R(tot)}$ is a nonalternating sine wave that varies from +22 V to +2 V, as shown in Figure 8–43(a).

FIGURE 8–43

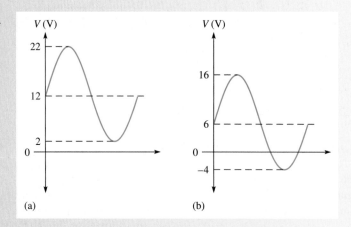

(a)   (b)

In Figure 8–42(b), the maximum voltage across R is

$$V_{max} = V_{DC} + V_p = 6\,V + 10\,V = \mathbf{16\,V}$$

The minimum voltage across R is

$$V_{min} = V_{DC} - V_p = \mathbf{-4\,V}$$

Therefore, $V_{R(tot)}$ is an alternating sine wave that varies from $+16$ V to -4 V, as shown in Figure 8–43(b).

Related Problem   Explain why the waveform in Figure 8–43(a) is nonalternating but the waveform in part (b) is considered to be alternating.

SECTION 8–7
REVIEW

1. What is the maximum positive value of the resulting total voltage when a sine wave with $V_p = 5$ V is added to a dc voltage of $+2.5$ V?

2. Will the resulting voltage in Question 1 alternate polarity?

3. If the dc voltage in Question 1 is -2.5 V, what is the maximum positive value of the resulting total voltage?

8–8 NONSINUSOIDAL WAVEFORMS

Sine waves are important in electronics, but they are not the only type of ac or time-varying waveform. Two other major types of waveforms are the pulse waveform and the triangular waveform.

After completing this section, you should be able to

◆ **Identify the characteristics of basic nonsinusoidal waveforms**

   ◆ Discuss the properties of a pulse waveform

   ◆ Define *duty cycle*

   ◆ Discuss the properties of triangular and sawtooth waveforms

   ◆ Discuss the harmonic content of a waveform

Pulse Waveforms

Basically, a **pulse** can be described as a very rapid transition (**leading edge**) from one voltage or current level (**baseline**) to another level; and then, after an interval of time, a very rapid transition (**trailing edge**) back to the original baseline level. The transitions in level are called *steps*. An ideal pulse consists of two opposite-going steps of equal amplitude. When the leading or trailing edge is positive-going, it is called a **rising edge.** When the leading or trailing edge is negative-going, it is called a **falling edge.**

Figure 8–44(a) shows an ideal positive-going pulse consisting of two equal but opposite instantaneous steps separated by an interval of time called the **pulse width**. Figure 8–44(b) shows an ideal negative-going pulse. The height of the pulse measured from the baseline is its voltage (or current) amplitude. Commonly, analysis is simplified by treating all pulses as ideal (composed of instantaneous steps and perfectly rectangular in shape).

(a) Positive-going pulse

(b) Negative-going pulse

◀ FIGURE 8–44

Ideal pulses.

Actual pulses, however, are never ideal. Pulses cannot change from one level to another instantaneously. Time is always required for a transition (step), as illustrated in Figure 8–45(a). As you can see, there is an interval of time during which the pulse is rising from its lower value to its higher value. This interval is called the *rise time, t_r.*

Rise time is the time required for the pulse to go from 10% of its amplitude to 90% of its amplitude.

The interval of time during which the pulse is falling from its higher value to its lower value is called the *fall time, t_f.*

Fall time is the time required for the pulse to go from 90% of its amplitude to 10% of its amplitude.

Pulse width (t_W) also requires a precise definition for the nonideal pulse because the leading and trailing edges are not vertical.

Pulse width is the time between the point on the leading edge where the value is 50% of the amplitude and the point on the trailing edge where the value is 50% of the amplitude.

Pulse width is shown in Figure 8–45(b).

(a) Rise and fall times

(b) Pulse width

◀ FIGURE 8–45

Nonideal pulse.

Repetitive Pulses Any waveform that repeats itself at fixed intervals is **periodic**. Figure 8–46 shows some examples of periodic pulse waveforms. Notice that in each case, the pulses repeat at regular intervals. The rate at which the pulses repeat is the **pulse repetition frequency,** which is the fundamental frequency of the waveform. The frequency can be expressed in hertz or in pulses per second. The time from one pulse to the corresponding point on the next pulse is the period (T). The relationship between frequency and period is the same as with the sine wave, $f = 1/T$.

(a)

(b)

(c)

▲ FIGURE 8–46

Repetitive pulse waveforms.

An important characteristic of periodic pulse waveforms is the duty cycle.

The duty cycle is the ratio of the pulse width (t_W) to the period (T) and is usually expressed as a percentage.

Equation 8–21

$$\text{Percent duty cycle} = \left(\frac{t_W}{T}\right)100\%$$

EXAMPLE 8–14

Determine the period, frequency, and duty cycle for the pulse waveform in Figure 8–47.

▲ FIGURE 8–47

Solution   As indicated in Figure 8–47, the period is

$$T = \textbf{10 } \boldsymbol{\mu}\textbf{s}$$

Use Equations 8–1 and 8–21 to determine the frequency and duty cycle.

$$f = \frac{1}{T} = \frac{1}{10\,\mu s} = \textbf{100 kHz}$$

$$\text{Percent duty cycle} = \left(\frac{t_W}{T}\right)100\% = \left(\frac{1\,\mu s}{10\,\mu s}\right)100\% = \textbf{10\%}$$

Related Problem   A certain pulse waveform has a frequency of 200 kHz and a pulse width of 0.25 μs. Determine the duty cycle expressed as a percentage.

Square Waves   A square wave is a pulse waveform with a duty cycle of 50%. Thus, the pulse width is equal to one-half of the period. A square wave is shown in Figure 8–48.

◀ **FIGURE 8–48**

Square wave.

The Average Value of a Pulse Waveform   The average value (V_{avg}) of a pulse waveform is equal to its baseline value plus the product of its duty cycle and its amplitude. The lower level of a positive-going waveform or the upper level of a negative-going waveform is taken as the baseline. The formula is as follows:

$$V_{avg} = \text{baseline} + (\text{duty cycle})(\text{amplitude})$$

Equation 8–22

The following example illustrates the calculation of the average value of pulse waveforms.

EXAMPLE 8–15   Determine the average value of each of the positive-going waveforms in Figure 8–49.

△ **FIGURE 8–49**

Solution   In Figure 8–49(a), the baseline is at 0 V, the amplitude is 2 V, and the duty cycle is 10%. The average value is

$$V_{avg} = \text{baseline} + (\text{duty cycle})(\text{amplitude})$$
$$= 0\,\text{V} + (0.1)(2\,\text{V}) = \textbf{0.2 V}$$

The waveform in Figure 8–49(b) has a baseline of +1 V, an amplitude of 5 V, and a duty cycle of 50%. The average value is

$$V_{avg} = \text{baseline} + (\text{duty cycle})(\text{amplitude})$$
$$= 1\,\text{V} + (0.5)(5\,\text{V}) = 1\,\text{V} + 2.5\,\text{V} = \textbf{3.5 V}$$

The waveform in Figure 8–49(c) is a square wave with a baseline of −1 V and an amplitude of 2 V. The duty cycle is 50%. The average value is

$$V_{avg} = \text{baseline} + (\text{duty cycle})(\text{amplitude})$$
$$= -1 \text{ V} + (0.5)(2 \text{ V}) = -1 \text{ V} + 1 \text{ V} = \mathbf{0 \text{ V}}$$

This is an alternating square wave, and, like an alternating sine wave, it has an average value of zero over a full cycle.

Related Problem   If the baseline of the waveform in Figure 8–49(a) is shifted to +1 V, what is the average value?

Triangular and Sawtooth Waveforms

Triangular and sawtooth waveforms are formed by voltage or current ramps. A **ramp** is a linear increase or decrease in the voltage or current. Figure 8–50 shows both positive- and negative-going ramps. In part (a), the ramp has a positive slope; in part (b), the ramp has a negative slope. The slope of a voltage ramp is $\pm V/t$ and the slope of a current ramp is $\pm I/t$.

(a) Positive ramp   (b) Negative ramp

▲ FIGURE 8–50

Ramps.

EXAMPLE 8–16   What are the slopes of the voltage ramps in Figure 8–51?

FIGURE 8–51

Solution   In Figure 8–51(a), the voltage increases from 0 V to +10 V in 5 ms. Thus, $V = 10$ V and $t = 5$ ms. The slope is

$$\frac{V}{t} = \frac{10 \text{ V}}{5 \text{ ms}} = \mathbf{2 \text{ V/ms}}$$

In Figure 8–51(b), the voltage decreases from +5 V to 0 V in 100 ms. Thus, $V = -5$ V and $t = 100$ ms. The slope is

$$\frac{V}{t} = \frac{-5\text{ V}}{100\text{ ms}} = -0.05\text{ V/ms}$$

Related Problem   A certain voltage ramp has a slope of +12 V/μs. If the ramp starts at zero, what is the voltage at 0.01 ms?

Triangular Waveforms   Figure 8–52 shows that a **triangular waveform** is composed of positive-going and negative-going ramps having equal slopes. The period of this waveform can be measured from one peak to the next corresponding peak, as illustrated. This particular triangular waveform is alternating and has an average value of zero.

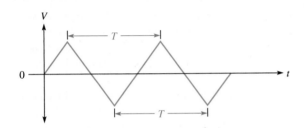

◀ FIGURE 8–52

Alternating triangular waveform.

Figure 8–53 depicts a triangular waveform with a nonzero average value. The frequency for triangular waves is determined in the same way as for sine waves, that is, $f = 1/T$.

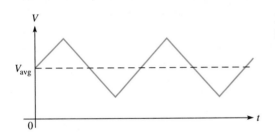

◀ FIGURE 8–53

Nonalternating triangular waveform.

Sawtooth Waveforms   The **sawtooth waveform** is actually a special case of the triangular waveform consisting of two ramps, one of much longer duration than the other. Sawtooth waveforms are used in many electronic systems. For example, the electron beam that sweeps across the screen of your TV receiver, creating the picture, is controlled by sawtooth voltages and currents. One sawtooth wave produces the horizontal beam movement, and the other produces the vertical beam movement. A sawtooth voltage is sometimes called a *sweep voltage*.

Figure 8–54 is an example of a sawtooth waveform. Notice that it consists of a positive-going ramp of relatively long duration, followed by a negative-going ramp of relatively short duration.

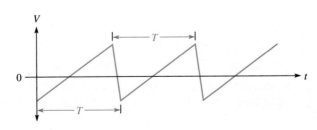

◀ FIGURE 8–54

Alternating sawtooth waveform.

Harmonics

A repetitive nonsinusoidal waveform contains sinusoidal waveforms with a fundamental frequency and harmonic frequencies. The **fundamental frequency** is the repetition rate of the waveform, and the **harmonics** are higher-frequency sine waves that are multiples of the fundamental.

Odd Harmonics *Odd harmonics* are frequencies that are odd multiples of the fundamental frequency of a waveform. For example, a 1 kHz square wave consists of a fundamental of 1 kHz and odd harmonics of 3 kHz, 5 kHz, 7 kHz, and so on. The 3 kHz frequency in this case is the third harmonic; the 5 kHz frequency is the fifth harmonic; and so on.

Even Harmonics *Even harmonics* are frequencies that are even multiples of the fundamental frequency. For example, if a certain wave has a fundamental of 200 Hz, the second harmonic is 400 Hz, the fourth harmonic is 800 Hz, the sixth harmonic is 1200 Hz, and so on. These are even harmonics.

Composite Waveform Any variation from a pure sine wave produces harmonics. A nonsinusoidal wave is a composite of the fundamental and the harmonics. Some types of waveforms have only odd harmonics, some have only even harmonics, and some contain both. The shape of the wave is determined by its harmonic content. Generally, only the fundamental frequency and the first few harmonics are of significant importance in determining the wave shape.

A square wave is an example of a waveform that consists of a fundamental frequency and only odd harmonics. When the instantaneous values of the fundamental and each odd harmonic are added algebraically at each point, the resulting curve will have the shape of a square wave, as illustrated in Figure 8–55. In part (a), the fundamental and the third harmonic produce a wave shape that begins to resemble a square wave. In part (b), the fundamental, third, and fifth harmonics produce a closer resemblance. When the seventh harmonic is included, as in part (c), the resulting wave shape becomes even more like a square wave. As more harmonics are included, a square wave is approached.

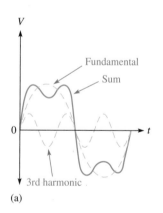

HANDS ON TIP The frequency response of an oscilloscope limits the accuracy with which waveforms can be accurately displayed. To view pulse waveforms, the frequency response must be high enough for all significant harmonics of the waveform. For example, a 100 MHz oscilloscope distorts a 100 MHz pulse waveform because the third, fifth, and higher harmonics are greatly attenuated.

(a)

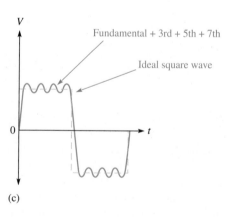

(b)

(c)

▲ FIGURE 8–55

Odd harmonics combine to produce a square wave.

SECTION 8–8 REVIEW

1. Define the following parameters:
   (a) rise time   (b) fall time   (c) pulse width
2. In a certain repetitive positive-going pulse waveform, the pulses are 200 μs wide and occur once every millisecond. What is the frequency of this waveform?

▷ FIGURE 8–56

3. Determine the duty cycle, amplitude, and average value of the waveform in Figure 8–56(a).
4. What is the period of the triangular wave in Figure 8–56(b)?
5. What is the frequency of the sawtooth wave in Figure 8–56(c)?
6. Define *fundamental frequency.*
7. What is the second harmonic of a fundamental frequency of 1 kHz?
8. What is the fundamental frequency of a square wave having a period of 10 μs?

8–9   THE OSCILLOSCOPE

The oscilloscope, or (scope for short) is a widely used and versatile test instrument for observing and measuring waveforms.

After completing this section, you should be able to

◆ **Use an oscilloscope to measure waveforms**

   ◆ Recognize common oscilloscope controls

   ◆ Measure the amplitude of a waveform

   ◆ Measure the period and frequency of a waveform

The **oscilloscope** is basically a graph-displaying device that traces a graph of a measured electrical signal on its screen. In most applications, the graph shows how signals change over time. The vertical axis of the display screen represents voltage and the horizontal axis represents time. You can measure amplitude, period, and frequency of a signal using an oscilloscope. Also, you can determine the pulse width, duty cycle, rise time, and fall time of a pulse waveform. Most scopes can display at least two signals on the screen at one time, enabling you to observe their time relationship. A typical oscilloscope is shown in Figure 8–57.

Two basic types of oscilloscopes, analog and digital, can be used to view digital waveforms. As shown in Figure 8–58(a), the analog scope works by applying the measured waveform directly to control the up and down motion of the electron beam in the cathode-ray tube (CRT) as it sweeps across the screen. As a result, the beam traces out the waveform pattern on the screen. As shown in Figure 8–58(b), the digital scope converts the measured

▶ FIGURE 8–57

Typical oscilloscopes. Copyright © Tektronix. Reproduced by permission.

▶ FIGURE 8–58

Basic comparison of analog and digital oscilloscopes.

(a) Analog   (b) Digital

waveform to digital information by a sampling process in an analog-to-digital converter (ADC). The digital information is then used to reconstruct the waveform on the screen.

The digital scope is more widely used than the analog scope. However, either type can be used in many applications; each has characteristics that make it more suitable for certain situations. An analog scope displays waveforms as they occur in "real time." Digital scopes are useful for measuring transient pulses that may occur randomly or only once. Also, because information about the measured waveform can be stored in a digital scope, it may be viewed at some later time, printed out, or thoroughly analyzed by a computer or other means.

Basic Operation of Analog Oscilloscopes   To measure a voltage, a probe must be connected from the scope to the point in a circuit at which the voltage is present. Generally, a ×10 probe is used that reduces (attenuates) the signal amplitude by ten. The signal goes through the probe into the vertical circuits where it is either further attenuated (reduced) or amplified depending on the actual amplitude and on where you set the vertical control of the scope. The vertical circuits then drive the vertical deflection plates of the CRT. Also, the signal goes to the trigger circuits that trigger the horizontal circuits to initiate repetitive horizontal sweeps of the electron beam across the screen using a sawtooth waveform. There are many sweeps per second so that the beam appears to form a solid line across the screen in the shape of the waveform. This basic operation is illustrated in Figure 8–59.

Block diagram of an analog oscilloscope.

Basic Operation of Digital Oscilloscopes   Some parts of a digital scope are similar to the analog scope. However, the digital scope is more complex than an analog scope and typically has an LCD screen rather than a CRT. Rather than displaying a waveform as it occurs, the digital scope first acquires the measured analog waveform and converts it to a digital format using an analog-to-digital converter (ADC). The digital data is stored and processed. The data then goes to the reconstruction and display circuits for display in its original analog form. Figure 8–60 shows a block diagram for a digital oscilloscope.

▲ FIGURE 8–60

Block diagram of a digital oscilloscope.

Oscilloscope Controls

A front panel view of a typical dual-channel oscilloscope is shown in Figure 8–61. Instruments vary depending on model and manufacturer, but most have certain common features. For example, the two vertical sections contain a Position control, a channel menu button, and a Volts/Div control. The horizontal section contains a Sec/Div control.

Some of the main controls are now discussed. Refer to the user manual for complete details of your particular scope.

▲ FIGURE 8–61

A typical dual-channel oscilloscope. Numbers below screen indicate the values for each division on the vertical (voltage) and horizontal (time) scales and can be varied using the vertical and horizontal controls on the scope.

Vertical Controls In the Vertical section of the scope in Figure 8–61, there are identical controls for each of the two channels (CH1 and CH2). The position control lets you move a displayed waveform up or down vertically on the screen. The Menu button provides for the selection of several items that appear on the screen, such as the coupling modes (ac, dc, or ground) and coarse or fine adjustment for the Volts/Div, as indicated in Figure 8–62(a). The Volts/Div control adjusts the number of volts represented by each vertical division on the screen. The Volts/Div setting for each channel is displayed on the bottom of the screen. The Math Menu button provides a selection of operations that can be performed on the input waveforms, such as subtraction and addition of signals, as indicated in Figure 8–62(b).

Horizontal Controls In the Horizontal section, the controls apply to both channels. The Position control lets you move a displayed waveform left to right horizontally on the screen. The Menu button provides for the selection of several items that appear on the screen such as the main time base, expanded view of a portion of a waveform, and other parameters. The Sec/Div control adjusts the time represented by each horizontal division or main time base. The Sec/Div setting is displayed at the bottom of the screen.

Trigger Controls In the Trigger section, the Level control determines the point on the triggering waveform where triggering occurs to initiate the sweep to display input waveforms. The Menu button provides for the selection of several items that appear on the screen including edge or slope triggering, trigger source, trigger mode, and other parameters, as shown in Figure 8–63. There is also an input for an external trigger signal.

(a) Example of channel menu selection

(b) Example of math menu selection

▲ FIGURE 8–62

Scope screens showing examples of menu selections.

◀ FIGURE 8–63

Example of the trigger menu.

Triggering stabilizes a waveform on the screen and properly triggers on a pulse that occurs only one time or randomly. Also it allows you to observe time delays between two waveforms. Figure 8–64 compares a triggered to an untriggered signal. The untriggered signal tends to drift across the screen producing what appears to be multiple waveforms.

(a) Untriggered waveform display

(b) Triggered waveform display

◀ FIGURE 8–64

Comparison of an untriggered and a triggered waveform on an oscilloscope.

Coupling a Signal into the Scope   Coupling is the method used to connect a signal voltage to be measured into the oscilloscope. The DC and AC coupling modes are selected from the Vertical menu. DC coupling allows a waveform including its dc component to be displayed. AC coupling blocks the dc component of a signal so that you see the waveform centered at 0 V. The Ground mode allows you to connect the channel input to ground to see where the 0 V reference is on the screen. Figure 8–65 illustrates the result of DC and AC coupling using a sinusoidal waveform that has a dc component.

▶ FIGURE 8–65

Displays of the same waveform having a dc component.

(a) DC coupled waveform

(b) AC coupled waveform

The voltage probe, shown in Figure 8–66, is used for connecting a signal to the scope. Since all instruments tend to affect the circuit being measured due to loading, most scope probes provide an attenuation network to minimize loading effects. Probes that attenuate the measured signal by a factor of 10 are called ×10 (times ten) probes. Probes with no attenuation are called ×1 (times one) probes. The oscilloscope adjusts its calibration for the attenuation of the type of probe being used. For most measurements, the ×10 probe should be used. However, if you are measuring very small signals, a ×1 may be the best choice.

▶ FIGURE 8–66

An oscilloscope voltage probe. Copyright © Tektronix, Inc. Reproduced by permission.

The probe has an adjustment that allows you to compensate for the input capacitance of the scope. Most scopes have a probe compensation output that provides a calibrated square wave for probe compensation. Before making a measurement, you should make sure that the probe is properly compensated to eliminate any distortion introduced. Typically, there is a screw or other means of adjusting compensation on a probe. Figure 8–67 shows scope waveforms for three probe conditions: properly compensated, undercompensated, and overcompensated. If the waveform appears either over- or undercompensated, adjust the probe until the properly compensated square wave is achieved.

Properly compensated   Undercompensated   Overcompensated

▲ FIGURE 8–67

Probe compensation conditions.

EXAMPLE 8–17

Determine the peak-to-peak value and period of each sine wave in Figure 8–68 from the digital scope screen displays and the settings for Volts/Div and Sec/Div, which are indicated under the screens. Sine waves are centered vertically on the screens.

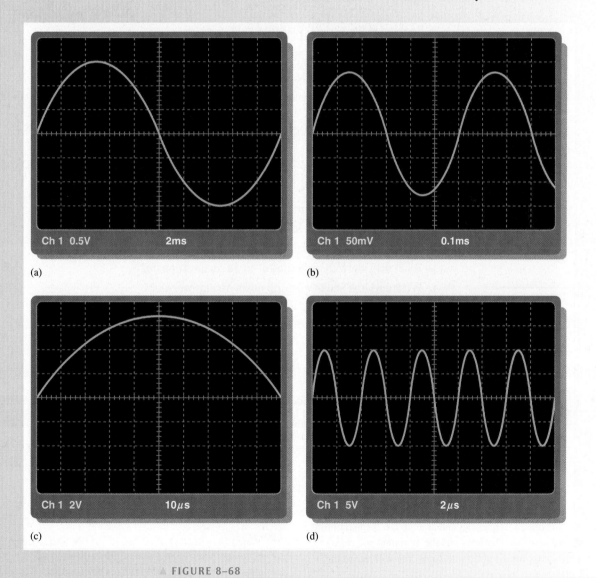

(a)

(b)

(c)

(d)

▲ FIGURE 8–68

Solution   Looking at the vertical scale in Figure 8–68(a),

$$V_{pp} = 6 \text{ divisions} \times 0.5 \text{ V/division} = \textbf{3.0 V}$$

From the horizontal scale (one cycle covers ten divisions),

$$T = 10 \text{ divisions} \times 2 \text{ ms/division} = \textbf{20 ms}$$

Looking at the vertical scale in Figure 8–68(b),

$$V_{pp} = 5 \text{ divisions} \times 50 \text{ mV/division} = \textbf{250 mV}$$

From the horizontal scale (one cycle covers six divisions),

$$T = 6 \text{ divisions} \times 0.1 \text{ ms/division} = 0.6 \text{ ms} = \textbf{600 } \boldsymbol{\mu}\textbf{s}$$

Looking at the vertical scale in Figure 8–68(c),

$$V_{pp} = 6.8 \text{ divisions} \times 2 \text{ V/division} = \textbf{13.6 V}$$

From the horizontal scale (one-half cycle covers ten divisions),

$$T = 20 \text{ divisions} \times 10 \text{ } \mu\text{s/division} = \textbf{200 } \boldsymbol{\mu}\textbf{s}$$

Looking at the vertical scale in Figure 8–68(d),

$$V_{pp} = 4 \text{ divisions} \times 5 \text{ V/division} = \textbf{20 V}$$

From the horizontal scale (one cycle covers two divisions),

$$T = 2 \text{ divisions} \times 2 \text{ } \mu\text{s/division} = \textbf{4 } \boldsymbol{\mu}\textbf{s}$$

Related Problem   Determine the rms value and the frequency for each waveform displayed in Figure 8–68.

**SECTION 8–9
REVIEW**

1. What is the main difference between a digital and an analog oscilloscope?
2. Is voltage read horizontally or vertically on a scope screen?
3. What does the Volts/Div control on an oscilloscope do?
4. What does the Sec/Div control on an oscilloscope do?
5. When should you use a ×10 probe for making a voltage measurement?

Application Assignment

PUTTING YOUR KNOWLEDGE
TO WORK

Assume you are assigned to check out a particular function generator that produces sine wave, triangular wave, and pulse outputs. For each type of output, you will analyze oscilloscope measurements of the minimum and maximum frequencies and amplitudes, the maximum positive and negative dc offsets, and the minimum and maximum duty cycles for the pulse waveform. You will record the measurements in a logical format.

Step 1: Familiarization with the Function Generator

The function generator is shown in Figure 8–69. Each control is marked by a circled number and a description follows.

1. *Power on/off switch*   Press this push-button switch to turn the power on. Press again to release the switch and turn the power off.

2. *Function switches*   Press one of the switches to select either a sinusoidal, triangular, sawtooth, or pulse output.

▲ FIGURE 8–69

Function generator.

3. *Frequency/amplitude range switches* These menu-selectable switches are used in conjunction with the adjustment control (4).

4. *Frequency adjustment control* Turn this dial to set a specific frequency in the range selected.

5. *DC offset/duty cycle control* This control adjusts the dc level of the ac output. You can add a positive or a negative dc level to a waveform and adjust the duty cycle of the pulse waveform output. The sine wave or triangular wave outputs are not affected by this control.

Step 2: Measuring the Sinusoidal Output

The output of the function generator is connected to the channel 1 (CH1) input of the scope and the sinusoidal output function is selected. The scope is set to dc coupling.

In Figure 8–70(a), assume the amplitude and frequency of the function generator are set to their minimum values. Measure and record these values. Express amplitude in both peak and rms.

In Figure 8–70(b), assume the amplitude and frequency are set to their maximum values. Measure and record these values. Express amplitude in both peak and rms.

Step 3: Measuring the DC Offset

Assume the sinusoidal amplitude and frequency of the function generator are set to arbitrary values for dc offset measurement. The scope is set to dc coupling.

In Figure 8–71(a), the dc offset of the function generator is adjusted to the maximum positive value. Measure and record this value.

In Figure 8–71(b), the dc offset is adjusted to the maximum negative value. Measure and record this value.

Step 4: Measuring the Triangular Output

The triangular output of the function generator is selected. The scope is set to ac coupling.

In Figure 8–72(a), the amplitude and frequency of the function generator are set to the minimum values. Measure and record these values.

In Figure 8–72(b), the amplitude and frequency are set to the maximum values. Measure and record these values.

▶ FIGURE 8–70

(a) The horizontal axis is 0 V.

(b) The horizontal axis is 0 V.

▷ FIGURE 8–71

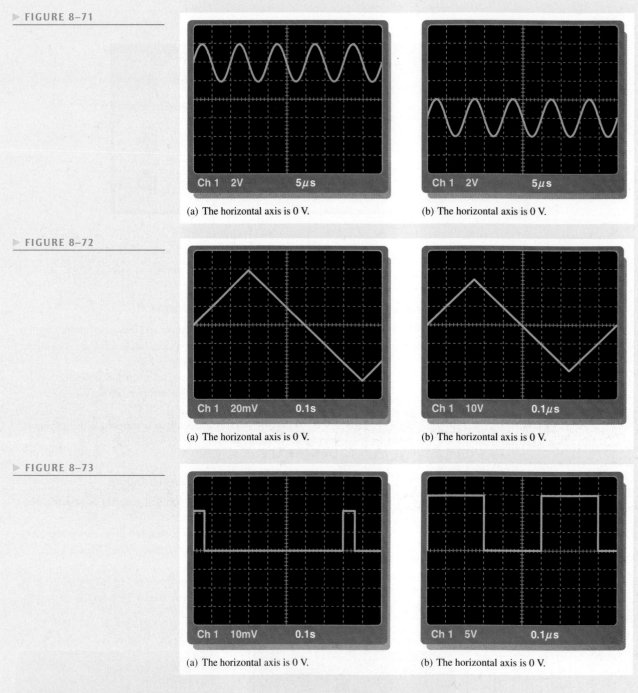

(a) The horizontal axis is 0 V. (b) The horizontal axis is 0 V.

▷ FIGURE 8–72

(a) The horizontal axis is 0 V. (b) The horizontal axis is 0 V.

▷ FIGURE 8–73

(a) The horizontal axis is 0 V. (b) The horizontal axis is 0 V.

Step 5: Measuring the Pulse Output

The pulse output of the function generator is selected. The scope is set to dc coupling.

In Figure 8–73(a), the amplitude from the baseline and frequency of the function generator are set to the minimum values. The duty cycle is adjusted to minimum. Measure and record these values. Express the duty cycle as a percentage.

In Figure 8–73(b), the amplitude and frequency are set to the maximum values. The duty cycle is adjusted to maximum. Measure and record these values. Express the duty cycle as a percentage.

Review

1. Generally, what setting of the Sec/Div control on a scope should be used to obtain the most accurate measurement of frequency?

2. Generally, what setting of the Volts/Div control on a scope should be used to obtain the most accurate measurement of amplitude?

3. Explain the purpose of each coupling mode setting (AC, DC, and GND) for each channel of an oscilloscope.

SUMMARY

◆ The sine wave is a time-varying, periodic waveform.

◆ The sine wave is the fundamental type of alternating current (ac) and alternating voltage.

◆ Alternating current changes direction in response to changes in the polarity of the source voltage.

◆ One cycle of an alternating sine wave consists of a positive alternation and a negative alternation.

◆ A sine wave voltage can be generated by a conductor rotating in a magnetic field.

◆ Two common sources of sine waves are the electromagnetic ac generator and the electronic oscillator circuit.

◆ A full cycle of a sine wave is 360°, or 2π radians. A half-cycle is 180°, or π radian. A quarter-cycle is 90° or $\pi/2$ radians.

◆ Phase angle is the difference in degrees (or radians) between two sine waves or between a sine wave and a reference wave.

◆ The angular position of a phasor represents the angle of a sine wave, and the length of the phasor represents the amplitude.

◆ Voltages and currents must all be expressed with consistent units when you apply Ohm's or Kirchhoff's laws in ac circuits.

◆ Power in a resistive ac circuit is determined using rms voltage and/or current values.

◆ A pulse consists of a transition from a baseline level to an amplitude level, followed by a transition back to the baseline level.

◆ A triangular or sawtooth wave consists of positive-going and negative-going ramps.

◆ Harmonic frequencies are odd or even multiples of the repetition rate (or fundamental frequency) of a nonsinusoidal waveform.

◆ Conversions of sine wave values are summarized in Table 8–2.

▶ TABLE 8–2

TO CHANGE FROM	TO	MULTIPLY BY
Peak	rms	0.707
Peak	Peak-to-peak	2
Peak	Average	0.637
rms	Peak	1.414
Peak-to-peak	Peak	0.5
Average	Peak	1.57

KEY TERMS

Key terms and other bold terms in the chapter are defined in the end-of-book glossary.

Amplitude   The maximum value of a voltage or current.

Average value   The average of a sine wave over one half-cycle. It is 0.637 times the peak value.

Cycle   One repetition of a periodic waveform.

Degree   The unit of angular measure corresponding to 1/360 of a complete revolution.

Duty cycle   A characteristic of a pulse waveform that indicates the percentage of time that a pulse is present during a cycle; the ratio of pulse width to period expressed as either a fraction or as a percentage.

Fall time (t_f)   The time interval required for a pulse to change from 90% to 10% of its amplitude.

Frequency (f)   A measure of the rate of change of a periodic function; the number of cycles completed in 1 s. The unit of frequency is the hertz.

Function generator   An instrument that produces more than one type of waveform.

Fundamental frequency   The repetition rate of a waveform.

Harmonics   The frequencies contained in a composite waveform, which are integer multiples of the pulse repetition frequency (fundamental).

Hertz (Hz)   The unit of frequency. One hertz equals one cycle per second.

Instantaneous value   The voltage or current value of a waveform at a given instant in time.

Oscillator   An electronic circuit that produces a time-varying signal without an external input signal using positive feedback.

Oscilloscope   A measurement instrument that displays signal waveforms on a screen.

Peak-to-peak value   The voltage or current value of a waveform measured from its minimum to its maximum points.

Peak value   The voltage or current value of a waveform at its maximum positive or negative points.

Period (T)   The time interval of one complete cycle of a periodic waveform.

Periodic   Characterized by a repetition at fixed-time intervals.

Phase   The relative angular displacement of a time-varying waveform in terms of its occurrence with respect to a reference.

Pulse   A type of waveform that consists of two equal and opposite steps in voltage or current separated by a time interval.

Pulse width (t_W)   The time interval between the opposite steps of an ideal pulse. For a nonideal pulse, the time between the 50% points on the leading and trailing edges.

Radian   A unit of angular measurement. There are 2π radians in one complete 360° revolution. One radian equals 57.3°.

Ramp   A type of waveform characterized by a linear increase or decrease in voltage or current.

Rise time (t_r)   The time interval required for a pulse to change from 10% to 90% of its amplitude.

rms value   The value of a sinusoidal voltage that indicates its heating effect, also known as the effective value. It is equal to 0.707 times the peak value. *rms* stands for root mean square.

Sine wave   A type of waveform that follows a cyclic sinusoidal pattern defined by the formula $v = A \sin \theta$.

Waveform   The pattern of variations of a voltage or current showing how the quantity changes with time.

FORMULAS

8–1	$f = \dfrac{1}{T}$	Frequency
8–2	$T = \dfrac{1}{f}$	Period
8–3	$f = $ **(number of pole pairs)(rps)**	Output frequency of a generator
8–4	$V_{pp} = 2V_p$	Peak-to-peak voltage (sine wave)
8–5	$I_{pp} = 2I_p$	Peak to peak current (sine wave)
8–6	$V_{rms} = 0.707V_p$	Root-mean-square voltage (sine wave)
8–7	$I_{rms} = 0.707I_p$	Root-mean-square current (sine wave)
8–8	$V_p = 1.414V_{rms}$	Peak voltage (sine wave)
8–9	$I_p = 1.414I_{rms}$	Peak current (sine wave)
8–10	$V_{pp} = 2.828V_{rms}$	Peak-to-peak voltage (sine wave)
8–11	$I_{pp} = 2.828I_{rms}$	Peak-to-peak current (sine wave)
8–12	$V_{avg} = 0.637V_p$	Half-cycle average voltage (sine wave)
8–13	$I_{avg} = 0.637I_p$	Half-cycle average current (sine wave)
8–14	$\text{rad} = \left(\dfrac{\pi \text{ rad}}{180°}\right) \times \text{degrees}$	Degrees to radian conversion

8–15	degrees $= \left(\dfrac{180°}{\pi \text{ rad}}\right) \times \text{rad}$	Radian to degrees conversion
8–16	$y = A \sin \theta$	General formula for a sine wave
8–17	$v = V_p \sin \theta$	Sinusoidal voltage
8–18	$i = I_p \sin \theta$	Sinusoidal current
8–19	$y = A \sin(\theta - \phi)$	Lagging sine wave
8–20	$y = A \sin(\theta + \phi)$	Leading sine wave
8–21	Percent duty cycle $= \left(\dfrac{t_W}{T}\right)100\%$	Duty cycle
8–22	$V_{\text{avg}} = \text{baseline} + (\text{duty cycle})(\text{amplitude})$	Average value of pulse waveform

SELF-TEST

Answers are at the end of the chapter.

1. The difference between alternating current (ac) and direct current (dc) is
   (a) ac changes value and dc does not
   (b) ac changes direction and dc does not
   (c) both (a) and (b)
   (d) neither (a) nor (b)

2. During each cycle, a sine wave reaches a peak value
   (a) one time   (b) two times
   (c) four times   (d) a number of times depending on the frequency

3. A sine wave with a frequency of 12 kHz is changing at a faster rate than a sine wave with a frequency of
   (a) 20 kHz   (b) 15,000 Hz   (c) 10,000 Hz   (d) 1.25 MHz

4. A sine wave with a period of 2 ms is changing at a faster rate than a sine wave with a period of
   (a) 1 ms   (b) 0.0025 s   (c) 1.5 ms   (d) 1000 μs

5. When a sine wave has a frequency of 60 Hz, in 10 s it goes through
   (a) 6 cycles   (b) 10 cycles   (c) 1/16 cycle   (d) 600 cycles

6. If the peak value of a sine wave is 10 V, the peak-to-peak value is
   (a) 20 V   (b) 5 V   (c) 100 V   (d) none of these

7. If the peak value of a sine wave is 20 V, the rms value is
   (a) 14.14 V   (b) 6.37 V   (c) 7.07 V   (d) 0.707 V

8. The average value of a 10 V peak sine wave over one complete cycle is
   (a) 0 V   (b) 6.37 V   (c) 7.07 V   (d) 5 V

9. The average half-cycle value of a sine wave with a 20 V peak is
   (a) 0 V   (b) 6.37 V   (c) 12.74 V   (d) 14.14 V

10. One sine wave has a positive-going zero crossing at 10° and another sine wave has a positive-going zero crossing at 45°. The phase angle between the two waveforms is
    (a) 55°   (b) 35°   (c) 0°   (d) none of these

11. The instantaneous value of a 15 A peak sine wave at a point 32° from its positive-going zero crossing is
    (a) 7.95 A   (b) 7.5 A   (c) 2.13 A   (d) 7.95 V

12. If the rms current through a 10 kΩ resistor is 5 mA, the rms voltage drop across the resistor is
    (a) 70.7 V   (b) 7.07 V   (c) 5 V   (d) 50 V

13. Two series resistors are connected to an ac source. If there is 6.5 V rms across one resistor and 3.2 V rms across the other, the peak source voltage is
    (a) 9.7 V   (b) 9.19 V   (c) 13.72 V   (d) 4.53 V

14. A 10 kHz pulse waveform consists of pulses that are 10 μs wide. Its duty cycle is

    (a) 100%   **(b)** 10%   **(c)** 1%   **(d)** not determinable

15. The duty cycle of a square wave

    (a) varies with the frequency   **(b)** varies with the pulse width

    (c) both (a) and (b)   **(d)** is 50%

TROUBLESHOOTING: SYMPTOM AND CAUSE

The purpose of these exercises is to help develop thought processes essential to troubleshooting. Answers are at the end of the chapter.

Determine the cause for each set of symptoms. Refer to Figure 8–74.

▶ FIGURE 8–74

The ac meters indicate the correct readings for this circuit.

1. *Symptom:* The voltmeter 1 reading is 0 V, and the voltmeter 2 reading is 20 V.

   Cause:

   (a) R_1 is open.

   (b) R_2 is open.

   (c) R_3 is open.

2. *Symptom:* The voltmeter 1 reading is 20 V, and the voltmeter 2 reading is 0 V.

   Cause:

   (a) R_1 is open.

   (b) R_2 is shorted.

   (c) R_3 is shorted.

3. *Symptom:* The voltmeter 1 reading is 18.2 V, and the voltmeter 2 reading is 1.8 V.

   Cause:

   (a) R_1 is open.

   (b) R_2 is open.

   (c) R_1 is shorted.

4. *Symptom:* Both voltmeter readings are 10 V.

   Cause:

   (a) R_1 is open.

   (b) R_1 is shorted.

   (c) R_2 is open.

5. *Symptom:* The voltmeter 1 reading is 16.7 V, and the voltmeter 2 reading is 3.3 V.

   Cause:

   (a) R_1 is shorted.

   (b) R_2 is 10 kΩ instead of 1 kΩ.

   (c) R_3 is 10 kΩ instead of 1 kΩ.

PROBLEMS

Answers to odd-numbered problems are at the end of the book.

BASIC PROBLEMS

SECTION 8–1 The Sinusoidal Waveform

1. Calculate the frequency for each of the following periods:

   (a) 1 s   (b) 0.2 s   (c) 50 ms   (d) 1 ms   (e) 500 μs   (f) 10 μs

2. Calculate the period for each of the following frequencies:

   (a) 1 Hz   (b) 60 Hz   (c) 500 Hz   (d) 1 kHz   (e) 200 kHz   (f) 5 MHz

3. A sine wave goes through 5 cycles in 10 μs. What is its period?

4. A sine wave has a frequency of 50 kHz. How many cycles does it complete in 10 ms?

SECTION 8–2 Sinusoidal Voltage Sources

5. The conductive wire loop on the rotor of a simple two-pole, single-phase generator rotates at a rate of 250 rps. What is the frequency of the induced output voltage?

6. A certain four-pole generator has a speed of rotation of 3600 rpm. What is the frequency of the voltage produced by this generator?

7. At what speed of rotation must a four-pole generator be operated to produce a 400 Hz sinusoidal voltage?

SECTION 8–3 Voltage and Current Values of Sine Waves

8. A sine wave has a peak value of 12 V. Determine the following voltage values:

   (a) rms   (b) peak-to-peak   (c) half-cycle average

9. A sinusoidal current has an rms value of 5 mA. Determine the following current values:

   (a) peak   (b) half-cycle average   (c) peak-to-peak

10. For the sine wave in Figure 8–75, determine the peak, peak-to-peak, rms, and average values.

11. If each horizontal division in Figure 8–75 is 1 ms, determine the instantaneous voltage value at

    (a) 1 ms   (b) 2 ms   (c) 4 ms   (d) 7 ms

▶ FIGURE 8–75

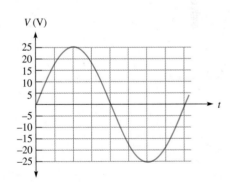

SECTION 8–4 Angular Measurement of a Sine Wave

12. In Figure 8–75, what is the instantaneous voltage at

    (a) 45°   (b) 90°   (c) 180°

13. Sine wave A has a positive-going zero crossing at 30° from a reference. Sine wave B has a positive-going zero crossing at 45° from the same reference. Determine the phase angle between the two signals. Which signal leads?

14. One sine wave has a positive peak at 75°. and another has a positive peak at 100°. How much is each sine wave shifted in phase from the 0° reference? What is the phase angle between them?

15. Draw two sine waves as follows: Sine wave A is the reference, and sine wave B lags A by 90°. Both have equal amplitudes.

16. Convert the following angular values from degrees to radians:

(a) 30°   (b) 45°   (c) 78°   (d) 135°   (e) 200°   (f) 300°

17. Convert the following angular values from radians to degrees:

(a) $\pi/8$ (b) $\pi/3$ (c) $\pi/2$ (d) $3\pi/5$ (e) $6\pi/5$ (f) 1.8π

SECTION 8–5   The Sine Wave Formula

18. A certain sine wave has a positive-going zero crossing at 0° and an rms value of 20 V. Calculate its instantaneous value at each of the following angles:

(a) 15°   (b) 33°   (c) 50°   (d) 110°

(e) 70°   (f) 145°   (g) 250°   (h) 325°

19. For a particular 0° reference sinusoidal current, the peak value is 100 mA. Determine the instantaneous value at each of the following points:

(a) 35°   (b) 95°   (c) 190°   (d) 215°   (e) 275°   (f) 360°

20. For a 0° reference sine wave with an rms value of 6.37 V, determine its instantaneous value at each of the following points:

(a) $\pi/8$ rad   (b) $\pi/4$ rad   (c) $\pi/2$ rad   (d) $3\pi/4$ rad

(e) π rad   (f) $3\pi/2$ rad   (g) 2π rad

21. Sine wave A lags sine wave B by 30°. Both have peak values of 15 V. Sine wave A is the reference with a positive-going crossing at 0°. Determine the instantaneous value of sine wave B at 30°, 45°, 90°, 180°, 200°, and 300°.

22. Repeat Problem 21 for the case when sine wave A leads sine wave B by 30°.

SECTION 8–6   Analysis of AC Circuits

23. A sinusoidal voltage is applied to the resistive circuit in Figure 8–76. Determine the following:

(a) I_{rms} (b) I_{avg} (c) I_p (d) I_{pp} (e) i at the positive peak

▶ FIGURE 8–76

24. Find the half-cycle average values of the voltages across R_1 and R_2 in Figure 8–77. All values shown are rms.

25. Determine the rms voltage across R_3 in Figure 8–78.

▲ FIGURE 8–77   ▲ FIGURE 8–78

SECTION 8–7   Superimposed DC and AC Voltages

26. A sine wave with an rms value of 10.6 V is riding on a dc level of 24 V. What are the maximum and minimum values of the resulting waveform?

27. How much dc voltage must be added to a 3 V rms sine wave in order to make the resulting voltage nonalternating (no negative values)?

28. A 6 V peak sine wave is riding on a dc voltage of 8 V. If the dc voltage is lowered to 5 V, how far negative will the sine wave go?

SECTION 8–8   Nonsinusoidal Waveforms

29. From the graph in Figure 8–79, determine the approximate values of t_r, t_f, t_W, and amplitude.

▲ FIGURE 8–79

30. Determine the duty cycle for each pulse waveform in Figure 8–80.

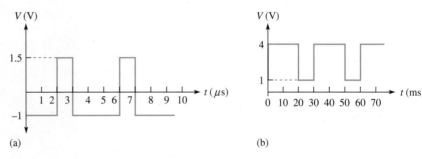

(a)   (b)

▲ FIGURE 8–80

31. Find the average value of each positive-going pulse waveform in Figure 8–80.

32. What is the frequency of each waveform in Figure 8–80.

33. What is the frequency of each sawtooth waveform in Figure 8–81?

(a)

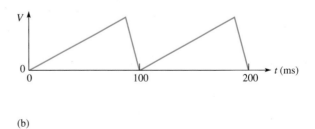

(b)

▲ FIGURE 8–81

34. A square wave has a period of 40 μs. List the first six odd harmonics.

35. What is the fundamental frequency of the square wave mentioned in Problem 34?

SECTION 8–9   **The Oscilloscope**

36. Determine the peak value and the period of the sine wave displayed on the scope screen in Figure 8–82. The horizontal axis is 0 V.

▶ FIGURE 8–82

37. Determine the rms value and the frequency of the sine wave displayed on the scope screen in Figure 8–82.

38. Determine the rms value and the frequency of the sine wave displayed on the scope screen in Figure 8–83. The horizontal axis is 0 V.

▶ FIGURE 8–83

39. Find the amplitude, pulse width, and duty cycle for the pulse waveform displayed on the scope screen in Figure 8–84. The horizontal axis is 0 V.

▶ FIGURE 8–84

ADVANCED PROBLEMS

40. A certain sine wave has a frequency of 2.2 kHz and an rms value of 25 V. Assuming a given cycle begins (zero crossing) at $t = 0$ s, what is the change in voltage from 0.12 ms to 0.2 ms?

41. Figure 8–85 shows a sinusoidal voltage source in series with a dc source. Effectively, the two voltages are superimposed. Draw the total voltage across R_L. Determine the maximum current through R_L and the average voltage across R_L.

◢ FIGURE 8–85

42. A nonsinusoidal waveform called a *stairstep* is shown in Figure 8–86. Determine its average value.

▲ FIGURE 8–86

43. Refer to the oscilloscope screen in Figure 8–87.

   (a) How many cycles are displayed?

   (b) What is the rms value of the sine wave?

   (c) What is the frequency of the sine wave?

◢ FIGURE 8–87

44. Accurately draw on a grid representing the scope screen in Figure 8–87 how the sine wave will appear if the Volts/Div control is moved to a setting of 5 V.

45. Accurately draw on a grid representing the scope screen in Figure 8–87 how the sine wave will appear if the Sec/Div control is moved to a setting of 10 μs.

46. Based on the instrument settings and an examination of the scope display and the circuit board in Figure 8–88, determine the frequency and peak value of the input signal and output signal. The waveform shown is channel 1. Draw the channel 2 waveform as it would appear on the scope with the indicated settings.

47. Examine the circuit board and the oscilloscope display in Figure 8–89 and determine the peak value and the frequency of the unknown input signal.

▲ FIGURE 8–88

Unknown input signal

▲ FIGURE 8–89

 MULTISIM TROUBLESHOOTING PROBLEMS

48. Open file P08-48 and measure the peak value and period of the voltage sine wave using the oscilloscope.

49. Open file P08-49 and determine if there is a fault. If so, identify it.

50. Open file P08-50 and determine if there is a fault. If so, identify it.

51. Open file P08-51 and measure the amplitude and period of the pulse waveform using the oscilloscope.

52. Open file P08-52 and determine if there is a fault. If so, identify it.

ANSWERS

SECTION REVIEWS

SECTION 8–1   The Sine Wave

1. One cycle goes from the zero crossing through a positive peak, then through zero to a negative peak and back to the zero crossing.

2. A sine wave changes polarity at the zero crossings.

3. A sine wave has two maximum points (peaks) in one cycle.

4. The period is measured from one zero crossing to the next corresponding zero crossing, or from one peak to the next corresponding peak.

5. Frequency is the number of cycles completed in one second and its unit is the hertz.

6. $f = 1/5\,\mu s = 200\,\text{kHz}$

7. $T = 1/120\,\text{Hz} = 8.33\,\text{ms}$

SECTION 8–2   **Sinusoidal Voltage Sources**

1. Two types of sine wave sources are electromagnetic and electronic.

2. Sine waves are generated electromagnetically by rotating a conductor in a magnetic field.

3. Frequency is dependent on the number of poles and the rps.

4. Amplitude is dependent on the number of turns and the rps.

SECTION 8–3   **Voltage and Current Values of Sine Waves**

1. **(a)** $V_{pp} = 2(1\,\text{V}) = 2\,\text{V}$

  (b) $V_{pp} = 2(1.414)(1.414\,\text{V}) = 4\,\text{V}$

  (c) $V_{pp} = 2(1.57)(3\,\text{V}) = 9.42\,\text{V}$

2. **(a)** $V_{rms} = (0.707)(2.5\,\text{V}) = 1.77\,\text{V}$

  (b) $V_{rms} = (0.5)(0.707)(10\,\text{V}) = 3.54\,\text{V}$

  (c) $V_{rms} = (0.707)(1.57)(1.5\,\text{V}) = 1.66\,\text{V}$

3. **(a)** $V_{avg} = (0.637)(10\,\text{V}) = 6.37\,\text{V}$

  (b) $V_{avg} = (0.637)(1.414)(2.3\,\text{V}) = 2.07\,\text{V}$

  (c) $V_{avg} = (0.637)(0.5)(60\,\text{V}) = 19.1\,\text{V}$

SECTION 8–4   **Angular Measurements of a Sine Wave**

1. **(a)** The positive peak is at $90°$.

  (b) The negative-going zero crossing is at $180°$.

  (c) The negative peak is at $270°$.

  (d) The cycle ends at $360°$.

2. A half-cycle is completed in $180°$ or π radians.

3. A full cycle is completed in $360°$ or 2π radians.

4. $\theta = 90° - 45° = 45°$

SECTION 8–5   **The Sine Wave Formula**

1. **(a)** $\sin 30° = 0.5$

  (b) $\sin 60° = 0.866$

  (c) $\sin 90° = 1$

2. $v = 10 \sin 120° = 8.66\,\text{V}$

3. $v = 10 \sin(45° + 10°) = 8.19\,\text{V}$

SECTION 8–6   **Analysis of AC Circuits**

1. $I_p = V_p/R = (1.57)(12.5\,\text{V})/330\,\Omega = 59.5\,\text{mA}$

2. $V_{s(rms)} = (0.707)(25.3\,\text{V}) = 17.9\,\text{V}$

SECTION 8–7   **Superimposed DC and AC Voltages**

1. $+V_{max} = 5\,\text{V} + 2.5\,\text{V} = 7.5\,\text{V}$

2. Yes, it will alternate.

3. $+V_{max} = 5\,\text{V} - 2.5\,\text{V} = 2.5\,\text{V}$

SECTION 8–8   **Nonsinusoidal Waveforms**

1. **(a)** Rise time is the time interval from 10% to 90% of the amplitude;

    (b) Fall time is the time interval from 90% to 10% of the amplitude;

    (c) Pulse width is the time interval from 50% of the leading pulse edge to 50% of the trailing pulse edge.

2. $f = 1/1\ \text{ms} = 1\ \text{kHz}$

3. d.c. $= (1/5)100\% = 20\%$; Ampl. 1.5 V; $V_{\text{avg}} = 0.5\ \text{V} + 0.2(1.5\ \text{V}) = 0.8\ \text{V}$

4. $T = 16\ \text{ms}$

5. $f = 1/T = 1/1\ \mu\text{s} = 1\ \text{MHz}$

6. Fundamental frequency is the repetition rate of the waveform.

7. 2nd harmonic: 2 kHz

8. $f = 1/10\ \mu\text{s} = 100\ \text{kHz}$

SECTION 8–9   **The Oscilloscope**

1. Digital: Signal is converted to digital for processing and then reconstructed for display.

    Analog: Signal drives display directly.

2. Voltage is measured vertically.

3. The Volts/Div control sets the amount of volts represented by each division on the vertical scale.

4. The Sec/Div control sets the amount of time represented by each division on the horizontal scale.

5. Use a ×10 probe most of the time except when measuring very small voltages.

Application Assignment

1. Lowest Sec/Div setting that allows frequency to be measured

2. Lowest Volts/Div setting that allows voltage to be measured

3. AC: Couples ac voltage only; GND: Grounds input so trace is at 0 V; DC: Couples ac and dc voltages

RELATED PROBLEMS FOR EXAMPLES

8–1   2.4 s

8–2   1.5 ms

8–3   20 kHz

8–4   200 Hz

8–5   1 ms

8–6   30 rps

8–7 $V_{pp} = 50\ \text{V}; V_{\text{rms}} = 17.7\ \text{V}; V_{\text{avg}} = 15.9\ \text{V}$

8–8   **(a)** $\pi/12\ \text{rad}$

       (b) 112.5°

8–9   8°

8–10   18.1 V

8–11 $I_{\text{rms}} = 4.53\ \text{mA}; V_{1(\text{rms})} = 4.53\ \text{V}; V_{2(\text{rms})} = 2.54\ \text{V}; P_{tot} = 32\ \text{mV}$

8–12   23.7 V

8–13   The waveform in part (a) never goes negative. The waveform in part (b) goes negative for a portion of its cycle.

8–14   5%

8–15   1.2 V

8–16   120 V

8–17 (a) $V_{rms} = 1.06\ V; f = 50\ Hz$

(b) $V_{rms} = 88.4\ mV; f = 1.67\ kHz$

(c) $V_{rms} = 4.81\ V; f = 5\ kHz$

(d) $V_{rms} = 7.07\ V; f = 250\ kHz$

SELF-TEST

1. (b) **2.** (b) **3.** (c) **4.** (b) **5.** (d) **6.** (a) **7.** (a)

8. (a) **9.** (c) **10.** (b) **11.** (a) **12.** (d) **13.** (c) **14.** (b)

15. (d)

TROUBLESHOOTING: SYMPTOM AND CAUSE

1. (c)

2. (c)

3. (b)

4. (a)

5. (b)

CAPACITORS

9

CHAPTER OBJECTIVES

- Describe the basic structure and characteristics of a capacitor
- Discuss various types of capacitors
- Analyze series capacitors
- Analyze parallel capacitors
- Describe how a capacitor operates in a dc switching circuit
- Describe how a capacitor operates in an ac circuit
- Discuss some capacitor applications

KEY TERMS

- Capacitor
- Dielectric
- Capacitance
- Farad (F)
- Coulomb's law
- Dielectric strength
- Temperature coefficient
- Dielectric constant
- Charging
- *RC* time constant
- Exponential
- Transient time
- Capacitive reactance
- Instantaneous power
- True power
- Reactive power
- VAR (volt-ampere reactive)
- Filter
- Ripple voltage
- Coupling
- Decoupling
- Bypass

APPLICATION ASSIGNMENT PREVIEW

Capacitors are used in many applications. The application assignment in this chapter focuses on the use of capacitors in amplifier circuits to couple an ac voltage from one point to another while blocking dc voltage. You will determine if voltages measured on an amplifier circuit board with an oscilloscope are correct; and if they are not correct, you will troubleshoot the problem. After studying this chapter, you should be able to complete the application assignment.

VISIT THE COMPANION WEBSITE

Study aids for this chapter are available at
http://www.prenhall.com/floyd

INTRODUCTION

The capacitor is a device that can store electrical charge, thereby creating an electric field which in turn stores energy. The measure of the charge-storing ability is called *capacitance.*

In this chapter, the basic capacitor is introduced and its characteristics are studied. The physical construction and electrical properties of various types of capacitors are discussed. Series and parallel combinations are analyzed, and the basic behavior of capacitors in both dc and ac circuits is studied. Representative applications also are discussed.

9–1 THE BASIC CAPACITOR

A **capacitor** is a passive electrical component that stores electrical charge and has the property of capacitance.

After completing this section, you should be able to

◆ **Describe the basic structure and characteristics of a capacitor**

◆ Explain how a capacitor stores charge

◆ Define *capacitance* and state its unit

◆ State Coulomb's law

◆ Explain how a capacitor stores energy

◆ Discuss voltage rating and temperature coefficient

◆ Explain capacitor leakage

◆ Specify how the physical characteristics affect the capacitance

Basic Construction

In its simplest form, a capacitor is an electrical device constructed of two parallel conductive plates separated by an insulating material called the **dielectric**. Connecting leads are attached to the parallel plates. A basic capacitor is shown in Figure 9–1(a), and the schematic symbol is shown in part (b).

▶ FIGURE 9–1

The basic capacitor.

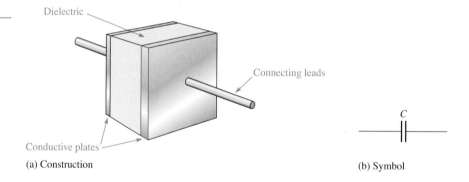

Dielectric

Connecting leads

Conductive plates

(a) Construction

C

(b) Symbol

How a Capacitor Stores Charge

In the neutral state, both plates of a capacitor have an equal number of free electrons, as indicated in Figure 9–2(a). When the capacitor is connected to a dc voltage source through a resistor, as shown in part (b), electrons (negative charge) are removed from plate *A*, and an equal number are deposited on plate *B*. As plate *A* loses electrons and plate *B* gains electrons, plate *A* becomes positive with respect to plate *B*. During this charging process, electrons flow only through the connecting leads and the source. No electrons flow through the dielectric of the capacitor because it is an insulator. The movement of electrons ceases when the voltage across the capacitor equals the source voltage, as indicated in Figure 9–2(c). If the capacitor is disconnected from the source, it retains the stored charge for a long period of time (the length of time depends on the type of capacitor) and still has the voltage across it, as shown in Figure 9–2(d). A charged capacitor can act as a temporary battery.

(a) Neutral (uncharged) capacitor (same charge on both plates)

(b) When connected to a voltage source, electrons flow from plate *A* to plate *B* as the capacitor charges.

(c) After the capacitor charges to V_S, no electrons flow.

(d) Ideally, the capacitor retains charge when disconnected from the voltage source.

▲ FIGURE 9–2

Illustration of a capacitor storing charge.

Capacitance

The amount of charge that a capacitor can store per unit of voltage across its plates is its capacitance, designated *C*. That is, **capacitance** is a measure of a capacitor's ability to store charge. The more charge per unit of voltage that a capacitor can store, the greater its capacitance, as expressed by the following formula:

$$C = \frac{Q}{V}$$

Equation 9–1

where *C* is capacitance, *Q* is charge, and *V* is voltage.

By rearranging the terms in Equation 9–1, you can obtain two other formulas.

$$Q = CV$$

Equation 9–2

$$V = \frac{Q}{C}$$

Equation 9–3

The Unit of Capacitance   The **farad (F)** is the basic unit of capacitance. Recall that the coulomb (C) is the unit of electrical charge.

One farad is the amount of capacitance when one coulomb of charge is stored with one volt across the plates.

Most capacitors that are used in electronics work have capacitance values in microfarads (μF) and picofarads (pF). A microfarad is one-millionth of a farad (1 μF $= 1 \times 10^{-6}$ F); and a picofarad is one-trillionth of a farad (1 pF $= 1 \times 10^{-12}$ F). Conversions for farads, microfarads, and picofarads are given in Table 9–1.

▶ TABLE 9–1

Conversions for farads, microfarads, and picofarads.

TO CONVERT FROM	TO	MOVE THE DECIMAL POINT
Farads	Microfarads	right 6 places ($\times 10^{6}$)
Farads	Picofarads	right 12 places ($\times 10^{12}$)
Microfarads	Farads	left 6 places ($\times 10^{-6}$)
Microfarads	Picofarads	right 6 places ($\times 10^{6}$)
Picofarads	Farads	left 12 places ($\times 10^{-12}$)
Picofarads	Microfarads	left 6 places ($\times 10^{-6}$)

EXAMPLE 9–1

(a) A certain capacitor stores 50 microcoulombs (50 μC) when 10 V are applied across its plates. What is its capacitance?

(b) A 2.2 μF capacitor has 100 V across its plates. How much charge does it store?

(c) Determine the voltage across a 100 pF capacitor that is storing 2 μC of charge.

Solution

(a) $C = \dfrac{Q}{V} = \dfrac{50\,\mu C}{10\,V} = \mathbf{5\,\mu F}$

(b) $Q = CV = (2.2\,\mu F)(100\,V) = \mathbf{220\,\mu C}$

(c) $V = \dfrac{Q}{C} = \dfrac{2\,\mu C}{100\,pF} = \mathbf{20\,kV}$

*Related Problem** Determine V if $C = 1000$ pF and $Q = 10\,\mu$C.

---

*Answers are at the end of the chapter.

EXAMPLE 9–2

Convert the following values to microfarads:

(a) 0.00001 F   (b) 0.0047 F   (c) 1000 pF   (d) 220 pF

Solution

(a) $0.00001\,F \times 10^{6}\,\mu F/F = \mathbf{10\,\mu F}$

(b) $0.0047\,F \times 10^{6}\,\mu F/F = \mathbf{4700\,\mu F}$

(c) $1000\,pF \times 10^{-6}\,\mu F/pF = \mathbf{0.001\,\mu F}$

(d) $220\,pF \times 10^{-6}\,\mu F/pF = \mathbf{0.00022\,\mu F}$

Related Problem Convert 47,000 pF to microfarads.

EXAMPLE 9–3

Convert the following values to picofarads:

(a) 0.1×10^{-8} F   (b) 0.000027 F   (c) 0.01 μF   (d) 0.0047 μF

Solution **(a)** $0.1 \times 10^{-8}\,\text{F} \times 10^{12}\,\text{pF/F} = \textbf{1000 pF}$

(b) $0.000027\,\text{F} \times 10^{12}\,\text{pF/F} = \textbf{27} \times \textbf{10}^{\textbf{6}}\,\textbf{pF}$

(c) $0.01\,\mu\text{F} \times 10^{6}\,\text{pF}/\mu\text{F} = \textbf{10,000 pF}$

(d) $0.0047\,\mu\text{F} \times 10^{6}\,\text{pF}/\mu\text{F} = \textbf{4700 pF}$

Related Problem Convert $100\,\mu\text{F}$ to picofarads.

How a Capacitor Stores Energy

A capacitor stores energy in an electric field that is established by the opposite charges stored on the two plates. The electric field is represented by lines of force between the positive and negative charges and is concentrated within the dielectric, as shown in Figure 9–3.

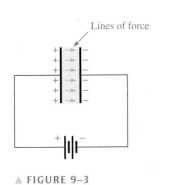

▲ **FIGURE 9–3**

The electric field stores energy in a capacitor. The beige area indicates the dielectric.

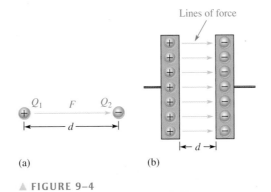

(a) (b)

▲ **FIGURE 9–4**

Lines of force are created by opposite charges.

Coulomb's law states

A force (F) exists between two point-source charges (Q_1, Q_2) that is directly proportional to the product of the two charges and inversely proportional to the square of the distance (d) between the charges.

Figure 9–4(a) illustrates a line of force between a positive and a negative charge. Figure 9–4(b) shows that many opposite charges distributed on the plates of a capacitor create many lines of force, which form an electric field that stores energy within the dielectric. Although the distributed charges no longer act as point-source charges and do not exactly obey Coulomb's law, the force is still dependent on the amount of charge and the distance between the plates.

The greater the forces between the charges on the plates of a capacitor, the more energy is stored. Therefore, the amount of energy stored is directly proportional to the capacitance because, from Coulomb's law, the more charge stored, the greater the force.

Also, from the equation $Q = CV$, the amount of charge stored is directly related to the voltage as well as the capacitance. Therefore, the amount of energy stored is also dependent on the square of the voltage across the plates of the capacitor. The formula for the energy stored by a capacitor is

$$W = \frac{1}{2}CV^2$$

Equation 9–4

When capacitance (C) is in farads and voltage (V) is in volts, the energy (W) is in joules.

Voltage Rating

Every capacitor has a limit on the amount of voltage that it can withstand across its plates. The voltage rating specifies the maximum dc voltage that can be applied without risk of damage to the device. If this maximum voltage, commonly called the *breakdown voltage* or *working voltage,* is exceeded, permanent damage to the capacitor can result.

You must consider both the capacitance and the voltage rating before you use a capacitor in a circuit application. The choice of capacitance value is based on particular circuit requirements. The voltage rating should always be above the maximum voltage expected in a particular application.

Dielectric Strength The breakdown voltage of a capacitor is determined by the **dielectric strength** of the dielectric material used. The dielectric strength is expressed in V/mil (1 mil = 0.001 in. = 2.54×10^{-5} meter). Table 9–2 lists typical values for several materials. Exact values vary depending on the specific composition of the material.

▶ TABLE 9–2

Some common dielectric materials and their typical dielectric strengths.

MATERIAL	DIELECTRIC STRENGTH (V/MIL)
Air	80
Oil	375
Ceramic	1000
Paper (paraffined)	1200
Teflon®	1500
Mica	1500
Glass	2000

The dielectric strength of a capacitor can best be explained by an example. Assume that a certain capacitor has a plate separation of 1 mil and that the dielectric material is ceramic. This particular capacitor can withstand a maximum voltage of 1000 V because its dielectric strength is 1000 V/mil. If the maximum voltage is exceeded, the dielectric may break down and conduct current, causing permanent damage to the capacitor. If the ceramic capacitor has a plate separation of 2 mils, its breakdown voltage is 2000 V.

Temperature Coefficient

The **temperature coefficient** indicates the amount and direction of a change in capacitance value with temperature. A positive temperature coefficient means that the capacitance increases with an increase in temperature or decreases with a decrease in temperature. A negative coefficient means that the capacitance decreases with an increase in temperature or increases with a decrease in temperature.

Temperature coefficients typically are specified in parts per million per Celsius degree (ppm/°C). For example, a negative temperature coefficient of 150 ppm/°C for a 1 μF capacitor means that for every degree Celsius rise in temperature, the capacitance decreases by 150 pF (there are one million picofarads in one microfarad).

Leakage

No insulating material is perfect. The dielectric of any capacitor will conduct some very small amount of current. Thus, the charge on a capacitor will eventually leak off. Some types of capacitors have higher leakages than others. An equivalent circuit for a nonideal capacitor is shown in Figure 9–5. The parallel resistor R_{leak} represents the extremely high resistance (several hundred kΩ or more) of the dielectric material through which there is leakage current.

▲ FIGURE 9–5

Equivalent circuit for a nonideal capacitor.

Physical Characteristics of a Capacitor

The following parameters are important in establishing the capacitance and the voltage rating of a capacitor: plate area, plate separation, and dielectric constant.

Plate Area *Capacitance is directly proportional to the physical size of the plates as determined by the plate area, A.* A large plate area produces more capacitance, and a smaller plate area produces less capacitance. Figure 9–6(a) shows that the plate area of a parallel plate capacitor is the area of one of the plates. If the plates are moved in relation to each other, as shown in Figure 9–6(b), the overlapping area determines the effective plate area. This variation in effective plate area is the basis for a certain type of variable capacitor.

Plate Separation *Capacitance is inversely proportional to the distance between the plates.* The plate separation is designated d, as shown in Figure 9–7. A greater separation of the plates produces a lesser capacitance, as illustrated in the figure. The breakdown voltage is directly proportional to the plate separation. The further the plates are separated, the greater the breakdown voltage.

(a) Full plate area:
   more capacitance

(b) Reduced plate area:
   less capacitance

▲ FIGURE 9–6

Capacitance is directly proportional
to plate area (A).

(a) Plates closer together:
   more capacitance

(b) Plates further apart:
   less capacitance

▲ FIGURE 9–7

Capacitance is inversely proportional
to the distance d between the plates.

Dielectric Constant As you know, the insulating material between the plates of a capacitor is called the *dielectric*. Every dielectric material has the ability to concentrate the lines of force of the electric field existing between the oppositely charged plates of a capacitor and thus increase the capacity for energy storage. The measure of a material's ability to establish an electric field is called the **dielectric constant** or *relative permittivity,* symbolized by ε_r (the Greek letter epsilon).

   Capacitance is directly proportional to the dielectric constant. The dielectric constant of a vacuum is defined as 1, and that of air is very close to 1. These values are used as a reference, and all other materials have values of ε_r specified with respect to that of a vacuum or air. For example, a material with $\varepsilon_r = 5$ can have a capacitance five times greater than that of air, with all other factors being equal.

   Table 9–3 lists several common dielectric materials and a typical dielectric constant for each. The values can vary because it depends on the specific composition of the material.

   The dielectric constant (relative permittivity) is dimensionless because it is a relative measure. It is a ratio of the absolute permittivity of a material, ε, to the absolute permittivity of a vacuum, ε_0, as expressed by the following formula:

$$\varepsilon_r = \frac{\varepsilon}{\varepsilon_0}$$

Equation 9–5

The value of ε_0 is 8.85×10^{-12} F/m (farads per meter).

▶ TABLE 9–3

Some common dielectric materials
and their typical dielectric constants.

MATERIAL	TYPICAL ε_r VALUE
Air (vacuum)	1.0
Teflon®	2.0
Paper (paraffined)	2.5
Oil	4.0
Mica	5.0
Glass	7.5
Ceramic	1200

Formula for Capacitance You have seen how capacitance is directly related to plate area, A, and the dielectric constant, ε_r, and inversely related to plate separation, d. An exact formula for calculating the capacitance in terms of these three quantities is

Equation 9–6

$$C = \frac{A\varepsilon_r(8.85 \times 10^{-12}\,\text{F/m})}{d}$$

where A is in square meters (m²), d is in meters (m), and C is in farads (F).

EXAMPLE 9–4

Determine the capacitance in μF of a parallel plate capacitor having a plate area of 0.01 m² and a plate separation of 1 mil (2.54×10^{-5} m). The dielectric is mica, which has a dielectric constant of 5.0.

Solution Use Equation 9–6.

$$C = \frac{A\varepsilon_r(8.85 \times 10^{-12}\,\text{F/m})}{d} = \frac{(0.01\,\text{m}^2)(5.0)(8.85 \times 10^{-12}\,\text{F/m})}{2.54 \times 10^{-5}\,\text{m}} = \mathbf{0.017\,\mu F}$$

Related Problem Determine C in μF where $A = 0.005$ m², $d = 3$ mil (7.62×10^{-5} m), and ceramic is the dielectric.

SECTION 9–1
REVIEW
Answers are at the end of the chapter.

1. Define *capacitance*.
2. (a) How many microfarads in one farad?
   (b) How many picofarads in one farad?
   (c) How many picofarads in one microfarad?
3. Convert 0.0015 μF to picofarads. To farads.
4. How much energy in joules is stored by a 0.01 μF capacitor with 15 V across its plates?
5. (a) When the plate area of a capacitor is increased, does the capacitance increase or decrease?
   (b) When the distance between the plates is increased, does the capacitance increase or decrease?
6. The plates of a ceramic capacitor are separated by 2 mils. What is the typical breakdown voltage?

9–2   TYPES OF CAPACITORS

Capacitors normally are classified according to the type of dielectric material. The most common types of dielectric materials are mica, ceramic, plastic-film, and electrolytic (aluminum oxide and tantalum oxide).

After completing this section, you should be able to

◆ **Discuss various types of capacitors**

   ◆ Describe the characteristics of mica, ceramic, plastic-film, and electrolytic capacitors

   ◆ Describe types of variable capacitors

   ◆ Identify capacitor labeling

   ◆ Discuss capacitance measurement

Fixed Capacitors

Mica Capacitors   Two types of mica capacitors are stacked-foil and silver-mica. The basic construction of the stacked-foil type is shown in Figure 9–8. It consists of alternate layers of metal foil and thin sheets of mica. The metal foil forms the plate, with alternate foil sheets connected together to increase the plate area. More layers are used to increase the plate area, thus increasing the capacitance. The mica/foil stack is encapsulated in an insulating material such as Bakelite®, as shown in Figure 9–8(b). The silver-mica capacitor is formed in a similar way by stacking mica sheets with silver electrode material screened on them.

(a) Stacked layer arrangement

(b) Layers are pressed together and encapsulated.

◀ FIGURE 9–8

Construction of a typical radial-lead mica capacitor.

Mica capacitors are generally available with capacitance values ranging from 1 pF to 0.1 μF and voltage ratings from 100 V dc to 2500 V dc and higher. Common temperature coefficients range from -20 ppm/°C to $+100$ ppm/°C. Mica has a typical dielectric constant of 5.

Ceramic Capacitors   Ceramic dielectrics provide very high dielectric constants (1200 is typical). As a result, comparatively high capacitance values can be achieved in a small physical size. Ceramic capacitors are commonly available in a ceramic disk form, as shown in Figure 9–9; in a multilayer radial-lead configuration, as shown in Figure 9–10; or in a leadless ceramic chip, as shown in Figure 9–11.

Ceramic capacitors typically are available in capacitance values ranging from 1 pF to 2.2 μF with voltage ratings up to 6 kV. A typical temperature coefficient for ceramic capacitors is 200,000 ppm/°C.

HANDS ON TIP

Chip capacitors are for surface mounting on a printed circuit board and have conductive terminals plated on the ends. These capacitors will withstand the molten solder temperatures encountered in reflow and wave soldering used in automated circuit board assembly. Chip capacitors are in great demand because of the move toward miniaturization.

Lead wire soldered
to silver electrode

Solder

Ceramic
dielectric

Dipped phenolic coating

Silver electrodes deposited on
top and bottom of ceramic disk

(a)

(b)

▲ FIGURE 9–9

A ceramic disk capacitor and its basic construction.

CK05
K50V
104K

75388
J 200 V
822K

KEMET
C512BX
104K   200V
7552

Solder

Ceramic
dielectric

Electrode

Lead wire

Molded case

Solder

(a) Typical capacitors

(b) Construction view

▲ FIGURE 9–10

Examples of ceramic capacitors.

▶ FIGURE 9–11

Construction view of a typical ceramic
chip capacitor used for surface
mounting on printed circuit boards.

Copper (barrier layer)

Ceramic
dielectric

Electrode

Solder

Plastic-Film Capacitors   Common dielectric materials used in plastic-film capacitors include polycarbonate, propylene, polyester, polystyrene, polypropylene, and mylar. Some of these types have capacitance values up to 100 μF but most are less than 1 μF.

Figure 9–12 shows a basic construction used in many plastic-film capacitors. A thin strip of plastic-film dielectric is sandwiched between two thin metal strips that act as plates. One lead is connected to the inner plate and one is connected to the outer plate as indicated. The strips are then rolled in a spiral configuration and encapsulated in a molded case. Thus, a large plate area can be packaged in a relatively small physical size, thereby achieving large capacitance values. Another method uses metal deposited directly on the film dielectric to form the plates.

Lead connected to outer foil

Lead connected to inner foil

Inner foil

Plastic film

Outer foil

◀ **FIGURE 9–12**

Basic construction of axial-lead tubular plastic-film dielectric capacitors.

Figure 9–13(a) shows typical plastic-film capacitors. Figure 9–13(b) shows a construction view for one type of an axial-lead plastic-film capacitor.

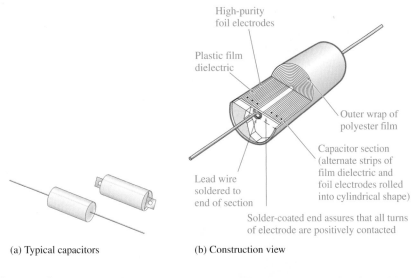

High-purity foil electrodes

Plastic film dielectric

Outer wrap of polyester film

Capacitor section (alternate strips of film dielectric and foil electrodes rolled into cylindrical shape)

Lead wire soldered to end of section

Solder-coated end assures that all turns of electrode are positively contacted

(a) Typical capacitors   (b) Construction view

◀ **FIGURE 9–13**

Examples of plastic-film capacitors.

Electrolytic Capacitors   Electrolytic capacitors are polarized so that one plate is positive and the other negative. These capacitors are generally used for high capacitance values from 1 μF up to over 200,000 μF, but they have relatively low breakdown voltages (350 V is a typical maximum but higher voltages are occasionally found) and high amounts of leakage.

Electrolytic capacitors offer much higher capacitance values than mica or ceramic capacitors, but their voltage ratings are typically lower. While other capacitors use two similar plates, the electrolytic capacitor consists of one plate made of aluminum foil and another plate made of a conducting electrolyte applied to a material such as plastic film. These two "plates" are separated by a layer of aluminum oxide that forms on the surface of the aluminum plate. Figure 9–14(a) illustrates the construction of a typical aluminum electrolytic capacitor with axial leads. Other electrolytic capacitors with radial leads are shown in Figure 9–14(b); the symbol for an electrolytic capacitor is shown in part (c).

SAFETY POINT

Be extremely careful with electrolytic capacitors because it does make a difference which way an electrolytic capacitor is connected. Always observe the proper polarity. If a polarized capacitor is connected backwards, it may explode and cause injury.

(a) Construction view of an axial-lead electrolytic capacitor

(b) Typical radial-lead electrolytics

(c) Symbol for an electrolytic capacitor.

▲ FIGURE 9–14

Examples of electrolytic capacitors.

Tantalum electrolytic capacitors can be in either a tubular configuration similar to Figure 9–14 or "tear drop" shape as shown in Figure 9–15. In the tear drop configuration, the positive plate is actually a pellet of tantalum powder rather than a sheet of foil. Tantalum pentoxide forms the dielectric, and manganese dioxide forms the negative plate.

Because of the process used for the insulating pentoxide dielectric, the metallic (aluminum or tantalum) plate is always positive with respect to the electrolyte plate, and thus all electrolytic capacitors are polarized. The metal plate (positive lead) is usually indicated by a plus sign or some other obvious marking and must always be connected in a dc circuit where the voltage across the capacitor does not change polarity. Reversal of the polarity of the voltage can result in complete destruction of the capacitor.

▶ FIGURE 9–15

Construction view of a typical "tear drop" shaped tantalum electrolytic capacitor.

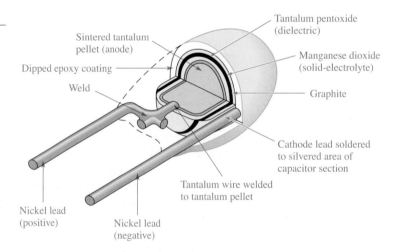

Variable Capacitors

Variable capacitors are used in a circuit when there is a need to adjust the capacitance value either manually or automatically. These capacitors are generally less than 300 pF but are available in larger values for specialized application. The schematic symbol for a variable capacitor is shown in Figure 9–16.

Adjustable capacitors that normally have slotted screw-type adjustments and are used for very fine adjustments in a circuit are called **trimmers.** Ceramic or mica is a common dielectric in these types of capacitors, and the capacitance usually is changed by adjusting the plate separation. Generally, trimmer capacitors have values less than 100 pF. Figure 9–17 shows some typical devices.

▲ FIGURE 9–16

Schematic symbol for a variable capacitor.

◀ FIGURE 9–17

Trimmer capacitors.

The **varactor** is a semiconductive device that exhibits a capacitance characteristic that is varied by changing the voltage across its terminals. This device usually is covered in detail in a course on electronic devices.

Capacitor Labeling

Capacitor values are indicated on the body of the capacitor either by numerical or alphanumerical labels and sometimes by color codes. Capacitor labels indicate various parameters such as capacitance, voltage rating, and tolerance.

Some capacitors carry no unit designation for capacitance. In these cases, the units are implied by the value indicated and are recognized by experience. For example, a ceramic capacitor marked .001 or .01 has units of microfarads because picofarad values that small are not available. As another example, a ceramic capacitor labeled 50 or 330 has units of picofarads because microfarad units that large normally are not available in this type. In some cases a 3-digit designation is used. The first two digits are the first two digits of the capacitance value. The third digit is the multiplier or number of zeros after the second digit. For example, 103 means 10,000 pF. In some instances, the units are labeled as pF or μF; sometimes the microfarad unit is labeled as MF or MFD.

A voltage rating appears on some types of capacitors with WV or WVDC and is omitted on others. When it is omitted, the voltage rating can be determined from information supplied by the manufacturer. The tolerance of the capacitor is usually labeled as a percentage, such as ±10%. The temperature coefficient is indicated by a *parts per million* marking. This type of label consists of a P or N followed by a number. For example, N750 means a negative temperature coefficient of 750 ppm/°C, and P30 means a positive temperature coefficient of 30 ppm/°C. An NP0 designation means that the positive and negative coefficients are zero; thus the capacitance does not change with temperature. Certain types of capacitors are color coded. Refer to Appendix B for additional capacitor labeling and color code information.

Capacitance Measurement

An *LCR* (inductance, capacitance, and resistance) meter, such as the one shown in Figure 9–18, can be used to check the value of a capacitor. Also, many DMMs provide a capacitance measurement feature. All capacitors change value over a period of time, some more than others. Ceramic capacitors, for example, often exhibit a 10% to 15% change in the value during the first year. Electrolytic capacitors are particularly subject to value change due to drying of the electrolytic solution. In other cases, capacitors may be labeled incorrectly or

▲ FIGURE 9–18

A typical *LCR* meter. (Courtesy of B+K Precision)

the wrong value may have been installed in the circuit. Although a value change represents less than 25% of defective capacitors, a value check should be made to quickly eliminate this as a source of trouble when troubleshooting a circuit. Values from 200 pF to 20 mF can be measured by simply connecting the capacitor, setting the switch, and reading the value on the display.

Some *LCR* meters can also be used to check for leakage current in capacitors. In order to check for leakage, a sufficient voltage must be applied across the capacitor to simulate operating conditions. This is automatically done by the test instrument. Over 40% of all defective capacitors have excessive leakage current and electrolytic capacitors are particularly susceptible to this problem.

SECTION 9–2 REVIEW	1. How are capacitors commonly classified?
	2. What is the difference between a fixed and a variable capacitor?
	3. What type of capacitor normally is polarized?
	4. What precautions must be taken when a polarized capacitor is installed in a circuit?
	5. An electrolytic capacitor is connected between a negative supply voltage and ground. Which capacitor lead should be connected to ground?

9–3 SERIES CAPACITORS

The total capacitance of a series connection of capacitors is less than the individual capacitance of any of the capacitors. Capacitors in series divide voltage across them in proportion to their capacitance.

After completing this section, you should be able to

- ◆ **Analyze series capacitors**
  - ◆ Determine total capacitance
  - ◆ Determine capacitor voltages

When capacitors are connected in series, the total capacitance is less than the smallest capacitance value because the effective plate separation increases. The calculation of total series capacitance is analogous to the calculation of total resistance of parallel resistors (Chapter 5).

Two capacitors can be used in series to show how the total capacitance is determined. Figure 9–19 shows two capacitors, which initially are uncharged, connected in series with a dc voltage source. When the switch is closed, as shown in part (a), current begins.

Recall that current is the same at all points in a series circuit and that current is defined as the rate of flow of charge ($I = Q/t$). In a certain period of time, a certain amount of charge moves through the circuit. Since current is the same everywhere in the circuit of Figure 9–19(a), the same amount of charge is moved from the negative side of the source to plate A of C_1, and from plate B of C_1 to plate A of C_2, and from plate B of C_2 to the positive side of the source. As a result, of course, the same amount of charge is deposited on the plates of both capacitors in a given period of time, and the total charge (Q_T) moved

Capacitors in series produce a total capacitance that is less than the smallest value.

(a) While charging, $I = Q/t$ is the same at all points. Capacitor voltages are increasing.

(b) Both capacitors store the same amount of charge ($Q_T = Q_1 = Q_2$).

through the circuit in that period of time equals the charge stored by C_1 and also equals the charge stored by C_2.

$$Q_T = Q_1 = Q_2$$

As the capacitors charge, the voltage across each one increases as indicated.

Figure 9–19(b) shows the capacitors after they have been completely charged and the current has ceased. Both capacitors store an equal amount of charge (Q), and the voltage across each one depends on its capacitance value ($V = Q/C$). By Kirchhoff's voltage law, which applies to capacitive circuits as well as to resistive circuits, the sum of the capacitor voltages equals the source voltage.

$$V_S = V_1 + V_2$$

Using the formula $V = Q/C$, you can substitute into the formula for Kirchhoff's law and get the following relationship (where $Q = Q_T = Q_1 = Q_2$):

$$\frac{Q}{C_T} = \frac{Q}{C_1} + \frac{Q}{C_2}$$

The Q can be factored out of the right side of the equation and canceled with the Q on the left side as follows:

$$\frac{\cancel{Q}}{C_T} = \cancel{Q}\left(\frac{1}{C_1} + \frac{1}{C_2}\right)$$

Thus, you have the following relationship for two capacitors in series:

$$\frac{1}{C_T} = \frac{1}{C_1} + \frac{1}{C_2}$$

Taking the reciprocal of both sides of this equation gives the formula for the total capacitance for two capacitors in series.

$$C_T = \frac{1}{\dfrac{1}{C_1} + \dfrac{1}{C_2}}$$

Equation 9–7

Equation 9–7 can also be expressed equivalently as

$$C_T = \frac{C_1 C_2}{C_1 + C_2}$$

EXAMPLE 9–5

Find the total capacitance C_T in Figure 9–20.

▶ FIGURE 9–20

Solution

$$C_T = \frac{C_1 C_2}{C_1 + C_2} = \frac{(100\,\text{pF})(330\,\text{pF})}{100\,\text{pF} + 330\,\text{pF}} = \textbf{76.7 pF}$$

Related Problem Determine C_T if $C_1 = 470\,\text{pF}$ and $C_2 = 680\,\text{pF}$ in Figure 9–20.

General Formula The equation for two series capacitors can be extended to any number of capacitors in series, as shown in Figure 9–21.

▶ FIGURE 9–21

General circuit with n capacitors in series.

The formula for total capacitance for any number of capacitors in series is developed as follows; the subscript n can be any number.

$$\frac{1}{C_T} = \frac{1}{C_1} + \frac{1}{C_2} + \frac{1}{C_3} + \cdots + \frac{1}{C_n}$$

Equation 9–8

$$C_T = \frac{1}{\dfrac{1}{C_1} + \dfrac{1}{C_2} + \dfrac{1}{C_3} + \cdots + \dfrac{1}{C_n}}$$

Remember,

The total series capacitance is always less than the smallest capacitance.

EXAMPLE 9–6

Determine the total capacitance in Figure 9–22.

▶ FIGURE 9–22

Solution
$$C_T = \frac{1}{\dfrac{1}{C_1} + \dfrac{1}{C_2} + \dfrac{1}{C_3}} = \frac{1}{\dfrac{1}{10\,\mu F} + \dfrac{1}{4.7\,\mu F} + \dfrac{1}{8.2\,\mu F}} = 2.30\,\mu F$$

Related Problem
If another 4.7 μF capacitor is connected in series with the three existing capacitors in Figure 9–22, what is the value of C_T?

Capacitor Voltages

The voltage across each capacitor in a series connection depends on its capacitance value according to the formula $V = Q/C$. You can determine the voltage across any individual capacitor in series with the following formula:

$$V_x = \left(\frac{C_T}{C_x}\right)V_S$$

Equation 9–9

where C_x is any capacitor in series, such as C_1, C_2, and C_3, and so on, and V_x is the voltage across C_x.

The largest-value capacitor in a series connection will have the smallest voltage across it. The smallest-value capacitor will have the largest voltage across it.

EXAMPLE 9–7

Find the voltage across each capacitor in Figure 9–23.

▶ FIGURE 9–23

Solution   Calculate the total capacitance.

$$C_T = \frac{1}{\dfrac{1}{C_1} + \dfrac{1}{C_2} + \dfrac{1}{C_3}} = \frac{1}{\dfrac{1}{0.1\,\mu F} + \dfrac{1}{0.47\,\mu F} + \dfrac{1}{0.22\,\mu F}} = 0.06\,\mu F$$

The voltages are as follows:

$$V_1 = \left(\frac{C_T}{C_1}\right)V_S = \left(\frac{0.06\,\mu F}{0.1\,\mu F}\right)25\,V = 15.0\,V$$

$$V_2 = \left(\frac{C_T}{C_2}\right)V_S = \left(\frac{0.06\,\mu F}{0.47\,\mu F}\right)25\,V = 3.19\,V$$

$$V_3 = \left(\frac{C_T}{C_3}\right)V_S = \left(\frac{0.06\,\mu F}{0.22\,\mu F}\right)25\,V = 6.82\,V$$

Related Problem   Another 0.47 μF capacitor is connected in series with the existing capacitors in Figure 9–23. Determine the voltage across the new capacitor, assuming all the capacitors are initially uncharged.

Open Multisim File E09-07 on your CD-ROM. Measure the voltage across each of the capacitors and compare with the calculated values. Connect another 0.47 μF capacitor in series with the other three and measure the voltage across the new capacitor. Also measure the voltage across C_1, C_2, and C_3 and compare with the previous voltages. Did the values increase or decrease after the fourth capacitor was added? Why?

SECTION 9–3 REVIEW

1. Is the total capacitance of series capacitors less than or greater than the value of the smallest capacitor?
2. The following capacitors are in series: 100 pF, 220 pF, and 560 pF. What is the total capacitance?
3. A 0.01 μF and a 0.015 μF capacitor are in series. Determine the total capacitance.
4. Determine the voltage across the 0.01 μF capacitor in Question 3 if 10 V are connected across the two series capacitors.

9–4 PARALLEL CAPACITORS

Capacitances add when they are connected in parallel.

After completing this section, you should be able to

◆ **Analyze parallel capacitors**

◆ Determine total capacitance

When capacitors are connected in parallel, the total capacitance is the sum of the individual capacitances because the effective plate area increases. The calculation of total parallel capacitance is analogous to the calculation of total series resistance (Chapter 4).

Figure 9–24 shows two parallel capacitors connected to a dc voltage source. When the switch is closed, as shown in part (a), current begins. A total amount of charge (Q_T) moves

▶ FIGURE 9–24

Capacitors in parallel produce a total capacitance that is the sum of the individual capacitances.

(a) The amount of charge on each capacitor is directly proportional to its capacitance value.

(b) $Q_T = Q_1 + Q_2$

through the circuit in a certain period of time. Part of the total charge is stored by C_1 and part by C_2. The portion of the total charge that is stored by each capacitor depends on its capacitance value according to the relationship $Q = CV$.

Figure 9–24(b) shows the capacitors after they have been completely charged and the current has stopped. Since the voltage across both capacitors is the same, the larger capacitor stores more charge. If the capacitors are equal in value, they store an equal amount of charge. The charge stored by both of the capacitors together equals the total charge that was delivered from the source.

$$Q_T = Q_1 + Q_2$$

Since $Q = CV$, Equation 9–2, you can use substitution to get the following relationship:

$$C_T V_S = C_1 V_S + C_2 V_S$$

Because all the V_S terms are equal, they can be canceled. Therefore, the total capacitance for two capacitors in parallel is

$$C_T = C_1 + C_2$$

Equation 9–10

EXAMPLE 9–8

What is the total capacitance in Figure 9–25? What is the voltage across each capacitor?

▶ FIGURE 9–25

Solution   The total capacitance is

$$C_T = C_1 + C_2 = 330\,\text{pF} + 220\,\text{pF} = \mathbf{550\,pF}$$

The voltage across each capacitor in parallel is equal to the source voltage.

$$V_S = V_1 = V_2 = \mathbf{5\,V}$$

Related Problem   What is C_T if a 100 pF capacitor is connected in parallel with C_1 and C_2 in Figure 9–25?

General Formula   Equation 9–10 can be extended to any number of capacitors in parallel, as shown in Figure 9–26. The expanded formula is as follows; the subscript n can be any number.

$$C_T = C_1 + C_2 + C_3 + \cdots + C_n$$

Equation 9–11

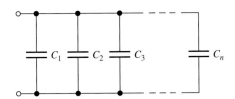

◀ FIGURE 9–26

General circuit with n capacitors in parallel.

EXAMPLE 9–9

Determine C_T in Figure 9–27.

◢ FIGURE 9–27

Solution

$$C_T = C_1 + C_2 + C_3 + C_4 + C_5 + C_6$$
$$= 0.01\,\mu F + 0.022\,\mu F + 0.01\,\mu F + 0.047\,\mu F + 0.022\,\mu F + 0.022\,\mu F$$
$$= \mathbf{0.133\,\mu F}$$

Related Problem

If three more $0.01\,\mu F$ capacitors are connected in parallel in Figure 9–27, what is C_T?

**SECTION 9–4
REVIEW**

1. How is total parallel capacitance determined?
2. In a certain application, you need $0.05\,\mu F$. The only capacitor value available is $0.01\,\mu F$, and this capacitor is available in large quantities. How can you get the total capacitance that you need?
3. The following capacitors are in parallel: 10 pF, 56 pF, 33 pF, and 68 pF. What is C_T?

9–5 CAPACITORS IN DC CIRCUITS

A capacitor will charge up when it is connected to a dc voltage source. The buildup of charge across the plates occurs in a predictable manner that is dependent on the capacitance and the resistance in a circuit.

After completing this section, you should be able to

◆ **Describe how a capacitor operates in a dc switching circuit**

  ◆ Describe the charging and discharging of a capacitor

  ◆ Define *RC time constant*

  ◆ Relate the time constant to charging and discharging

  ◆ Write equations for the charging and discharging curves

  ◆ Explain why a capacitor blocks constant dc

Charging a Capacitor

A capacitor will charge when it is connected to a dc voltage source, as shown in Figure 9–28. The capacitor in part (a) is uncharged; that is, plate *A* and plate *B* have equal numbers of free electrons. When the switch is closed, as shown in part (b), the source moves electrons

▲ FIGURE 9–28

Charging a capacitor.

away from plate *A* through the circuit to plate *B* as the arrows indicate. As plate *A* loses electrons and plate *B* gains electrons, plate *A* becomes positive with respect to plate *B*. As this **charging** process continues, the voltage across the plates builds up rapidly until it is equal to the source voltage, V_S, but opposite in polarity, as shown in part (c). When the capacitor is fully charged, there is no current.

A capacitor blocks constant dc.

When the charged capacitor is disconnected from the source, as shown in Figure 9–28(d), it remains charged for long periods of time, depending on its leakage resistance. The charge on an electrolytic capacitor generally leaks off more rapidly than in other types of capacitors.

Discharging a Capacitor

When a conductor is connected across a charged capacitor, as shown in Figure 9–29, the capacitor will discharge. In this particular case, a very low resistance path (the conductor) is connected across the capacitor with a switch. Before the switch is closed, the capacitor is charged to 50 V, as indicated in part (a). When the switch is closed, as shown in part (b), the excess electrons on plate *B* move through the circuit to plate *A* (indicated by the arrows); as a result of the current through the low resistance of the conductor, the energy stored by the capacitor is dissipated in the resistance of the conductor. The charge is neutralized when the numbers of free electrons on both plates are again equal. At this time, the voltage across the capacitor is zero, and the capacitor is completely discharged, as shown in part (c).

SAFETY POINT

Capacitors are capable of storing electrical charge for a long time after power has been turned off in a circuit. Be careful when touching or handling capacitors in or out of a circuit. If you touch the leads, you may be in for a shock as the capacitor discharges through you! It is usually good practice to discharge a capacitor using a shorting tool with an insulated grip of some sort before handling the capacitor.

(a) Retains charge   (b) Discharging   (c) Uncharged

◀ FIGURE 9–29

Discharging a capacitor.

Current and Voltage During Charging and Discharging

Notice in Figures 9–28 and 9–29 that the direction of electron flow during discharge is opposite to that during charging. It is important to understand that, ideally, *there is no current through the dielectric of the capacitor during charging or discharging because the dielectric is an insulating material.* There is current from one plate to the other only through the external circuit.

Figure 9–30(a) shows a capacitor connected in series with a resistor and a switch to a dc voltage source. Initially, the switch is open and the capacitor is uncharged with zero volts across its plates. At the instant the switch is closed, the current jumps to its maximum value and the capacitor begins to charge. The current is maximum initially because the capacitor

Current jumps to maximum at instant
switch is closed; then it decreases.

Voltage is
zero at instant
switch is
closed; then
it increases.

(a) Charging: Capacitor voltage increases as the current
    and resistor voltage decrease.

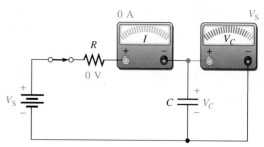

(b) Fully charged: Capacitor voltage equals source voltage.
    The current is zero.

Current jumps to maximum at instant
switch is closed; then it decreases.

Voltage decreases
as capacitor
discharges.

(c) Discharging: Capacitor voltage, resistor voltage, and the current decrease
    from their initial maximum values. Note that the discharge current is
    opposite to the charge current.

▲ FIGURE 9–30

Current and voltage in a charging and discharging capacitor.

has zero volts across it and, therefore, effectively acts as a short; thus, the current is limited
only by the resistance. As time passes and the capacitor charges, the current decreases and
the voltage across the capacitor (V_C) increases. The resistor voltage is proportional to the
current during this charging period.

After a certain period of time, the capacitor reaches full charge. At this point, the current
is zero and the capacitor voltage is equal to the dc source voltage, as shown in Figure
9–30(b). If the switch were opened now, the capacitor would retain its full charge (neglecting any leakage).

In Figure 9–30(c), the voltage source has been removed. When the switch is closed, the
capacitor begins to discharge. Initially, the current jumps to a maximum but in a direction
opposite to its direction during charging. As time passes, the current and capacitor voltage
decrease. The resistor voltage is always proportional to the current. When the capacitor has
fully discharged, the current and the capacitor voltage are zero.

Remember these two rules about capacitors in dc circuits:

1. A capacitor appears as an *open* to constant voltage.

2. A capacitor appears as a *short* to an instantaneous change in voltage.

Now let's examine in more detail how the voltage and current change with time in a capacitive circuit.

The *RC* Time Constant

In a practical situation, there cannot be capacitance without some resistance in a circuit. It
may simply be the small resistance of a wire, or it may be a designed-in resistance. Because
of this, the charging and discharging characteristics of a capacitor must always be considered

with the associated series resistance included. The resistance introduces the element of *time* in the charging and discharging of a capacitor.

When a capacitor charges or discharges through a resistance, a certain time is required for the capacitor to charge fully or discharge fully. The voltage across a capacitor cannot change instantaneously because a finite time is required to move charge from one point to another. The time constant of a series *RC* circuit determines the rate at which the capacitor charges or discharges.

> The *RC* **time constant is a fixed time interval that equals the product of the resistance and the capacitance in a series *RC* circuit.**

The time constant is expressed in units of seconds when resistance is in ohms and capacitance is in farads. It is symbolized by τ (Greek letter tau), and the formula is

$$\tau = RC$$

Equation 9–12

Recall that $I = Q/t$. The current depends on the amount of charge moved in a given time. When the resistance is increased, the charging current is reduced, thus increasing the charging time of the capacitor. When the capacitance is increased, the amount of charge increases; thus, for the same current, more time is required to charge the capacitor.

EXAMPLE 9–10

A series *RC* circuit has a resistance of $1.0\,M\Omega$ and a capacitance of $4.7\,\mu F$. What is the time constant?

Solution

$$\tau = RC = (1.0 \times 10^6\,\Omega)(4.7 \times 10^{-6}\,F) = \textbf{4.7\,s}$$

Related Problem

A series *RC* circuit has a $270\,k\Omega$ resistor and a $3300\,pF$ capacitor. What is the time constant in μs?

When a capacitor is charging or discharging between two voltage levels, the charge on the capacitor changes by approximately 63% of the difference in the levels in one time constant. An uncharged capacitor charges to approximately 63% of its fully charged voltage in one time constant. When a fully charged capacitor is discharging, its voltage drops to approximately $100\% - 63\% = 37\%$ of its initial voltage in one time constant. This change also corresponds to a 63% change.

The Charging and Discharging Curves

A capacitor charges and discharges following a nonlinear curve, as shown in Figure 9–31. In these graphs, the approximate percentage of full charge is shown at each time-constant

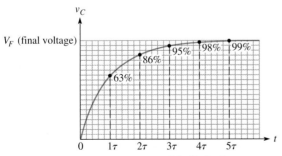

(a) Charging curve with percentages of the final voltage

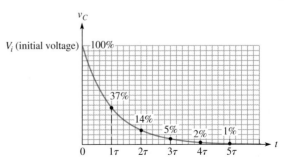

(b) Discharging curve with percentages of the initial voltage

▲ FIGURE 9–31

Exponential voltage curves for the charging and discharging of a capacitor in an *RC* circuit.

interval. This type of curve follows a precise mathematical formula and is called an **exponential** curve. The charging curve is an increasing exponential, and the discharging curve is a decreasing exponential. It takes five time constants to reach 99% (considered 100%) of the final voltage. This five time-constant interval is generally accepted as the time to fully charge or discharge a capacitor and is called the **transient time**.

General Formula The general expressions for either increasing or decreasing exponential curves are given in the following equations for both instantaneous voltage and current:

Equation 9–13
$$v = V_F + (V_i - V_F)e^{-t/\tau}$$

Equation 9–14
$$i = I_F + (I_i - I_F)e^{-t/\tau}$$

where V_F and I_F are the final values of voltage and current and V_i and I_i are the initial values of voltage and current. The lowercase italic letters v and i are the instantaneous values of the capacitor voltage and current at time t, and e is the base of natural logarithms. The e^x key on a calculator makes it easy to work with this exponential term.

Charging from Zero The formula for the special case in which an increasing exponential voltage curve begins at zero ($V_i = 0$), as shown in Figure 9–31(a), is given in Equation 9–15. It is developed as follows, starting with the general formula, Equation 9–13.

$$v = V_F + (V_i - V_F)e^{-t/\tau} = V_F + (0 - V_F)e^{-t/RC} = V_F - V_F e^{-t/RC}$$

Factoring out V_F, you have

Equation 9–15
$$v = V_F(1 - e^{-t/RC})$$

Using Equation 9–15, you can calculate the value of the charging voltage of a capacitor at any instant of time if it is initially uncharged. You can calculate an increasing current by substituting i for v and I_F for V_F in Equation 9–15.

EXAMPLE 9–11

In Figure 9–32, determine the capacitor voltage 50 μs after the switch is closed if the capacitor initially is uncharged. Draw the charging curve.

▶ FIGURE 9–32

Solution   The time constant is

$$\tau = RC = (8.2\text{ k}\Omega)(0.01\text{ }\mu\text{F}) = 82\text{ }\mu\text{s}$$

The voltage to which the capacitor will fully charge is 50 V (this is V_F). The initial voltage is zero. Notice that 50 μs is less than one time constant; so the capacitor will charge less than 63% of the full voltage in that time.

$$v_C = V_F(1 - e^{-t/RC}) = (50\text{ V})(1 - e^{-50\mu s/82\mu s}) = \textbf{22.8 V}$$

The charging curve for the capacitor is shown in Figure 9–33.

▶ FIGURE 9–33

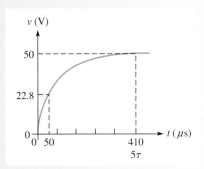

Related Problem   Determine the capacitor voltage 15 μs after the switch is closed in Figure 9–32.

Discharging to Zero   The formula for the special case in which a decreasing exponential voltage curve ends at zero ($V_F = 0$), as shown in Figure 9–31(b), is derived from the general formula as follows:

$$v = V_F + (V_i - V_F)e^{-t/\tau} = 0 + (V_i - 0)e^{-t/RC}$$

This reduces to

$$v = V_i e^{-t/RC}$$

Equation 9–16

where V_i is the voltage at the beginning of the discharge. You can use this formula to calculate the discharging voltage at any instant. The exponent $-t/RC$ can also be written as $-t/\tau$.

EXAMPLE 9–12

Determine the capacitor voltage in Figure 9–34 at a point in time 6 ms after the switch is closed. Draw the discharging curve.

▶ FIGURE 9–34

Solution   The discharge time constant is

$$\tau = RC = (10\,k\Omega)(2.2\,\mu F) = 22\,ms$$

The initial capacitor voltage is 10 V. Notice that 6 ms is less than one time constant, so the capacitor will discharge less than 63%. Therefore, it will have a voltage greater than 37% of the initial voltage at 6 ms.

$$v_C = V_i e^{-t/RC} = (10\,V)e^{-6ms/22ms} = \mathbf{7.61\,V}$$

The discharging curve for the capacitor is shown in Figure 9–35.

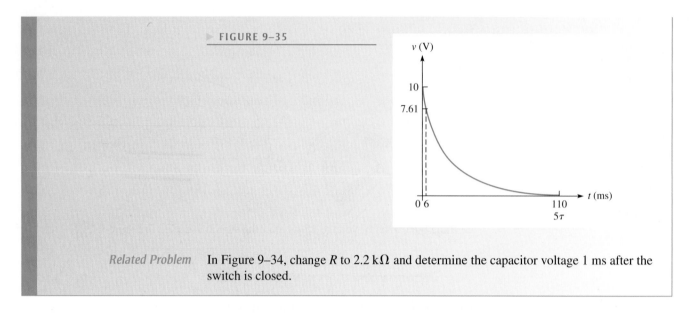

▶ FIGURE 9–35

Related Problem In Figure 9–34, change R to 2.2 kΩ and determine the capacitor voltage 1 ms after the switch is closed.

Graphical Method Using Universal Exponential Curves The universal curves in Figure 9–36 provide a graphic solution of the charge and discharge of capacitors. Example 9–13 illustrates this graphical method.

▶ FIGURE 9–36

Normalized universal exponential curves.

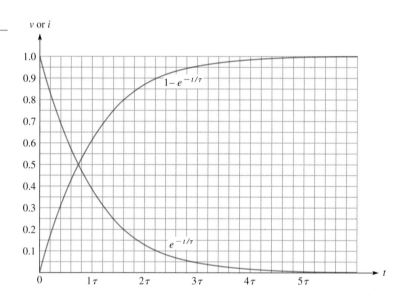

EXAMPLE 9–13

How long will it take the capacitor in Figure 9–37 to charge to 75 V? What is the capacitor voltage 2 ms after the switch is closed? Use the normalized universal curves in Figure 9–36 to determine the answers.

▶ FIGURE 9–37

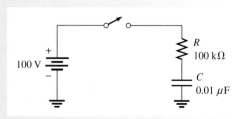

Solution   The final voltage is 100 V, which is the 100% level (1.0) on the graph. The value 75 V is 75% of the maximum, or 0.75 on the graph. You can see that this value occurs at 1.4 time constants. In this circuit one time constant is $RC = (100 \text{ k}\Omega)(0.01 \text{ } \mu\text{F}) = 1 \text{ ms}$. Therefore, the capacitor voltage reaches 75 V at 1.4 ms after the switch is closed.

The capacitor is at approximately 86 V (0.86 on the vertical axis) in 2 ms. These graphic solutions are shown in Figure 9–38.

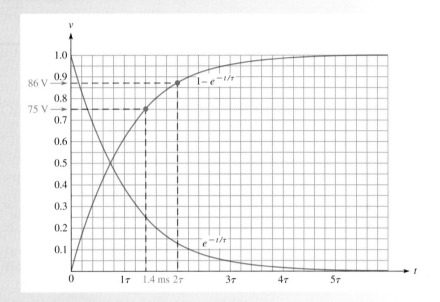

▲ FIGURE 9–38

Related Problem   Using the normalized universal exponential curves, determine how long it will take the capacitor in Figure 9–37 to charge to 50 V from zero. What is the capacitor voltage 3 ms after switch closure?

Response to a Square Wave

A common case that illustrates the rising and falling exponential occurs when an *RC* circuit is driven with a square wave that has a long period compared to the time constant. The square wave provides on and off action but, unlike a single switch, it provides a discharge path back through the generator when the wave drops back to zero.

When the square wave rises, the voltage across the capacitor rises exponentially toward the maximum value of the square wave in a time that depends on the time constant. When the square wave returns to the zero level, the capacitor voltage decreases exponentially, again depending on the time constant. The internal resistance of the square wave generator is part of the *RC* time constant; however, it can be ignored if it is small compared to *R*. The following example shows the waveforms for the case where the period is long compared to the time constant; other cases will be covered in detail in Chapter 15.

EXAMPLE 9–14   For the circuit in Figure 9–39(a), calculate the voltage across the capacitor every 0.1 ms for one complete period of the input waveform shown in Figure 9–39(b). Then sketch the capacitor waveform. Assume the internal resistance of the generator is negligible.

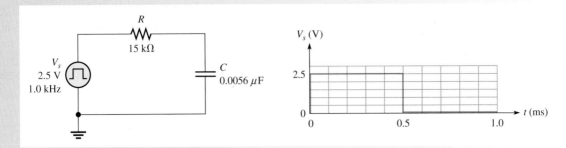

▲ FIGURE 9–39

Solution

$$\tau = RC = (15 \text{ k}\Omega)(0.0056 \,\mu\text{F}) = 0.084 \text{ ms}$$

The period of the square wave is 1 ms, which is approximately 12τ. This means that 6τ will elapse after each change of the pulse, allowing the capacitor to fully charge and fully discharge.

For the increasing exponential, $v = V_F(1 - e^{-t/RC})$.

At 0.1 ms: $v = 2.5 \text{ V}(1 - e^{-0.1\text{ms}/0.084\text{ms}}) = 1.74 \text{ V}$

At 0.2 ms: $v = 2.5 \text{ V}(1 - e^{-0.2\text{ms}/0.084\text{ms}}) = 2.27 \text{ V}$

At 0.3 ms: $v = 2.5 \text{ V}(1 - e^{-0.3\text{ms}/0.084\text{ms}}) = 2.43 \text{ V}$

At 0.4 ms: $v = 2.5 \text{ V}(1 - e^{-0.4\text{ms}/0.084\text{ms}}) = 2.48 \text{ V}$

At 0.5 ms: $v = 2.5 \text{ V}(1 - e^{-0.5\text{ms}/0.084\text{ms}}) = 2.49 \text{ V}$

For the decreasing exponential, $v = V_i(e^{-t/RC})$. In the equation, time is shown from the point when the change occurs (subtracting 0.5 ms from the actual time). For example, at 0.6 ms, $t = 0.6 \text{ ms} - 0.5 \text{ ms} = 0.1 \text{ ms}$.

At 0.6 ms: $v = 2.5 \text{ V}(e^{-0.1\text{ms}/0.084\text{ms}}) = 0.76 \text{ V}$

At 0.7 ms: $v = 2.5 \text{ V}(e^{-0.2\text{ms}/0.084\text{ms}}) = 0.23 \text{ V}$

At 0.8 ms: $v = 2.5 \text{ V}(e^{-0.3\text{ms}/0.084\text{ms}}) = 0.07 \text{ V}$

At 0.9 ms: $v = 2.5 \text{ V}(e^{-0.4\text{ms}/0.084\text{ms}}) = 0.02 \text{ V}$

At 1.0 ms: $v = 2.5 \text{ V}(e^{-0.5\text{ms}/0.084\text{ms}}) = 0.01 \text{ V}$

Figure 9–40 is a graph of these results.

▶ FIGURE 9–40

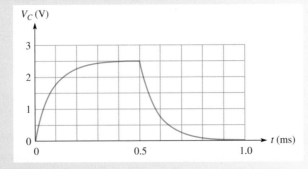

Related Problem   What is the capacitor voltage at 0.65 ms?

**SECTION 9–5
REVIEW**

1. Determine the time constant when $R = 1.2\,\text{k}\Omega$ and $C = 1000\,\text{pF}$.
2. If the circuit in Question 1 is charged with a 5 V source, how long will it take the initially uncharged capacitor to reach full charge? At full charge, what is the capacitor voltage?
3. A certain circuit has a time constant of 1 ms. If it is charged with a 10 V battery, what will the capacitor voltage be at each of the following times: 2 ms, 3 ms, 4 ms, and 5 ms? The capacitor is initially uncharged.
4. A capacitor is charged to 100 V. If it is discharged through a resistor, what is the capacitor voltage at one time constant?

9–6 CAPACITORS IN AC CIRCUITS

As you know, a capacitor blocks constant dc. A capacitor passes ac with an amount of opposition, called capacitive reactance, that depends on the frequency of the ac.

After completing this section, you should be able to

◆ **Describe how a capacitor operates in an ac circuit**

  ◆ Define *capacitive reactance*

  ◆ Determine the value of capacitive reactance in a given circuit

  ◆ Explain why a capacitor causes a phase shift between voltage and current

  ◆ Discuss instantaneous, true, and reactive power in a capacitor

Capacitive Reactance, X_C

In Figure 9–41, a capacitor is shown connected to a sinusoidal voltage source. When the source voltage is held at a constant amplitude value and its frequency is increased, the amplitude of the current increases. Also, when the frequency of the source is decreased, the current amplitude decreases.

Fixed amplitude ac voltage source

(a) Current increases when the frequency increases.

(b) Current decreases when the frequency decreases.

◀ FIGURE 9–41

The current in a capacitive circuit varies directly with the frequency of the source voltage.

When the frequency of the voltage increases, its rate of change also increases. This relationship is illustrated in Figure 9–42, where the frequency is doubled. Now, if the rate at which the voltage is changing increases, the amount of charge moving through the circuit

▶ FIGURE 9–42

Rate of change of a sine wave increases when frequency increases.

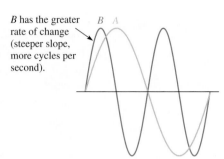

B has the greater rate of change (steeper slope, more cycles per second).

in a given period of time must also increase. More charge in a given period of time means more current. For example, a tenfold increase in frequency means that the capacitor is charging and discharging 10 times as much in a given time interval. The rate of charge movement has increased 10 times. This means the current has increased by 10 because $I = Q/t$.

An increase in the amount of current with a fixed amount of voltage indicates that opposition to the current has decreased. Therefore, the capacitor offers opposition to current, and that opposition varies *inversely* with frequency.

The opposition to sinusoidal current in a capacitor is called capacitive reactance.

The symbol for capacitive reactance is X_C, and its unit is the ohm (Ω).

You have just seen how frequency affects the opposition to current (capacitive reactance) in a capacitor. Now let's see how the capacitance (C) itself affects the reactance. Figure 9–43(a) shows that when a sinusoidal voltage with a fixed amplitude and fixed frequency is applied to a 1 μF capacitor, there is a certain amount of alternating current. When the capacitance value is increased to 2 μF, the current increases, as shown in Figure 9–43(b). Thus, when the capacitance is increased, the opposition to current (capacitive reactance) decreases. Therefore, not only is the capacitive reactance *inversely* proportional to frequency, but it is also *inversely* proportional to capacitance. This relationship can be stated as follows:

X_C is proportional to $\dfrac{1}{fC}$.

It can be proven that the constant of proportionality that relates X_C to $1/fC$ is $1/2\pi$. Therefore, the formula for capacitive reactance (X_C) is

Equation 9–17

$$X_C = \frac{1}{2\pi fC}$$

X_C is in ohms when f is in hertz and C is in farads. The 2π term comes from the fact that, as you learned in Chapter 8, a sine wave can be described in terms of rotational motion, and one revolution contains 2π radians.

▶ FIGURE 9–43

For a fixed voltage and fixed frequency, the current varies directly with the capacitance value.

1 μF

(a) Less capacitance, less current

2 μF

(b) More capacitance, more current

EXAMPLE 9–15

A sinusoidal voltage is applied to a capacitor, as shown in Figure 9–44. The frequency of the sine wave is 1 kHz. Determine the capacitive reactance.

▶ FIGURE 9–44

Solution

$$X_C = \frac{1}{2\pi fC} = \frac{1}{2\pi(1 \times 10^3 \text{ Hz})(0.0047 \times 10^{-6} \text{ F})} = \mathbf{33.9 \ k\Omega}$$

Related Problem   Determine the frequency required to make the capacitive reactance in Figure 9–44 equal to 10 kΩ.

Ohm's Law   The reactance of a capacitor is analogous to the resistance of a resistor. In fact, both are expressed in ohms. Since both R and X_C are forms of opposition to current, Ohm's law applies to capacitive circuits as well as to resistive circuits.

$$I = \frac{V}{X_C}$$

Equation 9–18

When applying Ohm's law in ac circuits, you must express both the current and the voltage in the same way, that is, both in rms, both in peak, and so on.

EXAMPLE 9–16

Determine the rms current in Figure 9–45.

▶ FIGURE 9–45

Solution   First, find X_C.

$$X_C = \frac{1}{2\pi fC} = \frac{1}{2\pi(10 \times 10^3 \text{ Hz})(0.0056 \times 10^{-6} \text{ F})} = 2.84 \ k\Omega$$

Then, apply Ohm's law.

$$I_{rms} = \frac{V_{rms}}{X_C} = \frac{5 \text{ V}}{2.84 \text{ k}\Omega} = \mathbf{1.76 \ mA}$$

Related Problem   Change the frequency in Figure 9–45 to 25 kHz and determine the rms value of the current.

Open Multisim file E09-16 on your CD-ROM. Measure the rms current and compare with the calculated value. Change the frequency of the source voltage to 25 kHz and measure the current.

Current Leads Capacitor Voltage by 90°

A sinusoidal voltage is shown in Figure 9–46. Notice that the rate at which the voltage is changing varies along the sine wave curve, as indicated by the "steepness" of the curve. At the zero crossings, the curve is changing at a faster rate than anywhere else along the curve. At the peaks, the curve has a zero rate of change because it has just reached its maximum and is at the point of changing direction.

▶ FIGURE 9–46

The rates of change of a sine wave.

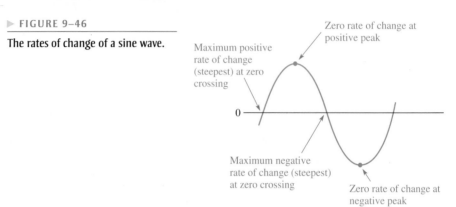

Maximum positive rate of change (steepest) at zero crossing

Zero rate of change at positive peak

Maximum negative rate of change (steepest) at zero crossing

Zero rate of change at negative peak

The amount of charge stored by a capacitor determines the voltage across it. Therefore, the rate at which the charge is moved ($Q/t = I$) from one plate to the other determines the rate at which the voltage changes. When the current is changing at its maximum rate (at the zero crossings), the voltage is at its maximum value (peak). When the current is changing at its minimum rate (zero at the peaks), the voltage is at its minimum value (zero). This phase relationship is illustrated in Figure 9–47. As you can see, the current peaks occur a quarter of a cycle before the voltage peaks. Thus, the current leads the voltage by 90°.

▶ FIGURE 9–47

Current is always leading the capacitor voltage by 90°.

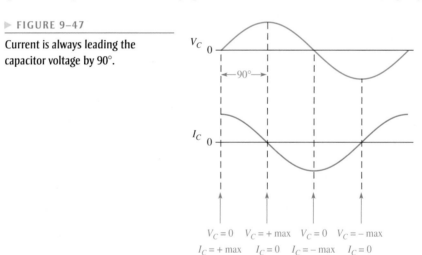

$V_C = 0$ $V_C = +\max$ $V_C = 0$ $V_C = -\max$
$I_C = +\max$ $I_C = 0$ $I_C = -\max$ $I_C = 0$

Power in a Capacitor

As discussed earlier in this chapter, a charged capacitor stores energy in the electric field within the dielectric. An ideal capacitor does not dissipate energy; it only stores energy temporarily. When an ac voltage is applied to a capacitor, energy is stored by the capacitor during one-quarter of the voltage cycle. Then the stored energy is returned to the source during another quarter of the cycle. There is no net energy loss. Figure 9–48 shows the power curve that results from one cycle of capacitor voltage and current.

Instantaneous Power (p)   The product of instantaneous voltage, *v*, and instantaneous current, *i*, gives **instantaneous power,** *p*. At points where *v* or *i* is zero, *p* is also zero. When both *v* and *i* are positive, *p* is also positive. When either *v* or *i* is positive and the other

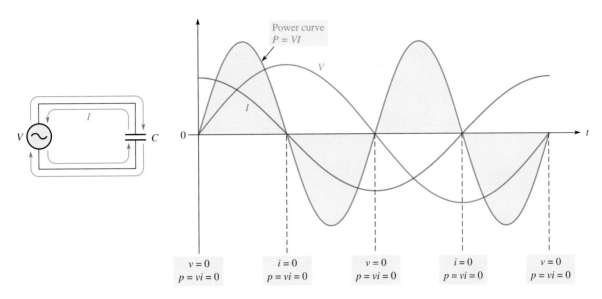

▲ FIGURE 9–48

Power curve for a capacitor.

negative, p is negative. When both v and i are negative, p is positive. As you can see, the power follows a sinusoidal-shaped curve. Positive values of power indicate that energy is stored by the capacitor. Negative values of power indicate that energy is returned from the capacitor to the source. Note that the power fluctuates at a frequency twice that of the voltage or current, as energy is alternately stored and returned to the source.

True Power (P_{true})   Ideally, all of the energy stored by a capacitor during the positive portion of the power cycle is returned to the source during the negative portion. No net energy is lost due to conversion to heat in the capacitor, so the **true power** is zero. Actually, because of leakage and foil resistance in a practical capacitor, a small percentage of the total power is dissipated in the form of true power.

Reactive Power (P_r)   The rate at which a capacitor stores or returns energy is called its **reactive power**, P_r. The reactive power is a nonzero quantity, because at any instant in time, the capacitor is actually taking energy from the source or returning energy to it. Reactive power does not represent an energy loss. The following formulas apply:

$$P_r = V_{rms} I_{rms}$$

Equation 9–19

$$P_r = \frac{V_{rms}^2}{X_C}$$

Equation 9–20

$$P_r = I_{rms}^2 X_C$$

Equation 9–21

Notice that these equations are of the same form as those introduced in Chapter 3 for true power in a resistor. The voltage and current are expressed as rms values. The unit of reactive power is **VAR (volt-ampere reactive)**.

EXAMPLE 9–17

Determine the true power and the reactive power in Figure 9–49.

▶ FIGURE 9–49

Solution The true power P_{true} is always **zero** for an ideal capacitor. Determine the reactive power by first finding the value for the capacitive reactance and then using Equation 9–20.

$$X_C = \frac{1}{2\pi fC} = \frac{1}{2\pi(2 \times 10^3\,\text{Hz})(0.01 \times 10^{-6}\,\text{F})} = 7.96\,\text{k}\Omega$$

$$P_r = \frac{V_{rms}^2}{X_C} = \frac{(2\,\text{V})^2}{7.96\,\text{k}\Omega} = 503 \times 10^{-6}\,\text{VAR} = \textbf{503}\,\boldsymbol{\mu}\textbf{VAR}$$

Related Problem If the frequency is doubled in Figure 9–49, what are the true power and the reactive power?

SECTION 9–6
REVIEW

1. Calculate X_C for $f = 5$ kHz and $C = 47$ pF.
2. At what frequency is the reactance of a 0.1 μF capacitor equal to 2 kΩ?
3. Calculate the rms current in Figure 9–50.
4. State the phase relationship between current and voltage in a capacitor.
5. A 1 μF capacitor is connected to an ac voltage source of 12 V rms. What is the true power?
6. In Question 5, determine the reactive power at a frequency of 500 Hz.

▶ FIGURE 9–50

$V_{rms} = 1$ V
$f = 1$ MHz

0.1 μF

9–7 CAPACITOR APPLICATIONS

Capacitors are widely used in electrical and electronic applications.

After completing this section, you should be able to

◆ **Discuss some capacitor applications**

  ◆ Describe a power supply filter

  ◆ Explain the purpose of coupling and bypass capacitors

  ◆ Discuss the basics of capacitors applied to tuned circuits, timing circuits, and computer memories

If you pick up any circuit board, open any power supply, or look inside any piece of electronic equipment, chances are you will find capacitors of one type or another. These components are used for a variety of purposes in both dc and ac applications.

Electrical Storage

One of the most basic applications of a capacitor is as a backup voltage source for low-power circuits such as certain types of semiconductor memories in computers. This particular application requires a very high capacitance value and negligible leakage.

A storage capacitor is connected between the dc power supply input to the circuit and ground. When the circuit is operating from its normal power supply, the capacitor remains fully charged to the dc power supply voltage. If the normal power source is disrupted, effectively removing the power supply from the circuit, the storage capacitor temporarily becomes the power source for the circuit.

A capacitor provides voltage and current to a circuit as long as its charge remains sufficient. As current is drawn by the circuit, charge is removed from the capacitor and the voltage decreases. For this reason, a storage capacitor can only be used as a temporary power source. The length of time that a capacitor can provide sufficient power to a circuit depends on the capacitance and the amount of current drawn by the circuit. The smaller the current and the higher the capacitance, the longer the time a capacitor can provide power to a circuit.

Power Supply Filtering

A basic dc power supply consists of a circuit known as a **rectifier** followed by a filter. The rectifier converts the 110 V, 60 Hz sinusoidal voltage available at a standard outlet to a pulsating dc voltage that can be either a half-wave rectified voltage or a full-wave rectified voltage, depending on the type of rectifier circuit. As shown in Figure 9–51(a), a half-wave rectifier removes each negative half-cycle of the sinusoidal voltage. As shown in Figure 9–51(b), a full-wave rectifier actually reverses the polarity of the negative portion of each cycle. Both half-wave and full-wave rectified voltages are dc because, even though they are changing, they do not alternate polarity.

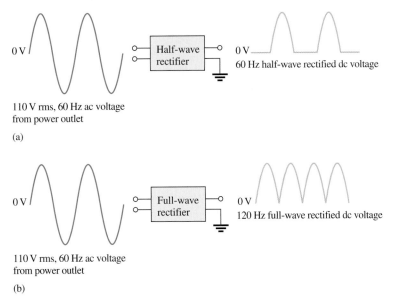

◀ FIGURE 9–51

Half-wave and full-wave rectifier operation.

To be useful for powering electronic circuits, the rectified voltage must be changed to constant dc voltage because all circuits require constant power. When connected to the rectifier output, the **filter** nearly eliminates the fluctuations in the rectified voltage and provides a smooth constant-value dc voltage to the load, which is the electronic circuit, as indicated in Figure 9–52.

The Capacitor as a Power Supply Filter   Capacitors are used as filters in dc power supplies because of their ability to store electrical charge. Figure 9–53(a) shows a dc power supply with a full-wave rectifier and a capacitor filter. The operation can be described from a charging and discharging point of view as follows. Assume the capacitor is initially

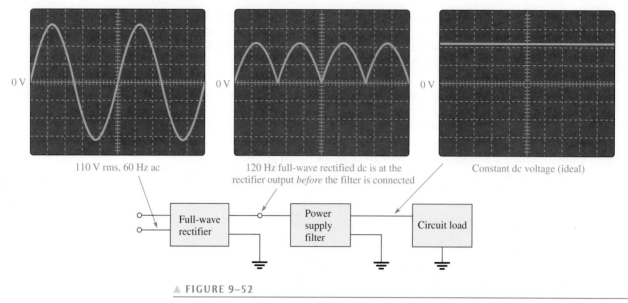

▲ FIGURE 9–52

Basic block diagram and operation of a dc power supply.

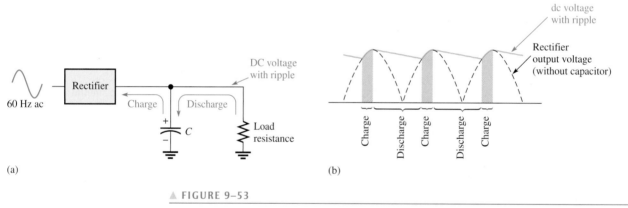

(a)   (b)

▲ FIGURE 9–53

Basic operation of a power supply filter capacitor.

uncharged. When the power supply is first turned on and the first cycle of the rectified voltage occurs, the capacitor will quickly charge through the low resistance of the rectifier. The capacitor voltage will follow the rectified voltage curve up to the peak of the rectified voltage. As the rectified voltage passes the peak and begins to decrease, the capacitor will begin to discharge very slowly through the high resistance of the load circuit, as indicated in Figure 9–53(b). The amount of discharge is typically very small and is exaggerated in the figure for purposes of illustration. The next cycle of the rectified voltage will recharge the capacitor back to the peak value by replenishing the small amount of charge lost since the previous peak. This pattern of a small amount of charging and discharging continues as long as the power is on.

A rectifier is designed so that it allows current only in the direction to charge the capacitor. The capacitor will not discharge back through the rectifier but will only discharge a small amount through the relatively high resistance of the load. The small fluctuation in voltage due to the charging and discharging of the capacitor is called the **ripple voltage**. A good dc power supply has a very small amount of ripple on its dc output. The discharge time constant of a power supply filter capacitor depends on its capacitance and the resistance of the load; consequently, the higher the capacitance value, the longer the discharge time and, therefore, the smaller the ripple voltage.

DC Blocking and AC Coupling

Capacitors are commonly used to block the constant dc voltage in one part of a circuit from getting to another part. As an example of this, a capacitor is connected between two stages of an amplifier to prevent the dc voltage at the output of stage 1 from affecting the dc voltage at the input of stage 2, as illustrated in Figure 9–54. Assume that, for proper operation, the output of stage 1 has a zero dc voltage and the input to stage 2 has a 3 V dc voltage. The capacitor prevents the 3 V dc at stage 2 from getting to the stage 1 output and affecting its zero value, and vice versa.

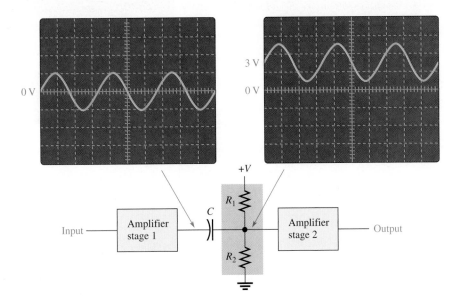

◄ FIGURE 9–54

An application of a capacitor used to block dc and couple ac in an amplifier.

If a sinusoidal signal voltage is applied to the input to stage 1, the signal voltage is increased (amplified) and appears on the output of stage 1, as shown in Figure 9–54. The amplified signal voltage is then coupled through the capacitor to the input of stage 2 where it is superimposed on the 3 V dc level and then again amplified by stage 2. In order for the signal voltage to be passed through the capacitor without being reduced, the capacitor must be large enough so that its reactance at the frequency of the signal voltage is negligible. In this type of application, the capacitor is known as a **coupling** capacitor, which ideally appears as an open to dc and as a short to ac. As the signal frequency is reduced, the capacitive reactance increases and, at some point, the capacitive reactance becomes large enough to cause a significant reduction in ac voltage between stage 1 and stage 2.

Power Line Decoupling

Capacitors connected from the dc supply voltage line to ground are used on circuit boards to decouple unwanted voltage transients or spikes that occur on the dc supply voltage because of fast switching digital circuits. A voltage **transient** contains higher frequencies that may affect the operation of the circuits. These transients are shorted to ground through the very low reactance of the decoupling capacitors. **Decoupling** capacitors are often used at various points along the supply voltage line on a circuit board, particularly near integrated circuits (ICs).

Bypassing

Bypass capacitors are used to bypass an ac voltage around a resistor in a circuit without affecting the dc voltage across the resistor. In amplifier circuits, for example, dc voltages called *bias voltages* are required at various points. For the amplifier to operate properly, certain bias voltages must remain constant and, therefore, any ac voltages must be removed. A sufficiently large capacitor connected from a bias point to ground provides a low reactance path to ground for ac voltages, leaving the constant dc bias voltage at the given point. This bypass application is illustrated in Figure 9–55. As frequencies decrease, the bypass capacitor becomes less effective because of its increased reactance.

Example of the operation of a bypass capacitor.

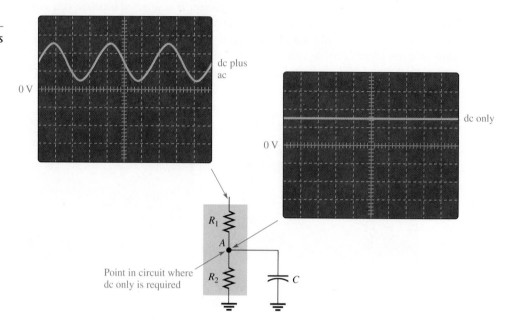

Signal Filters

Filters are used for selecting one ac signal with a certain specified frequency from a wide range of signals with many different frequencies or for selecting a certain band of frequencies and eliminating all others. A common example of this application is in radio and television receivers where it is necessary to select the signal transmitted from a given station and eliminate or filter out the signals transmitted from all the other stations in the area.

When you tune your radio or TV, you are actually changing the capacitance in the tuner circuit (which is a type of filter) so that only the signal from the station or channel you want passes through to the receiver circuitry. Capacitors are used in conjunction with resistors, inductors (covered in Chapter 11), and other components in these types of filters.

The main characteristic of a filter is its frequency selectivity, which is based on the fact that the reactance of a capacitor depends on frequency ($X_C = 1/2\pi fC$).

Timing Circuits

Another important area in which capacitors are used is in timing circuits that generate specified time delays or produce waveforms with specific characteristics. Recall that the time constant of a circuit with resistance and capacitance can be controlled by selecting appropriate values for R and C. The charging time of a capacitor can be used as a basic time delay in various types of circuits. An example is the circuit that controls the turn indicators on your car where the light flashes on and off at regular intervals.

Computer Memories

Dynamic computer memories use capacitors as the basic storage element for binary information, which consists of two digits, 1 and 0. A charged capacitor can represent a stored 1 and a discharged capacitor can represent a stored 0. Patterns of 1s and 0s that make up binary data are stored in a memory that consists of an array of capacitors with associated circuitry. You will study this topic in a computer or digital fundamentals course.

**SECTION 9–7
REVIEW**

1. Explain how half-wave or full-wave rectified dc voltages are smoothed out by a filter capacitor.

2. Explain the purpose of a coupling capacitor.

3. How large must a coupling capacitor be?

4. Explain the purpose of a decoupling capacitor.

5. Discuss how the relationship of frequency and capacitive reactance is important in frequency-selective circuits such as signal filters.

6. What parameter in a capacitor circuit is most important in time-delay applications?

Application Assignment

PUTTING YOUR KNOWLEDGE TO WORK

As you learned in this chapter, capacitors are used in certain types of amplifiers for coupling ac signals and blocking dc voltages. In this assignment, an amplifier circuit board contains two coupling capacitors. Your assignment is to check certain voltages on three identical amplifier circuit boards to determine if the capacitors are working properly. A knowledge of amplifier circuits is not necessary for this assignment.

All amplifier circuits contain transistors that require dc voltages to establish proper operating conditions for amplifying ac signals. These dc voltages are referred to as bias voltages. As indicated in Figure 9–56(a), a common type of dc bias circuit used in amplifiers is the voltage divider formed by R_1 and R_2, which sets up the proper dc voltage at the input to the amplifier.

When an ac signal voltage is applied to the amplifier, the input coupling capacitor, C_1, prevents the internal resistance of the

ac source from changing the dc bias voltage. Without the capacitor, the internal source resistance would appear in parallel with R_2 and drastically change the value of the dc voltage.

The coupling capacitance is chosen so that its reactance (X_C) at the frequency of the ac signal is very small compared to the bias resistor values. The coupling capacitance, therefore, efficiently couples the ac signal from the source to the input of the amplifier. On the source side of the input coupling capacitor there is only ac but on the amplifier side there is ac plus dc (the signal voltage is riding on the dc bias voltage set by the voltage divider), as indicated in Figure 9–56(a). Capacitor C_2 is the output coupling capacitor, which couples the amplified ac signal to another amplifier stage that would be connected to the output.

You will check three amplifier boards like the one in Figure 9–56(b) for the proper input voltages using an oscilloscope. If the voltages are incorrect, you will determine the most likely

(a) Amplifier schematic

(b) Amplifier board

▲ **FIGURE 9–56**

Capacitively coupled amplifier.

fault. For all measurements, assume the amplifier has no dc loading effect on the voltage-divider bias circuit.

Step 1: Comparing the Printed Circuit Board with the Schematic

Check the printed circuit board in Figure 9–56(b) to make sure it agrees with the amplifier schematic in part (a).

Step 2: Testing the Input to Board 1

The oscilloscope probe is connected from channel 1 to the board as shown in Figure 9–57.

The input signal from a sinusoidal voltage source is connected to the board and set to a frequency of 5 kHz with an amplitude of 1 V rms. Determine if the voltage and frequency displayed on the scope in Figure 9–57 are correct. If the scope measurement is incorrect, specify the most likely fault in the circuit.

Step 3: Testing the Input to Board 2

The oscilloscope probe is connected from channel 1 to board 2 the same as was shown in Figure 9–57 for board 1.

The input signal from the sinusoidal voltage source is the same as Step 2. Determine if the scope display in Figure 9–58 is correct. If the scope measurement is incorrect, specify the most likely fault in the circuit.

Step 4: Testing the Input to Board 3

The oscilloscope probe is connected from channel 1 to board 3 the same as was shown in Figure 9–57 for board 1.

The input signal from the sinusoidal voltage source is the same as Step 3. Determine if the scope display in Figure 9–59 is correct. If the scope measurement is incorrect, specify the most likely fault in the circuit.

Note: Ground reference has been established as indicated by 0 V.

▲ FIGURE 9–57

Testing board 1.

Note: Ground reference has been established as indicated by 0 V.

▲ FIGURE 9–58

Testing board 2.

Note: Ground reference has been established as indicated by 0 V.

▲ FIGURE 9–59

Testing board 3.

Review

1. Explain why the input coupling capacitor is necessary when one connects an ac source to the amplifier.

2. Capacitor C_2 in Figure 9–56 is an output coupling capacitor. Generally, what would you expect to measure at the point in the circuit labeled C and at the output of the circuit when an input signal is applied to the amplifier?

SUMMARY

◆ A capacitor is composed of two parallel conductive plates separated by an insulating material called the *dielectric*.

◆ A capacitor stores electrical charge on its plates.

◆ Energy is stored in a capacitor by the electric field created between the charged plates in the dielectric.

◆ Capacitance is measured in units of farads (F).

◆ Capacitance is directly proportional to the plate area and the dielectric constant and inversely proportional to the distance between the plates (the dielectric thickness).

◆ The dielectric constant is an indication of the ability of a material to establish an electric field.

◆ The dielectric strength is one factor that determines the breakdown voltage of a capacitor.

◆ Capacitors are commonly classified according to the dielectric material. Typical materials are mica, ceramic, plastic-film, and electrolytic (aluminum oxide and tantalum oxide).

◆ The total capacitance of series capacitors is less than the smallest capacitance.

◆ The total capacitance of parallel capacitors is the sum of all the capacitances.

◆ A capacitor blocks constant dc.

◆ The time constant determines the charging and discharging time of a capacitor with resistance in series.

◆ In an *RC* circuit, the voltage and current during charging and discharging make an approximate 63% change during each time-constant interval.

◆ Five time constants are required for a capacitor to fully charge or discharge. This is called the *transient time*.

◆ The approximate percentage of final charge after each charging time-constant interval is given in Table 9–4.

▶ TABLE 9–4

NUMBER OF TIME CONSTANTS	APPROXIMATE % OF FINAL CHARGE
1	63
2	86
3	95
4	98
5	99 (considered 100%)

▶ TABLE 9–5

NUMBER OF TIME CONSTANTS	APPROXIMATE % OF INITIAL CHARGE
1	37
2	14
3	5
4	2
5	1 (considered 0)

◆ The approximate percentage of initial charge after each discharging time-constant interval is given in Table 9–5.

◆ Alternating current in a capacitor leads the voltage by 90°.

◆ A capacitor passes ac to an extent that depends on its reactance and the resistance in the rest of the circuit.

◆ Capacitive reactance is the opposition to ac, expressed in ohms.

◆ Capacitive reactance (X_C) is inversely proportional to the frequency and to the capacitance value.

◆ Ideally, there is no energy loss in a capacitor and, thus, the true power (watts) is zero. However, in most capacitors there is some small energy loss due to leakage resistance.

KEY TERMS

Key terms and other bold terms in the chapter are defined in the end-of-book glossary.

Bypass   A capacitor connected from a point to ground to remove the ac signal without affecting the dc voltage. A special case of decoupling.

Capacitance   The ability of a capacitor to store electrical charge.

Capacitive reactance   The opposition of a capacitor to sinusoidal current. The unit is the ohm.

Capacitor   An electrical device consisting of two conductive plates separated by an insulating material and possessing the property of capacitance.

Charging   The process in which a current removes charge from one plate of a capacitor and deposits it on the other plate, making one plate more positive than the other.

Coulomb's law   A law that states a force exists between two charged bodies that is directly proportional to the product of the two charges and inversely proportional to the square of the distance between them.

Coupling   The method of connecting a capacitor from between two points in a circuit to allow ac to pass from one point to the other while blocking dc.

Decoupling   The method of connecting a capacitor from one point, usually the dc power supply line, to ground to short ac to ground without affecting the dc voltage.

Dielectric   The insulating material between the plates of a capacitor.

Dielectric constant   A measure of the ability of a dielectric material to establish an electric field.

Dielectric strength   A measure of the ability of a dielectric material to withstand voltage without breaking down.

Exponential A mathematical function described by a natural logarithm (base). The charging and discharging of a capacitor are described by an exponential function.

Farad (F) The unit of capacitance.

Filter A type of circuit that passes certain frequencies and rejects all others.

Instantaneous power (p) The value of power in a circuit at any given instant of time.

RC time constant A fixed time interval set by R and C values that determines the time response of a series RC circuit. It equals the product of the resistance and the capacitance.

Reactive power (P_r) The rate at which energy is alternately stored and returned to the source by a capacitor. The unit is the VAR.

Ripple voltage The small fluctuation in voltage due to the charging and discharging of a capacitor.

Temperature coefficient A constant specifying the amount of change in the value of a quantity for a given change in temperature.

Transient time An interval equal to approximately five time constants.

True power (P_{true}) The power that is dissipated in a circuit, usually in the form of heat.

VAR (volt-ampere reactive) The unit of reactive power.

FORMULAS

9–1	$C = \dfrac{Q}{V}$		Capacitance in terms of charge and voltage
9–2	$Q = CV$		Charge in terms of capacitance and voltage
9–3	$V = \dfrac{Q}{C}$		Voltage in terms of charge and capacitance
9–4	$W = \dfrac{1}{2}CV^2$		Energy stored by a capacitor
9–5	$\varepsilon_r = \dfrac{\varepsilon}{\varepsilon_0}$		Dielectric constant (relative permittivity)
9–6	$C = \dfrac{A\varepsilon_r(8.85 \times 10^{-12}\,\text{F/m})}{d}$		Capacitance in terms of physical parameters
9–7	$C_T = \dfrac{1}{\dfrac{1}{C_1} + \dfrac{1}{C_2}}$		Total series capacitance (two capacitors)
9–8	$C_T = \dfrac{1}{\dfrac{1}{C_1} + \dfrac{1}{C_2} + \dfrac{1}{C_3} + \cdots + \dfrac{1}{C_n}}$		Total series capacitance (general)
9–9	$V_x = \left(\dfrac{C_T}{C_x}\right)V_S$		Voltage across series capacitor
9–10	$C_T = C_1 + C_2$		Two capacitors in parallel
9–11	$C_T = C_1 + C_2 + C_3 + \cdots + C_n$		n capacitors in parallel
9–12	$\tau = RC$		RC time constant
9–13	$v = V_F + (V_i - V_F)e^{-t/\tau}$		Exponential voltage (general)
9–14	$i = I_F + (I_i - I_F)e^{-t/\tau}$		Exponential current (general)
9–15	$v = V_F(1 - e^{-t/RC})$		Increasing exponential voltage beginning at zero
9–16	$v = V_i e^{-t/RC}$		Decreasing exponential voltage ending at zero
9–17	$X_C = \dfrac{1}{2\pi fC}$		Capacitive reactance
9–18	$I = \dfrac{V}{X_C}$		Ohm's law for a capacitor

9-19 $\quad P_r = V_{rms}I_{rms}$ $\qquad$ Reactive power in a capacitor

9-20 $\quad P_r = \dfrac{V^2_{rms}}{X_C}$ $\qquad$ Reactive power in a capacitor

9-21 $\quad P_r = I^2_{rms}X_C$ $\qquad$ Reactive power in a capacitor

SELF-TEST

Answers are at the end of the chapter.

1. Which of the following statement(s) accurately describe(s) a capacitor?
   (a) The plates are conductive.
   (b) The dielectric is an insulator between the plates.
   (c) There is constant direct current (dc) through a fully charged capacitor.
   (d) A capacitor stores charge indefinitely when disconnected from the source.
   (e) none of the above answers (f) all the above answers (g) only answers (a) and (b)

2. Which one of the following statements is true?
   (a) There is current through the dielectric of a charging capacitor.
   (b) When a capacitor is connected to a dc voltage source, it will charge to the value of the source.
   (c) A capacitor can be discharged by disconnecting it from the voltage source.

3. A capacitance of 0.01 μF is larger than
   (a) 0.00001 F (b) 100,000 pF (c) 1000 pF (d) all of these answers

4. A capacitance of 1000 pF is smaller than
   (a) 0.01 μF (b) 0.001 μF (c) 0.00000001 F (d) answers (a) and (c)

5. When the voltage across a capacitor is increased, the stored charge
   (a) increases (b) decreases (c) remains constant (d) fluctuates

6. When the voltage across a capacitor is doubled, the stored charge
   (a) stays the same (b) is halved (c) increases by four (d) doubles

7. The voltage rating of a capacitor is increased by
   (a) increasing the plate separation (b) decreasing the plate separation
   (c) increasing the plate area (d) answers (b) and (c)

8. The capacitance value is increased by
   (a) decreasing plate area (b) increasing plate separation (c) decreasing plate separation
   (d) increasing plate area (e) answers (a) and (b) (f) answers (c) and (d)

9. A 1 μF, a 2.2 μF, and a 0.047 μF capacitor are connected in series. The total capacitance is less than
   (a) 1 μF (b) 2.2 μF (c) 0.047 μF (d) 0.001 μF

10. Four 0.022 μF capacitors are in parallel. The total capacitance is
    (a) 0.022 μF (b) 0.088 μF (c) 0.011 μF (d) 0.044 μF

11. An uncharged capacitor and a resistor are connected in series with a switch and a 12 V battery. At the instant the switch is closed, the voltage across the capacitor is
    (a) 12 V (b) 6 V (c) 24 V (d) 0 V

12. In Question 11, the voltage across the capacitor when it is fully charged is
    (a) 12 V (b) 6 V (c) 24 V (d) −6 V

13. In Question 11, the capacitor will reach full charge in a time equal to approximately
    (a) RC (b) $5RC$ (c) $12RC$ (d) cannot be predicted

14. A sinusoidal voltage is applied across a capacitor. When the frequency of the voltage is increased, the current
    (a) increases (b) decreases (c) remains constant (d) ceases

15. A capacitor and a resistor are connected in series to a sine wave generator. The frequency is set so that the capacitive reactance is equal to the resistance and, thus, an equal amount of voltage appears across each component. If the frequency is decreased,
    (a) $V_R > V_C$ (b) $V_C > V_R$ (c) $V_R = V_C$ (d) $V_C < V_R$

TROUBLESHOOTING: SYMPTOM AND CAUSE

The purpose of these exercises is to help develop thought processes essential to troubleshooting. Answers are at the end of the chapter.

Determine the cause for each set of symptoms. Refer to Figure 9–60.

► FIGURE 9–60

The ac meter indicates the correct reading for this circuit.

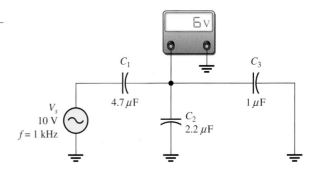

1. *Symptom:* The voltmeter reading is 0 V.
   Cause:
   (a) C_1 is shorted.   **(b)** C_2 is shorted.   **(c)** C_3 is open.

2. *Symptom:* The voltmeter reading is 10 V.
   Cause:
   (a) C_1 is shorted.   **(b)** C_2 is open.   **(c)** C_3 is open.

3. *Symptom:* The voltmeter reading is 6.86 V.
   Cause:
   (a) C_1 is open.   **(b)** C_2 is open.   **(c)** C_3 is open.

4. *Symptom:* The voltmeter reading is 0 V.
   Cause:
   (a) C_1 is open.   **(b)** C_2 is open.   **(c)** C_3 is open.

5. *Symptom:* The voltmeter reading is 8.28 V.
   Cause:
   (a) C_1 is shorted.   **(b)** C_2 is open.   **(c)** C_3 is open.

PROBLEMS

Answers to odd-numbered problems are at the end of the book.

BASIC PROBLEMS

SECTION 9–1 **The Basic Capacitor**

1. **(a)** Find the capacitance when $Q = 50 \ \mu C$ and $V = 10$ V.
   (b) Find the charge when $C = 0.001 \ \mu F$ and $V = 1$ kV.
   (c) Find the voltage when $Q = 2$ mC and $C = 200 \ \mu F$.

2. Convert the following values from microfarads to picofarads:
   (a) $0.1 \ \mu F$ **(b)** $0.0025 \ \mu F$ **(c)** $5 \ \mu F$

3. Convert the following values from picofarads to microfarads:
   (a) 1000 pF   **(b)** 3500 pF   **(c)** 250 pF

4. Convert the following values from farads to microfarads:
   (a) 0.0000001 F   **(b)** 0.0022 F   **(c)** 0.0000000015 F

5. What size capacitor is capable of storing 10 mJ of energy with 100 V across its plates?

6. A mica capacitor has a plate area of $20 \ cm^2$ and a dielectric thickness of 2.5 mils. What is its capacitance?

7. An air capacitor has plates with an area of 0.1 m². The plates are separated by 0.01 m. Calculate the capacitance.

8. A student wants to construct a 1 F capacitor out of two square plates for a science fair project. He plans to use a paper dielectric ($\varepsilon_r = 2.5$) that is 8×10^{-5} m thick. The science fair is to be held in the Astrodome. Will his capacitor fit in the Astrodome? What would be the size of the plates if it could be constructed?

9. A student decides to construct a capacitor using two conducting plates 30 cm on a side. He separates the plates with a paper dielectric ($\varepsilon_r = 2.5$) that is 8×10^{-5} m thick. What is the capacitance of his capacitor?

10. At ambient temperature (25°C), a certain capacitor is specified to be 1000 pF. It has a negative temperature coefficient of 200 ppm/°C. What is its capacitance at 75°C?

11. A 0.001 μF capacitor has a positive temperature coefficient of 500 ppm/°C. How much change in capacitance will a 25°C increase in temperature cause?

SECTION 9–2 Types of Capacitors

12. In the construction of a stacked-foil mica capacitor, how is the plate area increased?

13. What type of capacitor has the higher dielectric constant, mica or ceramic?

14. Show how to connect an electrolytic capacitor across points A and B in Figure 9–61.

▶ FIGURE 9–61

15. Determine the value of the typographically labeled ceramic disk capacitors in Figure 9–62.

▶ FIGURE 9–62

(a)   (b)   (c)   (d)

16. Name two types of electrolytic capacitors. How do electrolytics differ from other capacitors?

17. Identify the parts of the ceramic disk capacitor shown in the cutaway view of Figure 9–63 by referring to Figure 9–9(b).

▶ FIGURE 9–63

SECTION 9–3 Series Capacitors

18. Five 1000 pF capacitors are in series. What is the total capacitance?

19. Find the total capacitance for each circuit in Figure 9–64.

▶ FIGURE 9–64

(a)　　　　　　　　　(b)　　　　　　　　　(c)

20. For each circuit in Figure 9–64, determine the voltage across each capacitor.

21. The total charge stored by the series capacitors in Figure 9–65 is 10 μC. Determine the voltage across each of the capacitors.

▶ FIGURE 9–65

SECTION 9–4　Parallel Capacitors

22. Determine C_T for each circuit in Figure 9–66.

▶ FIGURE 9–66

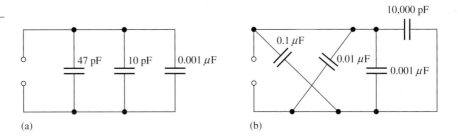

(a)　　　　　　　　　　　　　(b)

23. Determine C_T for each circuit in Figure 9–67.

24. What is the voltage between points A and B in each circuit in Figure 9–67?

(a)　　　　　　　　　(b)　　　　　　　　　(c) $C = 1$ μF for each capacitor

▲ FIGURE 9–67

SECTION 9–5　Capacitors in DC Circuits

25. Determine the time constant for each of the following series RC combinations:

    (a) $R = 100\ \Omega, C = 1\ \mu F$　　　　**(b)** $R = 10\ M\Omega, C = 56\ pF$

    (c) $R = 4.7\ k\Omega, C = 0.0047\ \mu F$　　**(d)** $R = 1.5\ M\Omega, C = 0.01\ \mu F$

26. Determine how long it takes the capacitor to reach full charge for each of the following combinations:

(a) $R = 47\,\Omega, C = 47\,\mu F$ (b) $R = 3300\,\Omega, C = 0.015\,\mu F$

(c) $R = 22\,k\Omega, C = 100\,pF$ (d) $R = 4.7\,M\Omega, C = 10\,pF$

27. In the circuit of Figure 9–68, the capacitor initially is uncharged. Determine the capacitor voltage at the following times after the switch is closed:

(a) 10 μs (b) 20 μs (c) 30 μs (d) 40 μs (e) 50 μs

▶ FIGURE 9–68

28. In Figure 9–69, the capacitor is charged to 25 V. Find the capacitor voltage at the following times when the switch is closed:

(a) 1.5 ms   (b) 4.5 ms   (c) 6 ms   (d) 7.5 ms

▶ FIGURE 9–69

29. Repeat Problem 27 for the following time intervals:

(a) 2 μs (b) 5 μs (c) 15 μs

30. Repeat Problem 28 for the following time intervals:

(a) 0.5 ms   (b) 1 ms   (c) 2 ms

SECTION 9–6   **Capacitors in AC Circuits**

31. Determine X_C for a 0.047 μF capacitor at each of the following frequencies:

(a) 10 Hz   (b) 250 Hz   (c) 5 kHz   (d) 100 kHz

32. What is the value of the total capacitive reactance in each circuit in Figure 9–70?

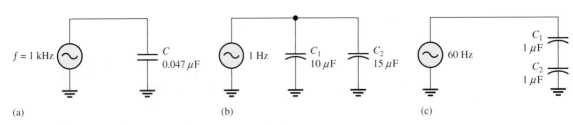

▲ FIGURE 9–70

33. In Figure 9–67, each dc voltage source is replaced by a 10 V rms, 2 kHz ac source. Determine the reactance in each case.

34. In each circuit of Figure 9–70, what frequency is required to produce an X_C of 100 Ω? An X_C of 1 kΩ?

35. A sinusoidal voltage of 20 V rms produces an rms current of 100 mA when connected to a certain capacitor. What is the reactance?

36. A 10 kHz voltage is applied to a 0.0047 μF capacitor, and 1 mA of rms current is measured. What is the rms value of the voltage?

37. Determine the true power and the reactive power in Problem 36.

SECTION 9–7   Capacitor Applications

38. If another capacitor is connected in parallel with the existing capacitor in the power supply filter of Figure 9–53, how is the ripple voltage affected?

39. Ideally, what should the reactance of a bypass capacitor be in order to eliminate a 10 kHz ac voltage at a given point in an amplifier circuit?

ADVANCED PROBLEMS

40. Two series capacitors (one 1 μF, the other of unknown value) are charged from a 12 V source. The 1 μF capacitor is charged to 8 V, and the other to 4 V. What is the value of the unknown capacitor?

41. How long does it take C to discharge to 3 V in Figure 9–69?

42. How long does it take C to charge to 8 V in Figure 9–68?

43. Determine the time constant for the circuit in Figure 9–71.

44. In Figure 9–72, the capacitor initially is uncharged. At $t = 10 \ \mu s$ after the switch is closed, the instantaneous capacitor voltage is 7.2 V. Determine the value of R.

▲ FIGURE 9–71

▲ FIGURE 9–72

45. (a) The capacitor in Figure 9–73 is uncharged when the switch is thrown into position 1. The switch remains in position 1 for 10 ms and then is thrown into position 2, where it remains indefinitely. Draw the complete waveform for the capacitor voltage.

   (b) If the switch is thrown back to position 1 after 5 ms in position 2, and then is left in position 1, how will the waveform appear?

46. Determine the ac voltage across each capacitor and the current in each branch of the circuit in Figure 9–74.

▲ FIGURE 9–73

▲ FIGURE 9–74

47. Find the value of C_1 in Figure 9–75.

▶ FIGURE 9–75

48. How much does the voltage across C_5 and C_6 change when the ganged switch is thrown from position 1 to position 2 in Figure 9–76?

▶ FIGURE 9–76

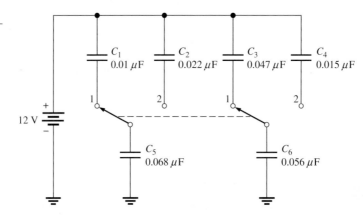

49. If C_4 in Figure 9–74 is open, determine the voltages that would be measured across the other capacitors.

MULTISIM TROUBLESHOOTING PROBLEMS

50. Open file P09-50 and determine if there is a fault. If so, identify it.

51. Open file P09-51 and determine if there is a fault. If so, identify it.

52. Open file P09-52 and determine if there is a fault. If so, identify it.

53. Open file P09-53 and determine if there is a fault. If so, identify it.

54. Open file P09-54 and determine if there is a fault. If so, identify it.

ANSWERS

SECTION REVIEWS

SECTION 9–1 **The Basic Capacitor**

1. Capacitance is the ability (capacity) to store electrical charge.

2. **(a)** There are 1,000,000 microfarads in one farad.

   (b) There are 1×10^{12} picofarads in one farad.

   (c) There are 1,000,000 picofarads in one microfarad.

3. $0.0015 \, \mu F \times 10^6 \, pF/\mu F = 1500 \, pF$; $0.0015 \, \mu F \times 10^{-6} \, F/\mu F = 0.0000000015 \, F$

4. $W = \frac{1}{2}CV^2 = \frac{1}{2}(0.01 \, \mu F)(15 \, V)^2 = 1.125 \, \mu J$

5. **(a)** Capacitance increases when plate area is increased.

   (b) Capacitance decreases when plate separation is increased.

6. $(1000 \, V/mil)(2 \, mils) = 2 \, kV$

SECTION 9–2 **Types of Capacitors**

    1. Capacitors are commonly classified by the dielectric material.

    2. A fixed capacitance cannot be changed; a variable capacitor can.

    3. Electrolytic capacitors are polarized.

    4. Be sure that the voltage rating is sufficient and connect the positive end to the positive side of the circuit when installing a polarized capacitor.

    5. The positive lead should be connected to ground.

SECTION 9–3 **Series Capacitors**

    1. C_T of series capacitors is less than the smallest value.

    2. $C_T = 61.2 \, \text{pF}$

    3. $C_T = 0.006 \, \mu\text{F}$

    4. $V = (0.006 \, \mu\text{F}/0.01 \, \mu\text{F})10 \, \text{V} = 6 \, \text{V}$

SECTION 9–4 **Parallel Capacitors**

    1. The individual parallel capacitors are added to get C_T.

    2. Use five $0.01 \, \mu\text{F}$ capacitors in parallel to get $0.05 \, \mu\text{F}$.

    3. $C_T = 167 \, \text{pF}$

SECTION 9–5 **Capacitors in DC Circuits**

    1. $\tau = RC = 1.2 \, \mu\text{s}$

    2. $5\tau = 6 \, \mu\text{s}$; V_C is approximately 5 V.

    3. $v_{2\text{ms}} = (0.86)10 \, \text{V} = 8.6 \, \text{V}$; $v_{3\text{ms}} = (0.95)10 \, \text{V} = 9.5 \, \text{V}$; $v_{4\text{ms}} = (0.98)10 \, \text{V} = 9.8 \, \text{V}$; $v_{5\text{ms}} = (0.99)10 \, \text{V} = 9.9 \, \text{V}$

    4. $v_C = (0.37)(100 \, \text{V}) = 37 \, \text{V}$

SECTION 9–6 **Capacitors in AC Circuits**

    1. $X_C = 1/2\pi fC = 677 \, \text{k}\Omega$

    2. $f = 1/2\pi C X_C = 796 \, \text{Hz}$

    3. $I_{\text{rms}} = 1 \, \text{V}/1.59 \, \Omega = 629 \, \text{mA}$

    4. Current leads voltage by 90°.

    5. $P_{\text{true}} = 0 \, \text{W}$

    6. $P_r = (12 \, \text{V})^2/318 \, \Omega = 0.453 \, \text{VAR}$

SECTION 9–7 **Capacitor Applications**

    1. Once the capacitor charges to the peak voltage, it discharges very little before the next peak thus smoothing the rectified voltage.

    2. A coupling capacitor allows ac to pass from one point to another, but blocks constant dc.

    3. A coupling capacitor must be large enough to have a negligible reactance at the frequency that is to be passed without opposition.

    4. A decoupling capacitor shorts power line voltage transients to ground.

    5. X_C is inversely proportional to frequency and so is the filter's ability to pass ac signals.

    6. The time constant is used in delay applications.

Application Assignment

    1. The coupling capacitor prevents the source from affecting the dc voltage but passes the ac input signal.

    2. An ac voltage superimposed on a dc voltage is at the point labeled C. There is an ac voltage only at the output.

RELATED PROBLEMS FOR EXAMPLES

9–1 10 kV

9–2 0.047 μF

9–3 100,000,000 pF

9–4 0.697 μF

9–5 278 pF

9–6 1.54 μF

9–7 2.83 V

9–8 650 pF

9–9 0.163 μF

9–10 891 μs

9–11 8.36 V

9–12 8.13 V

9–13 0.7 ms; 95 V

9–14 0.42 V

9–15 3.39 kHz

9–16 4.40 mA

9–17 0 W; 1.01 mVAR

SELF-TEST

1. (g)   **2.** (b)   **3.** (c)   **4.** (d)   **5.** (a)   **6.** (d)   **7.** (a)

8. (f)   **9.** (c)   **10.** (b)   **11.** (d)   **12.** (a)   **13.** (b)   **14.** (a)

15. (b)

TROUBLESHOOTING: SYMPTOM AND CAUSE

1. (b)   **2.** (a)   **3.** (c)   **4.** (a)   **5.** (b)

RC CIRCUITS

10

CHAPTER OBJECTIVES

◆ Describe the relationship between current and voltage in an *RC* circuit

◆ Determine impedance and phase angle in a series *RC* circuit

◆ Analyze a series *RC* circuit

◆ Determine impedance and phase angle in a parallel *RC* circuit

◆ Analyze a parallel *RC* circuit

◆ Analyze series-parallel *RC* circuits

◆ Determine power in *RC* circuits

◆ Discuss some basic *RC* applications

◆ Troubleshoot *RC* circuits

KEY TERMS

◆ Impedance (Z)
◆ Phase angle
◆ Capacitive susceptance (B_C)
◆ Admittance (Y)
◆ Apparent power (P_a)
◆ Power factor
◆ Frequency response
◆ Cutoff frequency
◆ Bandwidth

APPLICATION ASSIGNMENT PREVIEW

Your assignment will be to analyze frequency response measurements on a capacitively coupled amplifier used in a certain communications system. You will be concentrating on the *RC* input circuit of the amplifier and how it responds to different frequencies. The results of the measurements will be graphically documented with a frequency response curve. After studying this chapter, you should be able to complete the application assignment.

VISIT THE COMPANION WEBSITE

Study aids for this chapter are available at
http://www.prenhall.com/floyd

INTRODUCTION

An *RC* circuit, which contains both resistance and capacitance, is one of the basic types of reactive circuits. In this chapter, series and parallel *RC* circuits and their responses to sinusoidal voltages are covered. Series-parallel combinations are also examined. Power considerations in *RC* circuits are introduced, and practical aspects of power ratings are discussed. Three *RC* circuit applications are presented to give you an idea of how simple combinations of resistors and capacitors can be applied. Troubleshooting common faults in *RC* circuits is also covered.

The methods for analyzing reactive circuits are similar to those you studied in dc circuits. Reactive circuit problems can be solved at only one frequency at a time, and phasor math must be used.

10–1 SINUSOIDAL RESPONSE OF *RC* CIRCUITS

When a sinusoidal voltage is applied to a series or parallel *RC* circuit, each resulting voltage drop and the current in the circuit(s) are also sinusoidal and have the same frequency as the source voltage. The capacitance causes a phase shift between the voltage and current that depends on the relative values of the resistance and the capacitive reactance.

After completing this section, you should be able to

◆ **Describe the relationship between current and voltage in an *RC* circuit**

   ◆ Discuss voltage and current waveforms

   ◆ Discuss phase shift

   ◆ Describe types of signal generators

As shown in Figure 10–1 for the case of a series *RC* circuit, the resistor voltage (V_R), the capacitor voltage (V_C), and the current (I) are all sine waves with the frequency of the source. Phase shifts are introduced because of the capacitance. As you will learn, the resistor voltage and current are in phase with each other and lead the source voltage in phase. The capacitor voltage lags the source voltage. The phase angle between the current and the capacitor voltage is always 90°. These generalized phase relationships are indicated in Figure 10–1.

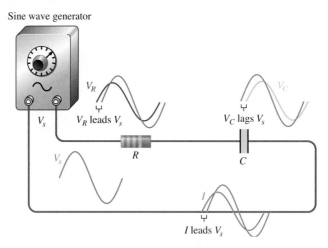

▲ FIGURE 10–1

Illustration of sinusoidal response with general phase relationships of V_R, V_C, and I relative to the source voltage. V_R and I are in phase, and V_R and V_C are 90° out of phase.

The amplitudes and the phase relationships of the voltages and current depend on the values of the resistance and the capacitive reactance. When a circuit is purely resistive, the phase angle between the source voltage and the total current is zero. When a circuit is purely capacitive, the phase angle between the source voltage and the total current is 90°, with the current leading the voltage. When there is a combination of both resistance and capacitive reactance in a circuit, the phase angle between the source voltage and the total current is somewhere between zero and 90°, depending on the relative values of the resistance and the capacitive reactance.

**SECTION 10–1
REVIEW**

Answers are at the end of the chapter.

1. A 60 Hz sinusoidal voltage is applied to an *RC* circuit. What is the frequency of the capacitor voltage? What is the frequency of the current?

2. What determines the phase shift between V_s and I in a series *RC* circuit?

3. When the resistance in an *RC* circuit is greater than the capacitive reactance, is the phase angle between the source voltage and the total current closer to 0° or to 90°?

10–2 IMPEDANCE AND PHASE ANGLE OF SERIES *RC* CIRCUITS

The **impedance** of a series *RC* circuit consists of resistance and capacitive reactance and is the total opposition to sinusoidal current. Its unit is the ohm. The **phase angle** is the phase difference between the total current and the source voltage.

After completing this section, you should be able to

◆ **Determine impedance and phase angle in a series *RC* circuit**

   ◆ Define *impedance*

   ◆ Draw an impedance triangle

   ◆ Calculate the total impedance magnitude

   ◆ Calculate the phase angle

In a purely resistive circuit, the impedance is simply equal to the total resistance. In a purely capacitive circuit, the impedance is the total capacitive reactance. The impedance of a series *RC* circuit is determined by both the resistance (R) and the capacitive reactance (X_C). These cases are illustrated in Figure 10–2. The magnitude of the impedance is symbolized by Z.

(a) $Z = R$

(b) $Z = X_C$

(c) Z includes both R and X_C

◄ **FIGURE 10–2**

Three cases of impedance.

In ac analysis, both R and X_C are treated as phasor quantities, as shown in the phasor diagram of Figure 10–3(a), with X_C appearing at a $-90°$ angle with respect to R. This relationship comes from the fact that the capacitor voltage in a series *RC* circuit lags the current, and thus the resistor voltage, by 90°. Since Z is the phasor sum of R and X_C, its phasor representation is as shown in Figure 10–3(b). A repositioning of the phasors, as shown in Figure 10–3(c), forms a right triangle, which is called the *impedance triangle*. The length of each phasor represents the magnitude in ohms, and the angle θ (the Greek letter theta) is the phase angle of the *RC* circuit and represents the phase difference between the source voltage and the current.

From right-triangle trigonometry (Pythagorean theorem), the magnitude (length) of the impedance can be expressed in terms of the resistance and capacitive reactance.

$$Z = \sqrt{R^2 + X_C^2}$$

Equation 10–1

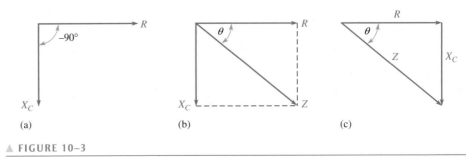

▲ **FIGURE 10–3**

Development of the impedance triangle for a series *RC* circuit.

The magnitude of the impedance (*Z*), as shown in the *RC* circuit in Figure 10–4, is expressed in ohms.

▲ **FIGURE 10–4**

Impedance in a series *RC* circuit.

The value of the phase angle, *θ*, is expressed as

Equation 10–2

$$\theta = \tan^{-1}\left(\frac{X_C}{R}\right)$$

The symbol $\tan^{-1}$ stands for *inverse tangent* and can be found on most calculators by pressing the 2nd and TAN^{-1} keys. Another term for inverse tangent is *arctangent* (arctan).

EXAMPLE 10–1

Determine the impedance and the phase angle of the *RC* circuit in Figure 10–5. Draw the impedance triangle.

▲ **FIGURE 10–5**

Solution   The impedance is

$$Z = \sqrt{R^2 + X_C^2} = \sqrt{(47\ \Omega)^2 + (100\ \Omega)^2} = \mathbf{110\ \Omega}$$

The phase angle is

$$\theta = \tan^{-1}\left(\frac{X_C}{R}\right) = \tan^{-1}\left(\frac{100\ \Omega}{47\ \Omega}\right) = \tan^{-1}(2.13) = \mathbf{64.8°}$$

The source voltage lags the current by 64.8°.

The impedance triangle is shown in Figure 10–6.

▶ FIGURE 10–6

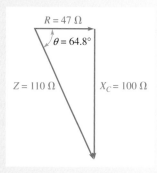

$R = 47\ \Omega$
$\theta = 64.8°$
$Z = 110\ \Omega$
$X_C = 100\ \Omega$

Related Problem*   Find Z and θ for $R = 1.0\ \text{k}\Omega$ and $X_C = 2.2\ \text{k}\Omega$ in Figure 10–5.

*Answers are at the end of the chapter.

**SECTION 10–2
REVIEW**

1. Define *impedance.*
2. Does the source voltage lead or lag the current in a series *RC* circuit?
3. What causes the phase angle in an *RC* circuit?
4. A series *RC* circuit has a resistance of 33 kΩ and a capacitive reactance of 50 kΩ. What is the value of the impedance? What is the phase angle?

10–3 ANALYSIS OF SERIES *RC* CIRCUITS

Ohm's law and Kirchhoff's voltage law are used in the analysis of series *RC* circuits to determine voltage, current, and impedance. Also in this section *RC* lead and lag circuits are examined.

After completing this section, you should be able to

◆ **Analyze a series *RC* circuit**

   ◆ Apply Ohm's law and Kirchhoff's voltage law to series *RC* circuits

   ◆ Determine the phase relationships of the voltages and current

   ◆ Show how impedance and phase angle vary with frequency

   ◆ Discuss and analyze the *RC* lag circuit

   ◆ Discuss and analyze the *RC* lead circuit

Ohm's Law

The application of Ohm's law to series *RC* circuits involves the use of the quantities of *Z*, *V*, and *I*. The three equivalent forms of Ohm's law are as follows:

Equation 10–3
$$V = IZ$$

Equation 10–4
$$I = \frac{V}{Z}$$

Equation 10–5
$$Z = \frac{V}{I}$$

The following two examples illustrate the use of Ohm's law.

EXAMPLE 10–2

The current in Figure 10–7 is 0.2 mA. Determine the source voltage and the phase angle. Draw the impedance triangle.

▶ FIGURE 10–7

Solution   The capacitive reactance is

$$X_C = \frac{1}{2\pi f C} = \frac{1}{2\pi(1000\text{ Hz})(0.01\,\mu\text{F})} = 15.9\text{ k}\Omega$$

The impedance is

$$Z = \sqrt{R^2 + X_C^2} = \sqrt{(10\text{ k}\Omega)^2 + (15.9\text{ k}\Omega)^2} = 18.8\text{ k}\Omega$$

Applying Ohm's law yields

$$V_s = IZ = (0.2\text{ mA})(18.8\text{ k}\Omega) = \textbf{3.76 V}$$

The phase angle is

$$\theta = \tan^{-1}\left(\frac{X_C}{R}\right) = \tan^{-1}\left(\frac{15.9\text{ k}\Omega}{10\text{ k}\Omega}\right) = \textbf{57.8°}$$

The source voltage has a magnitude of 3.76 V and lags the current by 57.8°. The impedance triangle is shown in Figure 10–8.

▶ FIGURE 10–8

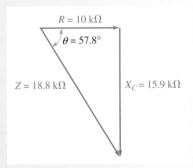

Related Problem   Determine V_s in Figure 10–7 if $f = 2$ kHz and $I = 200\,\mu$A.

EXAMPLE 10–3

Determine the current in the *RC* circuit of Figure 10–9.

▶ FIGURE 10–9

Solution The capacitive reactance is

$$X_C = \frac{1}{2\pi fC} = \frac{1}{2\pi(1.5 \text{ kHz})(0.022 \text{ }\mu\text{F})} = 4.82 \text{ k}\Omega$$

The impedance is

$$Z = \sqrt{R^2 + X_C^2} = \sqrt{(2.2 \text{ k}\Omega)^2 + (4.82 \text{ k}\Omega)^2} = 5.30 \text{ k}\Omega$$

Applying Ohm's law yields

$$I = \frac{V}{Z} = \frac{10 \text{ V}}{5.30 \text{ k}\Omega} = \textbf{1.89 mA}$$

Related Problem Determine the phase angle between V_s and I in Figure 10–9.

 Open Multisim file E10-03 on your CD-ROM. Measure the current and the voltages across the resistor and the capacitor.

Phase Relationships of the Current and Voltages

In a series *RC* circuit, the current is the same through both the resistor and the capacitor. Thus, the resistor voltage is in phase with the current, and the capacitor voltage lags the current by 90°. Therefore, there is a phase difference of 90° between the resistor voltage, V_R, and the capacitor voltage, V_C, as shown in the waveform diagram of Figure 10–10.

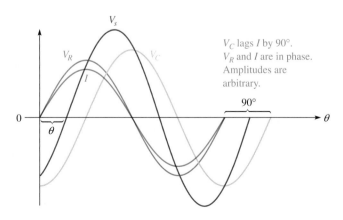

V_C lags *I* by 90°.
V_R and *I* are in phase.
Amplitudes are arbitrary.

▲ FIGURE 10–10

Phase relation of the voltages and current in a series *RC* circuit.

You know from Kirchhoff's voltage law that the sum of the voltage drops must equal the source voltage. However, since V_R and V_C are 90° out of phase with each other, they must be added as phasor quantities, with V_C lagging V_R, as shown in Figure 10–11(a). As shown in Figure 10–11(b), V_s is the phasor sum of V_R and V_C, as expressed in the following equation:

Equation 10–6

$$V_s = \sqrt{V_R^2 + V_C^2}$$

▶ FIGURE 10–11

Voltage phasor diagram for the waveforms in Figure 10–10.

(a)

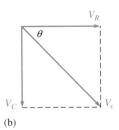

(b)

The value of the phase angle between the resistor voltage and the source voltage can be expressed as

Equation 10–7

$$\theta = \tan^{-1}\left(\frac{V_C}{V_R}\right)$$

Since the resistor voltage and the current are in phase, θ in Equation 10–7 also represents the phase angle between the source voltage and the current and is equivalent to $\tan^{-1}(X_C/R)$.

Figure 10–12 shows the voltage and current phasor diagram that represents the waveform diagram of Figure 10–10.

▶ FIGURE 10–12

Voltage and current phasor diagram for the waveforms in Figure 10–10.

EXAMPLE 10–4

Determine the source voltage and the phase angle in Figure 10–13. Draw the voltage phasor diagram.

▶ FIGURE 10–13

Solution Since V_R and V_C are 90° out of phase, you cannot add them directly. The source voltage is the phasor sum of V_R and V_C.

$$V_s = \sqrt{V_R^2 + V_C^2} = \sqrt{(10\ \text{V})^2 + (15\ \text{V})^2} = \textbf{18 V}$$

The phase angle between the resistor voltage and the source voltage is

$$\theta = \tan^{-1}\left(\frac{V_C}{V_R}\right) = \tan^{-1}\left(\frac{15\ V}{10\ V}\right) = \mathbf{56.3°}$$

The voltage phasor diagram is shown in Figure 10–14.

▶ FIGURE 10–14

Related Problem In a certain series *RC* circuit, $V_s = 10$ V and $V_R = 7$ V. Find V_C.

Variation of Impedance and Phase Angle with Frequency

As you know, capacitive reactance varies inversely with frequency. Since $Z = \sqrt{R^2 + X_C^2}$, you can see that when X_C increases, the entire term under the square root sign increases and thus the total impedance also increases; and when X_C decreases, the total impedance also decreases. Therefore, *in an RC circuit, Z is inversely dependent on frequency.*

Figure 10–15 illustrates how the voltages and current in a series *RC* circuit vary as the frequency increases or decreases, with the source voltage held at a constant value. Part (a) shows that as the frequency is increased, X_C decreases; so the voltage across the capacitor decreases. Also, Z decreases as X_C decreases, causing the current to increase. An increase in the current causes more voltage across R.

(a) As frequency is increased, Z decreases as X_C decreases, causing *I* and V_R to increase and V_C to decrease.

(b) As frequency is decreased, Z increases as X_C increases, causing *I* and V_R to decrease and V_C to increase.

▲ FIGURE 10–15

An illustration of how the variation of impedance affects the voltages and current as the source frequency is varied. The source voltage is held at a constant amplitude.

Figure 10–15(b) shows that as the frequency is decreased, X_C increases; so more voltage is dropped across the capacitor. Also, Z increases as X_C increases, causing the current to decrease. A decrease in the current causes less voltage across R.

Changes in Z and X_C can be observed as shown in Figure 10–16. As the frequency increases, the voltage across Z remains constant because V_s is constant ($V_s = V_Z$). Also, the voltage across C decreases. The increasing current indicates that Z is decreasing. It does so because of the inverse relationship stated in Ohm's law ($Z = V_Z/I$). The increasing current also indicates that X_C is decreasing ($X_C = V_C/I$). The decrease in V_C corresponds to the decrease in X_C.

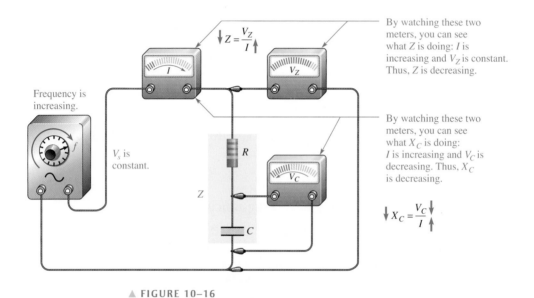

By watching these two meters, you can see what Z is doing: I is increasing and V_Z is constant. Thus, Z is decreasing.

By watching these two meters, you can see what X_C is doing: I is increasing and V_C is decreasing. Thus, X_C is decreasing.

▲ FIGURE 10–16

An illustration of how Z and X_C change with frequency.

Since X_C is the factor that introduces the phase angle in a series RC circuit, a change in X_C produces a change in the phase angle. As the frequency is increased, X_C becomes smaller, and thus the phase angle decreases. As the frequency is decreased, X_C becomes larger, and thus the phase angle increases. The angle between V_s and V_R is the phase angle of the circuit because I is in phase with V_R.

Figure 10–17 uses the impedance triangle to illustrate the variations in X_C, Z, and θ as the frequency changes. Of course, R remains constant. The key point is that because X_C varies inversely with the frequency, the magnitude of the total impedance and the phase angle also vary inversely with the frequency. Example 10–5 illustrates this.

▶ FIGURE 10–17

As the frequency increases, X_C decreases, Z decreases, and θ decreases. Each value of frequency can be visualized as forming a different impedance triangle.

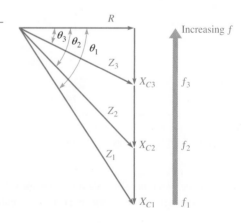

EXAMPLE 10–5

For the series *RC* circuit in Figure 10–18, determine the impedance and phase angle for each of the following values of frequency:

(a) 10 kHz   **(b)** 20 kHz   **(c)** 30 kHz

▶ FIGURE 10–18

Solution   **(a)** For $f = 10$ kHz, calculate the impedance as follows:

$$X_C = \frac{1}{2\pi fC} = \frac{1}{2\pi(10\,\text{kHz})(0.01\,\mu\text{F})} = 1.59\,\text{k}\Omega$$

$$Z = \sqrt{R^2 + X_C^2} = \sqrt{(1.0\,\text{k}\Omega)^2 + (1.59\,\text{k}\Omega)^2} = \mathbf{1.88\,k\Omega}$$

The phase angle is

$$\theta = \tan^{-1}\left(\frac{X_C}{R}\right) = \tan^{-1}\left(\frac{1.59\,\text{k}\Omega}{1.0\,\text{k}\Omega}\right) = \mathbf{57.8°}$$

(b) For $f = 20$ kHz,

$$X_C = \frac{1}{2\pi(20\,\text{kHz})(0.01\,\mu\text{F})} = 796\,\Omega$$

$$Z = \sqrt{(1.0\,\text{k}\Omega)^2 + (796\,\Omega)^2} = \mathbf{1.28\,k\Omega}$$

$$\theta = \tan^{-1}\left(\frac{796\,\Omega}{1.0\,\text{k}\Omega}\right) = \mathbf{38.5°}$$

(c) For $f = 30$ kHz,

$$X_C = \frac{1}{2\pi(30\,\text{kHz})(0.01\,\mu\text{F})} = 531\,\Omega$$

$$Z = \sqrt{(1.0\,\text{k}\Omega)^2 + (531\,\Omega)^2} = \mathbf{1.13\,k\Omega}$$

$$\theta = \tan^{-1}\left(\frac{531\,\Omega}{1.0\,\text{k}\Omega}\right) = \mathbf{28.0°}$$

Notice that as the frequency increases, X_C, Z, and θ decrease.

Related Problem   Find the total impedance and phase angle in Figure 10–18 for $f = 1$ kHz.

RC Lag Circuit

An ***RC*** **lag circuit** is a phase shift circuit in which the output voltage lags the input voltage by a specified angle, ϕ. Phase shift circuits are commonly used in electronic communication systems and in other application areas.

A basic series *RC* lag circuit is shown in Figure 10–19(a). Notice that the output voltage is taken across the capacitor, and the input voltage is the total voltage applied across the circuit. The relationship of the voltages is shown in the phasor diagram in Figure 10–19(b). Keep in mind that the circuit phase angle is the angle between V_{in} and the current. Notice in

(a) A basic RC lag circuit

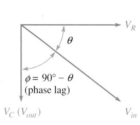

(b) Phasor voltage diagram showing the phase lag between V_{in} and V_{out}

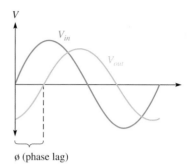

(c) Input and output voltage waveforms

▲ FIGURE 10–19

The RC lag circuit ($V_{out} = V_C$).

Figure 10–19(b) that the output voltage, V_{out}, lags V_{in} by an angle, designated ϕ, that is the difference between 90° and the circuit phase angle θ. The angle ϕ is called the phase lag when the output voltage lags the input voltage and the phase lead when the output voltage leads the input. Since $\theta = \tan^{-1}(X_C/R)$, the value of the phase lag, ϕ, can be expressed as

Equation 10–8

$$\phi = 90° - \tan^{-1}\left(\frac{X_C}{R}\right)$$

The input and output voltage waveforms of the lag circuit are shown in Figure 10–19(c). The exact amount of phase lag between the input and the output depends on the values of the resistance and the capacitive reactance. The magnitude of the output voltage depends on these values also.

EXAMPLE 10–6

Determine the amount of phase lag from input to output in the lag circuit in Figure 10–20.

▶ FIGURE 10–20

Solution   First determine the capacitive reactance.

$$X_C = \frac{1}{2\pi f C} = \frac{1}{2\pi(1\text{ kHz})(0.1\ \mu\text{F})} = 1.59\text{ k}\Omega$$

The phase lag between the output voltage and the input voltage is

$$\phi = 90° - \tan^{-1}\left(\frac{X_C}{R}\right) = 90° - \tan^{-1}\left(\frac{1.59\text{ k}\Omega}{680\ \Omega}\right) = \mathbf{23.2°}$$

The output voltage lags the input voltage by 23.2°.

Related Problem   In a lag circuit, what happens to the phase lag if the frequency increases?

The phase-lag circuit can be considered as a voltage divider with a portion of the input voltage dropped across R and a portion across C. The output voltage can be determined with the following formula:

$$V_{out} = \left(\frac{X_C}{\sqrt{R^2 + X_C^2}}\right)V_{in}$$

Equation 10–9

EXAMPLE 10–7

For the lag circuit in Figure 10–20 of Example 10–6, determine the output voltage when the input voltage has an rms value of 10 V. Draw the input and output waveforms showing the proper relationships. The values for X_C (1.59 kΩ) and ϕ (23.2°) were found in Example 10–6.

Solution   Use Equation 10–9 to determine the output voltage for the lag circuit in Figure 10–20.

$$V_{out} = \left(\frac{X_C}{\sqrt{R^2 + X_C^2}}\right)V_{in} = \left(\frac{1.59 \text{ k}\Omega}{\sqrt{(680 \text{ }\Omega)^2 + (1.59 \text{ k}\Omega)^2}}\right)10 \text{ V} = \textbf{9.2 V rms}$$

The waveforms are shown in Figure 10–21.

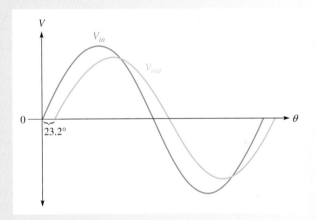

▲ FIGURE 10–21

Related Problem   In a lag circuit, what happens to the output voltage if the frequency increases?

Effects of Frequency on the Lag Circuit   Since the circuit phase angle, θ, decreases as frequency increases, the phase lag ϕ between the input and the output voltages increases. You can see this relationship by examining Equation 10–8. Also, the magnitude of V_{out} decreases as the frequency increases because X_C becomes smaller and less of the total input voltage is dropped across the capacitor. Figure 10–22 illustrates the changes in phase lag and output voltage magnitude with frequency.

RC Lead Circuit

An ***RC* lead circuit** is a phase shift circuit in which the output voltage leads the input voltage by a specified angle, ϕ. A basic *RC* lead circuit is shown in Figure 10–23(a). Notice

(a) When f increases, the phase lag ϕ increases and V_{out} decreases.

(b) When f decreases, ϕ decreases and V_{out} increases.

▲ FIGURE 10–22

Illustration of how the frequency affects the phase lag and the output voltage in an RC lag circuit with the amplitude of V_{in} held constant.

how it differs from the lag circuit. Here the output voltage is taken across the resistor. The relationship of the voltages is given in the phasor diagram in Figure 10–23(b). The output voltage, V_{out}, leads V_{in} by an angle that is the same as the circuit phase angle because V_R and I are in phase with each other.

(a) A basic RC lead circuit

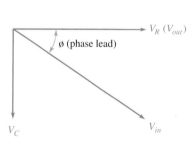

(b) Phasor voltage diagram showing the phase lead between V_{in} and V_{out}

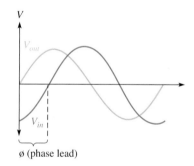

(c) Input and output voltage waveforms

▲ FIGURE 10–23

The RC lead circuit ($V_{out} = V_R$).

When the input and output waveforms are displayed on an oscilloscope, a relationship similar to that in Figure 10–23(c) is observed. Of course, the exact amount of phase lead and the output voltage magnitude depend on the values of R and X_C. The value of the phase lead, ϕ, is expressed as

Equation 10–10

$$\phi = \tan^{-1}\left(\frac{X_C}{R}\right)$$

The output voltage is expressed as

Equation 10–11

$$V_{out} = \left(\frac{R}{\sqrt{R^2 + X_C^2}}\right)V_{in}$$

EXAMPLE 10–8

Calculate the phase lead and the output voltage for the circuit in Figure 10–24.

▶ **FIGURE 10–24**

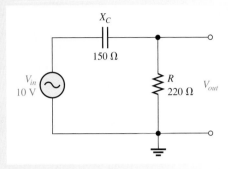

Solution   The phase lead is

$$\phi = \tan^{-1}\left(\frac{X_C}{R}\right) = \tan^{-1}\left(\frac{150\ \Omega}{220\ \Omega}\right) = \mathbf{34.3°}$$

The output leads the input by 34.3°.
  Use Equation 10–11 to determine the output voltage.

$$V_{out} = \left(\frac{R}{\sqrt{R^2 + X_C^2}}\right)V_{in} = \left(\frac{220\ \Omega}{\sqrt{(220\ \Omega)^2 + (150\ \Omega)^2}}\right)10\ V = \mathbf{8.26\ V}$$

Related Problem   How does an increase in *R* affect the phase lead and the output voltage in Figure 10–24?

Effects of Frequency on the Lead Circuit   Since the phase lead is the same as the circuit phase angle θ, it decreases as frequency increases. The output voltage increases with frequency because as X_C becomes smaller, more of the input voltage is dropped across the resistor. Figure 10–25 illustrates this relationship.

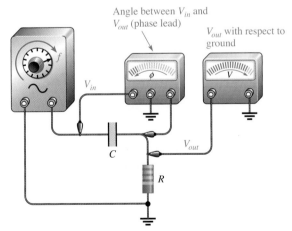

(a) When *f* increases, the phase lag ϕ decreases and V_{out} increases.

(b) When *f* decreases, ϕ increases and V_{out} decreases.

▲ **FIGURE 10–25**

Illustration of how the frequency affects the phase lead and the output voltage in an *RC* lead circuit with the amplitude of V_{in} held constant.

**SECTION 10–3
REVIEW**

1. In a certain series *RC* circuit, $V_R = 4$ V and $V_C = 6$ V. What is the magnitude of the source voltage?

2. In Question 1, what is the phase angle?

3. What is the phase difference between the capacitor voltage and the resistor voltage in a series *RC* circuit?

4. When the frequency of the source voltage in a series *RC* circuit is increased, what happens to each of the following?

   (a) the capacitive reactance   **(b)** the impedance   **(c)** the phase angle

5. A certain *RC* lag circuit consists of a 4.7 kΩ resistor and a 0.022 μF capacitor. Determine the phase lag between the input and output voltages at a frequency of 3 kHz.

6. An *RC* lead circuit has the same component values as the lag circuit in Question 5. What is the magnitude of the output voltage at 3 kHz when the input is 10 V rms?

10–4 IMPEDANCE AND PHASE ANGLE OF PARALLEL *RC* CIRCUITS

In this section, you will learn how to determine the impedance and phase angle of a parallel *RC* circuit. Also conductance (G), capacitive susceptance (B_C), and total admittance (Y_{tot}) are discussed because of their usefulness in parallel circuit analysis.

After completing this section, you should be able to

◆ **Determine impedance and phase angle in a parallel *RC* circuit**

  ◆ Express total impedance in a product-over-sum form

  ◆ Express the phase angle in terms of R and X_C

  ◆ Determine the conductance, capacitive susceptance, and admittance

  ◆ Convert admittance to impedance

Figure 10–26 shows a basic parallel *RC* circuit.

▶ FIGURE 10–26

Parallel *RC* circuit.

The expression for the impedance in Equation 10–12 is given in a product-over-sum form similar to the way two resistors in parallel can be expressed. In this case, the denominator is the phasor sum of R and X_C.

Equation 10–12

$$Z = \frac{RX_C}{\sqrt{R^2 + X_C^2}}$$

The value of the phase angle between the source voltage and the total current can be expressed in terms of R and X_C as shown in Equation 10–13.

Equation 10–13

$$\theta = \tan^{-1}\left(\frac{R}{X_C}\right)$$

This formula is derived from an equivalent formula using branch currents (Equ. 10–22), which is introduced in Section 10–5.

EXAMPLE 10–9

For each circuit in Figure 10–27, determine the impedance and the phase angle.

FIGURE 10–27

(a)   (b)

Solution   For the circuit in Figure 10–27(a), the impedance and phase angle are

$$Z = \frac{RX_C}{\sqrt{R^2 + X_C^2}} = \frac{(100 \text{ } \Omega)(50 \text{ } \Omega)}{\sqrt{(100 \text{ } \Omega)^2 + (50 \text{ } \Omega)^2}} = \mathbf{44.7 \text{ } \Omega}$$

$$\theta = \tan^{-1}\left(\frac{R}{X_C}\right) = \tan^{-1}\left(\frac{100 \text{ } \Omega}{50 \text{ } \Omega}\right) = \mathbf{63.4°}$$

For the circuit in Figure 10–27(b),

$$Z = \frac{(1.0 \text{ k}\Omega)(2 \text{ k}\Omega)}{\sqrt{(1.0 \text{ k}\Omega)^2 + (2 \text{ k}\Omega)^2}} = \mathbf{894 \text{ } \Omega}$$

$$\theta = \tan^{-1}\left(\frac{1.0 \text{ k}\Omega}{2 \text{ k}\Omega}\right) = \mathbf{26.6°}$$

Related Problem   Determine *Z* in Figure 10–27(a) if the frequency is doubled.

Conductance, Capacitive Susceptance, and Admittance

Recall that **conductance (*G*)** is the reciprocal of resistance and is expressed as

$$G = \frac{1}{R}$$

Equation 10–14

Two new terms are now introduced for use in parallel *RC* circuits. Susceptance is the reciprocal of reactance; therefore, **capacitive susceptance (*B_C*)** is the reciprocal of capacitive reactance and is a measure of the ability of a capacitor to permit current. It is expressed as

$$B_C = \frac{1}{X_C}$$

Equation 10–15

Admittance (*Y*) is the reciprocal of impedance and is expressed as

$$Y = \frac{1}{Z}$$

Equation 10–16

The unit of each of these three quantities is the siemens (S), which is the reciprocal of the ohm.

In working with parallel circuits, it is often easier to use conductance (*G*), capacitive susceptance (*B_C*), and admittance (*Y*) rather than resistance (*R*), capacitive reactance (*X_C*) and impedance (*Z*). In a parallel *RC* circuit, as shown in Figure 10–28(a), the total

▶ FIGURE 10–28

Admittance in a parallel *RC* circuit.

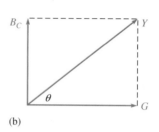

(a)   (b)

admittance is the phasor sum of the conductance and the capacitive susceptance, as shown in Figure 10–28(b).

Equation 10–17

$$Y_{tot} = \sqrt{G^2 + B_C^2}$$

EXAMPLE 10–10

Determine the total admittance in Figure 10–29, and then convert it to impedance.

▶ FIGURE 10–29

Solution   To determine *Y*, first calculate the values for *G* and B_C. Since $R = 330\,\Omega$,

$$G = \frac{1}{R} = \frac{1}{330\ \Omega} = 3.03\ \text{mS}$$

The capacitive reactance is

$$X_C = \frac{1}{2\pi fC} = \frac{1}{2\pi(1000\ \text{Hz})(0.22\ \mu\text{F})} = 723\ \Omega$$

The capacitive susceptance is

$$B_C = \frac{1}{X_C} = \frac{1}{723\ \Omega} = 1.38\ \text{mS}$$

Therefore, the total admittance is

$$Y_{tot} = \sqrt{G^2 + B_C^2} = \sqrt{(3.03\ \text{mS})^2 + (1.38\ \text{mS})^2} = \textbf{3.33 mS}$$

Convert to impedance.

$$Z = \frac{1}{Y_{tot}} = \frac{1}{3.33\ \text{mS}} = \textbf{300}\ \boldsymbol{\Omega}$$

Related Problem   Calculate the admittance in Figure 10–29 if *f* is increased to 2.5 kHz.

**SECTION 10–4
REVIEW**

1. Determine *Z* if a 1.0 kΩ resistance is in parallel with a 650 Ω capacitive reactance.
2. Define *conductance*, *capacitive susceptance*, and *admittance*.
3. If *Z* = 100 Ω, what is the value of *Y*?
4. In a certain parallel *RC* circuit, *R* = 50 Ω and X_C = 75 Ω. Determine *Y*.

10–5   ANALYSIS OF PARALLEL *RC* CIRCUITS

Ohm's law and Kirchhoff's current law are used in the analysis of *RC* circuits. Current and voltage relationships in a parallel *RC* circuit are examined.

After completing this section, you should be able to

◆ **Analyze a parallel *RC* circuit**

   ◆ Apply Ohm's law and Kirchhoff's current law to parallel *RC* circuits

   ◆ Show how impedance and phase angle vary with frequency

   ◆ Convert from a parallel circuit to an equivalent series circuit

For convenience in the analysis of parallel circuits, the Ohm's law formulas using impedance—Equations 10–3, 10–4, and 10–5—can be rewritten for admittance using the relation $Y = 1/Z$.

$$V = \frac{I}{Y}$$

Equation 10–18

$$I = VY$$

Equation 10–19

$$Y = \frac{I}{V}$$

Equation 10–20

EXAMPLE 10–11

Determine the total current and the phase angle in Figure 10–30.

▶ **FIGURE 10–30**

Solution   First, determine the total admittance. The capacitive reactance is

$$X_C = \frac{1}{2\pi fC} = \frac{1}{2\pi(1.5 \text{ kHz})(0.022 \ \mu\text{F})} = 4.82 \text{ k}\Omega$$

The conductance is

$$G = \frac{1}{R} = \frac{1}{2.2 \text{ k}\Omega} = 455 \ \mu\text{S}$$

The capacitive susceptance is

$$B_C = \frac{1}{X_C} = \frac{1}{4.82 \text{ k}\Omega} = 207 \ \mu\text{S}$$

Therefore, the total admittance is

$$Y_{tot} = \sqrt{G^2 + B_C^2} = \sqrt{(455 \ \mu\text{S})^2 + (207 \ \mu\text{S})^2} = 500 \ \mu\text{S}$$

Next, use Ohm's law to calculate the total current.

$$I_{tot} = VY_{tot} = (10 \text{ V})(500 \, \mu\text{S}) = \textbf{5.00 mA}$$

The phase angle is

$$\theta = \tan^{-1}\left(\frac{R}{X_C}\right) = \tan^{-1}\left(\frac{2.2 \text{ k}\Omega}{4.82 \text{ k}\Omega}\right) = \textbf{24.5}°$$

The total current is 5.00 mA, and it leads the source voltage by 24.5°.

Related Problem   What is the total current if the frequency is doubled?

Open Multisim file E10-11 on your CD-ROM. Verify the value of the total current that was calculated. Then measure each branch current. Double the frequency to 3 kHz and measure the total current.

Phase Relationships of the Currents and Voltages

Figure 10–31(a) shows all the currents and voltages in a basic parallel *RC* circuit. As you can see, the source voltage, V_s, appears across both the resistive and the capacitive branches, so V_s, V_R, and V_C are all in phase and of the same magnitude. The total current, I_{tot}, divides at the junction into the two branch currents, I_R and I_C.

▲ FIGURE 10–31

Currents and voltages in a parallel *RC* circuit. The current directions shown in (a) are instantaneous and, of course, reverse when the source voltage reverses. The current phasors in (b) rotate once per cycle.

The current through the resistor is in phase with the voltage. The current through the capacitor leads the voltage, and thus the resistive current, by 90°. By Kirchhoff's current law, the total current is the phasor sum of the two branch currents, as shown by the phasor diagram in Figure 10–31(b). The total current is expressed as

Equation 10–21
$$I_{tot} = \sqrt{I_R^2 + I_C^2}$$

The value of the phase angle between the resistor current and the total current is

Equation 10–22
$$\theta = \tan^{-1}\left(\frac{I_C}{I_R}\right)$$

Equation 10–22 is equivalent to Equation 10–13, $\theta = \tan^{-1}(R/X_C)$.

Figure 10–32 shows a complete current and voltage phasor diagram. Notice that I_C leads I_R by 90° and that I_R is in phase with the voltage ($V_s = V_R = V_C$).

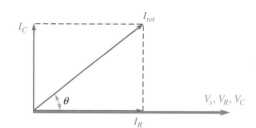

◀ FIGURE 10–32

Current and voltage phasor diagram for a parallel *RC* circuit (amplitudes are arbitrary).

EXAMPLE 10–12

Determine the value of each current in Figure 10–33, and describe the phase relationship of each with the source voltage. Draw the current phasor diagram.

▶ FIGURE 10–33

Solution   The resistor current, the capacitor current, and the total current are expressed as follows:

$$I_R = \frac{V_s}{R} = \frac{12\,\text{V}}{220\,\Omega} = \textbf{54.5 mA}$$

$$I_C = \frac{V_s}{X_C} = \frac{12\,\text{V}}{150\,\Omega} = \textbf{80 mA}$$

$$I_{tot} = \sqrt{I_R^2 + I_C^2} = \sqrt{(54.5\,\text{mA})^2 + (80\,\text{mA})^2} = \textbf{96.8 mA}$$

The phase angle is

$$\theta = \tan^{-1}\left(\frac{I_C}{I_R}\right) = \tan^{-1}\left(\frac{80\,\text{mA}}{54.5\,\text{mA}}\right) = 55.7°$$

I_R is in phase with the source voltage, I_C leads the source voltage by 90°, and I_{tot} leads the source voltage by 55.7°. The current phasor diagram is shown in Figure 10–34.

▶ FIGURE 10–34

I_C = 80 mA

I_{tot} = 96.8 mA

55.7°

I_R = 54.5 mA

Related Problem   In a certain parallel circuit, I_R = 100 mA and I_C = 60 mA. Determine the total current and the phase angle.

Conversion from Parallel to Series Form

For every parallel *RC* circuit, there is an equivalent series *RC* circuit for any given frequency. Two circuits are equivalent when they both present an equal impedance and phase angle.

To obtain the equivalent series circuit for a given parallel RC circuit, first find the impedance and phase angle of the parallel circuit. Then use the values of Z and θ to construct an impedance triangle, shown in Figure 10–35. The vertical and horizontal sides of the triangle represent the equivalent series resistance and capacitive reactance as indicated. You can find these values by using the following trigonometric relationships:

Equation 10–23

$$R_{eq} = Z\cos\theta$$

Equation 10–24

$$X_{C(eq)} = Z\sin\theta$$

The cosine (cos) and the sine (sin) functions are available on any scientific calculator.

▶ **FIGURE 10–35**

Impedance triangle for the series equivalent of a parallel RC circuit. Z and θ are the known values for the parallel circuit. R_{eq} and $X_{C(eq)}$ are the series equivalent values.

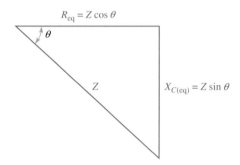

EXAMPLE 10–13

Convert the parallel circuit in Figure 10–36 to an equivalent series form.

▶ **FIGURE 10–36**

Solution First, find the total admittance of the parallel circuit as follows:

$$G = \frac{1}{R} = \frac{1}{18\ \Omega} = 55.6\ \text{mS}$$

$$B_C = \frac{1}{X_C} = \frac{1}{27\ \Omega} = 37.0\ \text{mS}$$

$$Y_{tot} = \sqrt{G^2 + B_C^2} = \sqrt{(55.6\ \text{mS})^2 + (37.0\ \text{mS})^2} = 66.8\ \text{mS}$$

Then, the total impedance is

$$Z_{tot} = \frac{1}{Y_{tot}} = \frac{1}{66.8\ \text{mS}} = 15.0\ \Omega$$

The phase angle is

$$\theta = \tan^{-1}\left(\frac{R}{X_C}\right) = \tan^{-1}\left(\frac{18\ \Omega}{27\ \Omega}\right) = 33.6°$$

The equivalent series values are

$$R_{eq} = Z\cos\theta = (15.0\ \Omega)\cos(33.6°) = \textbf{12.5\ } \boldsymbol{\Omega}$$

$$X_{C(eq)} = Z\sin\theta = (15.0\ \Omega)\sin(33.6°) = \textbf{8.3\ } \boldsymbol{\Omega}$$

The series equivalent circuit is shown in Figure 10–37. The value of C can only be determined if the frequency is known.

▶ FIGURE 10–37

Related Problem   The impedance of a parallel *RC* circuit is 10 kΩ and the phase angle is 26°. Convert to an equivalent series circuit.

Note that a parallel *RC* circuit becomes less reactive when X_C is increased. That is, the circuit phase angle becomes smaller. The reason for this effect is that when X_C is increased relative to R, less current is through the capacitive branch, and although the in-phase or resistive current does not increase, it becomes a greater percentage of the total current.

SECTION 10–5 REVIEW	1. The admittance of an *RC* circuit is 3.5 mS, and the source voltage is 6 V. What is the total current?
	2. In a certain parallel *RC* circuit, the resistor current is 10 mA, and the capacitor current is 15 mA. Determine the phase angle and the total current.
	3. What is the phase angle between the capacitor current and the source voltage in a parallel *RC* circuit?

10–6 ANALYSIS OF SERIES-PARALLEL *RC* CIRCUITS

The concepts studied in the previous sections are used to analyze circuits with combinations of both series and parallel R and C components.

After completing this section, you should be able to

◆ **Analyze series-parallel *RC* circuits**

  ◆ Determine total impedance

  ◆ Calculate currents and voltages

  ◆ Measure impedance and phase angle

The following example demonstrates the analysis of a series-parallel reactive circuit.

EXAMPLE 10–14

In the series-parallel *RC* circuit of Figure 10–38, determine the following:

(a) total impedance   **(b)** total current   **(c)** phase angle by which I_{tot} leads V_s

▲ FIGURE 10–38

Solution   **(a)** First, calculate the magnitudes of the capacitive reactances.

$$X_{C1} = \frac{1}{2\pi(5 \text{ kHz})(0.1 \ \mu\text{F})} = 318 \ \Omega$$

$$X_{C2} = \frac{1}{2\pi(5 \text{ kHz})(0.047 \ \mu\text{F})} = 677 \ \Omega$$

One approach is to find the series equivalent resistance and capacitive reactance for the parallel portion of the circuit; then add the resistances ($R_1 + R_{eq}$) to get total resistance and add the reactances ($X_{C1} + X_{C(eq)}$) to get total reactance. From these totals, you can determine the total impedance.

Find the impedance of the parallel portion (Z_2) by first finding the admittance.

$$G_2 = \frac{1}{R_2} = \frac{1}{680 \ \Omega} = 1.47 \text{ mS}$$

$$B_{C2} = \frac{1}{X_{C2}} = \frac{1}{677 \ \Omega} = 1.48 \text{ mS}$$

$$Y_2 = \sqrt{G_2^2 + B_{C2}^2} = \sqrt{(1.47 \text{ mS})^2 + (1.48 \text{ mS})^2} = 2.09 \text{ mS}$$

$$Z_2 = \frac{1}{Y_2} = \frac{1}{2.09 \text{ mS}} = 478 \ \Omega$$

The phase angle associated with the parallel portion of the circuit is

$$\theta_p = \tan^{-1}\left(\frac{R_2}{X_{C2}}\right) = \tan^{-1}\left(\frac{680 \ \Omega}{677 \ \Omega}\right) = 45.1°$$

The series equivalent values for the parallel portion are

$$R_{eq} = Z_2\cos\theta_p = (478 \ \Omega)\cos(45.1°) = 337 \ \Omega$$
$$X_{C(eq)} = Z_2\sin\theta_p = (478 \ \Omega)\sin(45.1°) = 339 \ \Omega$$

The total circuit resistance is

$$R_{tot} = R_1 + R_{eq} = 1000 \ \Omega + 337 \ \Omega = 1.34 \text{ k}\Omega$$

The total circuit reactance is

$$X_{C(tot)} = X_{C1} + X_{C(eq)} = 318 \ \Omega + 339 \ \Omega = 657 \ \Omega$$

The total circuit impedance is

$$Z_{tot} = \sqrt{R_{tot}^2 + X_{C(tot)}^2} = \sqrt{(1.34\,\text{k}\Omega)^2 + (657\,\Omega)^2} = \textbf{1.49 k}\boldsymbol{\Omega}$$

(b) Use Ohm's law to find the total current.

$$I_{tot} = \frac{V_s}{Z_{tot}} = \frac{10\,\text{V}}{1.49\,\text{k}\Omega} = \textbf{6.71 mA}$$

(c) To find the phase angle, view the circuit as a series combination of R_{tot} and $X_{C(tot)}$. The phase angle by which I_{tot} leads V_s is

$$\theta = \tan^{-1}\!\left(\frac{X_{C(tot)}}{R_{tot}}\right) = \tan^{-1}\!\left(\frac{657\,\Omega}{1.34\,\text{k}\Omega}\right) = \textbf{26.1}\boldsymbol{\degree}$$

Related Problem   Determine the voltages across Z_1 and Z_2 in Figure 10–38.

 Open Multisim file E10-14 on your CD-ROM. Verify the calculated value of the total current. Measure the current through R_2 and the current through C_2. Measure voltages across Z_1 and Z_2.

Circuit Measurements

Determining Z_{tot} Now, let's see how the value of Z_{tot} for the circuit in Example 10–14 can be determined by measurement. First, the total impedance is measured as outlined in the following steps and as illustrated in Figure 10–39 (other ways are also possible).

Step 1. Using a sine wave generator, set the source voltage to a known value (10 V) and the frequency to 5 kHz. Check the voltage with an ac voltmeter and the frequency with a frequency counter rather than relying on the marked values on the generator controls.

Step 2. Connect an ac ammeter as shown in Figure 10–39, and measure the total current. Alternately, you can measure the voltage across R_1 and calculate the current.

Step 3. Calculate the total impedance by using Ohm's law.

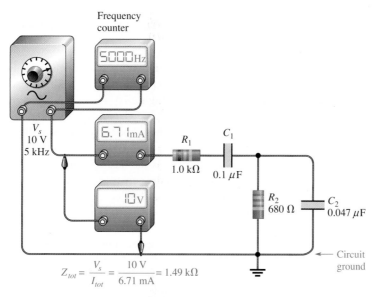

▲ FIGURE 10–39

Determining Z_{tot} by measurement of V_s and I_{tot}.

Determining θ To measure the phase angle, the source voltage and the total current must be displayed on an oscilloscope screen in the proper time relationship. Two basic types of scope probes are available to measure the quantities with an oscilloscope: the voltage probe and the current probe. The current probe is a convenient device, but it is often not as readily available as a voltage probe. We will confine our phase measurement technique to the use of voltage probes in conjunction with the oscilloscope. Although there are special isolation methods, a typical oscilloscope voltage probe has two points that are connected to the circuit: the probe tip and the ground lead. Thus, all voltage measurements must be referenced to ground.

Since only voltage probes are to be used, the total current cannot be measured directly. However, for phase measurement, the voltage across R_1 is in phase with the total current and can be used to establish the phase angle of the current.

Before proceeding with the actual phase measurement, there is a problem with displaying V_{R1}. If the scope probe is connected across the resistor, as indicated in Figure 10–40(a), the ground lead of the scope will short point B to ground, thus bypassing the rest of the components and effectively removing them from the circuit electrically, as illustrated in Figure 10–40(b) (assuming that the scope is not isolated from power line ground).

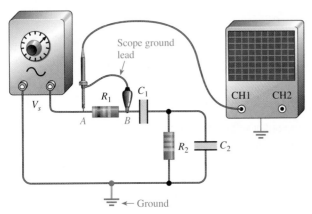

(a) Ground lead on scope probe grounds point B.

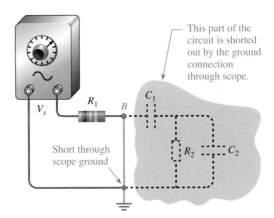

(b) The effect of grounding point B is to short out the rest of the circuit.

▲ FIGURE 10–40

Effects of measuring directly across a component when the instrument and the circuit are grounded.

To avoid this problem, you can switch the generator output terminals so that one end of R_1 is connected to the ground terminal, as shown in Figure 10–41(a). Now the scope can be connected across it to display V_{R1}, as indicated in Figure 10–41(b). The other probe is connected across the voltage source to display V_s as indicated. Now channel 1 of the scope has V_{R1} as an input, and channel 2 has V_s. The scope should be triggered from the source voltage (channel 2 in this case).

Before connecting the probes to the circuit, you should align the two horizontal lines (traces) so that they appear as a single line across the center of the scope screen. To do so, ground the probe tips and adjust the vertical position knobs to move the traces toward the center line of the screen until they are superimposed. This procedure ensures that both waveforms have the same zero crossing so that an accurate phase measurement can be made.

Once you have stabilized the waveforms on the scope screen, you can measure the period of the source voltage. Next, use the Volts/Div controls to adjust the amplitudes of the waveforms until they both appear to have the same amplitude. Now, spread the waveforms horizontally by using the Sec/Div control to expand the distance between them. This horizontal distance represents the time between the two waveforms. The number of divisions between the waveforms along any horizontal lines times the Sec/Div setting is equal to the

(a) Ground repositioned so that one end of R_1 is grounded.

(b) The scope displays V_{R1} and V_s. V_{R1} represents the phase of the total current.

▲ FIGURE 10–41

Repositioning ground so that a direct voltage measurement can be made with respect to ground without shorting out part of the circuit.

time between them, Δt. Also, you can use the cursors to determine Δt if your oscilloscope has this feature.

Once you have determined the period, T, and the time between the waveforms, Δt, you can calculate the phase angle with the following equation:

$$\theta = \left(\frac{\Delta t}{T}\right)360°$$

Equation 10–25

An example screen display is shown in Figure 10–42. In this illustration, there are 1.5 horizontal divisions between the two waveforms, as indicated, and the Sec/Div control is set at 10 μs. The period of these waveforms is 200 μs and the Δt is

$$\Delta t = 1.5 \text{ divisions} \times 10 \,\mu\text{s/division} = 15 \,\mu\text{s}$$

The phase angle is

$$\theta = \left(\frac{\Delta t}{T}\right)360° = \left(\frac{15 \,\mu\text{s}}{200 \,\mu\text{s}}\right)360° = 27°$$

$\Delta t = 1.5 \text{ divisions} \times 10 \,\mu\text{s/division} = 15 \,\mu\text{s}$

◀ FIGURE 10–42

Determining the phase angle on the oscilloscope.

SECTION 10–6 REVIEW

1. Determine the series equivalent circuit for the series-parallel circuit in Figure 10–38.
2. What is the voltage across R_1 in Figure 10–38?

10–7 Power in RC Circuits

In a purely resistive ac circuit, all of the energy delivered by the source is dissipated in the form of heat by the resistance. In a purely capacitive ac circuit, all of the energy delivered by the source is stored by the capacitor during a portion of the voltage cycle and then returned to the source during another portion of the cycle so that there is no net energy conversion to heat. When there is both resistance and capacitance, some of the energy is alternately stored and returned by the capacitance and some is dissipated by the resistance. The amount of energy converted to heat is determined by the relative values of the resistance and the capacitive reactance.

After completing this section, you should be able to

◆ **Determine power in RC circuits**

◆ Explain true and reactive power

◆ Draw the power triangle

◆ Define *power factor*

◆ Explain apparent power

◆ Calculate power in an RC circuit

When the resistance is greater than the capacitive reactance in a series RC circuit, more of the total energy delivered by the source is dissipated by the resistor than is stored by the capacitor. Likewise, when the reactance is greater than the resistance, more of the total energy is stored and returned than is converted to heat.

The formulas for the power dissipated in a resistor, sometimes called *true power* (P_{true}), and the power in a capacitor, called *reactive power* (P_r), are restated here. The unit of true power is the watt (W), and the unit of reactive power is the VAR (volt-ampere reactive).

Equation 10–26

$$P_{\text{true}} = I_{tot}^2 R$$

Equation 10–27

$$P_r = I_{tot}^2 X_C$$

The Power Triangle for RC Circuits

The generalized impedance phasor diagram for a series RC circuit is shown in Figure 10–43(a). A relationship for power can also be represented by a similar diagram because the respective magnitudes of the powers, P_{true} and P_r, differ from R and X_C by a factor of I_{tot}^2, as shown in Figure 10–43(b).

The resultant power, $I_{tot}^2 Z$, represents the **apparent power, P_a.** At any instant in time, P_a is the total power that appears to be transferred between the source and the RC circuit.

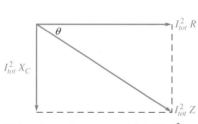

(a) Impedance phasors

(b) Impedance phasors are multiplied by I_{tot}^2 to get power

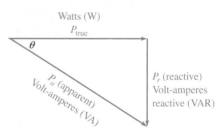

(c) Power triangle

▲ FIGURE 10–43

Development of the power triangle for a series RC circuit.

Part of the apparent power is true power, and part of it is reactive power. The unit of apparent power is the volt-ampere (VA). The expression for apparent power is

$$P_a = I_{tot}^2 Z$$

Equation 10–28

The diagram in Figure 10–43(b) can be rearranged in the form of a right triangle as shown in Figure 10–43(c), which is called the *power triangle*. Using the rules of trigonometry, P_{true} can be expressed as

$$P_{true} = P_a \cos \theta$$

Since P_a equals $I_{tot}^2 Z$ or $V_s I_{tot}$, the equation for true power can be written as

$$P_{true} = V_s I_{tot} \cos \theta$$

Equation 10–29

where V_s is the source voltage and I_{tot} is the total current.

For the case of a purely resistive circuit, $\theta = 0°$ and $\cos 0° = 1$, so P_{true} equals $V_s I_{tot}$. For the case of a purely capacitive circuit, $\theta = 90°$ and $\cos 90° = 0$, so P_{true} is zero. As you already know, there is no power dissipated in an ideal capacitor.

Power Factor

The term $\cos \theta$ is called the **power factor** and is stated as

$$PF = \cos \theta$$

Equation 10–30

As the phase angle between the source voltage and the total current increases, the power factor decreases, indicating an increasingly reactive circuit. The smaller the power factor, the smaller the power dissipation.

The power factor can vary from 0 for a purely reactive circuit to 1 for a purely resistive circuit. In an *RC* circuit, the power factor is referred to as a leading power factor because the current leads the voltage.

EXAMPLE 10–15

Determine the power factor and the true power in the *RC* circuit of Figure 10–44.

▶ FIGURE 10–44

Solution Calculate the capacitive reactance and phase angle.

$$X_C = \frac{1}{2\pi f C} = \frac{1}{2\pi(10 \text{ kHz})(0.0047 \text{ }\mu\text{F})} = 3.39 \text{ k}\Omega$$

$$\theta = \tan^{-1}\left(\frac{X_C}{R}\right) = \tan^{-1}\left(\frac{3.39 \text{ k}\Omega}{1.0 \text{ k}\Omega}\right) = 73.6°$$

The power factor is

$$PF = \cos \theta = \cos(73.6°) = \textbf{0.282}$$

The impedance is

$$Z = \sqrt{R^2 + X_C^2} = \sqrt{(1.0 \text{ k}\Omega)^2 + (3.39 \text{ k}\Omega)^2} = 3.53 \text{ k}\Omega$$

Therefore, the current is

$$I = \frac{V_s}{Z} = \frac{15 \text{ V}}{3.53 \text{ k}\Omega} = 4.25 \text{ mA}$$

The true power is

$$P_{\text{true}} = V_s I \cos \theta = (15 \text{ V})(4.25 \text{ mA})(0.282) = \textbf{18.0 mW}$$

Related Problem   What is the power factor if *f* is reduced by half in Figure 10–44?

 Open Multisim file E10-15 on your CD-ROM. Measure the current and compare to the calculated value. Measure the voltages across *R* and *C* at 10 kHz, 5 kHz, and 20 kHz. Explain your observations.

The Significance of Apparent Power

Apparent power is the power that *appears* to be transferred between the source and the load, and it consists of two components: a true power component and a reactive power component.

In all electrical and electronic systems, it is the true power that does the work. The reactive power is simply shuttled back and forth between the source and the load. Ideally, in terms of performing useful work, all of the power transferred to the load should be true power and none of it reactive power. However, in most practical situations the load has some reactance associated with it, and therefore you must deal with both power components.

For any reactive load, there are two components of the total current: the resistive component and the reactive component. If you consider only the true power (watts) in a load, you are dealing with only a portion of the total current that the load demands from a source. In order to have a realistic picture of the actual current that a load will draw, you must consider apparent power (in VA).

A source such as an ac generator can provide current to a load up to some maximum value. *If the load draws more than this maximum value, the source can be damaged.* Figure 10–45(a)

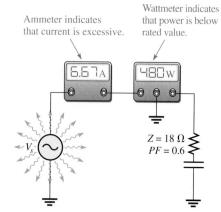

(a) Generator operating at its limits with a resistive load.

(b) Generator is in danger of internal damage due to excess current, even though the wattmeter indicates that the power is below the maximum wattage rating.

▲ FIGURE 10–45

The wattage rating of a source is inappropriate when the load is reactive. The rating should be in VA rather than in watts.

shows a 120 V generator that can deliver a maximum current of 5 A to a load. Assume that the generator is rated at 600 W and is connected to a purely resistive load of 24 Ω (power factor of 1). The ammeter shows that the current is 5 A, and the wattmeter indicates that the power is 600 W. The generator has no problem under these conditions, although it is operating at maximum current and power.

Now, consider what happens if the load is changed to a reactive one with an impedance of 18 Ω and a power factor of 0.6, as indicated in Figure 10–45(b). The current is 120 V/18 Ω = 6.67 A, which exceeds the maximum. Even though the wattmeter reads 480 W, which is less than the power rating of the generator, the excessive current probably will cause damage. This example shows that a true power rating can be deceiving and is inappropriate for ac sources. This particular ac generator should be rated at 600 VA, a rating the manufacturer would use, rather than 600 W.

EXAMPLE 10–16

For the circuit in Figure 10–46, find the true power, the reactive power, and the apparent power. X_C has been determined to be 2 kΩ.

▶ **FIGURE 10–46**

Solution First find the total impedance so that you can calculate the current.

$$Z_{tot} = \sqrt{R^2 + X_C^2} = \sqrt{(1.0\,\text{k}\Omega)^2 + (2\,\text{k}\Omega)^2} = 2.24\,\text{k}\Omega$$

$$I = \frac{V_s}{Z} = \frac{10\,\text{V}}{2.24\,\text{k}\Omega} = 4.46\,\text{mA}$$

The phase angle, θ, is

$$\theta = \tan^{-1}\left(\frac{X_C}{R}\right) = \tan^{-1}\left(\frac{2\,\text{k}\Omega}{1.0\,\text{k}\Omega}\right) = 63.4°$$

The true power is

$$P_{\text{true}} = V_s I \cos\theta = (10\,\text{V})(4.46\,\text{mA})\cos(63.4°) = \mathbf{20\,mW}$$

Note that the same result is realized if you use the formula $P_{\text{true}} = I^2R$.
The reactive power is

$$P_r = I^2 X_C = (4.46\,\text{mA})^2(2\,\text{k}\Omega) = \mathbf{39.8\,mVAR}$$

The apparent power is

$$P_a = I^2 Z = (4.46\,\text{mA})^2(2.24\,\text{k}\Omega) = \mathbf{44.6\,mVA}$$

The apparent power is also the phasor sum of P_{true} and P_r.

$$P_a = \sqrt{P_{\text{true}}^2 + P_r^2} = 44.6\,\text{mVA}$$

Related Problem What is the true power in Figure 10–46 if X_C = 10 kΩ?

SECTION 10–7 REVIEW

1. To which component in an *RC* circuit is the power dissipation due?
2. If the phase angle, θ, is 45°, what is the power factor?
3. A certain series *RC* circuit has the following parameter values: $R = 330\ \Omega$, $X_C = 460\ \Omega$, and $I = 2$ A. Determine the true power, the reactive power, and the apparent power.

10–8 BASIC APPLICATIONS

RC circuits are found in a variety of applications, often as part of a more complex circuit. Three applications are phase shift circuits applied to an oscillator, frequency-selective circuits (filters), and ac coupling.

After completing this section, you should be able to

◆ **Describe some basic *RC* applications**

  ◆ Discuss how the *RC* circuit is used in an oscillator

  ◆ Discuss how the *RC* circuit operates as a filter

  ◆ Discuss ac coupling

The Phase Shift Oscillator

As you know, a series *RC* circuit will shift the phase of the output voltage by an amount that depends on the values of *R* and *C* and the frequency of the signal. This ability to shift phase depending on frequency is vital in certain feedback oscillator circuits. An **oscillator** is a circuit that generates a periodic waveform and is an important circuit for many electronic systems. You will study oscillators in a devices course, so the focus here is on the application of *RC* circuits for shifting phase. The requirement is that a fraction of the output of the oscillator is returned to the input (called *feedback*) in the proper phase to reinforce the input and sustain oscillations. Generally, the requirement is to feed back the signal with a total of 180° of phase shift.

A single *RC* circuit is limited to phase shifts that are smaller than 90°. The basic *RC* lag circuit discussed in Section 10–3 can be "stacked" to form a complex *RC* network, as shown in Figure 10–47, which shows a specific circuit called a *phase shift oscillator*. The

▶ FIGURE 10–47

Phase shift oscillator.

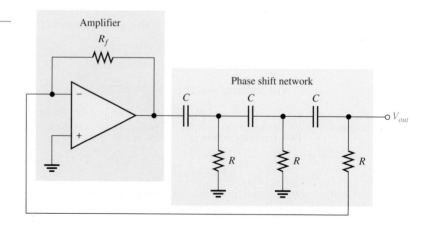

phase shift oscillator typically uses three equal-component *RC* circuits that produce the required 180° phase shift at a certain frequency, which will be the frequency at which the oscillator works. The output of the amplifier is phase shifted by the *RC* network and returned to the input of the amplifier, which provides sufficient gain to maintain oscillations.

The process of putting several *RC* circuits together results in a loading effect, so the overall phase shift is not the same as simply adding the phase shifts of the individual *RC* circuits. The detailed calculation for this circuit involves a lot of tedious phasor math, but the result is simple. With equal components, the frequency at which a 180° phase shift occurs is given by the following equation:

$$f_r = \frac{1}{2\pi\sqrt{6}RC}$$

It also turns out that the *RC* network attenuates (reduces) the signal from the amplifier by a factor of 29; the amplifier must make up for this attenuation by having a gain of −29 (the minus sign takes into account the phase shift).

EXAMPLE 10–17　　　　In Figure 10–48, calculate the output frequency.

▸ FIGURE 10–48

Solution　　$f_r = \dfrac{1}{2\pi\sqrt{6}RC} = \dfrac{1}{2\pi\sqrt{6}(15\text{ k}\Omega)(0.001\ \mu\text{F})} = 4.33\text{ kHz}$

Related Problem　　If all of the capacitors are changed to 0.0027 μF, what is the oscillator frequency?

The *RC* Circuit as a Filter

Frequency-selective circuits (filters) permit signals of certain frequencies to pass from the input to the output while blocking all others. That is, ideally all frequencies but the selected ones are filtered out.

Series *RC* circuits exhibit a frequency-selective characteristic. There are two types. The first one that we examine is a **low-pass circuit** that is realized by taking the output across the capacitor, just as in a lag circuit. The second type is a **high-pass circuit,** which is implemented by taking the output across the resistor, as in a lead circuit. In practice, *RC* circuits are used in conjunction with operational amplifiers to create active filters, which are much more effective than passive *RC* circuits.

Low-Pass Characteristic　　You have seen what happens to the phase angle and the output voltage in a series *RC* lag circuit. In terms of the filtering action of the series *RC* circuit, the variation in the magnitude of the output voltage as a function of frequency is important.

Figure 10–49 shows the filtering action of a series *RC* circuit using a specific series of measurements in which the frequency starts at 100 Hz and is increased in increments up to 20 kHz. At each value of frequency, the output voltage is measured. As you can see, the capacitive reactance decreases as frequency increases, thus dropping less voltage across the capacitor while the input voltage is held at a constant 10 V throughout each step. Table 10–1 summarizes the variation of the circuit parameters with frequency.

(a) $f = 0.1$ kHz, $X_C = 1.59$ kΩ, $V_{out} = 9.98$ V

(b) $f = 1$ kHz, $X_C = 159$ Ω, $V_{out} = 8.46$ V

(c) $f = 10$ kHz, $X_C = 15.9$ Ω, $V_{out} = 1.57$ V

(d) $f = 20$ kHz, $X_C = 7.96$ Ω, $V_{out} = 0.79$ V

▲ **FIGURE 10–49**

Example of low-pass filtering action. As frequency increases, V_{out} decreases.

▶ **TABLE 10–1**

f (kHz)	X_C (Ω)	Z_{tot} (Ω)	I (mA)	V_{out} (V)
0.1	1,590	≈1,590	≈6.29	9.98
1	159	188	53.2	8.46
10	15.9	101	99.0	1.57
20	7.96	≈100	≈100	0.79

The **frequency response** of the low-pass *RC* circuit in Figure 10–49 is shown in Figure 10–50, where the measured values are plotted on a graph of V_{out} versus f, and a smooth curve is drawn connecting the points. This graph, called a *response curve,* shows that the output voltage is greater at the lower frequencies and decreases as the frequency increases. The frequency scale is logarithmic.

High-Pass Characteristic   To illustrate *RC* high-pass filtering action, Figure 10–51 shows a series of specific measurements. The frequency starts at 10 Hz and is increased in increments up to 10 kHz. As you can see, the capacitive reactance decreases as the frequency increases, thus causing more of the total input voltage to be dropped across the resistor. Table 10–2 summarizes the variation of circuit parameters with frequency.

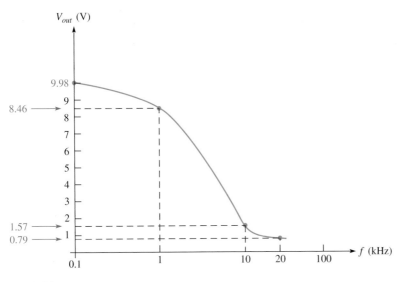

▲ FIGURE 10–50

Frequency response curve for the low-pass *RC* circuit in Figure 10–49.

(a) $f = 10$ Hz, $X_C = 15.9$ kΩ, $V_{out} = 0.063$ V

(b) $f = 100$ Hz, $X_C = 1.59$ kΩ, $V_{out} = 0.63$ V

(c) $f = 1$ kHz, $X_C = 159$ Ω, $V_{out} = 5.32$ V

(d) $f = 10$ kHz, $X_C = 15.9$ Ω, $V_{out} = 9.88$ V

▲ FIGURE 10–51

Example of high-pass filtering action. As frequency increases, V_{out} increases.

f (kHz)	X_C (Ω)	Z_{tot} (Ω)	I (mA)	V_{out} (V)
.01	15,900	≈15,900	0.629	0.063
.1	1590	1593	6.28	0.63
1	159	188	53.2	5.32
10	15.9	101	98.8	9.88

Frequency response curve for the high-pass *RC* circuit in Figure 10–51.

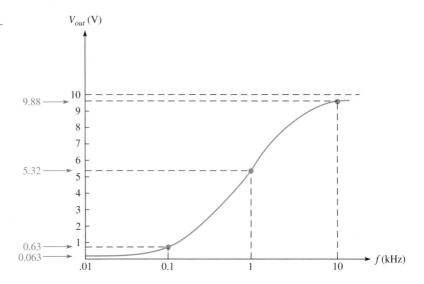

In Figure 10–52, the measured values for the high-pass *RC* circuit shown in Figure 10–51 have been plotted to produce a frequency response curve for this circuit. As you can see, the output voltage is greater at the higher frequencies and decreases as the frequency is reduced. The frequency scale is logarithmic.

The Cutoff Frequency and the Bandwidth of an RC Circuit The frequency at which the capacitive reactance equals the resistance in a low-pass or high-pass *RC* circuit is called the **cutoff frequency** and is designated f_c. This condition is expressed as $1/(2\pi f_c C) = R$. Solving for f_c results in the following formula:

Equation 10–31

$$f_c = \frac{1}{2\pi RC}$$

At f_c, the output voltage of the *RC* circuit is 70.7% of its maximum value. It is standard practice to consider the cutoff frequency as the limit of a circuit's performance in terms of passing or rejecting frequencies. For example, in a high-pass circuit, all frequencies above f_c are considered to be passed from the input to the output, and all those below f_c are considered to be rejected. The reverse is true for a low-pass circuit.

The range of frequencies that is considered to be passed from the input to the output of a circuit is called the **bandwidth**. Figure 10–53 illustrates the bandwidth and the cutoff frequency for a low-pass circuit.

Normalized general response curve of a low-pass *RC* circuit showing the cutoff frequency and the bandwidth.

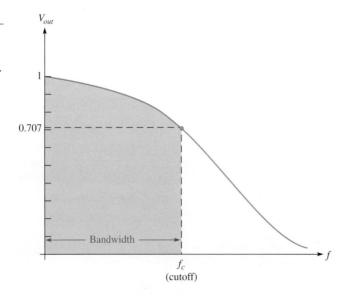

Coupling an AC Signal into a DC Bias Circuit

Figure 10–54 shows an *RC* circuit that is used to create a dc voltage level with an ac voltage superimposed on it. This type of circuit is commonly found in amplifiers in which the dc voltage is required to **bias** the amplifier to the proper operating point and the signal voltage to be amplified is coupled through a capacitor and superimposed on the dc level. The capacitor prevents the low internal resistance of the signal source from affecting the dc bias voltage.

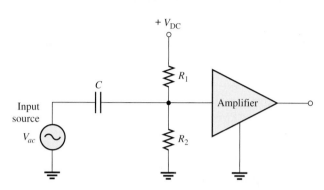

◀ FIGURE 10–54

Amplifier bias and signal-coupling circuit.

In this type of application, a relatively large value of capacitance is selected so that for the frequencies to be amplified, the reactance is very small compared to the resistance of the bias network. When the reactance is very small (ideally zero), there is practically no phase shift or signal voltage dropped across the capacitor. Therefore, all of the signal voltage passes from the source to the input to the amplifier.

Figure 10–55 illustrates the application of the superposition principle to the circuit in Figure 10–54. In part (a), the ac source has been effectively removed from the circuit and replaced with a short to represent its ideal internal resistance. Since *C* is open to dc, the voltage at point *A* is determined by the voltage-divider action of R_1 and R_2 and the dc voltage source.

(a) dc equivalent: ac source replaced by short. *C* is open to dc. R_1 and R_2 act as dc voltage divider.

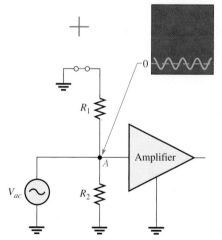

(b) ac equivalent: dc source is replaced by short. *C* is short to ac. All of V_{ac} is coupled to point *A*.

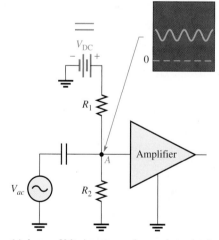

(c) dc + ac: Voltages are superimposed at point *A*.

▲ FIGURE 10–55

The superposition of dc and ac voltages in an *RC* bias and coupling circuit.

In Figure 10–55(b), the dc source has been effectively removed from the circuit and replaced with a short to represent its ideal internal resistance. Since *C* appears as a short at the frequency of the ac, the signal voltage is coupled directly to point *A* and appears across the parallel combination of R_1 and R_2. Figure 10–55(c) illustrates that the combined effect of the superposition of the dc and the ac voltages results in the signal voltage "riding" on the dc level.

10–9 TROUBLESHOOTING

Typical component failures or degradation have an effect on the response of basic *RC* circuits. The APM (analysis, planning, and measurement) method of troubleshooting can be used to locate problems in a circuit.

After completing this section, you should be able to

- ◆ **Troubleshoot *RC* circuits**
  - ◆ Find an open resistor
  - ◆ Find an open capacitor
  - ◆ Find a shorted capacitor
  - ◆ Find a leaky capacitor

Effect of an Open Resistor It is easy to see how an open resistor affects the operation of a basic series *RC* circuit, as shown in Figure 10–56. Obviously, there is no path for current, so the capacitor voltage remains at zero and the total voltage, V_s, appears across the open resistor.

Effect of an Open Capacitor When the capacitor is open, there is no current; thus, the resistor voltage drop is zero. The total source voltage appears across the open capacitor, as shown in Figure 10–57.

▲ FIGURE 10–56

Effect of an open resistor.

▲ FIGURE 10–57

Effect of an open capacitor.

Effect of a Shorted Capacitor When a capacitor shorts out, the voltage across it is zero, the current equals V_s/R, and the total voltage appears across the resistor, as shown in Figure 10–58.

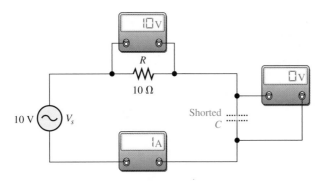

▲ FIGURE 10–58

Effect of a shorted capacitor.

Effect of a Leaky Capacitor When a capacitor exhibits a high leakage current, the leakage resistance effectively appears in parallel with the capacitor, as shown in Figure 10–59(a). When the leakage resistance is comparable in value to the circuit resistance, R, the circuit response is drastically affected. The circuit, looking from the capacitor toward the source, can be thevenized, as shown in Figure 10–59(b). The Thevenin equivalent resistance is R in parallel with R_{leak} (the source appears as a short), and the Thevenin equivalent voltage is determined by the voltage-divider action of R and R_{leak}.

$$R_{th} = R \| R_{leak} = \frac{RR_{leak}}{R + R_{leak}}$$

$$V_{th} = \left(\frac{R_{leak}}{R + R_{leak}}\right)V_{in}$$

As you can see, the voltage to which the capacitor will charge is reduced since $V_{th} < V_{in}$. Also, the current is increased. The Thevenin equivalent circuit is shown in Figure 10–59(c).

HANDS ON TIP

Some multimeters have a relatively low frequency response of 1 kHz or less, while others can measure voltages or currents with frequencies up to about 2 MHz. Always check to make sure that your meter is capable of making accurate measurements at the particular frequency you are working with.

(a)   (b)

(c)

▲ FIGURE 10–59

Effect of a leaky capacitor.

EXAMPLE 10–18

Assume that the capacitor in Figure 10–60 is degraded to a point where its leakage resistance is 10 kΩ. Determine the phase shift from input to output and the output voltage under the degraded condition.

▶ FIGURE 10–60

Solution   The effective circuit resistance is

$$R_{th} = \frac{RR_{leak}}{R + R_{leak}} = \frac{(4.7\,k\Omega)(10\,k\Omega)}{14.7\,k\Omega} = 3.2\,k\Omega$$

The phase lag is

$$\phi = 90° - \tan^{-1}\left(\frac{X_C}{R_{th}}\right) = 90° - \tan^{-1}\left(\frac{5\,k\Omega}{3.2\,k\Omega}\right) = \mathbf{32.6°}$$

To determine the output voltage, first calculate the Thevenin equivalent voltage.

$$V_{th} = \left(\frac{R_{leak}}{R + R_{leak}}\right)V_{in} = \left(\frac{10\,k\Omega}{14.7\,k\Omega}\right)10\,V = 6.80\,V$$

$$V_{out} = \left(\frac{X_C}{\sqrt{R_{th}^2 + X_C^2}}\right)V_{th} = \left(\frac{5\,k\Omega}{\sqrt{(3.2\,k\Omega)^2 + (5\,k\Omega)^2}}\right)6.8\,V = \mathbf{5.73\,V}$$

Related Problem   What would the output voltage be if the capacitor were not leaky?

Other Troubleshooting Considerations

When connecting protoboard circuits, always consistently use standard colors for universal connections such as signals, power supply voltage, and ground. For example, you can use green wires for signals, red wires for power supply voltage, and black wires for ground connections. This helps you identify wiring during connecting and troubleshooting.

Many times, the failure of a circuit to work properly is not the result of a faulty component. A loose wire, a bad contact, or a poor solder joint can cause an open circuit. A short can be caused by a wire clipping or solder splash. Things as simple as not plugging in a power supply or a function generator happen more often than you might think. Wrong values in a circuit (such as an incorrect resistor value), the function generator set at the wrong frequency, or the wrong output connected to the circuit can cause improper operation.

When you have problems with a circuit, always check to make sure that the instruments are properly connected to the circuits and to a power outlet. Also, look for obvious things such as a broken or loose contact, a connector that is not completely plugged in, or a piece of wire or a solder bridge that could be shorting something out.

The point is that you should consider all possibilities, not just faulty components, when a circuit is not working properly. The following example illustrates this approach with a simple circuit using the APM (analysis, planning, and measurement) method.

EXAMPLE 10–19

The circuit represented by the schematic in Figure 10–61 has no output voltage, which is the voltage across the capacitor. You expect to see about 7.4 V at the output. The circuit is physically constructed on a protoboard. Use your troubleshooting skills to find the problem.

▶ FIGURE 10–61

Solution   Apply the APM method to this troubleshooting problem.

Analysis: First think of the possible causes for the circuit to have no output voltage.

1. There is no source voltage or the frequency is so high that the capacitive reactance is almost zero.

2. There is a short between the output terminals. Either the capacitor could be internally shorted, or there could be some physical short.

3. There is an open between the source and the output. This would prevent current and thus cause the output voltage to be zero. The resistor could be open, or the conductive path could be open due to a broken or loose connecting wire or a bad protoboard contact.

4. There is an incorrect component value. The resistor could be so large that the current and, therefore, the output voltage are negligible. The capacitor could be so large that its reactance at the input frequency is near zero.

Planning: You decide to make some visual checks for problems such as the function generator power cord not plugged in or the frequency set at an incorrect value. Also, broken leads, shorted leads, as well as an incorrect resistor color code or capacitor label often can be found visually. If nothing is discovered after a visual check, then you will make voltage measurements to track down the cause of the problem. You decide to use a digital oscilloscope and a DMM to make the measurements.

Measurement: Assume that you find that the function generator is plugged in and the frequency setting appears to be correct. Also, you find no visible opens or shorts during your visual check, and the component values are correct.

The first step in the measurement process is to check the voltage from the source with the scope. Assume a 10 V rms sine wave with a frequency of 5 kHz is observed at the circuit input as shown in Figure 10–62(a). The correct voltage is present, so *the first possible cause has been eliminated.*

Next, check for a shorted capacitor by disconnecting the source and placing a DMM (set on the ohmmeter function) across the capacitor. If the capacitor is good, an open will be indicated by an OL (overload) in the meter display after a short charging time. Assume the capacitor checks okay, as shown in Figure 10–62(b). *The second possible cause has been eliminated.*

Since the voltage has been "lost" somewhere between the input and the output, you must now look for the voltage. You reconnect the source and measure the voltage across the resistor with the DMM (set on the voltmeter function) from one resistor lead to the other. The voltage across the resistor is zero. This means there is no current, which indicates an open somewhere in the circuit.

Now, you begin tracing the circuit back toward the source looking for the voltage (you could also start from the source and work forward). You can use either the scope or the DMM, but decide to use the multimeter with one lead connected to ground and the other used to probe the circuit. As shown in Figure 10–62(c), the

(a) Scope shows the correct voltage at the input.

(b) With function generator disconnected, the meter indicates the capacitor is not shorted.

(c) The voltage is found at point ③, indicating that one of the two used protoboard contacts in that row is bad.

▲ FIGURE 10–62

voltage on the right lead of the resistor, point ①, reads zero. Since you already have measured zero voltage across the resistor, the voltage on the left resistor lead at point ② must be zero as the meter indicates. Next, moving the meter probe to point ③, you read 10 V. You have found the voltage! Since there is zero volts on the left resistor lead, and there is 10 V at point ③, one of the two contacts in the protoboard hole into which the wire leads are inserted is bad. It could be that the small contacts were pushed in too far and were bent or broken so that the circuit lead does not make contact.

Move either or both the resistor lead and the wire to another hole in the same row. Assume that when the resistor lead is moved to the hole just above, you have voltage at the output of the circuit (across the capacitor).

Related Problem   Suppose you had measured 10 V across the resistor before the capacitor was checked. What would this have indicated?

SECTION 10–9 REVIEW

1. Describe the effect of a leaky capacitor on the dc response of an *RC* circuit.
2. In a series *RC* circuit, if all the applied voltage appears across the capacitor, what is the problem?
3. What faults can cause 0 V across the capacitor in a series *RC* circuit?

Application Assignment

PUTTING YOUR KNOWLEDGE TO WORK

In Chapter 9, you worked with the capacitively coupled input to an amplifier with voltage-divider bias. In this assignment, you will check the voltage of a similar amplifier's input circuit to determine how it changes with the frequency of the input signal. If too much voltage is dropped across the capacitor, the overall performance of the amplifier is adversely affected. To do this assignment, you do not have to be familiar with the details of the amplifier circuit but you should review the application assignment in Chapter 9 before proceeding.

As you learned in Chapter 9, the coupling capacitor (C_1) in Figure 10–63 passes the input signal voltage to the input of the amplifier (point *A* to point *B*) without affecting the dc level at point *B* produced by the resistive voltage divider (R_1 and R_2). If

the input frequency is high enough so that the reactance of the coupling capacitor is negligibly small, essentially no ac signal voltage is dropped across the capacitor. As the signal frequency is reduced, the capacitive reactance increases and more of the signal voltage is dropped across the capacitor. This lowers the output voltage of the amplifier.

The amount of signal voltage that is coupled from the input source (point *A*) to the amplifier input (point *B*) is determined by the values of the capacitor and the dc bias resistors (assuming the amplifier has no loading effect) in Figure 10–63. These components actually form a high-pass *RC* filter, as shown in Figure 10–64. The voltage-divider bias resistors are effectively in parallel with each other as far as the ac source is concerned. The lower end of R_2 goes to ground and the upper end of R_1 goes to the dc

▲ FIGURE 10–63

A capacitively coupled amplifier.

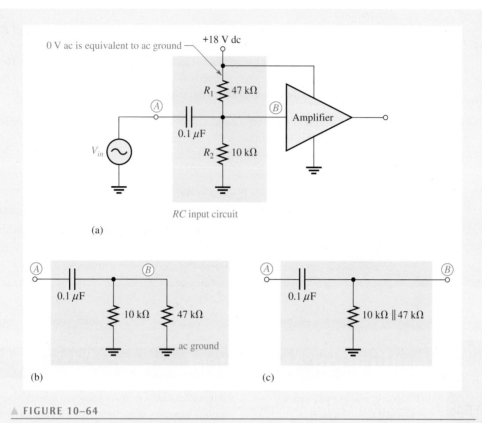

The *RC* input circuit acts effectively like a high-pass *RC* filter.

supply voltage as shown in Figure 10–64(a). Since there is no ac voltage at the +18 V dc terminal, the upper end of R_1 is at 0 V ac which is referred to as *ac ground*. The development of the circuit into an effective high-pass *RC* filter is shown in parts (b) and (c).

Step 1: Evaluating the Amplifier Input Circuit

Determine the value of the equivalent resistance of the input circuit. Assume the amplifier (shown inside the white dashed lines in Figure 10–65) has no loading effect on the input circuit.

▲ FIGURE 10–65

Measuring the input circuit response at frequency f_1. The channel 1 waveform is shown.

Step 2: Measuring the Response at Frequency f_1

Refer to Figure 10–65. The input signal voltage is applied to the amplifier circuit board and displayed on channel 1 of the oscilloscope, and channel 2 is connected to a point on the circuit board. Determine to what point on the circuit the channel 2 probe is connected, the frequency, and the voltage that should be displayed.

Step 3: Measuring the Response at Frequency f_2

Refer to Figure 10–66 and the circuit board in Figure 10–65. The input signal voltage displayed on channel 1 of the oscilloscope is applied to the amplifier circuit board. Determine the frequency and the voltage that should be displayed on channel 2.

State the difference between the channel 2 waveforms determined in Step 2 and Step 3. Explain the reason for the difference.

Step 4: Measuring the Response at Frequency f_3

Refer to Figure 10–67 and the circuit board in Figure 10–65. The input signal voltage displayed on channel 1 of the oscilloscope is applied to the amplifier circuit board. Determine the frequency and the voltage that should be displayed on channel 2.

State the difference between the channel 2 waveforms determined in Step 3 and Step 4. Explain the reason for the difference.

Step 5: Plotting a Response Curve

Determine the frequency at which the signal voltage at point B in Figure 10–63 is 70.7% of its maximum value. Plot the response curve using this voltage value and the values at frequencies f_1, f_2, and f_3. How does this curve show that the input circuit acts as a high-pass filter? What can you do to the circuit to lower the frequency at which the voltage is 70.7% of maximum without affecting the dc bias voltage?

Multisim Analysis

Using Multisim, connect the equivalent circuit in Figure 10–64(b).

1. Apply an input signal voltage at the same frequency and amplitude as shown in Figure 10–65. Measure the voltage at point B with the oscilloscope and compare the result from Step 2.

2. Apply an input signal voltage at the same frequency and amplitude as shown in Figure 10–66. Measure the voltage at point B with the oscilloscope and compare the result from Step 3.

3. Apply an input signal voltage at the same frequency and amplitude as shown in Figure 10–67. Measure the voltage at point B with the oscilloscope and compare the result from Step 4.

Review

1. Explain the effect on the response of the amplifier input circuit of reducing the value of the coupling capacitor.

2. What is the voltage at point B in Figure 10–63 if the coupling capacitor opens when the ac input signal is 10 mV rms?

3. What is the voltage at point B in Figure 10–63 if resistor R_1 is open when the ac input signal is 10 mV rms?

▲ FIGURE 10–66

Measuring the input circuit response at frequency f_2. The channel 1 waveform is shown.

▲ FIGURE 10–67

Measuring the input circuit response at frequency f_3. The channel 1 waveform is shown.

SUMMARY

◆ When a sinusoidal voltage is applied to an *RC* circuit, the current and all the voltage drops are also sine waves.

◆ Total current in a series or parallel *RC* circuit always leads the source voltage.

◆ The resistor voltage is always in phase with the current.

◆ The capacitor voltage always lags the current by 90°.

◆ In an *RC* circuit, the impedance is determined by both the resistance and the capacitive reactance combined.

◆ Impedance is expressed in units of ohms.

◆ The circuit phase angle is the angle between the total current and the source voltage.

◆ The impedance of a series *RC* circuit varies inversely with frequency.

◆ The phase angle (θ) of a series *RC* circuit varies inversely with frequency.

◆ In an *RC* lag circuit, the output voltage lags the input voltage in phase.

◆ In an *RC* lead circuit, the output voltage leads the input voltage.

◆ For each parallel *RC* circuit, there is an equivalent series circuit for any given frequency.

◆ The impedance of a circuit can be determined by measuring the source voltage and the total current and then applying Ohm's law.

◆ In an *RC* circuit, part of the power is resistive and part reactive.

◆ The phasor combination of resistive power (true power) and reactive power is called *apparent power.*

◆ Apparent power is expressed in volt-amperes (VA).

◆ The power factor (*PF*) indicates how much of the apparent power is true power.

◆ A power factor of 1 indicates a purely resistive circuit, and a power factor of 0 indicates a purely reactive circuit.

◆ In a circuit that exhibits frequency selectivity, certain frequencies are passed to the output while others are rejected.

KEY TERMS

Key terms and other bold terms in the chapter are defined in the end-of-book glossary.

Admittance (*Y*)   A measure of the ability of a reactive circuit to permit current; the reciprocal of impedance. The unit is the siemens (S).

Apparent power (*P$_a$*)   The phasor combination of resistive power (true power) and reactive power. The unit is the volt-ampere (VA).

Bandwidth   The range of frequencies that is considered to be passed from the input to the output of a circuit.

Capacitive susceptance (*B$_C$*)   The ability of a capacitor to permit current: the reciprocal of capacitive reactance. The unit is the siemens (S).

Cutoff frequency   The frequency at which the output voltage of a filter is 70.7% of the maximum output voltage.

Frequency response   In electric circuits, the variation in the output voltage (or current) over a specified range of frequencies.

Impedance (*Z*)   The total opposition to sinusoidal current expressed in ohms.

Phase angle   The angle between the source voltage and the total current in a reactive circuit.

Power factor   The relationship between volt-amperes and true power or watts. Volt-amperes multiplied by the power factor equals true power.

FORMULAS

10–1	$Z = \sqrt{R^2 + X_C^2}$	Series *RC* impedance
10–2	$\theta = \tan^{-1}\left(\dfrac{X_C}{R}\right)$	Series *RC* phase angle
10–3	$V = IZ$	Ohm's law
10–4	$I = \dfrac{V}{Z}$	Ohm's law

10–5 $Z = \dfrac{V}{I}$ Ohm's law

10–6 $V_s = \sqrt{V_R^2 + V_C^2}$ Total voltage in series RC circuits

10–7 $\theta = \tan^{-1}\left(\dfrac{V_C}{V_R}\right)$ Series RC phase angle

10–8 $\phi = 90° - \tan^{-1}\left(\dfrac{X_C}{R}\right)$ Phase angle of lag circuit

10–9 $V_{out} = \left(\dfrac{X_C}{\sqrt{R^2 + X_C^2}}\right)V_{in}$ Output voltage of lag circuit

10–10 $\phi = \tan^{-1}\left(\dfrac{X_C}{R}\right)$ Phase angle of lead circuit

10–11 $V_{out} = \left(\dfrac{R}{\sqrt{R^2 + X_C^2}}\right)V_{in}$ Output voltage of lead circuit

10–12 $Z = \dfrac{RX_C}{\sqrt{R^2 + X_C^2}}$ Parallel RC impedance

10–13 $\theta = \tan^{-1}\left(\dfrac{R}{X_C}\right)$ Parallel RC phase angle

10–14 $G = \dfrac{1}{R}$ Conductance

10–15 $B_C = \dfrac{1}{X_C}$ Capacitive susceptance

10–16 $Y = \dfrac{1}{Z}$ Admittance

10–17 $Y_{tot} = \sqrt{G^2 + B_C^2}$ Total admittance

10–18 $V = \dfrac{I}{Y}$ Ohm's law

10–19 $I = VY$ Ohm's law

10–20 $Y = \dfrac{I}{V}$ Ohm's law

10–21 $I_{tot} = \sqrt{I_R^2 + I_C^2}$ Total current in parallel RC circuits

10–22 $\theta = \tan^{-1}\left(\dfrac{I_C}{I_R}\right)$ Parallel RC phase angle

10–23 $R_{eq} = Z\cos\theta$ Equivalent series resistance

10–24 $X_{C(eq)} = Z\sin\theta$ Equivalent series reactance

10–25 $\theta = \left(\dfrac{\Delta t}{T}\right)360°$ Phase angle using time measurements

10–26 $P_{true} = I_{tot}^2 R$ True power (W)

10–27 $P_r = I_{tot}^2 X_C$ Reactive power (VAR)

10–28 $P_a = I_{tot}^2 Z$ Apparent power (VA)

10–29 $P_{true} = V_s I_{tot}\cos\theta$ True power

10–30 $PF = \cos\theta$ Power factor

10–31 $f_c = \dfrac{1}{2\pi RC}$ Cutoff frequency of an RC circuit

SELF-TEST

Answers are at the end of the chapter.

1. In a series RC circuit, the voltage across the resistance is

    (a) in phase with the source voltage   **(b)** lagging the source voltage by 90°

    (c) in phase with the current   **(d)** lagging the current by 90°

2. In a series *RC* circuit, the voltage across the capacitor is

   (a) in phase with the source voltage   **(b)** lagging the resistor voltage by 90°

   (c) in phase with the current   **(d)** lagging the source voltage by 90°

3. When the frequency of the voltage applied to a series *RC* circuit is increased, the impedance

   (a) increases   **(b)** decreases   **(c)** remains the same   **(d)** doubles

4. When the frequency of the voltage applied to a series *RC* circuit is decreased, the phase angle

   (a) increases   **(b)** decreases   **(c)** remains the same   **(d)** becomes erratic

5. In a series *RC* circuit when the frequency and the resistance are doubled, the impedance

   (a) doubles

   (b) is halved

   (c) is quadrupled

   (d) cannot be determined without values

6. In a series *RC* circuit, 10 V rms is measured across the resistor and 10 V rms is also measured across the capacitor. The rms source voltage is

   (a) 20 V   **(b)** 14.14 V   **(c)** 28.28 V   **(d)** 10 V

7. The voltages in Problem 6 are measured at a certain frequency. To make the resistor voltage greater than the capacitor voltage, the frequency

   (a) must be increased   **(b)** must be decreased

   (c) is held constant   **(d)** has no effect

8. When $R = X_C$, the phase angle is

   (a) 0°   **(b)** +90°   **(c)** −90°   **(d)** 45°

9. To decrease the phase angle below 45°, the following condition must exist:

   (a) $R = X_C$ **(b)** $R < X_C$ **(c)** $R > X_C$ **(d)** $R = 10X_C$

10. When the frequency of the source voltage is increased, the impedance of a parallel *RC* circuit

   (a) increases   **(b)** decreases   **(c)** does not change

11. In a parallel *RC* circuit, there is 1 A rms through the resistive branch and 1 A rms through the capacitive branch. The total rms current is

   (a) 1 A   **(b)** 2 A   **(c)** 2.28 A   **(d)** 1.414 A

12. A power factor of 1 indicates that the circuit phase angle is

   (a) 90°   **(b)** 45°   **(c)** 180°   **(d)** 0°

13. For a certain load, the true power is 100 W and the reactive power is 100 VAR. The apparent power is

   (a) 200 VA   **(b)** 100 VA   **(c)** 141.4 VA   **(d)** 141.4 W

14. Energy sources are normally rated in

   (a) watts   **(b)** volt-amperes   **(c)** volt-amperes reactive   **(d)** none of these

15. If the bandwidth of a certain low-pass filter is 1 kHz, the cutoff frequency is

   (a) 0 Hz   **(b)** 500 Hz   **(c)** 2 kHz   **(d)** 1000 Hz

TROUBLESHOOTING: SYMPTOM AND CAUSE

The purpose of these exercises is to help develop thought processes essential to troubleshooting. Answers are at the end of the chapter.

Determine the cause for each set of symptoms. Refer to Figure 10–68.

1. *Symptom:* The dc voltmeter reading is 0 V, and the ac voltmeter reading is 1.85 V.

   Cause:

   (a) *C* is shorted.

   (b) R_1 is open.

   (c) R_2 is open.

▲ FIGURE 10–68

The ac meters indicate the correct readings for this circuit.

2. *Symptom:* The dc voltmeter reading is 5.42 V, and the ac voltmeter reading is 0 V.

   Cause:

   (a) *C* is shorted.

   (b) *C* is open.

   (c) A resistor is open.

3. *Symptom:* The dc voltmeter reading is approximately 0 V, and the ac voltmeter reading is 2 V.

   Cause:

   (a) *C* is shorted.

   (b) *C* is open.

   (c) R_1 is shorted.

4. *Symptom:* The dc voltmeter reading is 10 V, and the ac voltmeter reading is 0 V.

   Cause:

   (a) *C* is open.

   (b) *C* is shorted.

   (c) R_1 is shorted.

5. *Symptom:* The dc voltmeter reading is 10 V, and the ac voltmeter reading is 1.8 V.

   Cause:

   (a) R_1 is shorted.

   (b) R_2 is open.

   (c) *C* is shorted.

PROBLEMS

Answers to odd-numbered problems are at the end of the book.

BASIC PROBLEMS

SECTION 10–1   Sinusoidal Response of *RC* Circuits

1. An 8 kHz sinusoidal voltage is applied to a series *RC* circuit. What is the frequency of the voltage across the resistor? Across the capacitor?

2. What is the waveshape of the current in the circuit of Problem 1?

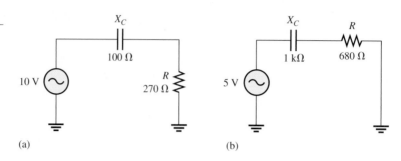

(a)   (b)

SECTION 10–2   Impedance and Phase Angle of Series *RC* Circuits

3. Find the impedance of each circuit in Figure 10–69.

4. Determine the impedance and the phase angle in each circuit in Figure 10–70.

(a)   (b)

▲ FIGURE 10–70

5. For the circuit of Figure 10–71, determine the impedance for each of the following frequencies:

    (a) 100 Hz   (b) 500 Hz   (c) 1 kHz   (d) 2.5 kHz

6. Repeat Problem 5 for $C = 0.0047 \ \mu F$.

▶ FIGURE 10–71

SECTION 10–3   Analysis of Series *RC* Circuits

7. Calculate the total current in each circuit of Figure 10–69.

8. Repeat Problem 7 for the circuits in Figure 10–70.

9. For the circuit in Figure 10–72, draw the phasor diagram showing all voltages and the total current. Indicate the phase angles.

10. For the circuit in Figure 10–73, determine the following:

    (a) Z (b) I (c) V_R (d) V_C

▲ FIGURE 10–72

▲ FIGURE 10–73

11. To what value must the rheostat be set in Figure 10–74 to make the total current 10 mA? What is the resulting phase angle?

▶ FIGURE 10–74

12. For the lag circuit in Figure 10–75, determine the phase lag between the input voltage and the output voltage for each of the following frequencies:

    (a) 1 Hz   **(b)** 100 Hz   **(c)** 1 kHz   **(d)** 10 kHz

13. Repeat Problem 12 for the lead circuit in Figure 10–76.

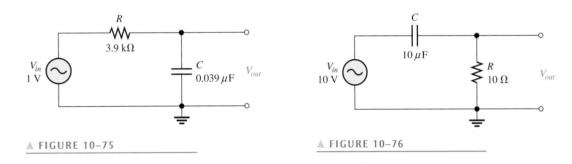

▲ FIGURE 10–75   ▲ FIGURE 10–76

SECTION 10–4   **Impedance and Phase Angle of Parallel *RC* Circuits**

14. Determine the impedance for the circuit in Figure 10–77.

15. Determine the impedance and the phase angle in Figure 10–78.

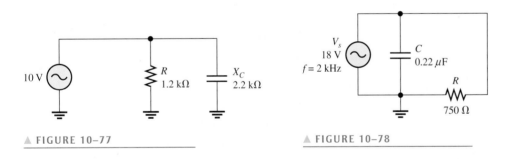

▲ FIGURE 10–77   ▲ FIGURE 10–78

16. Repeat Problem 15 for the following frequencies:

    (a) 1.5 kHz   **(b)** 3 kHz   **(c)** 5 kHz   **(d)** 10 kHz

17. Determine the impedance and phase angle in Figure 10–79.

▶ FIGURE 10–79

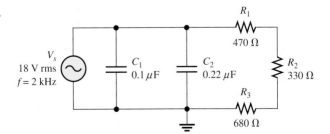

SECTION 10–5 **Analysis of Parallel *RC* Circuits**

18. For the circuit in Figure 10–80, find all the currents and voltages.

19. For the parallel circuit in Figure 10–81, find each branch current and the total current. What is the phase angle between the source voltage and the total current?

▲ FIGURE 10–80

▲ FIGURE 10–81

20. For the circuit in Figure 10–82, determine the following:

    (a) Z (b) I_R (c) I_C (d) I_{tot} (e) θ

21. Repeat Problem 20 for $R = 4.7\ \text{k}\Omega$, $C = 0.047\ \mu\text{F}$, and $f = 500\ \text{Hz}$.

22. Convert the circuit in Figure 10–83 to an equivalent series form.

▲ FIGURE 10–82

▲ FIGURE 10–83

SECTION 10–6 **Analysis of Series-Parallel *RC* Circuits**

23. Determine the voltages across each element in Figure 10–84. Find the phase angle of the circuit.

24. Is the circuit in Figure 10–84 predominantly resistive or predominantly capacitive?

25. Find the current through each branch and the total current in Figure 10–84.

26. For the circuit in Figure 10–85, determine the following:

    (a) I_{tot} (b) θ (c) V_{R1} (d) V_{R2} (e) V_{R3} (f) V_C

▲ FIGURE 10–84

▲ FIGURE 10–85

SECTION 10–7 **Power in *RC* Circuits**

27. In a certain series *RC* circuit, the true power is 2 W, and the reactive power is 3.5 VAR. Determine the apparent power.

28. In Figure 10–73, what is the true power and the reactive power?

29. What is the power factor for the circuit of Figure 10–83?

30. Determine P_{true}, P_r, P_a, and *PF* for the circuit in Figure 10–85. Draw the power triangle.

SECTION 10–8 **Basic Applications**

31. The lag circuit in Figure 10–75 also acts as a low-pass filter. Draw a response curve for this circuit by plotting the output voltage versus frequency for 0 Hz to 10 kHz in 1 kHz increments.

32. Plot the frequency response curve for the circuit in Figure 10–76 for a frequency range of 0 Hz to 10 kHz in 1 kHz increments.

33. Draw the voltage phasor diagram for each circuit in Figures 10–75 and 10–76 for a frequency of 5 kHz with V_{in} = 1 V rms.

34. The rms value of the signal voltage out of amplifier *A* in Figure 10–86 is 50 mV. If the input resistance to amplifier *B* is 10 kΩ, how much of the signal is lost due to the coupling capacitor (C_c) when the frequency is 3 kHz?

▲ FIGURE 10–86

35. Determine the cutoff frequency for each circuit in Figures 10–75 and 10–76.

36. Determine the bandwidth of the circuit in Figure 10–75.

SECTION 10–9 **Troubleshooting**

37. Assume that the capacitor in Figure 10–87 is excessively leaky. Show how this degradation affects the output voltage and phase angle, assuming that the leakage resistance is 5 kΩ and the frequency is 10 Hz.

▲ FIGURE 10–87

(a)

(b)

▲ FIGURE 10–88

38. Each of the capacitors in Figure 10–88 has developed a leakage resistance of 2 kΩ. Determine the output voltages under this condition for each circuit.

39. Determine the output voltage for the circuit in Figure 10–88(a) for each of the following failure modes, and compare it to the correct output:

    (a) R_1 open   **(b)** R_2 open   **(c)** C open   **(d)** C shorted

40. Determine the output voltage for the circuit in Figure 10–88(b) for each of the following failure modes, and compare it to the correct output:

    (a) C open   **(b)** C shorted   **(c)** R_1 open   **(d)** R_2 open   **(e)** R_3 open

ADVANCED PROBLEMS

41. A single 220 V, 60 Hz source drives two loads. Load A has an impedance of 50 Ω and a power factor of 0.85. Load B has an impedance of 72 Ω and a power factor of 0.95.

    (a) How much current does each load draw?

    (b) What is the reactive power in each load?

    (c) What is the true power in each load?

    (d) What is the apparent power in each load?

    (e) Which load has more voltage drop along the lines connecting it to the source?

42. What value of coupling capacitor is required in Figure 10–89 so that the signal voltage at the input of amplifier 2 is at least 70.7% of the signal voltage at the output of amplifier 1 when the frequency is 20 Hz? Disregard the input resistance of the amplifier.

▶ FIGURE 10–89

43. Determine the value of R_1 required to get a phase angle of 30° between the source voltage and the total current in Figure 10–90.

44. Draw the voltage and current phasor diagram for Figure 10–91.

▲ FIGURE 10–90

▲ FIGURE 10–91

45. A certain load dissipates 1.5 kW of power with an impedance of 12 Ω and a power factor of 0.75. What is its reactive power? What is its apparent power?

46. Determine the series element or elements that are in the block of Figure 10–92 to meet the following overall circuit requirements:

    (a) $P_{true} = 400\,\text{W}$ **(b)** leading power factor (I_{tot} leads V_s)

47. Determine the value of C_2 in Figure 10–93 when $V_A = V_B$.

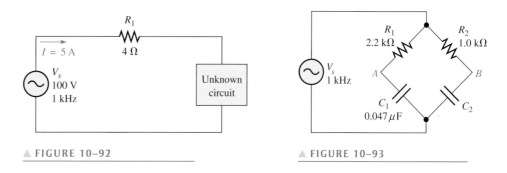

▲ FIGURE 10–92	▲ FIGURE 10–93

48. Draw the schematic for the circuit in Figure 10–94 and determine if the waveform on the scope is correct. If there is a fault in the circuit, identify it.

(a) Oscilloscope display

(b) Circuit with leads connected

▲ FIGURE 10–94

MULTISIM TROUBLESHOOTING PROBLEMS

49. Open file P10-49. Determine if there is a fault and, if so, identify it.

50. Open file P10-50. Determine if there is a fault and, if so, identify it.

51. Open file P10-51. Determine if there is a fault and, if so, identify it.

52. Open file P10-52. Determine if there is a fault and, if so, identify it.

53. Open file P10-53. Determine if there is a fault and, if so, identify it.

54. Open file P10-54. Determine if there is a fault and, if so, identify it.

ANSWERS

SECTION REVIEWS

SECTION 10–1   Sinusoidal Response of *RC* Circuits

1. V_C frequency is 60 Hz, I frequency is 60 Hz.

2. The capacitive reactance and resistance

3. θ is closer to 0° when $R > X_C$.

SECTION 10–2 **Impedance and Phase Angle of Series *RC* Circuits**

1. Impedance is the opposition to sinusoidal current.

2. V_s lags I.

3. The capacitive reactance produces the phase angle.

4. $Z = \sqrt{R^2 + X_C^2} = 59.9\,\text{k}\Omega; \theta = \tan^{-1}(X_C/R) = 56.6°$

SECTION 10–3 **Analysis of Series *RC* Circuits**

1. $V_s = \sqrt{V_R^2 + V_C^2} = 7.2\,\text{V}$

2. $\theta = \tan^{-1}(V_C/V_R) = 56.3°\text{s}$

3. $\theta = 90°$

4. **(a)** X_C decreases when f increases.

   (b) Z decreases when f increases.

   (c) θ decreases when f increases.

5. $\phi = 90° - \tan^{-1}(X_C/R) = 62.8°$

6. $V_{out} = (R/\sqrt{R^2 + X_C^2})V_{in} = 8.9\,\text{V rms}$

SECTION 10–4 **Impedance and Phase Angle of Parallel *RC* Circuits**

1. $Z = RX_C/\sqrt{R^2 + X_C^2} = 545\,\Omega$

2. *Conductance* is the reciprocal of resistance; *capacitive susceptance* is the reciprocal of capacitive reactance; and *admittance* is the reciprocal of impedance.

3. $Y = 1/Z = 10\,\text{mS}$

4. $Y = \sqrt{G^2 + B_C^2} = 24\,\text{mS}$

SECTION 10–5 **Analysis of Parallel *RC* Circuits**

1. $I_{tot} = V_s Y = 21\,\text{mA}$

2. $\theta = \tan^{-1}(I_C/I_R) = 56.3°; I_{tot} = \sqrt{I_R^2 + I_C^2} = 18\,\text{mA}$

3. $\theta = 90°$

SECTION 10–6 **Analysis of Series-Parallel *RC* Circuits**

1. See Figure 10–95.

2. $V_1 = I_{tot} R_1 = 6.71\,\text{V}$

▶ FIGURE 10–95

SECTION 10–7 **Power in *RC* Circuits**

1. Power dissipation is due to the resistance.

2. $PF = \cos 45° = 0.707$

3. $P_{true} = I_{tot}^2 R = 1.32\,\text{kW}; P_r = I_{tot}^2 X_C = 1.84\,\text{kVAR}; P_a = I_{tot}^2 Z = 2.26\,\text{kVA}$

SECTION 10–8 **Basic Applications**

1. $180°$

2. Output is across the capacitor.

SECTION 10–9 Troubleshooting

1. The leakage resistance acts in parallel with C, which alters the circuit time constant.

2. The capacitor is open.

3. A shorted capacitor, open resistor, no source voltage, or open contact can cause 0 V across the capacitor.

Application Assignment

1. A lower value coupling capacitor will increase the frequency at which a significant drop in voltage occurs.

2. $V_B = 3.16$ V dc

3. $V_B = 10$ mV rms

RELATED PROBLEMS FOR EXAMPLES

10–1 $2.42\,\text{k}\Omega; 65.6°$

10–2 2.56 V

10–3 65.5°

10–4 7.14 V

10–5 $15.9\,\text{k}\Omega; 86.4°$

10–6 Phase lag ϕ increases.

10–7 Output voltage decreases.

10–8 Phase lead ϕ decreases; output voltage increases.

10–9 24.3 Ω

10–10 4.60 mS

10–11 6.16 mA

10–12 117 mA; 31°

10–13 $R_{eq} = 8.99\,\text{k}\Omega; X_{C(eq)} = 4.38\,\text{k}\Omega$

10–14 $V_1 = 7.04$ V; $V_2 = 3.21$ V

10–15 0.146

10–16 990 μW

10–17 1.60 kHz

10–18 7.29 V

10–19 Resistor open

SELF-TEST

1. (c)	2. (b)	3. (b)	4. (a)	5. (d)
6. (b)	7. (a)	8. (d)	9. (c)	10. (b)
11. (d)	12. (d)	13. (c)	14. (b)	15. (d)

TROUBLESHOOTING: SYMPTOM AND CAUSE

1. (b)	2. (b)	3. (a)
4. (c)	5. (b)	

11

INDUCTORS

CHAPTER OBJECTIVES

◆ Describe the basic structure and characteristics of an inductor

◆ Discuss various types of inductors

 Analyze series and parallel inductors

 Analyze inductive dc switching circuits

 Analyze inductive ac circuits

 Discuss some inductor applications

KEY TERMS

Inductor   ◆ Faraday's law
Winding   ◆ Lenz's law
◆ Coil   ◆ *RL* time constant
◆ Induced voltage   ◆ Exponential
◆ Inductance (*L*)   ◆ Inductive reactance
◆ Henry (H)   ◆ Quality factor (*Q*)
◆ Winding resistance

APPLICATION ASSIGNMENT PREVIEW

While working on a piece of defective communications equipment, you are asked to check out the unmarked coils that have been removed from the system and determine their approximate inductance value by measuring the time constant. After studying this chapter, you should be able to complete the application assignment.

VISIT THE COMPANION WEBSITE

Study aids for this chapter are available at
http://www.prenhall.com/floyd

INTRODUCTION

Inductance is the property of a coil of wire that opposes a change in current. The basis for inductance is the electromagnetic field that surrounds any conductor when there is current through it. The electrical component designed to have the property of inductance is called an *inductor* or *coil*. Both of these terms refer to the same type of device.

 In this chapter, you will study the basic inductor and its characteristics. Various types of inductors are covered in terms of their physical construction and their electrical properties. The basic behavior of inductors in both dc and ac circuits is discussed, and series and parallel combinations are analyzed.

11–1 THE BASIC INDUCTOR

An **inductor** is a passive electrical component formed by a coil of wire and which exhibits the property of inductance.

After completing this section, you should be able to

◆ **Describe the basic structure and characteristics of an inductor**

  ◆ Define *inductance* and state its unit

  ◆ Discuss induced voltage

  ◆ Explain how an inductor stores energy

  ◆ Specify how the physical characteristics affect inductance

  ◆ Discuss winding resistance and winding capacitance

  ◆ State Faraday's law

  ◆ State Lenz's law

◀ FIGURE 11–1

Current through a coil creates a three-dimensional electromagnetic field. The resistor limits the current.

When a length of wire is formed into a coil, as shown in Figure 11–1, it becomes an inductor. Current through the coil produces an electromagnetic field. The magnetic lines of force around each loop (turn) in the **winding** of the coil effectively add to the lines of force around the adjoining loops, forming a strong magnetic field within and around the coil, as shown. The net direction of the total magnetic field creates a north and a south pole. A schematic symbol for the inductor is shown in Figure 11–2.

L

▲ FIGURE 11–2

Symbol for an inductor.

Inductance

When there is current through an inductor, an electromagnetic field is established. When the current changes, the electromagnetic field also changes. An increase in current expands the field, and a decrease in current reduces it. Therefore, a changing current produces a changing electromagnetic field around the inductor (also known as **coil** and in some applications, **choke**). In turn, the changing electromagnetic field causes an **induced voltage** across the coil in a direction to oppose the change in current. This property is called *self-inductance* but is usually referred to as simply *inductance,* symbolized by *L.*

> **Inductance is a measure of a coil's ability to establish an induced voltage as a result of a change in its current, and that induced voltage is in a direction to oppose that change in current.**

The Unit of Inductance   The **henry**, symbolized by H, is the basic unit of inductance. By definition, the inductance of a coil is one henry when current through the coil, changing at the rate of one ampere per second, induces one volt across the coil. The henry is a large unit, so in practical applications, millihenries (mH) and microhenries (μH) are the more common units.

Energy Storage   An inductor stores energy in the magnetic field created by the current. The energy stored is expressed as

Equation 11–1

$$W = \frac{1}{2}LI^2$$

As you can see, the energy stored is proportional to the inductance and the square of the current. When current (I) is in amperes and inductance (L) is in henries, the energy (W) is in joules.

Physical Characteristics of an Inductor

The following characteristics are important in establishing the inductance of a coil: the permeability of the core material, the number of turns of wire, the core length, and the cross-sectional area of the core.

Core Material   As discussed earlier, an inductor is basically a coil of wire. The material around which the coil is formed is called the **core.** Coils are wound on either non-magnetic or magnetic materials. Examples of nonmagnetic materials are air, wood, copper, plastic, and glass. The permeabilities of these materials are the same as for a vacuum. Examples of magnetic materials are iron, nickel, steel, cobalt, or alloys. These materials have permeabilities that are hundreds or thousands of times greater than that of a vacuum and are classified as *ferromagnetic*. A ferromagnetic core provides a lower reluctance path for the magnetic lines of force and thus permits a stronger magnetic field.

As you learned in Chapter 7, the permeability (μ) of the core material determines how easily a magnetic field can be established. The inductance is directly proportional to the permeability of the core material.

Physical Parameters   As indicated in Figure 11–3, the number of turns of wire, the length, and the cross-sectional area of the core are factors in setting the value of inductance. The inductance is inversely proportional to the length of the core and directly proportional to the cross-sectional area. Also, the inductance is directly related to the number of turns squared. This relationship is as follows:

Equation 11–2

$$L = \frac{N^2 \mu A}{l}$$

where L is the inductance in henries (H), N is the number of turns, μ is the permeability in henries per meter (H/m), A is the cross-sectional area in meters squared (m²), and l is the core length in meters (m).

BIOGRAPHY

Joseph Henry
1797–1878

Henry began his career as a professor at a small school in Albany, NY, and later became the first director of the Smithsonian Institution. He was the first American since Franklin to undertake original scientific experiments. He was the first to superimpose coils of wire wrapped on an iron core and first observed the effects of electromagnetic induction in 1830, a year before Faraday, but he did not publish his findings. Henry did obtain credit for the discovery of self-induction, however. The unit of inductance is named in his honor. (Photo credit: Courtesy of the Smithsonian Institution. Photo number 52,054.)

▶ FIGURE 11–3

Factors that determine the inductance of a coil.

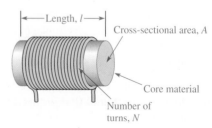

EXAMPLE 11–1

Determine the inductance of the coil in Figure 11–4. The permeability of the core is 0.25×10^{-3} H/m.

▶ FIGURE 11–4

1.5 cm

0.5 cm

$N = 350$

Solution   1 cm = 0.01 m. Therefore, 1.5 cm = 0.015 m and 0.5 cm = 0.005 m.

$$A = \pi r^2 = \pi (0.25 \times 10^{-2}\,\text{m})^2 = 1.96 \times 10^{-5}\,\text{m}^2$$

$$L = \frac{N^2 \mu A}{l} = \frac{(350)^2 (0.25 \times 10^{-3}\,\text{H/m})(1.96 \times 10^{-5}\,\text{m}^2)}{0.015\,\text{m}} = \textbf{40 mH}$$

Related Problem*   Determine the inductance of a coil with 400 turns on a core that is 2 cm long and has a diameter of 1 cm. The permeability is 0.25×10^{-3} H/m.

*Answers are at the end of the chapter.

Winding Resistance

When a coil is made of a certain material (for example, insulated copper wire), that wire has a certain resistance per unit of length. When many turns of wire are used to construct a coil, the total resistance may be significant. This inherent resistance is called the *dc resistance* or the **winding resistance (R_W)**.

Although this resistance is distributed along the length of the wire, as shown in Figure 11–5(a), it is sometimes indicated in a schematic as resistance appearing in series with the inductance of the coil, as shown in Figure 11–5(b). In many applications, the winding resistance can be ignored and the coil can be considered an ideal inductor. In other cases, the resistance must be considered.

(a) The wire has resistance distributed along its length.

R_W L

(b) Equivalent circuit

▲ FIGURE 11–5

Winding resistance of a coil.

Winding Capacitance

When two conductors are placed side by side, there is always some capacitance between them. Thus, when many turns of wire are placed close together in a coil, a certain amount of stray capacitance, called *winding capacitance (C_W)*, is a natural side effect. In many applications, this winding capacitance is very small and has no significant effect. In other cases, particularly at high frequencies, it may become quite important.

SAFETY POINT

Be careful when working with inductors because high induced voltages can be developed due to a rapidly changing magnetic field. This occurs when the current is interrupted or its value abruptly changed.

The equivalent circuit for an inductor with both its winding resistance (R_W) and its winding capacitance (C_W) is shown in Figure 11–6. The capacitance effectively acts in parallel. The total of the stray capacitances between each loop of the winding is indicated in a schematic as a capacitance appearing in parallel with the coil and its winding resistance, as shown in Figure 11–6(b).

(a) Stray capacitance between each loop appears as a total parallel capacitance (C_W).

(b) Equivalent circuit

▲ FIGURE 11–6

Winding capacitance of a coil.

Review of Faraday's Law

Faraday's law was introduced in Chapter 7 and is reviewed here because of its importance in the study of inductors. Faraday found that by moving a magnet through a coil of wire, a voltage was induced across the coil, and that when a complete path was provided, the induced voltage caused an induced current. He observed that

> **The amount of voltage induced in a coil is directly proportional to the rate of change of the magnetic field with respect to the coil.**

This principle is illustrated in Figure 11–7, where a bar magnet is moved through a coil of wire. An induced voltage is indicated by the voltmeter connected across the coil. The faster the magnet is moved, the greater the induced voltage.

▶ FIGURE 11–7

Induced voltage is created by a changing magnetic field.

When a wire is formed into a certain number of loops or turns and is exposed to a changing magnetic field, a voltage is induced across the coil. The induced voltage is proportional to the number of turns, N, of the wire in the coil and to the rate at which the magnetic field changes.

Lenz's Law

Lenz's law, also introduced in Chapter 7, adds to Faraday's law by defining the direction of induced voltage.

> **When the current through a coil changes and an induced voltage is created as a result of the changing magnetic field, the direction of the induced voltage is such that it always opposes the change in current.**

Figure 11–8 illustrates Lenz's law. In part (a), the current is constant and is limited by R_1. There is no induced voltage because the magnetic field is unchanging. In part (b), the switch suddenly is closed, placing R_2 in parallel with R_1 and thus reducing the resistance. Naturally, the current tries to increase and the magnetic field begins to expand, but the induced voltage opposes this attempted increase in current for an instant.

In Figure 11–8(c), the induced voltage gradually decreases, allowing the current to increase. In part (d), the current has reached a constant value as determined by the parallel

(a) Switch open: Constant current and constant magnetic field; no induced voltage.

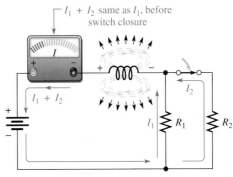

(b) At instant of switch closure: Expanding magnetic field induces voltage, which opposes an increase in total current. The total current remains the same at this instant.

(c) Right after switch closure: The rate of expansion of the magnetic field decreases, allowing the current to increase exponentially as induced voltage decreases.

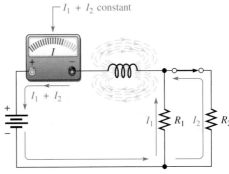

(d) Switch remains closed: Current and magnetic field reach constant value.

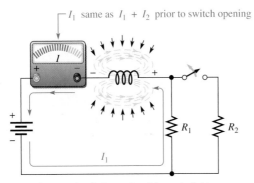

(e) At instant of switch opening: Magnetic field begins to collapse, creating an induced voltage, which opposes a decrease in current.

(f) After switch opening: Rate of collapse of magnetic field decreases, allowing current to decrease exponentially back to original value.

▲ FIGURE 11–8

Demonstration of Lenz's law in an inductive circuit: When the current tries to change suddenly, the electromagnetic field changes and induces a voltage in a direction that opposes that change in current.

resistors, and the induced voltage is zero. In part (e), the switch has been suddenly opened, and, for an instant, the induced voltage prevents any decrease in current. In part (f), the induced voltage gradually decreases, allowing the current to decrease back to a value determined by R_1. Notice that the induced voltage has a polarity that opposes any current change. The polarity of the induced voltage is opposite that of the battery voltage for an increase in current and aids the battery voltage for a decrease in current.

SECTION 11–1
REVIEW
Answers are at the end of the chapter.
	1. List the parameters that contribute to the inductance of a coil.
	2. Describe what happens to L when
	  (a) N is increased
	  (b) the core length is increased
	  (c) the cross-sectional area of the core is decreased
	  (d) a ferromagnetic core is replaced by an air core
	3. Explain why inductors have some winding resistance.
	4. Explain why inductors have some winding capacitance.

11–2 TYPES OF INDUCTORS

Inductors normally are classified according to the type of core material.

After completing this section, you should be able to

- ◆ **Discuss various types of inductors**
  - ◆ Describe the basic types of fixed inductors
  - ◆ Distinguish between fixed and variable inductors

HANDS ON TIP

When breadboarding circuits that include small inductors, it is best to use encapsulated inductors for structural strength. Inductors generally have extremely fine coil wire that is connected to a much larger size of lead wires.

In unencapsulated inductors, these contact points are very vulnerable to breaking if the inductor is frequently inserted and removed from a protoboard.

Inductors are made in a variety of shapes and sizes. Basically, they fall into two general categories: fixed and variable. The standard schematic symbols are shown in Figure 11–9.

Both fixed and variable inductors can be classified according to the type of core material. Three common types are the air core, the iron core, and the ferrite core. Each has a unique symbol, as shown in Figure 11–10.

(a) Fixed   (b) Variable

▲ FIGURE 11–9

Symbols for fixed and variable inductors.

(a) Air core   (b) Iron core   (c) Ferrite core

▲ FIGURE 11–10

Inductor symbols.

Adjustable (variable) inductors usually have a screw-type adjustment that moves a sliding core in and out, thus changing the inductance. A wide variety of inductors exists, and some are shown in Figure 11–11. Small fixed inductors are usually encapsulated in an insulating material that protects the fine wire in the coil. Encapsulated inductors have an appearance similar to a small resistor.

Typical inductors.

SECTION 11–2 REVIEW	1. Name two general categories of inductors. 2. Identify the inductor symbols in Figure 11–12.

FIGURE 11–12

(a) (b) (c)

11–3 SERIES AND PARALLEL INDUCTORS

When inductors are connected in series, the total inductance increases. When inductors are connected in parallel, the total inductance decreases.

After completing this section, you should be able to

- ◆ **Analyze series and parallel inductors**
  - ◆ Determine total series inductance
  - ◆ Determine total parallel inductance

Total Series Inductance

When inductors are connected in series, as in Figure 11–13, the total inductance, L_T, is the sum of the individual inductances. The formula for L_T is expressed in the following equation for the general case of n inductors in series:

$$L_T = L_1 + L_2 + L_3 + \cdots + L_n$$

Equation 11–3

▶ FIGURE 11–13

Induction in series.

L_1 L_2 L_3 L_n

Notice that the calculation of total inductance in series is analogous to the calculations of total resistance in series (Chapter 4) and total capacitance in parallel (Chapter 9).

EXAMPLE 11–2

Determine the total inductance for each of the series connections in Figure 11–14.

▶ FIGURE 11–14

1 H   2 H   1.5 H   5 H

(a)

5 mH   2 mH   10 mH   1000 µH

(b)

Solution   In Figure 11–14(a),

$$L_T = 1\,\text{H} + 2\,\text{H} + 1.5\,\text{H} + 5\,\text{H} = \mathbf{9.5\,H}$$

In Figure 11–14(b),

$$L_T = 5\,\text{mH} + 2\,\text{mH} + 10\,\text{mH} + 1\,\text{mH} = \mathbf{18\,mH}$$

Note: 1000 µH = 1 mH

Related Problem   What is the total inductance of three 50 µH inductors in series?

Total Parallel Inductance

When inductors are connected in parallel, as in Figure 11–15, the total inductance is less than the smallest inductance. The general formula states that the reciprocal of the total inductance is equal to the sum of the reciprocals of the individual inductances.

$$\frac{1}{L_T} = \frac{1}{L_1} + \frac{1}{L_2} + \frac{1}{L_3} + \cdots + \frac{1}{L_n}$$

You can calculate total inductance, L_T, by taking the reciprocals of both sides of the previous equation.

Equation 11–4

$$L_T = \frac{1}{\dfrac{1}{L_1} + \dfrac{1}{L_2} + \dfrac{1}{L_3} + \cdots + \dfrac{1}{L_n}}$$

Notice that this calculation of total inductance in parallel is analogous to the calculations of total parallel resistance (Chapter 5) and total series capacitance (Chapter 9).

▶ FIGURE 11–15

Inductors in parallel.

EXAMPLE 11–3

Determine L_T in Figure 11–16.

▶ **FIGURE 11–16**

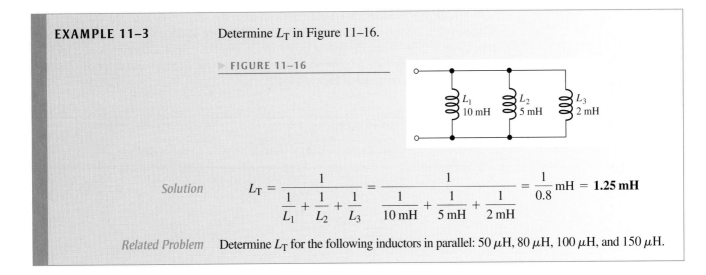

Solution

$$L_T = \frac{1}{\dfrac{1}{L_1} + \dfrac{1}{L_2} + \dfrac{1}{L_3}} = \frac{1}{\dfrac{1}{10\text{ mH}} + \dfrac{1}{5\text{ mH}} + \dfrac{1}{2\text{ mH}}} = \frac{1}{0.8}\text{ mH} = \mathbf{1.25\text{ mH}}$$

Related Problem Determine L_T for the following inductors in parallel: 50 μH, 80 μH, 100 μH, and 150 μH.

For series-parallel combinations of inductors, determine the total inductance in the
some way as total resistance in series-parallel resistive circuits.

**SECTION 11–3
REVIEW**

1. State the rule for combining inductors in series.
2. What is L_T for a series connection of 100 μH, 500 μH, and 2 mH?
3. Five 100 mH coils are connected in series. What is the total inductance?
4. Compare the total inductance in parallel with the smallest-value individual inductor.
5. The calculation of total parallel inductance is analogous to that for total parallel resistance.   (True or False)
6. Determine L_T for each parallel combination:
   (a) 100 mH, 50 mH, and 10 mH
   (b) 40 μH and 60 μH
   (c) Ten 1 H coils

11–4 INDUCTORS IN DC CIRCUITS

Energy is stored in the electromagnetic field of an inductor when it is connected to a
dc voltage source. The buildup of current through the inductor occurs in a predictable
manner, which is dependent on both the time constant determined by the inductance
and the resistance in a circuit.

After completing this section, you should be able to

◆ **Analyze inductive dc switching circuits**

  ◆ Define *RL time constant*

  ◆ Describe the increase and decrease of current in an inductor

  ◆ Relate the time constant to the energizing and deenergizing of an inductor

  ◆ Describe induced voltage

  ◆ Write the exponential equations for current in an inductor

When there is constant direct current in an inductor, there is no induced voltage. There is, however, a voltage drop due to the winding resistance of the coil. The inductance itself appears as a short to dc. Energy is stored in the magnetic field according to the formula $W = \frac{1}{2}LI^2$. The only energy conversion to heat occurs in the winding resistance ($P = I^2 R_W$). This condition is illustrated in Figure 11–17.

▲ FIGURE 11–17

Energy storage and conversion to heat in an inductor.

The *RL* Time Constant

Because the inductor's basic action is to develop a voltage that opposes a change in its current, it follows that current cannot change instantaneously in an inductor. A certain time is required for the current to make a change from one value to another. The rate at which the current changes is determined by the *RL* time constant.

The *RL* time constant is a fixed time interval that equals the ratio of the inductance to the resistance.

The formula is

Equation 11–5

$$\tau = \frac{L}{R}$$

where τ is in seconds when inductance (L) is in henries and resistance (R) is in ohms.

EXAMPLE 11–4

A series *RL* circuit has a resistance of 1.0 kΩ and an inductance of 1 mH. What is the time constant?

Solution

$$\tau = \frac{L}{R} = \frac{1 \text{ mH}}{1.0 \text{ k}\Omega} = \frac{1 \times 10^{-3} \text{ H}}{1 \times 10^3 \, \Omega} = 1 \times 10^{-6} \text{ s} = \mathbf{1 \, \mu s}$$

Related Problem Find the time constant for $R = 2.2$ kΩ and $L = 500 \, \mu$H.

Current in an Inductor

Increasing Current In a series *RL* circuit, the current will increase to approximately 63% of its full value in one time-constant interval after voltage is applied. This buildup of current (analogous to the buildup of capacitor voltage during the charging in an *RC* circuit) follows an **exponential** curve and reaches the approximate percentage of final current as indicated in Table 11–1 and as illustrated in Figure 11–18.

▼ TABLE 11–1

Percentage of final current after each time-constant interval during current buildup.

NUMBER OF TIME CONSTANTS	APPROXIMATE % OF FINAL CURRENT
1	63
2	86
3	95
4	98
5	99 (considered 100%)

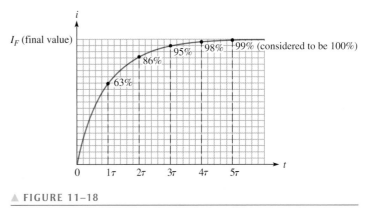

▲ FIGURE 11–18

Increasing current in an inductor.

The change in current over five time-constant intervals is illustrated in Figure 11–19. When the current reaches its final value at approximately 5τ, it ceases to change. At this time, the inductor acts as a short (except for winding resistance) to the constant current. The final value of the current is

$$I_F = \frac{V_S}{R} = \frac{10\,\text{V}}{1.0\,\text{k}\Omega} = 10\,\text{mA}$$

▲ FIGURE 11–19

Illustration of the exponential buildup of current in an inductor. The current increases approximately 63% during each time-constant interval after the switch is closed. A voltage (v_L) is induced in the coil that tends to oppose the increase in current.

EXAMPLE 11–5

Calculate the *RL* time constant for Figure 11–20. Then determine the current and the time at each time-constant interval, measured from the instant the switch is closed.

▲ FIGURE 11–20

Solution   The *RL* time constant is

$$\tau = \frac{L}{R} = \frac{10\,\text{mH}}{1.2\,\text{k}\Omega} = \mathbf{8.33\,\mu s}$$

The final current is

$$I_F = \frac{V_S}{R} = \frac{12\,\text{V}}{1.2\,\text{k}\Omega} = 10\,\text{mA}$$

Use the time-constant percentage values from Table 11–1.

At 1τ: $i = 0.63(10\,\text{mA}) = \mathbf{6.3\,mA};\, t = \mathbf{8.33\,\mu s}$

At 2τ: $i = 0.86(10\,\text{mA}) = \mathbf{8.6\,mA};\, t = \mathbf{16.7\,\mu s}$

At 3τ: $i = 0.95(10\,\text{mA}) = \mathbf{9.5\,mA};\, t = \mathbf{25.0\,\mu s}$

At 4τ: $i = 0.98(10\,\text{mA}) = \mathbf{9.8\,mA};\, t = \mathbf{33.3\,\mu s}$

At 5τ: $i = 0.99(10\,\text{mA}) = 9.9\,\text{mA} \cong \mathbf{10\,mA};\, t = \mathbf{41.7\,\mu s}$

Related Problem   Repeat the calculations if $R = 680\,\Omega$ and $L = 100\,\mu\text{H}$.

Decreasing Current   Current in an inductor decreases exponentially according to the approximate percentage values shown in Table 11–2 and in Figure 11–21.

▼ TABLE 11–2

Percentage of initial current after each time-constant interval while current is decreasing.

NUMBER OF TIME CONSTANTS	APPROXIMATE % OF INITIAL CURRENT
1	37
2	14
3	5
4	2
5	1 (considered 0)

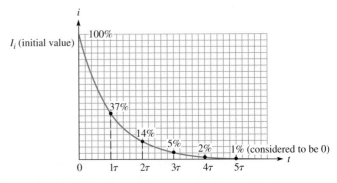

▲ FIGURE 11–21

Decreasing current in an inductor.

The change in current over five time-constant intervals is illustrated in Figure 11–22. When the current reaches its final value of approximately 0 A, it ceases to change. Before the switch is opened, the current through L is at a constant value of 10 mA, which is determined by R_1 because L acts ideally as a short. When the switch is opened, the induced inductor voltage initially provides 10 mA through R_2. The current then decreases by 63% during each time constant interval.

(a) Initially ($t = 0$)   (b) At $t = 1\tau$ (c) At $t = 2\tau$

(d) At $t = 3\tau$ (e) At $t = 4\tau$ (f) At $t = 5\tau$ (i is assumed to be 0)

▲ FIGURE 11–22

A good way to demonstrate both increasing and decreasing current in an RL circuit is to use a square wave voltage as the input. The square wave is a useful signal for observing the dc response of a circuit because it provides on and off action similar to a switch. Pulse response will be covered further in Chapter 15. When the square wave goes from its low level to its high level, the current in the circuit responds by exponentially increasing to its final value. When the square wave returns to the zero level, the current in the circuit responds by exponentially decreasing to its zero value. Figure 11–23 shows input voltage and current waveforms.

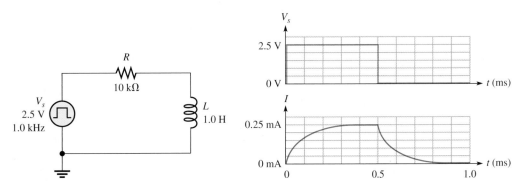

▲ FIGURE 11–23

EXAMPLE 11–6

For the circuit in Figure 11–23, what is the current at 0.1 ms and at 0.6 ms?

Solution The *RL* time constant for the circuit is

$$\tau = \frac{L}{R} = \frac{1.0\,\text{H}}{10\,\text{k}\Omega} = 0.1\,\text{ms}$$

If the square wave generator period is long enough for the current to reach its maximum value in 5τ, the current will increase exponentially and during each time constant interval will have a value equal to the percentage of the final current given in Table 11–1. The final current is

$$I_F = \frac{V_s}{R} = \frac{2.5\,\text{V}}{10\,\text{k}\Omega} = 0.25\,\text{mA}$$

The current at 0.1 ms is

$$i = 0.63(0.25\,\text{mA}) = \mathbf{0.158\,mA}$$

At 0.6 ms, the square wave input has been at the 0 V level for 0.1 ms, or 1τ; and, the current decreases from the maximum value toward its final value of 0 mA by 63%. Therefore,

$$i = 0.25\,\text{mA} - 0.63(0.25\,\text{mA}) = \mathbf{0.092\,mA}$$

Related Problem What is the current at 0.2 ms and 0.8 ms?

Voltages in the Series *RL* Circuit

As you know, when current changes in an inductor, a voltage is induced. Let's examine what happens to the induced voltage across the inductor in the series circuit in Figure 11–24 during one complete cycle of a square wave input. Keep in mind that the generator produces a level that is like switching a dc source on and then puts an "automatic" low resistance (ideally zero) path across the source when it returns to its zero level.

An ammeter placed in the circuit shows the current in the circuit at any instant in time. The V_L waveform is the voltage across the inductor. In Figure 11–24(a), the square wave has just transitioned from zero to its maximum value of 2.5 V. In accordance with Lenz's law, a voltage is induced across the inductor that opposes this *change* as the magnetic field surrounding the inductor builds up. There is no current in the circuit due to the equal but opposing voltages.

As the magnetic field builds up, the induced voltage across the inductor decreases, and current is in the circuit. After 1τ, the induced voltage across the inductor has decreased by 63%, which causes the current to increase by 63% to 0.158 mA. This is shown in Figure 11–24(b) at the end of one time constant (0.1 ms).

The voltage on the inductor continues to exponentially decrease to zero, at which point the current is limited only by the circuit resistance. Then the square wave goes back to zero (at $t = 0.5$ ms) as shown in Figure 11–24(c). Again a voltage is induced across the inductor opposing this change. This time, the polarity of the inductor voltage is reversed due to the collapsing magnetic field. Although the source voltage is 0, the collapsing magnetic field maintains current in the same direction until the current decreases to zero, as shown in Figure 11–24(d).

(a)

(b)

(c)

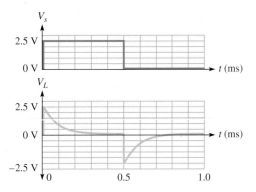

(d)

▲ FIGURE 11–24

EXAMPLE 11–7

(a) The circuit in Figure 11–25 has a square wave input. What is the highest frequency that can be used and still observe the complete waveform across the inductor?

(b) Assume the generator is set to the frequency determined in (a). Describe the voltage waveform across the resistor?

▶ **FIGURE 11–25**

Solution (a)

$$\tau = \frac{L}{R} = \frac{15\,\text{mH}}{33\,\text{k}\Omega} = 0.454\,\mu\text{s}$$

The period needs to be ten times longer than τ to observe the entire wave.

$$T = 10\tau = 4.54\,\mu\text{s}$$

$$f = \frac{1}{T} = \frac{1}{4.54\,\mu\text{s}} = \textbf{220 kHz}$$

(b) The voltage across the resistor has the same shape as the current waveform. The general shape was shown in Figure 11–24 and has a maximum value of 10 V (the same as V_s, assuming no winding resistance).

Related Problem What is the maximum voltage across the resistor for $f = 220\,\text{kHz}$?

 Open Multisim file E11-07 on your CD-ROM. Set the frequency to the calculated value and observe the voltage waveform across the inductor.

The Exponential Formulas

The formulas for the exponential current and voltage in an *RL* circuit are similar to those used in Chapter 9 for the *RC* circuit, and the universal exponential curves in Figure 9–36 apply to inductors as well as capacitors. The general formulas for *RL* circuits are stated as follows:

Equation 11–6
$$v = V_F + (V_i - V_F)e^{-Rt/L}$$

Equation 11–7
$$i = I_F + (I_i - I_F)e^{-Rt/L}$$

where V_F and I_F are the final values, V_i and I_i are the initial values, and v and i are the instantaneous values of the inductor voltage or current at time t.

Increasing Current The formula for the special case in which an increasing exponential current curve begins at zero ($I_i = 0$) is

Equation 11–8
$$i = I_F(1 - e^{-Rt/L})$$

Using Equation 11–8, you can calculate the value of the increasing inductor current at any instant of time. You can calculate voltage by substituting v for i and V_F for I_F in Equation 11–8. The exponent $-Rt/L$ can also be written as $-t/(L/R) = -t/\tau$.

EXAMPLE 11–8

In Figure 11–26, determine the inductor current 30 μs after the switch is closed.

▶ FIGURE 11–26

Solution   The *RL* time constant is

$$\tau = \frac{L}{R} = \frac{100\ \text{mH}}{2.2\ \text{k}\Omega} = 45.5\ \mu\text{s}$$

The final current is

$$I_F = \frac{V_S}{R} = \frac{12\ \text{V}}{2.2\ \text{k}\Omega} = 5.45\ \text{mA}$$

The initial current is zero. Notice that 30 μs is less than one time constant, so the current will reach less than 63% of its final value in that time.

$$i_L = I_F(1 - e^{-Rt/L}) = 5.45\ \text{mA}(1 - e^{-0.66}) = \textbf{2.63 mA}$$

Related Problem   In Figure 11–26, determine the inductor current 55 μs after the switch is closed.

Decreasing Current   The formula for the special case in which a decreasing exponential current has a final value of zero is

$$i = I_i e^{-Rt/L}$$

Equation 11–9

This formula can be used to calculate the decreasing inductor current at any instant.

EXAMPLE 11–9

In Figure 11–27, what is the current at each microsecond interval for one complete cycle of the input square wave as shown? After calculating the current at each time, sketch the current waveform.

▲ FIGURE 11–27

Solution   The *RL* time constant is

$$\tau = \frac{L}{R} = \frac{560\ \mu\text{H}}{680\ \Omega} = 0.824\ \mu\text{s}$$

When the pulse goes from 0 V to 10 V at $t = 0$, the current increases exponentially. The final current is

$$I_F = \frac{V_s}{R} = \frac{10\,\text{V}}{680\,\Omega} = 14.7\,\text{mA}$$

For the increasing current, $i = I_F(1 - e^{-Rt/L}) = I_F(1 - e^{-t/\tau})$.

At 1 µs: $i = 14.7\,\text{mA}(1 - e^{-1\mu s/0.824\mu s}) = 10.3\,\text{mA}$
At 2 µs: $i = 14.7\,\text{mA}(1 - e^{-2\mu s/0.824\mu s}) = 13.4\,\text{mA}$
At 3 µs: $i = 14.7\,\text{mA}(1 - e^{-3\mu s/0.824\mu s}) = 14.3\,\text{mA}$
At 4 µs: $i = 14.7\,\text{mA}(1 - e^{-4\mu s/0.824\mu s}) = 14.6\,\text{mA}$
At 5 µs: $i = 14.7\,\text{mA}(1 - e^{-5\mu s/0.824\mu s}) = 14.7\,\text{mA}$

When the pulse goes from 10 V to 0 V at $t = 5$ µs, the current decreases exponentially. For the decreasing current, $i = I_i(e^{-Rt/L}) = I_i(e^{-t/\tau})$. The initial current is the value at 5 µs, which is 14.7 mA.

At 6 µs: $i = 14.7\,\text{mA}(e^{-1\mu s/0.824\mu s}) = 4.37\,\text{mA}$
At 7 µs: $i = 14.7\,\text{mA}(e^{-2\mu s/0.824\mu s}) = 1.30\,\text{mA}$
At 8 µs: $i = 14.7\,\text{mA}(e^{-3\mu s/0.824\mu s}) = 0.38\,\text{mA}$
At 9 µs: $i = 14.7\,\text{mA}(e^{-4\mu s/0.824\mu s}) = 0.11\,\text{mA}$
At 10 µs: $i = 14.7\,\text{mA}(e^{-5\mu s/0.824\mu s}) = 0.03\,\text{mA}$

Figure 11–28 is a graph of these results.

▶ FIGURE 11–28

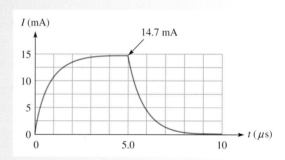

Related Problem   What is the current at 0.5 µs?

   Open Multisim file E11-09 on your CD-ROM. Measure the current by placing a very small-value series resistor between the inductor and ground and observing the voltage across it.

SECTION 11–4 REVIEW

1. A 15 mH inductor with a winding resistance of 10 Ω has a constant direct current of 10 mA through it. What is the voltage drop across the inductor?

2. A 20 V dc source is connected to a series *RL* circuit with a switch. At the instant of switch closure, what are the values of *i* and v_L?

3. In the same circuit as in Question 2, after a time interval equal to 5τ from switch closure, what is v_L?

4. In a series *RL* circuit where $R = 1.0\,\text{k}\Omega$ and $L = 500\,\mu\text{H}$, what is the time constant? Determine the current 0.25 µs after a switch connects 10 V across the circuit.

11–5 INDUCTORS IN AC CIRCUITS

An inductor passes ac but with an amount of opposition that depends on the frequency of the ac.

After completing this section, you should be able to

◆ **Analyze inductive ac circuits**

   ◆ Define *inductive reactance*

   ◆ Determine the value of inductive reactance in a given circuit

   ◆ Discuss instantaneous, true, and reactive power in an inductor

Inductive Reactance, X_L

In Figure 11–29, an inductor is shown connected to a sinusoidal voltage source. When the source voltage is held at a constant amplitude value and its frequency is increased, the amplitude of the current decreases. Also, when the frequency of the source is decreased, the current amplitude increases.

(a) Current decreases when the frequency increases.

(b) Current increases when the frequency decreases.

◀ **FIGURE 11–29**

The current in an inductive circuit varies inversely with the frequency of the source voltage.

When the frequency of the source voltage increases, its rate of change also increases, as you already know. Now, if the frequency of the source voltage is increased, the frequency of the current also increases. According to Faraday's and Lenz's laws, this increase in frequency induces more voltage across the inductor in a direction to oppose the current and causes it to decrease in amplitude. Similarly, a decrease in frequency will cause an increase in current.

A decrease in the amount of current with an increase in frequency for a fixed amount of voltage indicates that opposition to the current has increased. Thus, the inductor offers opposition to current, and that opposition varies *directly* with frequency.

Inductive reactance is the opposition to sinusoidal current in an inductor.

The symbol for inductive reactance is X_L, and its unit is the ohm (Ω).

You have just seen how frequency affects the opposition to current (inductive reactance) in an inductor. Now let's see how the inductance, L, affects the reactance. Figure 11–30(a) shows that when a sinusoidal voltage with a fixed amplitude and fixed frequency is applied to a 1 mH inductor, there is a certain amount of alternating current. When the inductance value is increased to 2 mH, the current decreases, as shown in part (b). Thus, when the inductance is increased, the opposition to current (inductive reactance) increases. So not only

▶ FIGURE 11–30

For a fixed voltage and fixed frequency, the current varies inversely with the inductance value.

(a) Less inductance, more current.

(b) More inductance, less current.

is the inductive reactance *directly* proportional to frequency, but it is also *directly* proportional to inductance. This relationship can be stated as follows:

X_L is proportional to fL.

It can be proven that the constant of proportionality is 2π, so the formula for inductive reactance (X_L) is

Equation 11–10

$$X_L = 2\pi fL$$

X_L is in ohms when f is in hertz and L is in henries. As with capacitive reactance, the 2π term comes from the relationship of the sine wave to rotational motion.

EXAMPLE 11–10

A sinusoidal voltage is applied to the circuit in Figure 11–31. The frequency is 10 kHz. Determine the inductive reactance.

▶ FIGURE 11–31

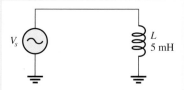

Solution Convert 10 kHz to 10×10^3 Hz and 5 mH to 5×10^{-3} H. Then, the inductive reactance is

$$X_L = 2\pi fL = 2\pi(10 \times 10^3 \text{ Hz})(5 \times 10^{-3} \text{ H}) = \textbf{314 } \boldsymbol{\Omega}$$

Related Problem What is X_L in Figure 11–31 if the frequency is increased to 35 kHz?

Ohm's Law The reactance of an inductor is analogous to the resistance of a resistor. In fact, X_L, just like X_C and R, is expressed in ohms. Since inductive reactance is a form of opposition to current, Ohm's law applies to inductive circuits as well as to resistive circuits and capacitive circuits; and it is stated as follows:

Equation 11–11

$$I = \frac{V}{X_L}$$

When applying Ohm's law in ac circuits, you must express both the current and the voltage in the same way, that is, both in rms, both in peak, and so on.

EXAMPLE 11–11

Determine the rms current in Figure 11–32.

▶ FIGURE 11–32

Solution

Convert 10 kHz to 10×10^3 Hz and 100 mH to 100×10^{-3} H. Then calculate X_L.

$$X_L = 2\pi fL = 2\pi(10 \times 10^3 \text{ Hz})(100 \times 10^{-3} \text{ H}) = 6283 \, \Omega$$

Apply Ohm's law.

$$I_{rms} = \frac{V_{rms}}{X_L} = \frac{5 \text{ V}}{6283 \, \Omega} = \textbf{796 } \boldsymbol{\mu} \textbf{A}$$

Related Problem

Determine the rms current in Figure 11–32 for the following values: $V_{rms} = 12$ V, $f = 4.9$ kHz, and $L = 680 \, \mu$H.

Open Multisim file E11-11 on your CD-ROM. Measure the rms current and compare to the calculated value. Change the circuit values to those given in the related problem and measure the rms current.

Current Lags Inductor Voltage by 90°

As you know, a sinusoidal voltage has a maximum rate of change at its zero crossings and a zero rate of change at the peaks. From Faraday's law (Chapter 7) you know that the amount of voltage induced across a coil is directly proportional to the rate at which the current is changing. Therefore, the coil voltage is maximum at the zero crossings of the current where the rate of change of the current is the greatest. Also, the amount of voltage is zero at the peaks of the current where the rate of change is zero. This phase relationship is illustrated in Figure 11–33. As you can see, the current peaks occur a quarter cycle after the voltage peaks. Thus, the current *lags* the voltage by 90°. Recall that in a capacitor, the current *leads* the voltage by 90°.

◀ FIGURE 11–33

Current is always lagging the inductor voltage by 90°.

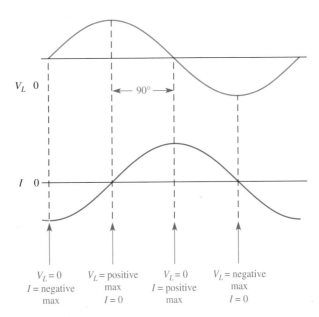

$V_L = 0$ $V_L = $ positive $V_L = 0$ $V_L = $ negative
$I = $ negative   max $I = $ positive   max
max $I = 0$ max $I = 0$

Power in an Inductor

As discussed earlier, an inductor stores energy in its magnetic field when there is current through it. An ideal inductor (assuming no winding resistance) does not dissipate energy; it only stores it. When an ac voltage is applied to an inductor, energy is stored by the inductor during a portion of the cycle; then the stored energy is returned to the source during another portion of the cycle. No net energy is lost in an ideal inductor due to conversion to heat. Figure 11–34 shows the power curve that results from one cycle of inductor current and voltage.

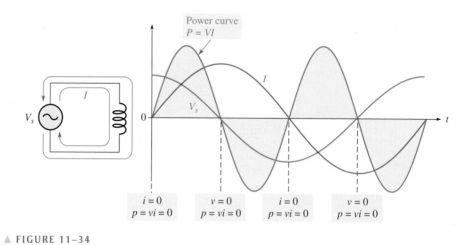

▲ FIGURE 11–34

Power curve for an inductor.

Instantaneous Power (p)   The product of instantaneous voltage, v, and instantaneous current, i, gives instantaneous power, p. At points where v or i is zero, p is also zero. When both v and i are positive, p is also positive. When either v or i is positive and the other negative, p is negative. When both v and i are negative, p is positive. As you can see in Figure 11–34, the power follows a sinusoidal-shaped curve. Positive values of power indicate that energy is stored by the inductor. Negative values of power indicate that energy is returned from the inductor to the source. Note that the power fluctuates at a frequency twice that of the voltage or current, as energy is alternately stored and returned to the source.

True Power (P_{true})   Ideally, all of the energy stored by an inductor during the positive portion of the power cycle is returned to the source during the negative portion. No net energy is lost due to conversion to heat in the inductor, so the power is zero. Actually, because of winding resistance in a practical inductor, some power is always dissipated, and there is a very small amount of true power, which can normally be neglected.

Equation 11–12
$$P_{\text{true}} = I_{\text{rms}}^2 R_W$$

Reactive Power (P_r)   The rate at which an inductor stores or returns energy is called its **reactive power**, P_r, with a unit of VAR (volt-ampere reactive). The reactive power is a nonzero quantity because at any instant in time the inductor is actually taking energy from the source or returning energy to it. Reactive power does not represent an energy loss due to conversion to heat. The following formulas apply:

Equation 11–13
$$P_r = V_{\text{rms}} I_{\text{rms}}$$

Equation 11–14
$$P_r = \frac{V_{\text{rms}}^2}{X_L}$$

Equation 11–15
$$P_r = I_{\text{rms}}^2 X_L$$

EXAMPLE 11–12

A 10 V rms signal with a frequency of 1 kHz is applied to a 10 mH coil with a winding resistance of 5 Ω. Determine the reactive power (P_r) and the true power (P_{true}).

Solution

First, calculate the inductive reactance and current values.

$$X_L = 2\pi f L = 2\pi(1\,\text{kHz})(10\,\text{mH}) = 62.8\,\Omega$$

$$I = \frac{V_s}{X_L} = \frac{10\,\text{V}}{62.8\,\Omega} = 159\,\text{mA}$$

Then using Equation 11–15,

$$P_r = I^2 X_L = (159\,\text{mA})^2(62.8\,\Omega) = \mathbf{1.59\,VAR}$$

The true power is

$$P_{true} = I^2 R_W = (159\,\text{mA})^2(5\,\Omega) = \mathbf{126\,mW}$$

Related Problem

What happens to the reactive power if the frequency increases?

The Quality Factor (Q)

The **quality factor (Q)** is the ratio of the reactive power in the inductor to the true power in the winding resistance of the coil. It is a ratio of the power in L to the power in R_W. The quality factor is important in resonant circuits, which are studied in Chapter 13. A formula for Q is developed as follows:

$$Q = \frac{\text{reactive power}}{\text{true power}} = \frac{P_r}{P_{true}} = \frac{I^2 X_L}{I^2 R_W}$$

The I^2 terms cancel, leaving

$$Q = \frac{X_L}{R_W}$$

Equation 11–16

Note that Q is a ratio of like units and, therefore, has no unit itself. The quality factor is also known as unloaded Q because it is defined with no load across the coil.

**SECTION 11–5
REVIEW**

1. State the phase relationship between current and voltage in an inductor.
2. Calculate X_L for $f = 5$ kHz and $L = 100$ mH.
3. At what frequency is the reactance of a 50 μH inductor equal to 800 Ω?
4. Calculate the rms current in Figure 11–35.
5. An ideal 50 mH inductor is connected to a 12 V rms source. What is the true power? What is the reactive power at a frequency of 1 kHz?

FIGURE 11–35

$V_{rms} = 1$ V
$f = 1$ MHz

L
$10\,\mu$H

11–6 INDUCTOR APPLICATIONS

Inductors are not as versatile as capacitors and tend to be more limited in their application due, in part, to size, cost factors, and nonideal behavior (internal resistance, etc.). One of the most common applications for inductors is noise reduction applications.

After completing this section, you should be able to

◆ **Discuss some inductor applications**

   ◆ Discuss two ways in which noise enters a circuit

   ◆ Describe the suppression of electromagnetic interference (EMI)

   ◆ Explain how a ferrite bead is used

   ◆ Discuss the basics of tuned circuits

Noise Suppression

One of the most important applications of inductors has to do with suppressing unwanted electrical noise. The inductors used in these applications are generally wound on a closed core to avoid having the inductor become a source of radiated noise itself. Two types of noise are conductive noise and radiated noise.

Conductive Noise   Many systems have common conductive paths connecting different parts of the system, which can conduct high frequency noise from one part of the system to another. Consider the case of two circuits connected with common lines as shown in Figure 11–36(a). A path for high frequency noise exists though the common grounds, creating a condition known as a *ground loop*. Ground loops are particularly a problem in instrumentation systems, where a transducer may be located a distance from the recording system and noise current in the ground can affect the signal.

If the signal of interest changes slowly, a special inductor, called a *longitudinal choke,* can be installed in the signal line as shown in Figure 11–36(b). The longitudinal choke is a form of transformer (covered in Chapter 14) that acts as an inductor in each signal line. The ground loop sees a high impedance path, thus reducing the noise, while the low-frequency signal is coupled through the low impedance of the choke.

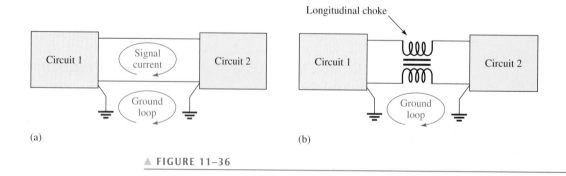

(a)   (b)

▲ FIGURE 11–36

Switching circuits also tend to generate high frequency noise (above 10 MHz) by virtue of the high-frequency components present. (Recall from Section 8–7 that a fast pulse contains many high-frequency components.) Certain types of power supplies use high-speed switching circuits, which are a source of conductive noise themselves. Because an inductor's impedance increases with frequency, inductors are good for blocking electrical noise from these supplies, which should carry only dc. Inductors are frequently installed in the power supply lines to suppress this conductive noise so that one circuit does not adversely affect another circuit. One or more capacitors may also be used in conjunction with the inductor to improve filtering action.

Radiated Noise   Noise can also enter a circuit by way of the electric field. The noise source can be an adjacent circuit or a nearby power supply. There are several approaches to reducing the effects of radiated noise. Usually, the first step is to determine the cause of the noise and isolate it using shielding or filtering. Inductors are widely used in filters that are used to suppress radio-frequency noise. The inductor used for noise suppression must be carefully selected so as not to become a source of radiated noise itself. For high frequencies (>20 MHz), inductors wound on highly permeable toroidal cores are widely used, as they tend to keep the magnetic flux restricted to the core.

RF Chokes

Inductors used for the purpose of blocking very high frequencies are called *radio frequency (RF) chokes*. RF chokes are used for conductive or radiated noise. They are special inductors designed to block high frequencies from getting into or leaving parts of a system by providing a high impedance path for high frequencies. In general, the choke is placed in series with the line for which RF suppression is required. Depending on the frequency of the interference, different types of chokes are required. A common type of electromagnetic interference (EMI) filter wraps the signal line on a toroidal core several times. The toroidal configuration is desired because it contains the magnetic field so that the choke does not become a source of noise itself.

Another common type of RF choke is a ferrite bead. All wires have inductance, and the ferrite bead is a small ferromagnetic material that is strung onto the wire to increase its inductance. The impedance presented by the bead is a function of both the material and the frequency, as well as the size of the bead. It is an effective and inexpensive "choke" for high frequencies. Ferrite beads are common in high-frequency communication systems. Sometimes several are strung together in series to increase the effective inductance.

Tuned Circuits

Inductors are used in conjunction with capacitors to provide frequency selection in communications systems. These tuned circuits allow a narrow band of frequencies to be selected while all other frequencies are rejected. The tuners in your TV and radio receivers are based on this principle and permit you to select one channel or station out of the many that are available.

Frequency selectivity is based on the fact that the reactances of both capacitors and inductors depend on the frequency and on the interaction of these two components when connected in series or parallel. Since the capacitor and the inductor produce opposite phase shifts, their combined opposition to current can be used to obtain a desired response at a selected frequency. Tuned (resonant) *RLC* circuits are covered in detail in Chapter 13.

SECTION 11–6 REVIEW	1. Name two types of unwanted noise.
	2. What do the letters EMI stand for?
	3. How is a ferrite bead used?

Application Assignment

You are given two unmarked coils and asked to find their inductance values. You cannot find an inductance bridge, which is an instrument for measuring inductance directly. After scratching your head for awhile, you decide to use the time-constant characteristic of inductive circuits to determine the unknown inductances. A test setup consisting of a square wave generator and an oscilloscope is used to make the measurements.

The method is to place the coil in series with a resistor of known value and measure the time constant by applying a square wave to the circuit and observing the resulting voltage across the resistor with an oscilloscope. Knowing the time constant and the resistance value, you can calculate the inductance L.

Each time the square wave input voltage goes high, the inductor current increases exponentially; and each time the square wave goes back to zero, the inductor current decreases exponen-

tially. The time it takes for the exponential resistor voltage to increase to approximately its final value equals five time constants. This operation is illustrated in Figure 11–37. To make sure that the winding resistance of the coil can be neglected, it must be measured; and the value of the resistor used in the circuit must be selected to be considerably larger than the winding and source resistance.

Step 1: Measuring the Coil Resistance and Selecting a Series Resistor

Assume that the winding resistance has been measured with an ohmmeter and found to be 85 Ω. To make the winding resistance negligible, a 10 kΩ series resistor is used in the circuit.

Step 2: Determining the Inductance of Coil 1

Refer to Figure 11–38. To determine the inductance, a 10 V square wave is applied to the breadboarded circuit. The frequency of the square wave is adjusted so that the inductor

▲ FIGURE 11–37

Circuit for time-constant measurement.

▲ FIGURE 11–38

Testing coil 1.

current has time to reach its final value during each square wave pulse; the scope is set to view a complete exponential curve as shown. Determine the approximate circuit time constant from the scope display and calculate the inductance of coil 1.

Step 3: Determining the Inductance of Coil 2

Refer to Figure 11–39. To determine the inductance, a 10 V square wave is applied to the breadboarded circuit. The frequency of the square wave is adjusted so that the inductor current has time to reach its final value during each square wave pulse; the scope is set to view a complete exponential curve as shown. Determine the approximate circuit time constant from the scope display and calculate the inductance of coil 2. Discuss any difficulty you find with this method.

Step 4: Another Way to Find Unknown Inductance

Determination of the time constant is not the only way that you can use to find an unknown inductance. Specify a method using a sinusoidal input voltage instead of the square wave.

Review

1. What is the maximum square wave frequency that can be used in Figure 11–38?

2. What is the maximum square wave frequency that can be used in Figure 11–39?

3. What happens if the frequency exceeds the maximum you determined in Questions 1 and 2? Explain how your measurements would be affected.

▲ FIGURE 11–39

Testing coil 2.

SUMMARY

◆ Inductance is a measure of a coil's ability to establish an induced voltage as a result of a change in its current.

◆ An inductor opposes a change in its own current.

◆ Faraday's law states that relative motion between a magnetic field and a coil induces a voltage across the coil.

◆ Lenz's law states that the polarity of induced voltage is such that the resulting induced current is in a direction that opposes the change in the magnetic field that produced it.

◆ Energy is stored by an inductor in its magnetic field.

◆ One henry is the amount of inductance when current, changing at the rate of one ampere per second, induces one volt across the inductor.

◆ Inductance is directly proportional to the square of the turns, the permeability, and the cross-sectional area of the core. It is inversely proportional to the length of the core.

◆ The permeability of a core material is an indication of the ability of the material to establish a magnetic field.

- Inductors add in series.
- Total parallel inductance is less than that of the smallest inductor in parallel.
- The time constant for a series *RL* circuit is the inductance divided by the resistance.
- In an *RL* circuit, the increasing or decreasing voltage and current in an inductor make an approximately 63% change during each time-constant interval.
- Increasing and decreasing current and voltage follow exponential curves.
- Voltage leads current by 90° in an inductor.
- Inductive reactance (X_L) is directly proportional to frequency and inductance.
- The true power in an inductor is zero; that is, there is no energy conversion to heat in an ideal inductor, only in its winding resistance.

KEY TERMS

Key terms and other bold terms in the chapter are defined in the end-of-book glossary.

Coil   A common term for an inductor.

Exponential   A mathematical function described by a natural logarithm (base). Increasing and decreasing current and voltage for an inductor are described by exponential functions.

Faraday's law   A law stating that the voltage induced across a coil of wire equals the number of turns in the coil times the rate of change of the magnetic flux.

Henry (H)   The unit of inductance.

Induced voltage   Voltage produced as a result of a changing magnetic field.

Inductance   The property of an inductor whereby a change in current causes the inductor to produce a voltage that opposes the change in current.

Inductive reactance   The opposition of an inductor to sinusoidal current. The unit is the ohm.

Inductor   An electrical device formed by a wire wound around a core having the property of inductance: also known as *coil*.

Lenz's law   A physical law that states when the current through a coil changes, the polarity of the induced voltage created by the changing magnetic field is such that it always opposes the change that caused it. The current cannot change instantaneously.

Quality factor (*Q*)   The ratio of reactive power to true power.

RL time constant   A fixed time interval, set by the *L* and *R* values, that determines the time response of a circuit.

Winding   The loops or turns of wire in an inductor.

Winding resistance   The resistance of the length of wire that makes up a coil.

FORMULAS

11–1	$W = \dfrac{1}{2}LI^2$	Energy stored by an inductor
11–2	$L = \dfrac{N^2 \mu A}{l}$	Inductance in terms of physical parameters
11–3	$L_T = L_1 + L_2 + L_3 + \cdots + L_n$	Series inductance
11–4	$L_T = \dfrac{1}{\dfrac{1}{L_1} + \dfrac{1}{L_2} + \dfrac{1}{L_3} + \cdots + \dfrac{1}{L_n}}$	Total parallel inductance
11–5	$\tau = \dfrac{L}{R}$	*RL* time constant
11–6	$v = V_F + (V_i - V_F)e^{-Rt/L}$	Exponential voltage (general)
11–7	$i = I_F + (I_i - I_F)e^{-Rt/L}$	Exponential current (general)
11–8	$i = I_F(1 - e^{-Rt/L})$	Increasing exponential current beginning at zero
11–9	$i = I_i e^{-Rt/L}$	Decreasing exponential current ending at zero

11–10	$X_L = 2\pi fL$	Inductive reactance
11–11	$I = \dfrac{V}{X_L}$	Ohm's law
11–12	$P_{\text{true}} = I_{\text{rms}}^2 R_W$	True power
11–13	$P_r = V_{\text{rms}} I_{\text{rms}}$	Reactive power
11–14	$P_r = \dfrac{V_{\text{rms}}^2}{X_L}$	Reactive power
11–15	$P_r = I_{\text{rms}}^2 X_L$	Reactive power
11–16	$Q = \dfrac{X_L}{R_W}$	Quality factor

SELF-TEST

Answers are at the end of the chapter.

1. An inductance of 0.05 μH is larger than

   (a) 0.0000005 H   (b) 0.000005 H   (c) 0.000000008 H   (d) 0.00005 mH

2. An inductance of 0.33 mH is smaller than

   (a) 33 μH   (b) 330 μH   (c) 0.05 mH   (d) 0.0005 H

3. When the current through an inductor increases, the amount of energy stored in the electromagnetic field

   (a) decreases   (b) remains constant   (c) increases   (d) doubles

4. When the current through an inductor doubles, the stored energy

   (a) doubles   (b) quadruples   (c) is halved   (d) does not change

5. The winding resistance of a coil can be decreased by

   (a) reducing the number of turns   (b) using a larger wire

   (c) changing the core material   (d) either answer (a) or (b)

6. The inductance of an iron-core coil increases if

   (a) the number of turns is increased   (b) the iron core is removed

   (c) the length of the core is increased   (d) larger wire is used

7. Four 10 mH inductors are in series. The total inductance is

   (a) 40 mH   (b) 2.5 mH   (c) 40,000 μH   (d) answers (a) and (c)

8. A 1 mH, a 3.3 mH, and a 0.1 mH inductor are connected in parallel. The total inductance is

   (a) 4.4 mH   (b) greater than 3.3 mH   (c) less than 0.1 mH   (d) answers (a) and (b)

9. An inductor, a resistor, and a switch are connected in series to a 12 V battery. At the instant the switch is closed, the inductor voltage is

   (a) 0 V   (b) 12 V   (c) 6 V   (d) 4 V

10. A sinusoidal voltage is applied across an inductor. When the frequency of the voltage is increased, the current

    (a) decreases   (b) increases   (c) does not change   (d) momentarily goes to zero

11. An inductor and a resistor are in series with a sinusoidal voltage source. The frequency is set so that the inductive reactance is equal to the resistance. If the frequency is increased, then

    (a) $V_R > V_L$ (b) $V_L < V_R$ (c) $V_L = V_R$ (d) $V_L > V_R$

TROUBLESHOOTING: SYMPTOM AND CAUSE

The purpose of these exercises is to help develop thought processes essential to troubleshooting. Answers are at the end of the chapter.

Determine the cause for each set of symptoms. Refer to Figure 11–40.

1. *Symptom:* All of the voltmeter readings are 0 V.

   Cause:

   (a) The source is off or faulty.

   (b) L_1 is open.

   (c) either (a) or (b)

▲ FIGURE 11–40

The ac meters indicate the correct readings for this circuit.

2. *Symptom:* All of the voltmeter readings are 0 V.

   Cause:

   (a) L_4 is completely shorted.

   (b) L_5 is completely shorted.

   (c) L_6 is completely shorted.

3. *Symptom:* The voltmeter 1 reading is 5 V, and the voltmeter 2 and voltmeter 3 readings are 0 V.

   Cause:

   (a) L_4 is open.

   (b) L_2 is open.

   (c) L_5 is shorted.

4. *Symptom:* The voltmeter 1 reading is 4 V, the voltmeter 2 reading is 2 V, and the voltmeter 3 reading is 0 V.

   Cause:

   (a) L_3 is open.

   (b) L_6 is shorted.

   (c) either (a) or (b)

5. *Symptom:* The voltmeter 1 reading is 4 V, the voltmeter 2 reading is 2 V, and the voltmeter 3 reading is 2 V.

   Cause:

   (a) L_3 is shorted.

   (b) L_6 is open.

   (c) either (a) or (b)

PROBLEMS

Answers to odd-numbered problems are at the end of the book.

BASIC PROBLEMS

SECTION 11–1 The Basic Inductor

1. Convert the following to millihenries:

   (a) 1 H (b) 250 μH (c) 10 μH (d) 0.0005 H

2. Convert the following to microhenries:

   (a) 300 mH (b) 0.08 H (c) 5 mH (d) 0.00045 mH

3. How many turns are required to produce 30 mH with a coil wound on a cylindrical core having a cross-sectional area of 10×10^{-5} m² and a length of 0.05 m? The core has a permeability of 1.26×10^{-6}.

4. A 12 V battery is connected across a coil with a winding resistance of 12 Ω. How much current is there in the coil?

5. How much energy is stored by a 100 mH inductor with a current of 1 A?

6. The current through a 100 mH coil is changing at a rate of 200 mA/s. How much voltage is induced across the coil?

SECTION 11–3   Series and Parallel Inductors

7. Five inductors are connected in series. The lowest value is 5 μH. If the value of each inductor is twice that of the preceding one, and if the inductors are connected in order of ascending values, what is the total inductance?

8. Suppose that you require a total inductance of 50 mH. You have available a 10 mH coil and a 22 mH coil. How much additional inductance do you need?

9. Determine the total parallel inductance for the following coils in parallel: 75 μH, 50 μH, 25 μH, and 15 μH.

10. You have a 12 mH inductor, and it is your smallest value. You need an inductance of 8 mH. What value can you use in parallel with the 12 mH to obtain 8 mH?

11. Determine the total inductance of each circuit in Figure 11–41.

(a)   (b)   (c)

▲ FIGURE 11–41

12. Determine the total inductance of each circuit in Figure 11–42.

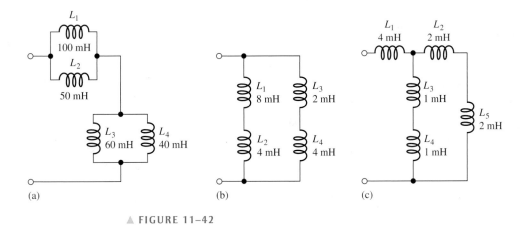

(a)   (b)   (c)

▲ FIGURE 11–42

SECTION 11–4   Inductors in DC Circuits

13. Determine the time constant for each of the following series RL combinations:

   (a) $R = 100\ \Omega$, $L = 100\ \mu$H   (b) $R = 4.7\ k\Omega$, $L = 10\ mH$

   (c) $R = 1.5\ M\Omega$, $L = 3\ H$

14. In a series RL circuit, determine how long it takes the current to build up to its full value for each of the following:

   (a) $R = 56\ \Omega$, $L = 50\ \mu$H   (b) $R = 3300\ \Omega$, $L = 15\ mH$

   (c) $R = 22\ k\Omega$, $L = 100\ mH$

15. In the circuit of Figure 11–43, there is initially no current. Determine the inductor voltage at the following times after the switch is closed:

(a) 10 μs   (b) 20 μs   (c) 30 μs   (d) 40 μs   (e) 50 μs

▶ FIGURE 11–43

16. In Figure 11–44, calculate the current at each of the following times. Assume an ideal inductor and voltage source.

(a) 10 μs   (b) 20 μs   (c) 30 μs

▲ FIGURE 11–44

SECTION 11–6   Inductors in AC Circuits

17. Find the total reactance for each circuit in Figure 11–41 when a voltage with a frequency of 5 kHz is applied across the terminals.

18. Find the total reactance for each circuit in Figure 11–42 when a 400 Hz voltage is applied.

19. Determine the total rms current in Figure 11–45. What are the currents through L_2 and L_3?

▶ FIGURE 11–45

20. What frequency will produce a total rms current of 500 mA in each circuit of Figure 11–42 with an rms input voltage of 10 V?

21. Determine the reactive power in Figure 11–45 neglecting the winding resistance.

ADVANCED PROBLEMS

22. Determine the time constant for the circuit in Figure 11–46.

23. (a) What is the current in the inductor 1.0 μs after the switch closes in Figure 11–46.

(b) What is the current after 5τ have elapsed?

24. For the circuit in Figure 11–46, assume the switch has been closed for more than 5τ and is opened. What is the current in the inductor 1.0 μs after the switch is opened?

▶ FIGURE 11–46

25. Determine the value of I_{L2} in Figure 11–47.

26. What is the total inductance between terminals A and B for each switch position in Figure 11–48?

▲ FIGURE 11–47

▲ FIGURE 11–48

MULTISIM TROUBLESHOOTING PROBLEMS

27. Open file P11-27 and test the circuit. If there is a fault, identify it.

28. Open file P11-28 and test the circuit. If there is a fault, identify it.

29. Determine if there is a fault in the circuit in file P11-29. If so, identify it.

30. Find and specify any faulty component in the circuit in file P11-30.

31. Is there a short or an open in the circuit in file P11-31? If so, identify the component that is faulty.

ANSWERS

SECTION REVIEWS

SECTION 11–1 The Basic Inductor

1. Parameters that determine inductance are turns of wire, permeability, cross-sectional area, and core length.

2. (a) When N increases, L increases.

    (b) When the core length increases, L decreases.

    (c) When the cross-sectional area decreases, L decreases.

    (d) For an air core, L decreases.

3. All wire has some resistance, and because inductors are made from turns of wire, there is always resistance in the winding.

4. Adjacent turns of wire in a coil act as plates of a capacitor and produce a small capacitance.

SECTION 11–2   Types of Inductors

1. Two categories of inductors are fixed and variable.

2. **(a)** air core   **(b)** iron core   **(c)** variable

SECTION 11–3   Series and Parallel Inductors

1. Inductances are added in series.

2. $L_T = 2600\,\mu H$

3. $L_T = 5 \times 100\,mH = 500\,mH$

4. The total parallel inductance is smaller than that of the smallest-value individual inductor in parallel.

5. True

6. **(a)** $L_T = 7.69\,mH$ **(b)** $L_T = 24\,\mu H$ **(c)** $L_T = 100\,mH$

SECTION 11–4   Inductors in DC Circuits

1. $V_L = (10\,mA)(10\,\Omega) = 100\,mV$

2. Initially, $i = 0\,V, v_L = 20\,V$

3. After 5τ, $v_L = 0\,V$

4. $\tau = 500\,\mu H/1.0\,k\Omega = 500\,ns, i_L = 3.93\,mA$

SECTION 11–5   Inductors in AC Circuits

1. Voltage leads current by 90° in an inductor.

2. $X_L = 2\pi fL = 3.14\,k\Omega$

3. $f = X_L/2\pi L = 2.55\,MHz$

4. $I_{rms} = 15.9\,mA$

5. $P_{true} = 0\,W, P_r = 458\,mVAR$

SECTION 11–6   Inductor Applications

1. Conductive and radiated

2. Electromagnetic interference

3. It is placed on a wire to increase its inductance, creating an RF choke.

Application Assignment

1. $f_{max} = 143\,kHz\,(5\tau = 3.5\,\mu s)$

2. $f_{max} = 3.57\,kHz\,(5\tau = 140\,\mu s)$

3. If $f > f_{max}$, the inductor current would not reach final value because $T/2 < 5\tau$.

RELATED PROBLEMS FOR EXAMPLES

11–1   157 mH

11–2   150 μH

11–3   20.3 μH

11–4   227 ns

11–5 $I_F = 17.6\,mA, \tau = 147\,ns$

At 1τ: $i = 11.1\,mA$; $t = 147\,ns$

At 2τ: $i = 15.1\,mA$; $t = 294\,ns$

At 3τ: $i = 16.7\,mA$; $t = 441\,ns$

At 4τ: $i = 17.2\,mA$; $t = 588\,ns$

At 5τ: $i = 17.4\,mA$; $t = 735\,ns$

11–6   At 0.2 ms: $i = 0.215\,mA$

At 0.8 ms: $i = 0.0125\,mA$

11–7   10 V if R_W is neglected.

11–8   3.83 mA

11–9   6.7 mA

11–10   1100 Ω

11–11   573 mA

11–12 P_r decreases.

SELF-TEST

1. (c)   **2.** (d)   **3.** (c)   **4.** (b)   **5.** (d)   **6.** (a)   **7.** (d)

8. (c)   **9.** (b)   **10.** (a)   **11.** (d)

TROUBLESHOOTING: SYMPTOM AND CAUSE

1. (c)   **2.** (a)   **3.** (b)   **4.** (a)   **5.** (b)

12

RL CIRCUITS

CHAPTER OBJECTIVES

◆ Describe the relationship between current and voltage in an *RL* circuit

◆ Determine impedance and phase angle in a series *RL* circuit

◆ Analyze a series *RL* circuit

◆ Determine impedance and phase angle in a parallel *RL* circuit

◆ Analyze a parallel *RL* circuit

◆ Analyze series-parallel *RL* circuits

◆ Determine power in *RL* circuits

◆ Discuss some basic *RL* applications

◆ Troubleshoot *RL* circuits

KEY TERMS

◆ Impedance (Z)
◆ Phase angle
◆ Inductive susceptance (B_L)
◆ Admittance (Y)
◆ Reactive power

◆ Apparent power
◆ Power factor
◆ Frequency response
◆ Cutoff frequency
◆ Bandwidth

APPLICATION ASSIGNMENT PREVIEW

The assignment will be to identify the types of *RL* circuits contained in two sealed modules that have been removed from a communications system. You will use your knowledge of *RL* circuits and basic measurements to determine the circuit arrangement and component values. After studying this chapter, you should be able to complete the application assignment.

VISIT THE COMPANION WEBSITE

Study aids for this chapter are available at
http://www.prenhall.com/floyd

INTRODUCTION

An *RL* circuit contains both resistance and inductance. In this chapter, series and parallel *RL* circuits and their responses to sinusoidal voltages are covered. In addition, series-parallel combinations are examined. Power considerations in *RL* circuits are introduced, and practical aspects of the power factor are discussed. A method of improving the power factor is presented, and two basic *RL* circuit applications are covered. Troubleshooting common faults in *RL* circuits is also covered.

The methods for analyzing reactive circuits are similar to those you studied in dc circuits. Reactive circuit problems can be solved at only one frequency at a time, and phasor math must be used.

As you study this chapter, note both the differences and the similarities in the response of *RL* circuits compared to *RC* circuits.

12–1 SINUSOIDAL RESPONSE OF *RL* CIRCUITS

As with an *RC* circuit, all currents and voltages in any type of *RL* circuit are sinusoidal when the input voltage is sinusoidal. The inductance causes a phase shift between the voltage and the current that depends on the relative values of the resistance and the inductive reactance. Because of its winding resistance, the inductor is generally not as "ideal" as a resistor or capacitor. However, it will usually be treated as ideal for purposes of illustration.

After completing this section, you should be able to

◆ **Describe the relationship between current and voltage in an *RL* circuit**

   ◆ Discuss voltage and current waveforms

   ◆ Discuss phase shift

In an *RL* circuit, the resistor voltage and the current lag the source voltage. The inductor voltage leads the source voltage. Ideally, the phase angle between the current and the inductor voltage is always 90°. These generalized phase relationships are indicated in Figure 12–1. Notice how they differ from those of the *RC* circuit that was discussed in Chapter 10.

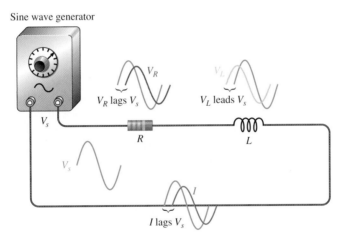

Sine wave generator

V_R
V_R lags V_s

V_L
V_L leads V_s

V_s

R L

V_s

I
I lags V_s

◀ FIGURE 12–1

Illustration of sinusoidal response with general phase relationships of V_R, V_L, and I relative to the source voltage. V_R and I are in phase; V_R and V_L are 90° out of phase with each other.

The amplitudes and the phase relationships of the voltages and current depend on the values of the resistance and the inductive reactance. When a circuit is purely inductive, the phase angle between the source voltage and the total current is 90°, with the current lagging the voltage. When there is a combination of both resistance and inductive reactance in a circuit, the phase angle is somewhere between zero and 90°, depending on the relative values of the resistance and the inductive reactance. Because all inductors have winding resistance, ideal conditions may be approached but never reached in practice.

SECTION 12–1 REVIEW Answers are at the end of the chapter.	1. A 1 kHz sinusoidal voltage is applied to an *RL* circuit. What is the frequency of the resulting current?
	2. When the resistance in an *RL* circuit is greater than the inductive reactance, is the phase angle between the source voltage and the total current closer to 0° or to 90°?

12–2 IMPEDANCE AND PHASE ANGLE OF SERIES *RL* CIRCUITS

The **impedance** of an *RL* circuit is the total opposition to sinusoidal current and its unit is the ohm. The **phase angle** is the phase difference between the total current and the source voltage.

After completing this section, you should be able to

◆ **Determine impedance and phase angle in a series *RL* circuit**

  ◆ Draw the impedance triangle

  ◆ Calculate impedance magnitude

  ◆ Calculate the phase angle

The impedance of a series *RL* circuit is determined by the resistance (*R*) and the inductive reactance (X_L), as indicated in Figure 12–2.

▶ FIGURE 12–2

Impedance of a series *RL* circuit.

In ac analysis, both *R* and X_L are treated as phasor quantities, as shown in the phasor diagram of Figure 12–3(a), with X_L appearing at a +90° angle with respect to *R*. This relationship comes from the fact that the inductor voltage leads the current, and thus the resistor voltage, by 90°. Since *Z* is the phasor sum of *R* and X_L, its phasor representation is as shown in Figure 12–3(b). A repositioning of the phasors, as shown in part (c), forms a right triangle. This formation, as you have learned, is called the *impedance triangle*. The length of each phasor represents the magnitude of the quantity, and θ is the phase angle between the source voltage and the current in the *RL* circuit.

▶ FIGURE 12–3

Development of the impedance triangle for a series *RL* circuit.

(a)

(b)

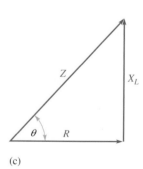

(c)

The magnitude of the impedance, *Z*, of the series *RL* circuit can be expressed in terms of the resistance and reactance as

Equation 12–1

$$Z = \sqrt{R^2 + X_L^2}$$

where *Z* is expressed in ohms.

The phase angle, θ, is expressed as

$$\theta = \tan^{-1}\left(\frac{X_L}{R}\right)$$

Equation 12–2

EXAMPLE 12–1

Determine the impedance and phase angle of the circuit in Figure 12–4. Draw the impedance triangle.

▶ FIGURE 12–4

Solution   The impedance is

$$Z = \sqrt{R^2 + X_L^2} = \sqrt{(5.6\,\text{k}\Omega)^2 + (10\,\text{k}\Omega)^2} = \textbf{11.5 k}\boldsymbol{\Omega}$$

The value of the phase angle is

$$\theta = \tan^{-1}\left(\frac{X_L}{R}\right) = \tan^{-1}\left(\frac{10\,\text{k}\Omega}{5.6\,\text{k}\Omega}\right) = \textbf{60.8°}$$

The source voltage leads the current by 60.8°. The impedance triangle is shown in Figure 12–5.

▶ FIGURE 12–5

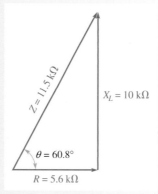

*Related Problem**   In a series *RL* circuit, $R = 1.8\,\text{k}\Omega$ and $X_L = 950\,\Omega$. Determine the impedance and phase angle.

---

*Answers are at the end of the chapter.

**SECTION 12–2
REVIEW**

1. Does the source voltage lead or lag the current in a series *RL* circuit?
2. What causes the phase angle in a series *RL* circuit?
3. How does the frequency response of an *RL* circuit differ from that of an *RC* circuit?
4. A series *RL* circuit has a resistance of 33 kΩ and an inductive reactance of 50 kΩ. Determine *Z* and θ.

12–3 ANALYSIS OF SERIES *RL* CIRCUITS

Ohm's law and Kirchhoff's voltage law are used in the analysis of series *RL* circuits to determine voltage, current, and impedance. Also, in this section *RL* lead and lag circuits are examined.

After completing this section, you should be able to

◆ **Analyze a series *RL* circuit**

   ◆ Apply Ohm's law and Kirchhoff's voltage law to series *RL* circuits

   ◆ Determine the phase relationships of the voltages and current

   ◆ Show how impedance and phase angle vary with frequency

   ◆ Discuss and analyze the *RL* lag circuit

   ◆ Discuss and analyze the *RL* lead circuit

Ohm's Law

The application of Ohm's law to series *RL* circuits involves the use of the quantities of Z, V, and I. The three equivalent forms of Ohm's law were stated in Chapter 10 for *RC* circuits. They apply also to *RL* circuits and are restated here:

$$V = IZ \qquad I = \frac{V}{Z} \qquad Z = \frac{V}{I}$$

The following example illustrates the use of Ohm's law.

EXAMPLE 12–2

The current in Figure 12–6 is 200 μA. Determine the source voltage.

▶ **FIGURE 12–6**

Solution   From Equation 11–10, the inductive reactance is

$$X_L = 2\pi fL = 2\pi(10\,\text{kHz})(100\,\text{mH}) = 6.28\,\text{k}\Omega$$

The impedance is

$$Z = \sqrt{R^2 + X_L^2} = \sqrt{(10\,\text{k}\Omega)^2 + (6.28\,\text{k}\Omega)^2} = 11.8\,\text{k}\Omega$$

Applying Ohm's law yields

$$V_s = IZ = (200\,\mu\text{A})(11.8\,\text{k}\Omega) = \textbf{2.36 V}$$

Related Problem   If the source voltage in Figure 12–6 is 5 V, what would be the current?

Open Multisim file E12-02 on your CD-ROM. Measure the current at 10 kHz, 5 kHz, and 20 kHz. Explain the results of your measurement.

Phase Relationships of the Current and Voltages

In a series *RL* circuit, the current is the same through both the resistor and the inductor. Thus, the resistor voltage is in phase with the current, and current lags the inductor voltage by 90°. Therefore, there is a phase difference of 90° between the resistor voltage, V_R, and the inductor voltage, V_L, as shown in the waveform diagram of Figure 12–7.

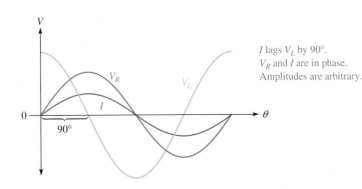

I lags V_L by 90°.
V_R and *I* are in phase.
Amplitudes are arbitrary.

◀ FIGURE 12–7

Phase relation of current and voltages in a series *RL* circuit.

From Kirchhoff's voltage law, the sum of the voltage drops must equal the source voltage. However, since V_R and V_L are not in phase with each other, they must be added as phasor quantities with V_L leading V_R by 90°, as shown in Figure 12–8(a). As shown in part (b), V_s is the phasor sum of V_R and V_L. This equation can be expressed as

$$V_s = \sqrt{V_R^2 + V_L^2}$$

Equation 12–3

The phase angle between the resistor voltage and the source voltage can be expressed as

$$\theta = \tan^{-1}\left(\frac{V_L}{V_R}\right)$$

Equation 12–4

Since the resistor voltage and the current are in phase, θ in Equation 12–4 also represents the phase angle between the source voltage and the current and is equivalent to $\tan^{-1}(X_L/R)$.

Figure 12–9 shows a voltage and current phasor diagram that represents the waveform diagram of Figure 12–7.

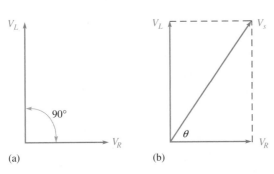

(a)   (b)

▲ FIGURE 12–8

Voltage phasor diagram for the waveforms in Figure 12–7.

▲ FIGURE 12–9

Voltage and current phasor diagram for the waveforms in Figure 12–7.

EXAMPLE 12–3

Determine the source voltage and the phase angle in Figure 12–10. Draw the voltage phasor diagram.

▶ FIGURE 12–10

Solution Since V_R and V_L are 90° out of phase, you cannot add them directly. The source voltage is the phasor sum of V_R and V_L.

$$V_s = \sqrt{V_R^2 + V_L^2} = \sqrt{(50 \text{ V})^2 + (35 \text{ V})^2} = \textbf{61 V}$$

The phase angle between the resistor voltage and the source voltage is

$$\theta = \tan^{-1}\left(\frac{V_L}{V_R}\right) = \tan^{-1}\left(\frac{35 \text{ V}}{50 \text{ V}}\right) = \textbf{35°}$$

The voltage phasor diagram is shown in Figure 12–11.

▶ FIGURE 12–11

$V_L = 35$ V $V_s = 61$ V
$\theta = 35°$
$V_R = 50$ V

Related Problem With the information given, can you determine the current in Figure 12–10?

Variation of Impedance and Phase Angle with Frequency

As you know, inductive reactance varies directly with frequency. When X_L increases, the total impedance also increases; and when X_L decreases, the total impedance decreases. Thus, *in an RL circuit, Z is directly dependent on frequency.*

Figure 12–12 illustrates how the voltages and current in a series *RL* circuit vary as the frequency increases or decreases, with the source voltage held at a constant value. Part (a) shows that as the frequency is increased, X_L increases; so more of the total voltage is dropped across the inductor. Also, Z increases as X_L increases, causing the current to decrease. A decrease in current causes less voltage across *R*.

Figure 12–12(b) shows that as the frequency is decreased, X_L decreases; so the voltage across the inductor decreases. Also, Z decreases as X_L decreases, causing the current to increase. An increase in current causes more voltage across *R*.

(a) As frequency is increased, *I* and V_R decrease and V_L increases.

(b) As frequency is decreased, *I* and V_R increase and V_L decreases.

▲ FIGURE 12–12

An illustration of how the variation of impedance affects the voltages and current as the source frequency is varied. The source voltage is held at a constant amplitude.

Changes in *Z* and X_L can be observed as shown in Figure 12–13. As the frequency increases, the voltage across *Z* remains constant because V_s is constant ($V_s = V_Z$), but the voltage across *L* increases. The decreasing current indicates that *Z* is increasing. It does so because of the inverse relationship stated in Ohm's law ($Z = V_Z/I$). The decreasing current also indicates that X_L is increasing. The increase in V_L corresponds to the increase in X_L.

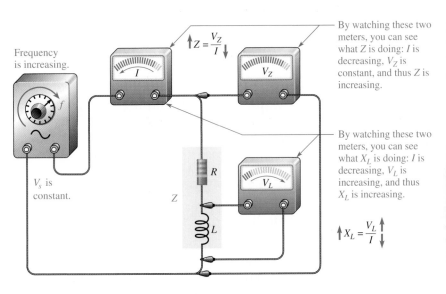

By watching these two meters, you can see what *Z* is doing: *I* is decreasing, V_Z is constant, and thus *Z* is increasing.

By watching these two meters, you can see what X_L is doing: *I* is decreasing, V_L is increasing, and thus X_L is increasing.

◀ FIGURE 12–13

Observing changes in *Z* and X_L with frequency by watching the meters and recalling Ohm's law.

HANDS ON TIP

As you know, some multimeters have a relatively low frequency response. There are other things of which you should be aware. One is that most ac meters are accurate only if the waveform being measured is sinusoidal. Another is that accuracy when measuring small ac voltage is usually less than for dc measurements. Finally, loading can affect the accuracy of meter readings.

Since X_L is the factor that introduces the phase angle in a series *RL* circuit, a change in X_L produces a change in the phase angle. As the frequency is increased, X_L becomes greater, and thus the phase angle increases. As the frequency is decreased, X_L becomes smaller, and thus the phase angle decreases. The angle between V_s and V_R is the phase angle of the circuit because *I* is in phase with V_R. The variations of phase angle with frequency are illustrated with the impedance triangle as shown in Figure 12–14.

▶ FIGURE 12–14

As the frequency increases, the phase angle θ increases.

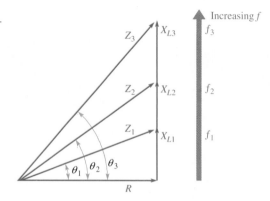

EXAMPLE 12–4

For the series *RL* circuit in Figure 12–15, determine the impedance and the phase angle for each of the following frequencies:

(a) 10 kHz   **(b)** 20 kHz   **(c)** 30 kHz

▶ FIGURE 12–15

Solution   **(a)** For $f = 10$ kHz, calculate the impedance as follows:

$$X_L = 2\pi f L = 2\pi (10 \text{ kHz})(20 \text{ mH}) = 1.26 \text{ k}\Omega$$

$$Z = \sqrt{R^2 + X_L^2} = \sqrt{(1.0 \text{ k}\Omega)^2 + (1.26 \text{ k}\Omega)^2} = \textbf{1.61 k}\Omega$$

The phase angle is

$$\theta = \tan^{-1}\left(\frac{X_L}{R}\right) = \tan^{-1}\left(\frac{1.26 \text{ k}\Omega}{1.0 \text{ k}\Omega}\right) = \textbf{51.6°}$$

(b) For $f = 20$ kHz,

$$X_L = 2\pi (20 \text{ kHz})(20 \text{ mH}) = 2.51 \text{ k}\Omega$$

$$Z = \sqrt{(1.0 \text{ k}\Omega)^2 + (2.51 \text{ k}\Omega)^2} = \textbf{2.70 k}\Omega$$

$$\theta = \tan^{-1}\left(\frac{2.51 \text{ k}\Omega}{1.0 \text{ k}\Omega}\right) = \textbf{68.3°}$$

(c) For $f = 30$ kHz,

$$X_L = 2\pi (30 \text{ kHz})(20 \text{ mH}) = 3.77 \text{ k}\Omega$$

$$Z = \sqrt{(1.0 \text{ k}\Omega)^2 + (3.77 \text{ k}\Omega)^2} = \textbf{3.90 k}\Omega$$

$$\theta = \tan^{-1}\left(\frac{3.77 \text{ k}\Omega}{1.0 \text{ k}\Omega}\right) = \textbf{75.1°}$$

Notice that as the frequency increases, X_L, Z, and θ also increase.

Related Problem   Determine Z and θ in Figure 12–15 if $f = 100$ kHz.

RL Lag Circuit

The **RL lag circuit** is a phase shift circuit in which the output voltage lags the input voltage by a specified angle, ϕ. A basic series *RL* lag circuit is shown in Figure 12–16(a). Notice that the output voltage is taken across the resistor and the input voltage is the total voltage applied across the circuit. The relationship of the voltages is shown in the phasor diagram in Figure 12–16(b), and a waveform diagram is shown in Figure 12–16(c). Notice that the output voltage, V_{out}, lags V_{in} by an angle, designated ϕ, that is the same as the circuit phase angle. The angles are equal, of course, because V_R and I are in phase with each other.

(a) A basic *RL* lag circuit

(b) Phasor voltage diagram showing phase lag between V_{in} and V_{out}

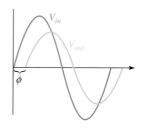

(c) Input and output waveforms

▲ FIGURE 12–16

The *RL* lag circuit ($V_{out} = V_R$).

The phase lag, ϕ, can be expressed as

$$\phi = \tan^{-1}\left(\frac{X_L}{R}\right)$$

Equation 12–5

EXAMPLE 12–5

Calculate the phase lag for each circuit in Figure 12–17.

▸ FIGURE 12–17

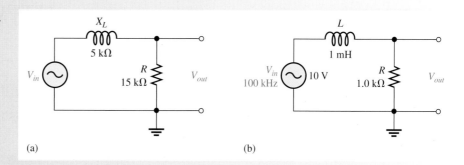

(a) (b)

Solution   For the circuit in Figure 12–17(a),

$$\phi = \tan^{-1}\left(\frac{X_L}{R}\right) = \tan^{-1}\left(\frac{5\,k\Omega}{15\,k\Omega}\right) = \mathbf{18.4°}$$

The output lags the input by 18.4°.

For the circuit in Figure 12–17(b), first determine the inductive reactance.

$$X_L = 2\pi f L = 2\pi(100\,kHz)(1\,mH) = 628\,\Omega$$

The phase lag is

$$\phi = \tan^{-1}\left(\frac{X_L}{R}\right) = \tan^{-1}\left(\frac{628\ \Omega}{1.0\ k\Omega}\right) = \mathbf{32.1°}$$

The output lags the input by 32.1°.

Related Problem In a certain lag circuit, $R = 5.6\ k\Omega$ and $X_L = 3.5\ k\Omega$. Determine the phase lag between input and output.

The phase-lag circuit can be considered as a voltage divider with a portion of the input voltage dropped across L and a portion across R. The output voltage can be determined with the following formula:

Equation 12–6
$$V_{out} = \left(\frac{R}{\sqrt{R^2 + X_L^2}}\right)V_{in}$$

EXAMPLE 12–6

The input voltage in Figure 12–17(b) of Example 12–5 has an rms value of 10 V. Determine the output voltage for the lag circuit shown in Figure 12–17(b). Draw the waveform relationships for the input and output voltages. The phase lag (32.1°) and X_L (628 Ω) were found in Example 12–5.

Solution Use Equation 12–6 to determine the output voltage for the lag circuit in Figure 12–17(b).

$$V_{out} = \left(\frac{R}{\sqrt{R^2 + X_L^2}}\right)V_{in} = \left(\frac{1.0\ k\Omega}{1.18\ k\Omega}\right)10\ V = \mathbf{8.47\ V\ rms}$$

The waveforms are shown in Figure 12–18.

▶ **FIGURE 12–18**

Related Problem In a lag circuit, $R = 4.7\ k\Omega$ and $X_L = 6\ k\Omega$. If the rms input voltage is 20 V, what is the output voltage?

Open Multisim file E12-06 on your CD-ROM. Measure the output voltage and compare to the calculated value.

Effects of Frequency on the Lag Circuit Since the circuit phase angle and the phase lag are the same, an increase in frequency causes an increase in phase lag. Also, an increase in frequency causes a decrease in the magnitude of the output voltage because X_L becomes greater and more of the total voltage is dropped across the inductor and less across the resistor. Figure 12–19 illustrates the changes in phase lag, ϕ, and output voltage magnitude with frequency.

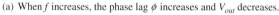

(a) When f increases, the phase lag ϕ increases and V_{out} decreases.   (b) When f decreases, ϕ decreases and V_{out} increases.

▲ **FIGURE 12–19**

Illustration of how the frequency affects the phase lag and the output voltage in an *RL* lag circuit with the amplitude of V_{in} held constant.

RL Lead Circuit

The ***RL* lead circuit** is a phase shift circuit in which the output voltage leads the input voltage by a specified angle, ϕ. A basic series *RL* lead circuit is shown in Figure 12–20(a). Notice how this circuit differs from the lag circuit. Here the output voltage is taken across the inductor rather than across the resistor. The relationship of the voltages is shown in the phasor diagram of Figure 12–20(b) and in the waveform plot of Figure 12–20(c). Notice that the output voltage, V_{out}, leads V_{in} by an angle (phase lead) that is the difference between $90°$ and the circuit phase angle θ.

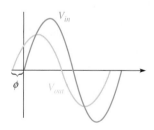

◀ **FIGURE 12–20**

The *RL* lead circuit ($V_{out} = V_L$).

(a) A basic *RL* lead circuit   (b) Phasor voltage diagram   (c) Input and output voltage
                                showing V_{out} leading V_{in} waveforms

Since $\theta = \tan^{-1}(X_L/R)$, the phase lead, ϕ, can be expressed as

$$\phi = 90° - \tan^{-1}\left(\frac{X_L}{R}\right)$$

Equation 12–7

Equivalently,

$$\phi = \tan^{-1}\left(\frac{R}{X_L}\right)$$

Again, the phase-lead circuit can be considered as a voltage divider with the voltage across L being the output. The expression for the output voltage is

$$V_{out} = \left(\frac{X_L}{\sqrt{R^2 + X_L^2}}\right)V_{in}$$

Equation 12–8

EXAMPLE 12–7

Determine the amount of phase lead and output voltage in the lead circuit in Figure 12–21.

▶ FIGURE 12–21

Solution   First, determine the inductive reactance.

$$X_L = 2\pi fL = 2\pi(1\ \text{kHz})(50\ \text{mH}) = 314\ \Omega$$

The phase lead is

$$\phi = 90° - \tan^{-1}\left(\frac{X_L}{R}\right) = 90° - \tan^{-1}\left(\frac{314\ \Omega}{680\ \Omega}\right) = \mathbf{65.2°}$$

The output leads the input by 65.2°.
   The output voltage is

$$V_{out} = \left(\frac{X_L}{\sqrt{R^2 + X_L^2}}\right)V_{in} = \left(\frac{314\ \Omega}{\sqrt{(680\ \Omega)^2 + (314\ \Omega)^2}}\right)5\ \text{V} = \mathbf{2.1\ V}$$

Related Problem   In a certain lead circuit, $R = 2.2\ \text{k}\Omega$ and $X_L = 1\ \text{k}\Omega$. What is the phase lead?

Open Multisim file E12-07 on your CD-ROM. Measure the output voltage and compare to the calculated value.

Effects of Frequency on the Lead Circuit   Since the circuit phase angle, θ, increases as frequency increases, the phase lead between the input and the output voltages decreases. Also, the amplitude of the output voltage increases as the frequency increases because X_L becomes greater and more of the total input voltage is dropped across the inductor. Figure 12–22 illustrates the changes in the phase lead (ϕ) and output voltage with frequency.

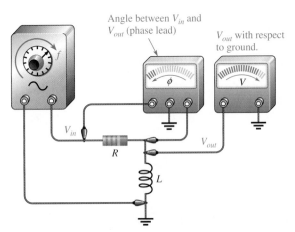

(a) When f increases, the phase lead ϕ decreases and V_{out} increases.

(b) When f decreases, ϕ increases and V_{out} decreases.

▲ FIGURE 12–22

Illustration of how the frequency affects the phase lead and the output voltage in an *RL* lead circuit with the amplitude of V_{in} held constant.

**SECTION 12–3
REVIEW**

1. In a certain series *RL* circuit, V_R = 2 V and V_L = 3 V. What is the magnitude of the total voltage?

2. In Question 1, what is the phase angle?

3. When the frequency of the source voltage in a series *RL* circuit is increased, what happens to the inductive reactance? What happens to the impedance? What happens to the phase angle?

4. A certain *RL* lead circuit consists of a 3.3 kΩ resistor and a 15 mH inductor. Determine the phase lead between input and output at a frequency of 5 kHz.

5. An *RL* lag circuit has the same component values as the lead circuit in Question 4. What is the magnitude of the output voltage at 5 kHz when the input is 10 V rms?

12–4 IMPEDANCE AND PHASE ANGLE OF PARALLEL *RL* CIRCUITS

In this section, you will learn how to determine the impedance and phase angle of a parallel *RL* circuit. Also, inductive susceptance and admittance of a parallel *RL* circuit are introduced.

After completing this section, you should be able to

◆ **Determine impedance and phase angle in a parallel *RL* circuit**

   ◆ Express total impedance in a product-over-sum form

   ◆ Express the phase angle in terms of R and X_L

   ◆ Determine inductive susceptance and admittance

   ◆ Convert admittance to impedance

A basic parallel *RL* circuit is shown in Figure 12–23. The expression for the impedance, using the product-over-sum rule, is

$$Z = \frac{RX_L}{\sqrt{R^2 + X_L^2}}$$

Equation 12–9

The phase angle between the source voltage and the total current can be expressed in terms of R and X_L as

$$\theta = \tan^{-1}\left(\frac{R}{X_L}\right)$$

Equation 12–10

◀ **FIGURE 12–23**

Parallel *RL* circuit.

EXAMPLE 12–8

For each circuit in Figure 12–24, determine the impedance and the phase angle.

FIGURE 12–24

(a)   (b)

Solution   For the circuit in Figure 12–24(a), the impedance and phase angle are

$$Z = \frac{RX_L}{\sqrt{R^2 + X_L^2}} = \frac{(100\,\Omega)(50\,\Omega)}{\sqrt{(100\,\Omega)^2 + (50\,\Omega)^2}} = \textbf{44.7}\,\boldsymbol{\Omega}$$

$$\theta = \tan^{-1}\left(\frac{R}{X_L}\right) = \tan^{-1}\left(\frac{100\,\Omega}{50\,\Omega}\right) = \textbf{63.4°}$$

For the circuit in Figure 12–24(b),

$$Z = \frac{(1.0\,k\Omega)(2\,k\Omega)}{\sqrt{(1.0\,k\Omega)^2 + (2\,k\Omega)^2}} = \textbf{894}\,\boldsymbol{\Omega}$$

$$\theta = \tan^{-1}\left(\frac{1.0\,k\Omega}{2\,k\Omega}\right) = \textbf{26.6°}$$

The voltage leads the current, compared to the parallel *RC* case where the voltage lags the current.

Related Problem   In a parallel *RL* circuit $R = 10\,k\Omega$ and $X_L = 14\,k\Omega$. Find Z and θ.

Conductance, Susceptance, and Admittance

As you know from Section 10–4, conductance (*G*) is the reciprocal of resistance, susceptance (*B*) is the reciprocal of reactance, and admittance (*Y*) is the reciprocal of impedance. For parallel *RL* circuits, **conductance (*G*)** is expressed as

Equation 12–11

$$G = \frac{1}{R}$$

Inductive susceptance (*B$_L$*) is expressed as

Equation 12–12

$$B_L = \frac{1}{X_L}$$

Admittance (*Y*) is expressed as

Equation 12–13

$$Y = \frac{1}{Z}$$

As with the *RC* circuit, the unit for *G*, *B$_L$*, and *Y* is the siemens (S).

In the basic parallel *RL* circuit shown in Figure 12–25(a), the total admittance is the phasor sum of the conductance and the inductive susceptance, as shown in part (b).

Equation 12–14

$$Y_{tot} = \sqrt{G^2 + B_L^2}$$

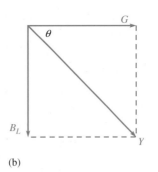

$$Y = \sqrt{G^2 + B_L^2}$$

Admittance in a parallel *RL* circuit.

(a)   (b)

EXAMPLE 12–9

Determine the total admittance for the circuit in Figure 12–26; then convert it to impedance.

▶ FIGURE 12–26

Solution   To determine Y, first calculate the values for G and B_L. Since $R = 330\ \Omega$,

$$G = \frac{1}{R} = \frac{1}{330\ \Omega} = 3.03\ \text{mS}$$

The inductive reactance is

$$X_L = 2\pi f L = 2\pi(1000\ \text{Hz})(100\ \text{mH}) = 628\ \Omega$$

The inductive susceptance is

$$B_L = \frac{1}{X_L} = \frac{1}{628\ \Omega} = 1.59\ \text{mS}$$

Therefore, the total admittance is

$$Y_{tot} = \sqrt{G^2 + B_L^2} = \sqrt{(3.03\ \text{mS})^2 + (1.59\ \text{mS})^2} = \textbf{3.42 mS}$$

Convert to impedance.

$$Z = \frac{1}{Y_{tot}} = \frac{1}{3.42\ \text{mS}} = \textbf{292 }\boldsymbol{\Omega}$$

Related Problem   What is the total admittance of the circuit in Figure 12–26 if f is increased to 2 kHz?

SECTION 12–4
REVIEW

1. If $Y = 50\ \text{mS}$, what is the value of Z?
2. In a certain parallel *RL* circuit, $R = 47\ \Omega$ and $X_L = 75\ \Omega$. Determine the admittance.
3. In the circuit of Question 2, does the total current lead or lag the source voltage and by what phase angle?

12–5 ANALYSIS OF PARALLEL *RL* CIRCUITS

Ohm's law and Kirchhoff's current law are used in the analysis of *RL* circuits. Current and voltage relationships in a parallel *RL* circuit are examined.

After completing this section, you should be able to

 ◆ **Analyze a parallel *RL* circuit**

  ◆ Apply Ohm's law and Kirchhoff's current law to parallel *RL* circuits

  ◆ Determine total current and phase angle

The following example applies Ohm's law to the analysis of a parallel *RL* circuit.

EXAMPLE 12–10

Determine the total current and the phase angle in the circuit of Figure 12–27.

▶ FIGURE 12–27

Solution First, determine the total admittance. The inductive reactance is

$$X_L = 2\pi fL = 2\pi(1.5\text{ kHz})(150\text{ mH}) = 1.41\text{ k}\Omega$$

The conductance is

$$G = \frac{1}{R} = \frac{1}{2.2\text{ k}\Omega} = 455\ \mu\text{S}$$

The inductive susceptance is

$$B_L = \frac{1}{X_L} = \frac{1}{1.41\text{ k}\Omega} = 709\ \mu\text{S}$$

Therefore, the total admittance is

$$Y_{tot} = \sqrt{G^2 + B_L^2} = \sqrt{(455\ \mu\text{S})^2 + (709\ \mu\text{S})^2} = 842\ \mu\text{S}$$

Next, use Ohm's law to calculate the total current.

$$I_{tot} = VY_{tot} = (10\text{ V})(842\ \mu\text{S}) = \textbf{8.42 mA}$$

The phase angle is

$$\theta = \tan^{-1}\left(\frac{R}{X_L}\right) = \tan^{-1}\left(\frac{2.2\text{ k}\Omega}{1.41\text{ k}\Omega}\right) = \textbf{57.3°}$$

The total current is 8.42 mA, and it lags the source voltage by 57.3°.

Related Problem Determine the total current and the phase angle if the frequency is reduced to 800 Hz in Figure 12–27.

Open Multisim file E12-10 on your CD-ROM. Measure the total current and each branch current. Change the frequency to 800 Hz and measure I_{tot}.

Phase Relationships of the Currents and Voltages

Figure 12–28(a) shows all the currents and voltages in a basic parallel *RL* circuit. As you can see, the source voltage, V_s, appears across both the resistive and the inductive branches, so V_s, V_R, and V_L are all in phase and of the same magnitude. The total current, I_{tot}, divides at the junction into the two branch currents, I_R and I_L. The current and voltage phasor diagram is shown in Figure 12–28(b).

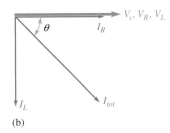

◀ FIGURE 12–28

Currents and voltages in a parallel *RL* circuit. The current directions shown in part (a) are instantaneous and, of course, reverse when the source voltage reverses during each cycle.

(a)   (b)

The current through the resistor is in phase with the voltage. The current through the inductor lags the voltage and the resistor current by 90°. By Kirchhoff's current law, the total current is the phasor sum of the two branch currents. The total current is expressed as

$$I_{tot} = \sqrt{I_R^2 + I_L^2}$$

Equation 12–15

The phase angle between the resistor current and the total current is

$$\theta = \tan^{-1}\left(\frac{I_L}{I_R}\right)$$

Equation 12–16

EXAMPLE 12–11   Determine the value of each current in Figure 12–29, and describe the phase relationship of each with the source voltage. Draw the current phasor diagram.

▶ FIGURE 12–29

Solution   Calculate the resistor current, the inductor current, and the total current.

$$I_R = \frac{V_s}{R} = \frac{12\text{ V}}{220\text{ }\Omega} = \textbf{54.5 mA}$$

$$I_L = \frac{V_s}{X_L} = \frac{12\text{ V}}{150\text{ }\Omega} = \textbf{80 mA}$$

$$I_{tot} = \sqrt{I_R^2 + I_L^2} = \sqrt{(54.5\text{ mA})^2 + (80\text{ mA})^2} = \textbf{96.8 mA}$$

The phase angle is

$$\theta = \tan^{-1}\left(\frac{R}{X_L}\right) = \tan^{-1}\left(\frac{220\text{ }\Omega}{150\text{ }\Omega}\right) = 55.7°$$

The resistor current is 54.5 mA and is in phase with the source voltage. The inductor current is 80 mA and lags the source voltage by 90°. The total current is 96.8 mA and lags the source voltage by 55.7°. The current phasor diagram is shown in Figure 12–30.

▶ FIGURE 12–30

Related Problem   Find I_{tot} and θ if $X_L = 300\text{ }\Omega$ in Figure 12–30.

SECTION 12–5 REVIEW

1. The admittance of a parallel *RL* circuit is 4 mS, and the source voltage is 8 V. What is the total current?

2. In a certain parallel *RL* circuit, the resistor current is 12 mA, and the inductor current is 20 mA. Determine the phase angle and the total current.

3. What is the phase angle between the inductor current and the source voltage in a parallel *RL* circuit?

12–6   ANALYSIS OF SERIES-PARALLEL *RL* CIRCUITS

The concepts studied in the previous sections are used to analyze circuits with combinations of both series and parallel *R* and *L* components.

After completing this section, you should be able to

◆ **Analyze series-parallel *RL* circuits**

  ◆ Determine total impedance and phase angle

  ◆ Calculate currents and voltages

The following two examples illustrate the procedures used to analyze a series-parallel reactive circuit.

EXAMPLE 12–12

In the series-parallel *RL* circuit of Figure 12–31, determine the values of the following:

(a) Z_{tot} (b) I_{tot} (c) θ

▶ FIGURE 12–31

Solution (a) First, calculate the magnitudes of the inductive reactances.

$$X_{L1} = 2\pi f L_1 = 2\pi(5 \text{ kHz})(250 \text{ mH}) = 7.85 \text{ k}\Omega$$
$$X_{L2} = 2\pi f L_2 = 2\pi(5 \text{ kHz})(100 \text{ mH}) = 3.14 \text{ k}\Omega$$

One approach is to find the series equivalent resistance and inductive reactance for the parallel portion of the circuit; then add the resistances ($R_1 + R_{eq}$) to get the total resistance and add the reactances ($X_{L1} + X_{L(eq)}$) to get the total reactance. From these totals, you can determine the total impedance.
Determine the impedance of the parallel portion (Z_2) as follows:

$$G_2 = \frac{1}{R_2} = \frac{1}{3.3 \text{ k}\Omega} = 303 \text{ }\mu\text{S}$$

$$B_{L2} = \frac{1}{X_{L2}} = \frac{1}{3.14 \text{ k}\Omega} = 318 \text{ }\mu\text{S}$$

$$Y_2 = \sqrt{G_2^2 + B_L^2} = \sqrt{(303 \text{ }\mu\text{S})^2 + (318 \text{ }\mu\text{S})^2} = 439 \text{ }\mu\text{S}$$

Then

$$Z_2 = \frac{1}{Y_2} = \frac{1}{439 \text{ }\mu\text{S}} = 2.28 \text{ k}\Omega$$

The phase angle associated with the parallel portion of the circuit is

$$\theta_p = \tan^{-1}\left(\frac{R_2}{X_{L2}}\right) = \tan^{-1}\left(\frac{3.3 \text{ k}\Omega}{3.14 \text{ k}\Omega}\right) = 46.4°$$

The series equivalent values for the parallel portion are found using Equations 10–23 and 10–24, adapted for parallel *RL* circuits as follows:

$$R_{eq} = Z_2\cos\theta_p = (2.28 \text{ k}\Omega)\cos(46.4°) = 1.57 \text{ k}\Omega$$
$$X_{L(eq)} = Z_2\sin\theta_p = (2.28 \text{ k}\Omega)\sin(46.4°) = 1.65 \text{ k}\Omega$$

The total circuit resistance is

$$R_{tot} = R_1 + R_{eq} = 4.7 \text{ k}\Omega + 1.57 \text{ k}\Omega = 6.27 \text{ k}\Omega$$

The total circuit reactance is

$$X_{L(tot)} = X_{L1} + X_{L(eq)} = 7.85 \text{ k}\Omega + 1.65 \text{ k}\Omega = 9.50 \text{ k}\Omega$$

The total circuit impedance is

$$Z_{tot} = \sqrt{R_{tot}^2 + X_{L(tot)}^2} = \sqrt{(6.27 \text{ k}\Omega)^2 + (9.50 \text{ k}\Omega)^2} = \mathbf{11.4 \text{ k}\Omega}$$

(b) Use Ohm's law to find the total current.

$$I_{tot} = \frac{V_s}{Z_{tot}} = \frac{10\text{ V}}{11.4\text{ k}\Omega} = \textbf{877 }\boldsymbol{\mu}\textbf{A}$$

(c) To find the phase angle, view the circuit as a series combination of R_{tot} and $X_{L(tot)}$. The phase angle by which I_{tot} lags V_s is

$$\theta = \tan^{-1}\left(\frac{X_{L(tot)}}{R_{tot}}\right) = \tan^{-1}\left(\frac{9.50\text{ k}\Omega}{6.27\text{ k}\Omega}\right) = \textbf{56.6°}$$

Related Problem   **(a)** Determine the voltage across the series part of the circuit in Figure 12–31.

(b) Determine the voltage across the parallel part of the circuit.

Open Multisim file E12-12 on your CD-ROM. Measure the current through each component. Measure the voltage across Z_1 and Z_2.

EXAMPLE 12–13

Determine the voltage across each component in Figure 12–32. Draw a voltage phasor diagram.

▶ **FIGURE 12–32**

Solution   First, calculate X_{L1} and X_{L2}.

$$X_{L1} = 2\pi fL_1 = 2\pi(2\text{ MHz})(50\text{ }\mu\text{H}) = 628\text{ }\Omega$$
$$X_{L2} = 2\pi fL_2 = 2\pi(2\text{ MHz})(100\text{ }\mu\text{H}) = 1.26\text{ k}\Omega$$

Now, determine the impedance of each branch.

$$Z_1 = \sqrt{R_1^2 + X_{L1}^2} = \sqrt{(330\text{ }\Omega)^2 + (628\text{ }\Omega)^2} = 709\text{ }\Omega$$
$$Z_2 = \sqrt{R_2^2 + X_{L2}^2} = \sqrt{(1.0\text{ k}\Omega)^2 + (1.26\text{ k}\Omega)^2} = 1.61\text{ k}\Omega$$

Calculate each branch current.

$$I_1 = \frac{V_s}{Z_1} = \frac{10\text{ V}}{709\text{ }\Omega} = 14.1\text{ mA}$$

$$I_2 = \frac{V_s}{Z_2} = \frac{10\text{ V}}{1.61\text{ k}\Omega} = 6.21\text{ mA}$$

Now, use Ohm's law to find the voltage across each component.

$$V_{R1} = I_1R_1 = (14.1\text{ mA})(330\text{ }\Omega) = \textbf{4.65 V}$$
$$V_{L1} = I_1X_{L1} = (14.1\text{ mA})(628\text{ }\Omega) = \textbf{8.85 V}$$
$$V_{R2} = I_2R_2 = (6.21\text{ mA})(1.0\text{ k}\Omega) = \textbf{6.21 V}$$
$$V_{L2} = I_2X_{L2} = (6.21\text{ mA})(1.26\text{ k}\Omega) = \textbf{7.82 V}$$

Now determine the values of the angles associated with each branch current.

$$\theta_1 = \tan^{-1}\left(\frac{X_{L1}}{R_1}\right) = \tan^{-1}\left(\frac{628\ \Omega}{330\ \Omega}\right) = 62.3°$$

$$\theta_2 = \tan^{-1}\left(\frac{X_{L2}}{R_2}\right) = \tan^{-1}\left(\frac{1.26\ k\Omega}{1.0\ k\Omega}\right) = 51.6°$$

Thus, I_1 lags V_s by 62.3°, and I_2 lags V_s by 51.6°, as indicated in Figure 12–33(a).

FIGURE 12–33

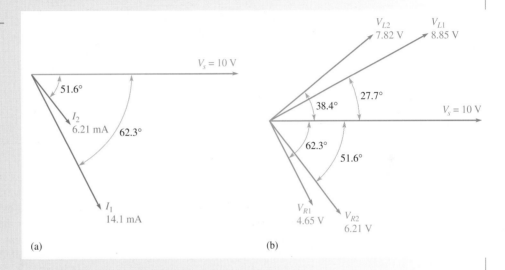

(a)

(b)

The phase relationships of the voltages are determined as follows:

◆ V_{R1} is in phase with I_1 and therefore lags V_s by 62.3°.

◆ V_{L1} leads I_1 by 90°, so its angle is 90° − 62.3° = 27.7°.

◆ V_{R2} is in phase with I_2 and therefore lags V_s by 51.6°.

◆ V_{L2} leads I_2 by 90°, so its angle is 90° − 51.6° = 38.4°.

These phase relationships are shown in Figure 12–33(b).

Related Problem   What effect does an increase in frequency have on the total current in Figure 12–33?

 Open Multisim file E12-13 on your CD-ROM. Measure the voltage across each component and compare to the calculated values.

SECTION 12–6
REVIEW

1. Determine the total current for the circuit in Figure 12–32. *Hint:* Find the sum of the horizontal components of I_1 and I_2 and the sum of the vertical components of I_1 and I_2. Then apply the Pythagorean theorem to get I_{tot}.
2. What is the total impedance of the circuit in Figure 12–32?

12–7 POWER IN *RL* CIRCUITS

In a purely resistive ac circuit, all of the energy delivered by the source is dissipated in the form of heat by the resistance. In a purely inductive ac circuit, all of the energy delivered by the source is stored by the inductor in its magnetic field during a portion of the voltage cycle and then returned to the source during another portion of the cycle so that there is no net energy conversion to heat. When there is both resistance and inductance, some of the energy is alternately stored and returned by the inductance and some is dissipated by the resistance. The amount of energy converted to heat is determined by the relative values of the resistance and the inductive reactance.

After completing this section, you should be able to

◆ **Determine power in *RL* circuits**

   ◆ Explain true and reactive power

   ◆ Draw the power triangle

   ◆ Define *power factor*

   ◆ Explain power factor correction

When the resistance in a series *RL* circuit is greater than the inductive reactance, more of the total energy delivered by the source is dissipated by the resistance than is stored and returned by the inductor. When the reactance is greater than the resistance, more of the total energy is stored and returned than is converted to heat.

As you know, the power dissipated in a resistor is called the true power. The power in an inductor is **reactive power** and is expressed as

Equation 12–17

$$P_r = I^2 X_L$$

The generalized power triangle for a series *RL* circuit is shown in Figure 12–34. The **apparent power,** P_a, is the resultant of the true power, P_{true}, and the reactive power, P_r.

▶ FIGURE 12–34

Generalized power triangle for an *RL* circuit.

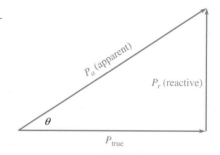

P_a (apparent)

P_r (reactive)

θ

P_{true}

EXAMPLE 12–14

Determine the power factor, the true power, the reactive power, and the apparent power in Figure 12–35.

▶ FIGURE 12–35

R X_L

1.0 kΩ   2 kΩ

V_s
10 V

Solution   The impedance of the circuit is

$$Z = \sqrt{R^2 + X_L^2} = \sqrt{(1.0\,k\Omega)^2 + (2\,k\Omega)^2} = 2.24\,k\Omega$$

The current is

$$I = \frac{V_s}{Z} = \frac{10\,V}{2.24\,k\Omega} = 4.46\,mA$$

The phase angle is

$$\theta = \tan^{-1}\left(\frac{X_L}{R}\right) = \tan^{-1}\left(\frac{2\,k\Omega}{1.0\,k\Omega}\right) = 63.4°$$

Therefore, the power factor is

$$PF = \cos\theta = \cos(63.4°) = \mathbf{0.448}$$

The true power is

$$P_{\text{true}} = V_s I \cos\theta = (10\,V)(4.46\,mA)(0.448) = \mathbf{20\,mW}$$

The reactive power is

$$P_r = I^2 X_L = (4.46\,mA)^2(2\,k\Omega) = \mathbf{39.8\,mVAR}$$

The apparent power is

$$P_a = I^2 Z = (4.46\,mA)^2(2.24\,k\Omega) = \mathbf{44.6\,mVA}$$

Related Problem   If the frequency in Figure 12–35 is increased, what happens to P_{true}, P_r, and P_a?

The Power Factor

Recall that the **power factor** equals the cosine of θ ($PF = \cos\theta$). As the phase angle between the source voltage and the total current increases, the power factor decreases, indicating an increasingly reactive circuit. A smaller power factor indicates less true power and more reactive power. The power factor of inductive loads is called a *lagging power factor* because the current lags the source voltage.

As you learned in Chapter 10, the power factor (PF) is important in determining how much useful power (true power) is transferred to a load. The highest power factor is 1, which indicates that all of the current to a load is in phase with the voltage (resistive). When the power factor is 0, all of the current to a load is 90° out of phase with the voltage (reactive).

Generally, a power factor as close to 1 as possible is desirable because then most of the power transferred from the source to the load is useful or true power. True power goes only one way—from source to load—and performs work on the load in terms of energy dissipation. Reactive power simply goes back and forth between the source and the load with no net work being done. Energy must be used in order for work to be done.

Many practical loads have inductance as a result of their particular function, and it is essential for their proper operation. Examples are transformers, electric motors, and speakers, to name a few. Therefore, inductive (and capacitive) loads are important considerations.

To see the effect of the power factor on system requirements, refer to Figure 12–36. This figure shows a representation of a typical inductive load consisting effectively of inductance and resistance in parallel. Part (a) shows a load with a relatively low power factor (0.75), and part (b) shows a load with a relatively high power factor (0.95). Both loads dissipate equal amounts of power as indicated by the wattmeters. Thus, an equal amount of work is done on both loads.

Although both loads are equivalent in terms of the amount of work done (true power), the low-power factor load in Figure 12–36(a) draws more current from the source than does the high-power factor load in Figure 12–36(b), as indicated by the ammeters. Therefore, the source

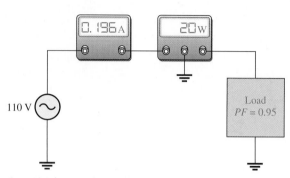

(a) A lower power factor means more total current for a given power dissipation (watts). A larger source is required to deliver the true power (watts).

(b) A higher power factor means less total current for a given power dissipation. A smaller source can deliver the same true power (watts).

▲ FIGURE 12–36

Illustration of the effect of the power factor on system requirements such as source rating (VA) and conductor size.

in part (a) must have a higher VA rating than the one in part (b). Also, the lines connecting the source to the load must be a larger wire gauge than those in part (b), a condition that becomes significant when very long transmission lines are required, such as in power distribution.

Figure 12–36 has demonstrated that a higher power factor is an advantage in delivering power more efficiently to a load. Also, because the electric company charges for apparent power, it is less expensive to have a high power factor.

Power Factor Correction The power factor of an inductive load can be increased by the addition of a capacitor in parallel, as shown in Figure 12–37. The capacitor compensates for the phase lag of the total current by creating a capacitive component of current that is 180° out of phase with the inductive component. This has a canceling effect and reduces the phase angle, thus increasing the power factor as well as the total current, as illustrated in the figure.

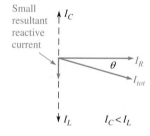

(a) Total current is the resultant of I_R and I_L.

(b) I_C subtracts from I_L, leaving only a small reactive current, thus decreasing I_{tot} and the phase angle.

▲ FIGURE 12–37

Example of how the power factor can be increased by the addition of a compensating capacitor (C_c). As θ decreases, *PF* increases.

SECTION 12–7 REVIEW

1. To which component in an *RL* circuit is the power dissipation due?
2. Calculate the power factor when $\theta = 50°$.
3. A certain series *RL* circuit consists of a 470 Ω resistor and an inductive reactance of 620 Ω at the operating frequency. Determine P_{true}, P_r, and P_a when $I = 100$ mA.

12–8 BASIC APPLICATIONS

Two applications of *RL* circuits are covered in this section. The first application is a basic frequency selective (filter) circuit. The second application is the switching regulator, a widely used circuit in power supplies because of its high efficiency. The switching regulator uses other components, but the *RL* circuit is emphasized.

After completing this section, you should be able to

♦ Describe two examples of *RL* circuit applications

  ♦ Discuss how the *RL* circuit operates as a filter

  ♦ Discuss the advantage of an inductor in a switching regulator

The *RL* Circuit as a Filter

Like *RC* circuits, series *RL* circuits also exhibit a frequency-selective characteristic.

Low-Pass Characteristic You have seen what happens to the phase angle and the output voltage in a series *RC* lag circuit. In terms of the filtering action of the series *RL* circuit, the variation in the magnitude of the output voltage as a function of frequency is important.

Figure 12–38 shows the filtering action of a series *RL* circuit using a specific series of measurements in which the frequency starts at 100 Hz and is increased in increments up to 20 kHz. At each value of frequency, the output voltage is measured. As you can see, the inductive reactance increases as frequency increases, thus causing less voltage to be dropped across the resistor while the input voltage is held at a constant 10 V throughout each step.

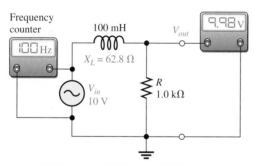

(a) $f = 100$ Hz, $X_L = 62.8\ \Omega$, $V_{out} = 9.98$ V

(b) $f = 1$ kHz, $X_L = 628\ \Omega$, $V_{out} = 8.47$ V

(c) $f = 10$ kHz, $X_L = 6.28$ kΩ, $V_{out} = 1.57$ V

(d) $f = 20$ kHz, $X_L = 12.6$ kΩ, $V_{out} = 791$ mV

▲ FIGURE 12–38

Example of low-pass filtering action. Winding resistance has been neglected. As the input frequency increases, the output voltage decreases.

(a) $f = 10$ Hz, $X_L = 6.28$ Ω, $V_{out} = 62.8$ mV

(b) $f = 100$ Hz, $X_L = 62.8$ Ω, $V_{out} = 627$ mV

(c) $f = 1$ kHz, $X_L = 628$ Ω, $V_{out} = 5.32$ V

(d) $f = 10$ kHz, $X_L = 6.28$ kΩ, $V_{out} = 9.88$ V

▲ FIGURE 12–39

Example of high-pass filtering action. Winding resistance has been neglected. As the input frequency increases, the output voltage increases.

The **frequency response** curve for these particular values would appear similar to the response curve in Figure 10–50 for the low-pass *RC* circuit.

High-Pass Characteristic   To illustrate *RL* high-pass filtering action, Figure 12–39 shows a series of specific measurements. The frequency starts at 10 Hz and is increased in increments up to 10 kHz. As you can see, the inductive reactance increases as the frequency increases, thus causing more voltage to be dropped across the inductor. Again, when the values are plotted, the response curve is similar to the one for the high-pass *RC* circuit that was shown in Figure 10–52.

The Cutoff Frequency of an RL Circuit   The frequency at which the inductive reactance equals the resistance in a low-pass or high-pass *RL* circuit is called the **cutoff frequency** and is designated f_c. This condition is expressed as $2\pi f_c L = R$. Solving for f_c results in the following formula:

Equation 12–18

$$f_c = \frac{R}{2\pi L}$$

As with the *RC* circuit, the output voltage is 70.7% of its maximum value at f_c. In a high-pass circuit, all frequencies above f_c are considered to be passed and all those below f_c are considered to be rejected. The reverse, of course, is true for a low-pass circuit. **Bandwidth**, defined in Chapter 10, applies to both *RC* and *RL* series circuits.

The Switching Regulator

In high frequency switching power supplies, small inductors are used as an essential part of the filter section. A switching power supply is much more efficient at converting ac to dc than any other type of supply. For this reason it is widely used in computers and other electronic systems. A switching regulator precisely controls the dc voltage. One type of switching regulator is shown in Figure 12–40. It uses a transistor switch to change unregulated dc to high

◀ FIGURE 12–40

Switching regulator block diagram.

frequency pulses. The output is the average value of the pulses. The pulse width is controlled by the pulse width modulator, which rapidly turns on and off a transistor switch and then is filtered by the filter section to produce regulated dc (Ripple in the figure is exaggerated to show the cycle). The pulse width modulator can increase pulse width if the output drops, or decrease it if the output rises, thus maintaining a constant average output for varying conditions.

Figure 12–41 illustrates the basic filtering action. The filter consists of a diode, an inductor, and a capacitor. The diode is a one-way device for current that you will study in a devices course. In this application the diode acts as an on-off switch that allows current in only one direction.

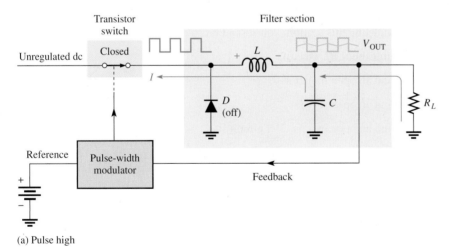

◀ FIGURE 12–41

Switching regulator action.

(a) Pulse high

(b) Pulse low

An important component of the filter section is the inductor, which in this type of regulator will always have current in it. The average voltage and the load resistor determine the amount of current. Recall that Lenz's law states that an induced voltage is created across a coil that opposes a *change* in current. When the transistor switch is closed, the pulse is high and current is through the inductor and the load as shown in Figure 12–41(a). The diode is off at this time. Notice that the inductor has an induced voltage across it that opposes a change in current. When the pulse goes low, as in Figure 12–41(b), the transistor is off and the inductor develops a voltage in the opposite direction than before. The diode acts as a closed switch, which provides a path for current. This action tends to keep the load current constant. The capacitor adds to this smoothing action by charging and discharging a small amount during the process.

SECTION 12–8 REVIEW	1. To achieve a low-pass characteristic with a series *RL* circuit, across which component is the output taken?
	2. What is the major advantage of a switching regulator?
	3. What happens to the pulse width of a switching regulator if the output voltage drops?

12–9 TROUBLESHOOTING

Typical component failures have an effect on the frequency response of basic *RL* circuits. An example of troubleshooting using the APM (analysis, planning, and measurement) method is presented.

After completing this section, you should be able to

◆ **Troubleshoot *RL* circuits**

   ◆ Find an open inductor

   ◆ Find an open resistor

   ◆ Find an open in a parallel circuit

   ◆ Find an inductor with shorted windings

Effect of an Open Inductor   The most common failure mode for inductors occurs when the winding opens as a result of excessive current or a mechanical contact failure. It is easy to see how an open coil affects the operation of a basic series *RL* circuit, as shown in Figure 12–42. Obviously, there is no path for current, so the resistor voltage is zero and the total source voltage appears across the open inductor.

▶ FIGURE 12–42

Effect of an open coil.

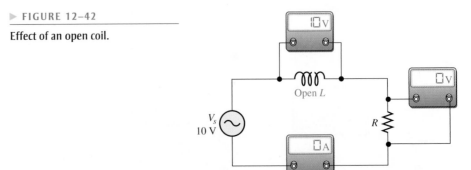

Effect of an Open Resistor When the resistor is open, there is no current, and the inductor voltage is zero. The total input voltage appears across the open resistor, as shown in Figure 12–43.

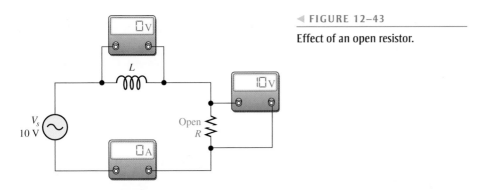

◀ FIGURE 12–43

Effect of an open resistor.

Open Components in Parallel Circuits In a parallel *RL* circuit, an open resistor or inductor will cause the total current to decrease because the total impedance will increase. Obviously, the branch with the open component will have zero current. Figure 12–44 illustrates these conditions.

(a) Before failure

(b) After *L* opens

▲ FIGURE 12–44

Effect of an open component in a parallel circuit with V_s constant.

Effect of an Inductor with Shorted Windings Although a rare occurrence, it is possible for some of the windings of coils to short together as a result of damaged insulation. This failure mode is much less likely than the open coil. A sufficient number of shorted windings may result in a reduction in inductance because the inductance of a coil is proportional to the square of the number of turns.

Other Troubleshooting Considerations

The failure of a circuit to work properly is not always the result of a faulty component. A loose wire, a bad contact, or a poor solder joint can cause an open circuit. A short can be caused by a wire clipping or solder splash. Things as simple as not plugging in a power supply or a function generator happen more often than you might think. Wrong values in a circuit (such as an incorrect resistor value), the function generator set at the wrong frequency, or the wrong output connected to the circuit can cause improper operation.

Always check to make sure that the instruments are properly connected to the circuits and to a power outlet. Also, look for obvious things such as a broken or loose contact, a connector that is not completely plugged in, or a piece of wire or a solder bridge that could be shorting something out.

The following example illustrates a troubleshooting approach to a circuit containing inductors and resistors using the APM (analysis, planning, and measurement) method and half-splitting.

EXAMPLE 12–15

The circuit represented by the schematic in Figure 12–45 has no output voltage, which is across R_4. The circuit is physically constructed on a protoboard. Use your troubleshooting skills to find the problem.

FIGURE 12–45

Solution   Apply the APM method to this troubleshooting problem.

Analysis: First think of the possible causes for the circuit to have no output voltage.

1. There is no source voltage or the frequency is so high that the inductors appear to be open because their reactances are extremely high compared to the resistance values.

2. There is a short between one of the resistors and ground. Either a resistor could be shorted, or there could be some physical short. A shorted resistor is not a very common fault.

3. There is an open between the source and the output. This would prevent current and thus cause the output voltage to be zero. An inductor could be open, or the conductive path could be open due to a broken or loose connecting wire or a bad protoboard contact.

4. There is an incorrect component value. A resistor could be so small that the voltage across it is negligible. An inductor could be so large that its reactance at the input frequency is extremely high.

Planning: You decide to make some visual checks for problems such as the function generator power cord not plugged in or the frequency set at an incorrect value. Also, broken leads, shorted leads, as well as an incorrect resistor color code or inductor value often can be found visually. If nothing is discovered after a visual check, then you will make voltage measurements to track down the cause of the problem. You decide to use a digital oscilloscope and a DMM to make the measurements using the half-splitting technique to more quickly isolate the fault.

Measurement: Assume that you find that the function generator is plugged in and the frequency setting appears to be correct. Also, you find no visible opens or shorts during your visual check, and the component values are correct.

The first step in the measurement process is to check the voltage from the source with the scope. Assume a 10 V rms sine wave with a frequency of 5 kHz is observed at the circuit input as shown in Figure 12–46(a). The correct ac voltage is present, so *the first possible cause has been eliminated.*

Next, check for a short by disconnecting the source and placing the DMM (set on the ohmmeter function) across each resistor. If any resistor is shorted (unlikely), the meter will read zero or a very small resistance. Assuming the meter readings are okay, *the second possible cause has been eliminated.*

Since the voltage has been "lost" somewhere between the input and the output, you must now look for the voltage. You reconnect the source and, using the half-splitting approach, measure the voltage at point ③ (the middle of the circuit) with respect to

(a) Scope shows the correct voltage at the input.

(b) A zero voltage at point ③ indicates the fault is between point ③ and the source. A reading of 8.31 V at point ② shows that L_2 is open.

▲ FIGURE 12–46

ground. The DMM test lead is placed on the right lead of inductor L_2, as indicated in Figure 12–46(b). Assume the voltage at this point is zero. This tells you that the part of the circuit to the right of point ③ is probably okay and the fault is in the circuit between point ③ and the source.

Now, you begin tracing the circuit back toward the source looking for the voltage (you could also start from the source and work forward). Placing the meter test lead on point ②, at the left lead of inductor L_2, results in a reading of 8.31 V as shown in Figure 12–46(b). This, of course, indicates that L_2 is open. Fortunately, in this case, a component, and not a contact on the board, is faulty. It is usually easier to replace a component than to repair a bad contact.

Related Problem   Suppose you had measured 0 V at the left lead of L_2 and 10 V at the right lead of L_1. What would this have indicated?

**SECTION 12–9
REVIEW**

1. Describe the effect of an inductor with shorted windings on the response of a series *RL* circuit.

2. In the circuit of Figure 12–47, indicate whether I_{tot}, V_{R1}, and V_{R2} increase or decrease as a result of *L* opening.

FIGURE 12–47

Application Assignment

PUTTING YOUR KNOWLEDGE TO WORK

You are given two sealed modules that have been removed from a communications system that is being modified. Each module has three terminals and is labeled as an *RL* circuit, but no specifications are given. Your assignment is to test the modules to determine the type of circuit and the component values.

The sealed modules have three terminals labeled IN, GND, and OUT as shown in Figure 12–48. You will apply your knowledge of series *RL* circuits and some basic measurements to determine the internal circuit configuration and the component values.

Step 1: Resistance Measurements of Module 1

Determine the arrangement of the components and the values of the resistor and winding resistance for module 1 indicated by the meter readings in Figure 12–48.

Step 2: AC Measurements of Module 1

Determine the inductance value for module 1 indicated by the test setup in Figure 12–49.

Step 3: Resistance Measurements of Module 2

Determine the arrangement of the components and the values of the resistor and the winding resistance for module 2 indicated by the meter readings in Figure 12–50.

▲ FIGURE 12–48

Resistance measurements of module 1.

▲ FIGURE 12–49

AC measurements for module 1.

▶ FIGURE 12–50

Resistance measurements of module 2.

▲ FIGURE 12–51

AC measurements for module 2.

Step 4: AC Measurements of Module 2

Determine the inductance value for module 2 indicated by the test setup in Figure 12–51.

Review

1. If the inductor in module 1 were open, what would you measure on the output with the test setup of Figure 12–49?

2. If the inductor in module 2 were open, what would you measure on the output with the test setup of Figure 12–51?

SUMMARY

◆ When a sinusoidal voltage is applied to an *RL* circuit, the current and all the voltage drops are also sine waves.

◆ Total current in an *RL* circuit always lags the source voltage.

◆ The resistor voltage is always in phase with the current.

◆ In an ideal inductor, the voltage always leads the current by 90°.

◆ In an *RL* lag circuit, the output voltage lags the input voltage in phase.

◆ In an *RL* lead circuit, the output voltage leads the input voltage in phase.

◆ In an *RL* circuit, the impedance is determined by both the resistance and the inductive reactance combined.

◆ Impedance is expressed in units of ohms.

◆ The impedance of an *RL* circuit varies directly with frequency.

◆ The phase angle (θ) of a series *RL* circuit varies directly with frequency.

◆ You can determine the impedance of a circuit by measuring the source voltage and the total current and then applying Ohm's law.

◆ In an *RL* circuit, part of the power is resistive and part reactive.

◆ The phasor combination of resistive power (true power) and reactive power is called *apparent power.*

◆ The power factor indicates how much of the apparent power is true power.

◆ A power factor of 1 indicates a purely resistive circuit, and a power factor of 0 indicates a purely reactive circuit.

◆ In a circuit that exhibits frequency selectivity, certain frequencies are passed to the output while others are rejected.

KEY TERMS

Key terms and other bold terms in the chapter are defined in the end-of-book glossary.

Admittance (Y)   A measure of the ability of a reactive circuit to permit current; the reciprocal of impedance. The unit is the siemens (S).

Apparent power (P_a)   The phasor combination of resistive power (true power) and reactive power. The unit is the volt-ampere (VA).

Bandwidth   The range of frequencies that is considered to be passed from the input to the output of a circuit.

Cutoff frequency   The frequency at which the output voltage of a filter is 70.7% of the maximum output voltage.

Frequency response   In electric circuits, the variation in the output voltage (or current) over a specified range of frequencies.

Impedance (Z)   The total opposition to sinusoidal current expressed in ohms.

Inductive susceptance (B_L)   The reciprocal of inductive reactance. The unit is the siemens.

Phase angle   The angle between the source voltage and the total current in a reactive circuit.

Power factor   The relationship between volt-amperes and true power or watts. Volt-amperes multiplied by the power factor equals true power.

FORMULAS

12–1 $Z = \sqrt{R^2 + X_L^2}$ Series RL impedance

12–2 $\theta = \tan^{-1}\left(\dfrac{X_L}{R}\right)$ Series RL phase angle

12–3 $V_s = \sqrt{V_R^2 + V_L^2}$ Total voltage in a series RL circuit

12–4 $\theta = \tan^{-1}\left(\dfrac{V_L}{V_R}\right)$ Series RL phase angle

12–5 $\phi = \tan^{-1}\left(\dfrac{X_L}{R}\right)$ Phase angle of lag circuit

12–6 $V_{out} = \left(\dfrac{R}{\sqrt{R^2 + X_L^2}}\right)V_{in}$ Output voltage of lag circuit

12–7 $\phi = 90° - \tan^{-1}\left(\dfrac{X_L}{R}\right)$ Phase angle of lead circuit

12–8 $V_{out} = \left(\dfrac{X_L}{\sqrt{R^2 + X_L^2}}\right)V_{in}$ Output voltage of lead circuit

12–9 $Z = \dfrac{RX_L}{\sqrt{R^2 + X_L^2}}$ Parallel RL impedance

12–10 $\theta = \tan^{-1}\left(\dfrac{R}{X_L}\right)$ Parallel RL phase angle

12–11 $G = \dfrac{1}{R}$ Conductance

12–12 $B_L = \dfrac{1}{X_L}$ Inductive susceptance

12–13 $Y = \dfrac{1}{Z}$ Admittance

12–14 $Y_{tot} = \sqrt{G^2 + B_L^2}$ Total admittance

12–15 $I_{tot} = \sqrt{I_R^2 + I_L^2}$ Total current in parallel RL circuit

12–16 $\theta = \tan^{-1}\left(\dfrac{I_L}{I_R}\right)$ Parallel RL phase angle

$$12\text{–}17 \quad P_r = I^2 X_L \qquad\qquad\qquad \text{Reactive power}$$

$$12\text{–}18 \quad f_c = \frac{R}{2\pi L} \qquad\qquad\qquad \text{Cutoff frequency of } RL \text{ circuit}$$

SELF-TEST

Answers are at the end of the chapter.

1. In a series *RL* circuit, the resistor voltage
   - (a) leads the source voltage
   - (b) lags the source voltage
   - (c) is in phase with the source voltage
   - (d) is in phase with the current
   - (e) answers (a) and (d)
   - (f) answers (b) and (d)

2. When the frequency of the voltage applied to a series *RL* circuit is increased, the impedance
   - (a) decreases   (b) increases   (c) does not change

3. When the frequency of the voltage applied to a series *RL* circuit is decreased, the phase angle
   - (a) decreases   (b) increases   (c) does not change

4. If the frequency is doubled and the resistance is halved, the impedance of a series *RL* circuit
   - (a) doubles   (b) halves
   - (c) remains constant   (d) cannot be determined without values

5. To reduce the current in a series *RL* circuit, the frequency should be
   - (a) increased   (b) decreased   (c) constant

6. In a series *RL* circuit, 10 V rms is measured across the resistor, and 10 V rms is measured across the inductor. The peak value of the source voltage is
   - (a) 14.14 V   (b) 28.28 V   (c) 10 V   (d) 20 V

7. The voltages in Question 6 are measured at a certain frequency. To make the resistor voltage greater than the inductor voltage, the frequency is
   - (a) increased   (b) decreased   (c) doubled   (d) not a factor

8. When the resistor voltage in a series *RL* circuit becomes greater than the inductor voltage, the phase angle
   - (a) increases   (b) decreases   (c) is not affected

9. When the frequency is increased, the impedance of a parallel *RL* circuit
   - (a) increases   (b) decreases   (c) remains constant

10. In a parallel *RL* circuit, there are 2 A rms in the resistive branch and 2 A rms in the inductive branch. The total rms current is
    - (a) 4 A   (b) 5.656 A   (c) 2 A   (d) 2.828 A

11. You are observing two voltage waveforms on an oscilloscope. The time base (sec/div) of the scope is set to 10 μs. One half-cycle of the waveforms covers the ten horizontal divisions. The positive-going zero crossing of one waveform is at the leftmost division, and the positive-going zero crossing of the other is three divisions to the right. The phase angle between these two waveforms is
    - (a) 18°   (b) 36°   (c) 54°   (d) 180°

12. Which of the following power factors results in the least energy conversion to heat in an *RL* circuit?
    - (a) 1   (b) 0.9   (c) 0.5   (d) 0.1

13. If a load is purely inductive and the reactive power is 10 VAR, the apparent power is
    - (a) 0 VA   (b) 10 VA   (c) 14.14 VA   (d) 3.16 VA

14. For a certain load, the true power is 10 W and the reactive power is 10 VAR. The apparent power is
    - (a) 5 VA   (b) 20 VA   (c) 14.14 VA   (d) 100 VA

15. The cutoff frequency of a certain low-pass *RL* circuit is 20 kHz. The bandwidth is
    - (a) 20 kHz   (b) 40 kHz   (c) 0 kHz   (d) unknown

TROUBLESHOOTING: SYMPTOM AND CAUSE

The purpose of these exercises is to help develop thought processes essential to troubleshooting. Answers are at the end of the chapter.

Determine the cause for each set of symptoms. Refer to Figure 12–52.

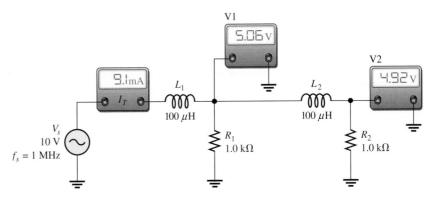

▲ FIGURE 12–52

The ac meters indicate the correct readings for this circuit.

1. *Symptom:* The ammeter reading is 15.9 mA, and the voltmeter 1 and voltmeter 2 readings are zero.

   Cause:

   (a) L_1 is open.

   (b) L_2 is open.

   (c) R_1 is shorted.

2. *Symptom:* The ammeter reading is 8.47 mA, the voltmeter 1 reading is 8.47 V, and the voltmeter 2 reading is 0 V.

   Cause:

   (a) L_2 is open.

   (b) R_2 is open.

   (c) R_2 is shorted.

3. *Symptom:* The ammeter reading is slightly less than 20 mA, and both voltmeter readings are slightly less than 10 V.

   Cause:

   (a) L_1 is shorted.

   (b) R_1 is open.

   (c) The source frequency is incorrectly set very low.

4. *Symptom:* The ammeter reading is 4.55 mA, voltmeter 1 reads 2.53 V, and voltmeter 2 reads 2.15 V.

   Cause:

   (a) The source frequency is incorrectly set at 500 kHz.

   (b) The source voltage is incorrectly set at 5 V.

   (c) The source frequency is incorrectly set at 2 MHz.

5. *Symptom:* All meter readings are zero.

   Cause:

   (a) The voltage source is faulty or off.

   (b) L_1 is open.

   (c) Either (a) or (b)

PROBLEMS

Answers to odd-numbered problems are at the end of the book.

BASIC PROBLEMS

SECTION 12–1 **Sinusoidal Response of RL Circuits**

1. A 15 kHz sinusoidal voltage is applied to a series RL circuit. Determine the frequency of I, V_R, and V_L.

2. What are the waveshapes of I, V_R, and V_L in Problem 1?

SECTION 12–2 **Impedance and Phase Angle of Series RL Circuits**

3. Find the impedance of each circuit in Figure 12–53.

▶ FIGURE 12–53

(a)   (b)

4. Determine the impedance and phase angle in each circuit in Figure 12–54.

▶ FIGURE 12–54

(a)   (b)

5. In Figure 12–55, determine the impedance at each of the following frequencies:
   (a) 100 Hz   (b) 500 Hz   (c) 1 kHz   (d) 2 kHz

▶ FIGURE 12–55

6. Determine the values of R and X_L in a series RL circuit for the following values of impedance and phase angle:
   (a) $Z = 20\ \Omega, \theta = 45°$ (b) $Z = 500\ \Omega, \theta = 35°$
   (c) $Z = 2.5\ k\Omega, \theta = 72.5°$ (d) $Z = 998\ \Omega, \theta = 45°$

SECTION 12–3 **Analysis of Series RL Circuits**

7. If the frequency of the source is increased to 1 kHz in the circuit in Figure 12–54(a), calculate the voltage across the total resistance.

8. Determine the voltage across the total resistance and across the total inductance in Figure 12–54(b).

9. Find the current for each circuit of Figure 12–53.

10. Calculate the total current in each circuit of Figure 12–54.

11. Determine θ for the circuit in Figure 12–56.

12. If the inductance in Figure 12–56 is doubled, does θ increase or decrease, and by how many degrees?

13. Draw the waveforms for V_s, V_R, and V_L in Figure 12–56. Show the proper phase relationships.

14. For the circuit in Figure 12–57, find V_R and V_L for each of the following frequencies:

    (a) 60 Hz   **(b)** 200 Hz   **(c)** 500 Hz   **(d)** 1 kHz

▲ FIGURE 12–56

▲ FIGURE 12–57

15. For the lag circuit in Figure 12–58, determine the phase lag of the output voltage with respect to the input for the following frequencies:

    (a) 1 Hz   **(b)** 100 Hz   **(c)** 1 kHz   **(d)** 10 kHz

16. Repeat Problem 15 for the lead circuit in Figure 12–59.

▲ FIGURE 12–58

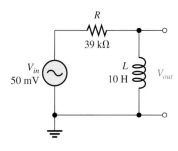

▲ FIGURE 12–59

SECTION 12–4   **Impedance and Phase Angle of Parallel *RL* Circuits**

17. What is the impedance for the circuit in Figure 12–60?

18. Repeat Problem 17 for the following frequencies:

    (a) 1.5 kHz   **(b)** 3 kHz   **(c)** 5 kHz   **(d)** 10 kHz

19. At what frequency does X_L equal R in Figure 12–60?

SECTION 12–5   **Analysis of Parallel *RL* Circuits**

20. Find the total current and each branch current in Figure 12–61.

▲ FIGURE 12–60   ▲ FIGURE 12–61

21. Determine the following quantities in Figure 12–62:

(a) Z (b) I_R (c) I_L (d) I_{tot} (e) θ

22. Convert the circuit in Figure 12–63 to an equivalent series form.

▲ FIGURE 12–62

▲ FIGURE 12–63

SECTION 12–6 Analysis of Series-Parallel *RL* Circuits

23. Determine the voltage across each element in Figure 12–64.

24. Is the circuit in Figure 12–64 predominantly resistive or predominantly inductive?

25. Find the current in each branch and the total current in Figure 12–64.

▶ FIGURE 12–64

SECTION 12–7 Power in *RL* Circuits

26. In a certain *RL* circuit, the true power is 100 mW, and the reactive power is 340 mVAR. What is the apparent power?

27. Determine the true power and the reactive power in Figure 12–56.

28. What is the power factor in Figure 12–61?

29. Determine P_{true}, P_r, P_a, and *PF* for the circuit in Figure 12–64. Draw the power triangle.

SECTION 12–8 Basic Applications

30. Plot the response curve for the circuit in Figure 12–58. Show the output voltage versus frequency in 1 kHz increments from 0 Hz to 5 kHz.

31. Using the same procedure as in Problem 30, plot the response curve for Figure 12–59.

32. Draw the voltage phasor diagram for each circuit in Figures 12–58 and 12–59 for a frequency of 8 kHz.

SECTION 12–9 Troubleshooting

33. Determine the voltage across each component in Figure 12–65 if L_1 were open.

34. Determine the output voltage in Figure 12–66 for each of the following failure modes:

(a) L_1 open   (b) L_2 open   (c) R_1 open   (d) a short across R_2

▶ FIGURE 12–65

▶ FIGURE 12–66

ADVANCED PROBLEMS

35. Determine the voltage across the inductors in Figure 12–67.

▶ FIGURE 12–67

36. Is the circuit in Figure 12–67 predominantly resistive or predominantly inductive?

37. Find the total current in Figure 12–67.

38. For the circuit in Figure 12–68, determine the following:

    (a) Z_{tot} **(b)** I_{tot} **(c)** θ **(d)** V_L **(e)** V_{R3}

39. For the circuit in Figure 12–69, determine the following:

    (a) I_{R1} **(b)** I_{L1} **(c)** I_{L2} **(d)** I_{R2}

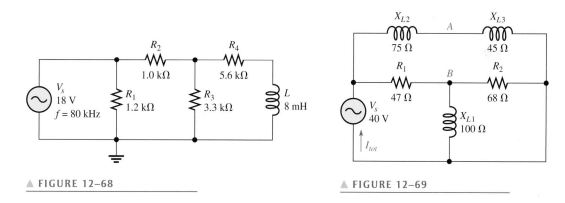

▲ FIGURE 12–68   ▲ FIGURE 12–69

40. Determine the phase shift and attenuation (ratio of V_{out} to V_{in}) from the input to the output for the circuit in Figure 12–70.

41. Determine the attenuation from the input to the output for the circuit in Figure 12–71.

▲ FIGURE 12–70

▲ FIGURE 12–71

42. Design an ideal inductive switching circuit that will provide a momentary voltage of 2.5 kV from a 12 V dc source when a switch is thrown instantaneously from one position to another. The drain on the source must not exceed 1 A.

43. Draw the schematic for the circuit in Figure 12–72 and determine if the waveforms on the scope are correct. If there is a fault in the circuit, identify it.

(a) Oscilloscope display

(b) Circuit with leads connected

▲ FIGURE 12–72

MULTISIM TROUBLESHOOTING PROBLEMS

44. Open file P12-44. Determine if there is a fault and, if so, identify it.

45. Open file P12-45. Determine if there is a fault and, if so, identify it.

46. Open file P12-46. Determine if there is a fault and, if so, identify it.

47. Open file P12-47. Determine if there is a fault and, if so, identify it.

48. Open file P12-48. Determine if there is a fault and, if so, identify it.

49. Open file P12-49. Determine if there is a fault and, if so, identify it.

ANSWERS

SECTION REVIEWS

SECTION 12–1 **Sinusoidal Response of *RL* Circuits**

1. The current frequency is at 1 kHz.

2. θ is closer to $0°$ when $R > X_L$.

SECTION 12–2 **Impedance and Phase Angle of Series *RL* Circuits**

1. V_s leads I.

2. The inductive reactance produces the phase angle.

3. An *RL* circuit has an opposite phase angle compared to an *RC* circuit.

4. $Z = \sqrt{R^2 + X_L^2} = 59.9\ \text{k}\Omega;\ \theta = \tan^{-1}(X_L/R) = 56.6°$

SECTION 12–3 **Analysis of Series *RL* Circuits**

1. $V_s = \sqrt{V_R^2 + V_L^2} = 3.61\ \text{V}$

2. $\theta = \tan^{-1}(X_L/V_R) = 56.3°$

3. When f increases, X_L increases, Z increases, and θ increases.

4. $\phi = 90° - \tan^{-1}(X_L/R) = 81.9°$

5. $V_{out} = \left(\dfrac{R}{\sqrt{R^2 + X_L^2}} \right) V_{in} = 9.90\ \text{V}$

SECTION 12–4   Impedance and Phase Angle of Parallel *RL* Circuits

1. $Z = 1/Y = 20 \, \Omega$
2. $Y = \sqrt{G^2 + B_L^2} = 25 \, \text{mS}$
3. I_{tot} lags V_s by 32.1°.

SECTION 12–5   Analysis of Parallel *RL* Circuits

1. $I_{tot} = V_s Y = 32 \, \text{mA}$
2. $\theta = \tan^{-1}(I_L/I_R) = 59.0°$; $I_{tot} = \sqrt{I_R^2 + I_L^2} = 23.3 \, \text{mA}$
3. $\theta = 90°$

SECTION 12–6   Analysis of Series-Parallel *RL* Circuits

1. $I_{tot} = \sqrt{(I_1 \cos \theta_1 + I_2 \cos \theta_2)^2 + (I_1 \sin \theta_1 + I_2 \sin \theta_2)^2} = 20.2 \, \text{mA}$
2. $Z = V_s/I_{tot} = 494 \, \Omega$

SECTION 12–7   Power in *RL* Circuits

1. Power dissipation is in the resistor.
2. $PF = \cos 50° = 0.643$
3. $P_{\text{true}} = I^2 R = 4.7 \, \text{W}$; $P_r = I^2 X_L = 6.2 \, \text{VAR}$; $P_a = \sqrt{P_{\text{true}}^2 + P_r^2} = 7.78 \, \text{VA}$

SECTION 12–8   Basic Applications

1. Output is across the resistor.
2. The switching regulator is more efficient than other types.
3. The pulse width increases.

SECTION 12–9   Troubleshooting

1. Shorted windings reduce L and thereby reduce X_L at any given frequency.
2. I_{tot} decreases, V_{R1} decreases, and V_{R2} increases when L opens.

Application Assignment

1. 0 V on output
2. Output same as input

RELATED PROBLEMS FOR EXAMPLES

12–1 2.04 kΩ; 27.8°
12–2 423 μA
12–3 No
12–4 12.6 kΩ; 85.5°
12–5 32°
12–6 12.3 V rms
12–7 65.6°
12–8 8.14 kΩ; 35.5°
12–9 3.13 mS
12–10 14.0 mA; 71.1°
12–11 67.6 mA; 36.3°
12–12 **(a)** 8.04 V   **(b)** 2.00 V
12–13 Current decreases.
12–14 P_{true}, P_r, and P_a decrease.
12–15 Open connection between L_1 and L_2

SELF-TEST

1. (f) **2.** (b) **3.** (a) **4.** (d) **5.** (a) **6.** (d) **7.** (b)
8. (b) **9.** (a) **10.** (d) **11.** (c) **12.** (d) **13.** (b) **14.** (c)
15. (a)

TROUBLESHOOTING: SYMPTOM AND CAUSE

1. (c) **2.** (a) **3.** (c) **4.** (b) **5.** (c)

RLC CIRCUITS AND RESONANCE

13

CHAPTER OUTLINE

CHAPTER OBJECTIVES

◆ Determine the impedance and phase angle of a series *RLC* circuit

◆ Analyze series *RLC* circuits

◆ Analyze a circuit for series resonance

◆ Analyze series resonant filters

◆ Analyze parallel *RLC* circuits

◆ Analyze a circuit for parallel resonance

◆ Analyze the operation of parallel resonant filters

◆ Discuss some applications of resonant circuits

KEY TERMS

◆ Series resonance
◆ Resonant frequency
◆ Band-pass filter
◆ Cutoff frequency
◆ Half-power frequency
◆ Decibel (dB)
◆ Selectivity
◆ Band-stop filter
◆ Parallel resonance

APPLICATION ASSIGNMENT PREVIEW

The application assignment in this chapter requires that you plot a frequency response curve for a resonant filter with unknown characteristics. From the frequency response measurements, you will identify the type of filter and determine the resonant frequency and the bandwidth. After studying this chapter, you should be able to complete the application assignment.

VISIT THE COMPANION WEBSITE

Study aids for this chapter are available at
http://www.prenhall.com/floyd

INTRODUCTION

In this chapter, you will learn about frequency response of circuits with combinations of resistance, capacitance, and inductance (*RLC*). Both series and parallel *RLC* circuits, including the concepts of series and parallel resonance will be discussed.

Because it is the basis for frequency selectivity, resonance in electrical circuits is very important to the operation of many types of electronic systems, particularly in the area of communications. For example, the ability of a radio or television receiver to select a certain frequency transmitted by a particular station and to eliminate frequencies from other stations is based on the principle of resonance.

The operation of both band-pass and band-stop filters is based on resonance of circuits containing inductance and capacitance, and these filters are discussed in this chapter. Also, certain system applications are presented.

13–1 IMPEDANCE AND PHASE ANGLE OF SERIES RLC CIRCUITS

A series RLC circuit contains resistance, inductance, and capacitance. Since inductive reactance and capacitive reactance have opposite effects on the circuit phase angle, the total reactance is less than either individual reactance.

After completing this section, you should be able to

◆ **Determine the impedance and phase angle of a series RLC circuit**

　◆ Calculate total reactance

　◆ Determine whether a circuit is predominately inductive or capacitive

A series RLC circuit is shown in Figure 13–1. It contains resistance, inductance, and capacitance.

▶ FIGURE 13–1

Series RLC circuit.

As you know, inductive reactance (X_L) causes the total current to lag the source voltage. Capacitive reactance (X_C) has the opposite effect: It causes the current to lead the voltage. Thus, X_L and X_C tend to offset each other. When they are equal, they cancel, and the total reactance is zero. In any case, the total reactance in a series circuit is

Equation 13–1
$$X_{tot} = |X_L - X_C|$$

The term $|X_L - X_C|$ means the absolute value of the difference of the two reactances. That is, the sign of the result is considered positive no matter which reactance is greater. For example, $3 - 7 = -4$, but the absolute value is

$$|3 - 7| = 4$$

When $X_L > X_C$, the circuit is predominantly inductive; and when $X_C > X_L$, the circuit is predominantly capacitive.

The total impedance for a series RLC circuit is given by

Equation 13–2
$$Z_{tot} = \sqrt{R^2 + X_{tot}^2}$$

and the value of the phase angle between V_s and I is

Equation 13–3
$$\theta = \tan^{-1}\left(\frac{X_{tot}}{R}\right)$$

EXAMPLE 13–1

Determine the total impedance and the phase angle for the series RLC circuit in Figure 13–2.

Solution　First, find X_C and X_L.

$$X_C = \frac{1}{2\pi fC} = \frac{1}{2\pi(1 \text{ kHz})(0.56 \ \mu\text{F})} = 284 \ \Omega$$

$$X_L = 2\pi fL = 2\pi(1 \text{ kHz})(100 \text{ mH}) = 628 \ \Omega$$

▶ FIGURE 13–2

In this case, X_L is greater than X_C, so the circuit is more inductive than capacitive. The magnitude of the total reactance is

$$X_{tot} = |X_L - X_C| = |628 \ \Omega - 284 \ \Omega| = 344 \ \Omega \qquad \text{(inductive)}$$

The total circuit impedance is

$$Z_{tot} = \sqrt{R^2 + X_{tot}^2} = \sqrt{(560 \ \Omega)^2 + (344 \ \Omega)^2} = \mathbf{657 \ \Omega}$$

The phase angle (between I and V_s) is

$$\theta = \tan^{-1}\left(\frac{X_{tot}}{R}\right) = \tan^{-1}\left(\frac{344 \ \Omega}{560 \ \Omega}\right) = \mathbf{31.6°} \qquad \text{(current lagging } V_s\text{)}$$

Related Problem*   Increase the frequency in Figure 13–2 to 2000 Hz and determine Z and θ.

*Answers are at the end of the chapter.

As you have seen, when the inductive reactance is greater than the capacitive reactance, the circuit appears to be inductive, and the current lags the source voltage. When the capacitive reactance is greater, the circuit appears to be capacitive, and the current leads the source voltage.

SECTION 13–1 REVIEW
Answers are at the end of the chapter.

1. Explain how you can determine if a series *RLC* circuit is inductive or capacitive.
2. In a given series *RLC* circuit, X_C is 150 Ω and X_L is 80 Ω. What is the total reactance in ohms? Is the circuit inductive or capacitive?
3. Determine the impedance for the circuit in Question 2 when $R = 45 \ \Omega$. What is the phase angle? Is the current leading or lagging the source voltage?

13–2 ANALYSIS OF SERIES *RLC* CIRCUITS

Recall that capacitive reactance varies inversely with frequency and that inductive reactance varies directly with frequency. In this section, the combined effects of the reactances as a function of frequency are examined.

After completing this section, you should be able to

◆ **Analyze series *RLC* circuits**

   ◆ Determine current in a series *RLC* circuit

   ◆ Determine the voltages in a series *RLC* circuit

   ◆ Determine the phase angle

Figure 13–3 shows that for a typical series *RLC* circuit the total reactance behaves as follows: Starting at a very low frequency, X_C is high, X_L is low, and the circuit is predominantly capacitive. As the frequency is increased, X_C decreases and X_L increases until a value is reached where $X_C = X_L$ and the two reactances cancel, making the circuit purely resistive. This condition is **series resonance** and will be studied in Section 13–3. As the frequency is increased further, X_L becomes greater than X_C, and the circuit is predominantly inductive. Example 13–2 illustrates how the impedance and phase angle change as the source frequency is varied.

▶ **FIGURE 13–3**

How X_C and X_L vary with frequency.

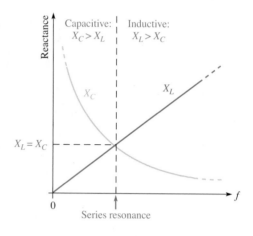

The graph of X_L is a straight line, and the graph of X_C is curved, as shown in Figure 13–3. The general equation for a straight line is $y = mx + b$, where m is the slope of the line and b is the y-axis intercept point. The formula $X_L = 2\pi fL$ fits this general straight-line formula, where $y = X_L$ (a variable), $m = 2\pi L$ (a constant), $x = f$ (a variable), and $b = 0$ as follows: $X_L = 2\pi Lf + 0$.

The X_C curve is called a *hyperbola*, and the general equation of a hyperbola is $xy = k$. The equation for capacitive reactance, $X_C = 1/2\pi fC$, can be rearranged as $X_C f = 1/2\pi C$ where $x = X_C$ (a variable), $y = f$ (a variable), and $k = 1/2\pi C$ (a constant).

EXAMPLE 13–2

For each of the following frequencies of the source voltage, find the impedance and the phase angle for the circuit in Figure 13–4. Note the change in the impedance and the phase angle with frequency.

(a) $f = 1$ kHz   **(b)** $f = 3.5$ kHz   **(c)** $f = 5$ kHz

▶ **FIGURE 13–4**

Solution   **(a)** At $f = 1$ kHz,

$$X_C = \frac{1}{2\pi fC} = \frac{1}{2\pi(1 \text{ kHz})(0.022 \ \mu\text{F})} = 7.23 \text{ k}\Omega$$

$$X_L = 2\pi fL = 2\pi(1 \text{ kHz})(100 \text{ mH}) = 628 \ \Omega$$

The circuit is highly capacitive because X_C is much larger than X_L. The magnitude of the total reactance is

$$X_{tot} = |X_L - X_C| = |628\,\Omega - 7.23\,k\Omega| = 6.6\,k\Omega$$

The impedance is

$$Z = \sqrt{R^2 + X_{tot}^2} = \sqrt{(3.3\,k\Omega)^2 + (6.6\,k\Omega)^2} = \textbf{7.38 k}\boldsymbol{\Omega}$$

The value of the phase angle is

$$\theta = \tan^{-1}\left(\frac{X_{tot}}{R}\right) = \tan^{-1}\left(\frac{6.60\,k\Omega}{3.3\,k\Omega}\right) = \textbf{63.4}^\circ$$

I leads V_s by 63.4°.

(b) At $f = 3.5\,kHz$,

$$X_C = \frac{1}{2\pi(3.5\,kHz)(0.022\,\mu F)} = 2.07\,k\Omega$$

$$X_L = 2\pi(3.5\,kHz)(100\,mH) = 2.20\,k\Omega$$

The circuit is very close to being purely resistive but is slightly inductive because X_L is slightly larger than X_C. The total reactance, impedance, and phase angle are

$$X_{tot} = |2.20\,k\Omega - 2.07\,k\Omega| = 130\,\Omega$$

$$Z = \sqrt{(3.3\,k\Omega)^2 + (130\,\Omega)^2} = \textbf{3.30 k}\boldsymbol{\Omega}$$

$$\theta = \tan^{-1}\left(\frac{130\,\Omega}{3.3\,k\Omega}\right) = \textbf{2.26}^\circ$$

I lags V_s by 2.26°.

(c) At $f = 5\,kHz$,

$$X_C = \frac{1}{2\pi(5\,kHz)(0.022\,\mu F)} = 1.45\,k\Omega$$

$$X_L = 2\pi(5\,kHz)(100\,mH) = 3.14\,k\Omega$$

The circuit is now predominantly inductive because $X_L > X_C$. The total reactance, impedance, and phase angle are

$$X_{tot} = |3.14\,k\Omega - 1.45\,k\Omega| = 1.69\,k\Omega$$

$$Z = \sqrt{(3.3\,k\Omega)^2 + (1.69\,k\Omega)^2} = \textbf{3.71 k}\boldsymbol{\Omega}$$

$$\theta = \tan^{-1}\left(\frac{1.69\,k\Omega}{3.3\,k\Omega}\right) = \textbf{27.1}^\circ$$

I lags V_s by 27.1°.

Notice how the circuit changed from capacitive to inductive as the frequency increased. The phase condition changed from the current leading to the current lagging. It is important to note that both the impedance and the phase angle decreased to a minimum and then began increasing again as the frequency went up.

Related Problem   Determine Z for $f = 7\,kHz$ in Figure 13–4.

In a series *RLC* circuit, the capacitor voltage and the inductor voltage are always 180° out of phase with each other. For this reason, V_C and V_L subtract from each other, and thus the voltage across *L* and *C* combined is always less than the larger individual voltage across either component, as illustrated in Figure 13–5 and in the waveform diagram of Figure 13–6.

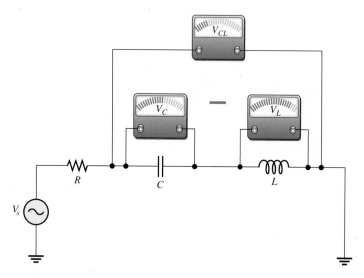

▲ **FIGURE 13–5**

The voltage across the series combination of *C* and *L* is always less than the larger individual voltage across either *C* or *L*.

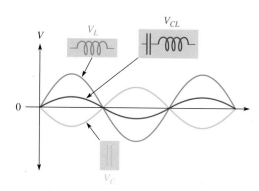

▲ **FIGURE 13–6**

Inductor voltage and capacitor voltage effectively subtract because they are out of phase.

In the next example, Ohm's law is used to find the current and voltages in a series *RLC* circuit.

EXAMPLE 13–3

Find the voltage across each component in Figure 13–7, and draw a complete voltage phasor diagram. Also find the voltage across *L* and *C* combined.

FIGURE 13–7

Solution   First, find the total reactance.

$$X_{tot} = |X_L - X_C| = |25\,k\Omega - 60\,k\Omega| = 35\,k\Omega$$

The total impedance is

$$Z_{tot} = \sqrt{R^2 + X_{tot}^2} = \sqrt{(75\,k\Omega)^2 + (35\,k\Omega)^2} = 82.8\,k\Omega$$

Apply Ohm's law to find the current.

$$I = \frac{V_s}{Z_{tot}} = \frac{10\ V}{82.8\ k\Omega} = 121\ \mu A$$

Now, apply Ohm's law to find the voltages across R, L, and C.

$$V_R = IR = (121\ \mu A)(75\ k\Omega) = \textbf{9.08 V}$$
$$V_L = IX_L = (121\ \mu A)(25\ k\Omega) = \textbf{3.03 V}$$
$$V_C = IX_C = (121\ \mu A)(60\ k\Omega) = \textbf{7.26 V}$$

The voltage across L and C combined is

$$V_{CL} = V_C - V_L = 7.26\ V - 3.03\ V = \textbf{4.23 V}$$

The circuit phase angle is

$$\theta = \tan^{-1}\left(\frac{X_{tot}}{R}\right) = \tan^{-1}\left(\frac{35\ k\Omega}{75\ k\Omega}\right) = 25°$$

Since the circuit is capacitive ($X_C > X_L$), the current leads the source voltage by 25°.

The phasor diagram is shown in Figure 13–8. Notice that V_L is leading V_R by 90°, and V_C is lagging V_R by 90°. Also, there is a 180° phase difference between V_L and V_C. If the current phasor were shown, it would be at the same angle as V_R.

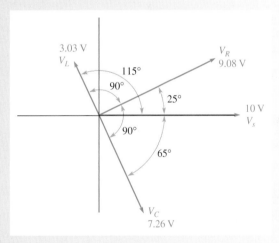

▲ FIGURE 13–8

Related Problem   What will happen to the current as the frequency of the source voltage in Figure 13–7 is increased?

**SECTION 13–2
REVIEW**

1. The following voltages occur in a certain series *RLC* circuit: $V_R = 24\ V$, $V_L = 15\ V$, $V_C = 45\ V$. Determine the source voltage.

2. When $R = 10\ k\Omega$, $X_C = 18\ k\Omega$, and $X_L = 12\ k\Omega$, does the current lead or lag the source voltage? Why?

3. Determine the total reactance in Question 2.

13–3 SERIES RESONANCE

In a series RLC circuit, series resonance occurs when $X_L = X_C$. The frequency at which resonance occurs is called the **resonant frequency** and is designated f_r.

After completing this section, you should be able to

◆ **Analyze a circuit for series resonance**

   ◆ Define *resonant frequency*

   ◆ Explain why the reactances cancel at resonance

   ◆ Determine the series resonant frequency

   ◆ Calculate the current and voltages at resonance

   ◆ Determine the impedance at resonance

Figure 13–9 illustrates the series resonant condition. Since the reactances are equal and effectively cancel, the impedance is purely resistive. These resonant conditions are stated as

$$X_L = X_C$$

$$Z_r = R$$

▶ FIGURE 13–9

At the resonant frequency (f_r), the reactances are equal in magnitude and effectively cancel, leaving $Z_r = R$.

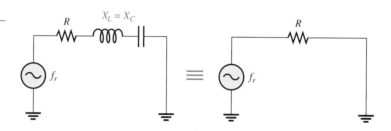

EXAMPLE 13–4

For the series RLC circuit in Figure 13–10, determine X_C and Z at resonance.

▶ FIGURE 13–10

Solution X_L equals X_C at resonance; therefore,

$$X_C = X_L = \textbf{50 } \Omega$$

Since the reactances cancel each other, the impedance equals the resistance.

$$Z_r = R = \textbf{100 } \Omega$$

Related Problem Just below the resonant frequency, is the circuit more inductive or more capacitive?

At the series resonant frequency, the voltages across C and L are equal in magnitude because the reactances are equal. The same current is through both since they are in series ($IX_C = IX_L$). Also, V_L and V_C are always 180° out of phase with each other.

During any given cycle of the input voltage, the polarities of the voltages across C and L are opposite, as shown in parts (a) and (b) of Figure 13–11. The equal and opposite voltages across C and L cancel, leaving zero volts from point A to point B as shown in the figure. Since there is no voltage drop from A to B but there is still current, the total reactance must be zero, as indicated in Figure 13–11(c). Also, the voltage phasor diagram in part (d) shows that V_C and V_L are equal in magnitude and $180°$ out of phase with each other.

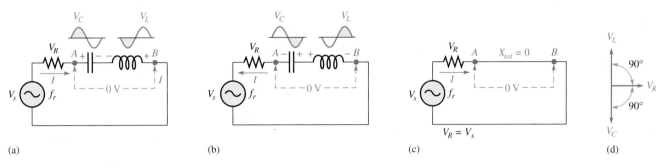

(a) (b) (c) (d)

▲ FIGURE 13–11

At the resonant frequency, f_r, the voltages across C and L are equal in magnitude. Since they are $180°$ out of phase with each other, they cancel, leaving 0 V across the CL combination (point A to point B). The section of the circuit from A to B effectively looks like a short at resonance (neglecting winding resistance).

Series Resonant Frequency

For a given series RLC circuit, resonance occurs at only one specific frequency. A formula for this resonant frequency is developed as follows:

$$X_L = X_C$$

Substitute the reactance formulas, and solve for the resonant frequency (f_r).

$$2\pi f_r L = \frac{1}{2\pi f_r C}$$

$$(2\pi f_r L)(2\pi f_r C) = 4\pi^2 f_r^2 LC = 1$$

$$f_r^2 = \frac{1}{4\pi^2 LC}$$

Take the square root of both sides. The formula for resonant frequency is

$$f_r = \frac{1}{2\pi\sqrt{LC}}$$

Equation 13–4

EXAMPLE 13–5

Find the series resonant frequency for the circuit in Figure 13–12.

▶ FIGURE 13–12

R — $10\ \Omega$
C — $470\ \text{pF}$
L — $0.5\ \text{mH}$
V_s

Solution The resonant frequency is

$$f_r = \frac{1}{2\pi\sqrt{LC}} = \frac{1}{2\pi\sqrt{(0.5\ \text{mH})(470\ \text{pF})}} = \textbf{328 kHz}$$

Related Problem If $C = 0.01$ μF in Figure 13–12, what is the resonant frequency?

Open Multisim file E13-05 on your CD-ROM. Determine the series resonant frequency by measurement.

Voltage and Current Amplitudes in a Series *RLC* Circuit

The current and voltage amplitudes in a series *RLC* circuit vary as the frequency is increased from below the resonant frequency, through resonance, and then above resonance. Figure 13–13 illustrates the general response of a circuit in terms of changes in the current

▶ **FIGURE 13–13**

An illustration of how the voltage and current amplitudes respond in a series *RLC* circuit as the frequency is increased from below to above its resonant value. The source voltage is held at a constant amplitude.

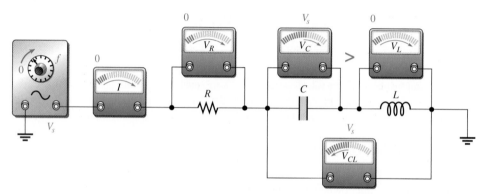

(a) As frequency is increased below resonance from 0: $X_C > X_L$, I increases from 0, V_R increases from 0, V_C increases from V_s, V_L increases from 0, and V_{CL} decreases from V_s.

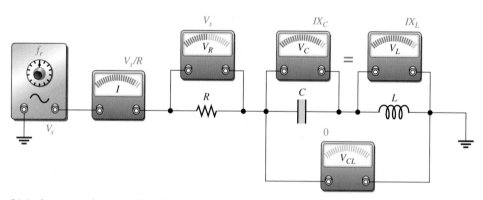

(b) At the resonant frequency, $X_C = X_L$.

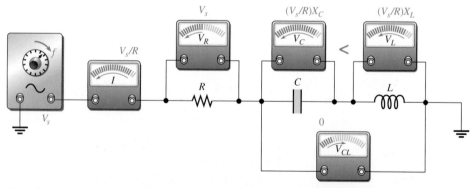

(c) As frequency is increased above resonance: $X_C < X_L$, I decreases from V_s/R, V_R decreases from V_s, V_C decreases from $(V_s/R)X_C$, V_L decreases from $(V_s/R)X_L$, and V_{CL} increases from 0.

and in the voltage drops. The Q (quality factor) of the circuit is assumed to be sufficiently high so it has no effect on the response. The Q is the ratio of reactive power to true power and is discussed later in this chapter.

Below the Resonant Frequency   Figure 13–13(a) indicates the response as the source frequency is increased from zero toward f_r. At $f = 0\,\text{Hz}$ (dc), the capacitor appears open and blocks the current. Thus, there is no voltage across R or L, and the entire source voltage appears across C. The impedance of the circuit is infinitely large at 0 Hz because X_C is infinite (C is open). As the frequency begins to increase, X_C decreases and X_L increases, causing the total reactance, $X_C - X_L$, to decrease. As a result, the impedance decreases and the current increases. As the current increases, V_R also increases, and both V_C and V_L increase. The voltage across C and L combined decreases from its maximum value of V_s because as V_C and V_L approach the same value, their difference becomes less.

At the Resonant Frequency   When the frequency reaches its resonant value, f_r, as shown in Figure 13–13(b), V_C and V_L can each be much larger than the source voltage. V_C and V_L cancel, leaving 0 V across the combination of C and L because the voltages are equal in magnitude but opposite in phase. At this point the total impedance is equal to R and is at its minimum value because the total reactance is zero. Thus, the current is at its maximum value, V_s/R, and V_R is at its maximum value, which is equal to the source voltage.

Above the Resonant Frequency   As the frequency is increased above resonance, as indicated in Figure 13–13(c), X_L continues to increase and X_C continues to decrease, causing the total reactance, $X_L - X_C$, to increase. As a result, there is an increase in impedance and a decrease in current. As the current decreases, V_R also decreases and V_C and V_L decrease. As V_C and V_L decrease, their difference becomes greater, so V_{CL} increases. As the frequency becomes very high, the current approaches zero, both V_R and V_C approach zero, and V_L approaches V_s.

Figure 13–14(a) and (b) illustrate the responses of current and voltage to increasing frequency, respectively. As frequency is increased, the current increases below resonance,

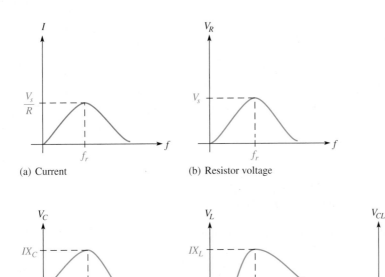

(a) Current

(b) Resistor voltage

(c) Capacitor voltage

(d) Inductor voltage

(e) Voltage across C and L combined

▲ FIGURE 13–14

Generalized current and voltage magnitudes as a function of frequency in a series *RLC* circuit. V_C and V_L can be much larger than the source voltage. The shapes of the graphs depend on particular circuit values.

reaches a peak at the resonant frequency, and then decreases above resonance. The resistor voltage responds in the same way as the current.

The general slopes of the V_C and V_L curves are indicated in Figure 13–14(c) and (d). The voltages are maximum at resonance but drop off above and below f_r. The voltages across L and C at resonance are exactly equal in magnitude but $180°$ out of phase, so they cancel. Thus, the total voltage across both L and C is zero, and $V_R = V_s$ at resonance. Individually, V_L and V_C can be much greater than the source voltage. Keep in mind that V_L and V_C are always opposite in polarity regardless of the frequency, but only at resonance are their magnitudes equal. The voltage across the C and L combination decreases as the frequency increases below resonance, reaching a minimum of zero at the resonant frequency; then it increases above resonance, as shown in Figure 13–14(e).

EXAMPLE 13–6

Find I, V_R, V_L, and V_C at resonance in Figure 13–15.

▲ FIGURE 13–15

Solution At resonance, I is maximum and equal to V_s/R.

$$I = \frac{V_s}{R} = \frac{50 \text{ mV}}{22 \text{ }\Omega} = \textbf{2.27 mA}$$

Apply Ohm's law to obtain the voltages.

$$V_R = IR = (2.27 \text{ mA})(22 \text{ }\Omega) = \textbf{50 mV}$$
$$V_L = IX_L = (2.27 \text{ mA})(100 \text{ }\Omega) = \textbf{227 mV}$$
$$V_C = IX_C = (2.27 \text{ mA})(100 \text{ }\Omega) = \textbf{227 mV}$$

Notice that all of the source voltage is dropped across the resistor. Also, of course, V_L and V_C are equal in magnitude but opposite in phase. This causes the voltages to cancel, making the total reactive voltage zero.

Related Problem What is the current at resonance in Figure 13–15 if $X_L = X_C = 1 \text{ k}\Omega$?

The Impedance of a Series *RLC* Circuit

Figure 13–16 shows a general graph of impedance versus frequency superimposed on the curves for X_C and X_L. At zero frequency, both X_C and Z are infinitely large and X_L is zero because the capacitor looks like an open at 0 Hz and the inductor looks like a short. As the frequency increases, X_C decreases and X_L increases. Since X_C is larger than X_L at frequencies below f_r, Z decreases along with X_C. At f_r, $X_C = X_L$ and $Z = R$. At frequencies above f_r, X_L becomes increasingly larger than X_C, causing Z to increase.

Z (Ω)

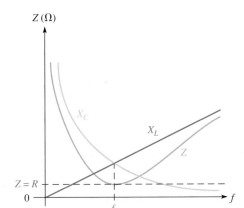

Series *RLC* impedance as a function of frequency.

EXAMPLE 13–7

For the circuit in Figure 13–17, determine the impedance at the following frequencies:

(a) f_r **(b)** 1 kHz below f_r **(c)** 1 kHz above f_r

▶ FIGURE 13–17

Solution   **(a)** At f_r, the impedance is equal to R.

$$Z = R = \mathbf{100\ \Omega}$$

To determine the impedance above and below f_r, first calculate the resonant frequency.

$$f_r = \frac{1}{2\pi\sqrt{LC}} = \frac{1}{2\pi\sqrt{(100\ \text{mH})(0.01\ \mu\text{F})}} = 5.03\ \text{kHz}$$

(b) At 1 kHz below f_r, the frequency and reactances are as follows:

$$f = f_r - 1\ \text{kHz} = 5.03\ \text{kHz} - 1\ \text{kHz} = 4.03\ \text{kHz}$$

$$X_C = \frac{1}{2\pi fC} = \frac{1}{2\pi(4.03\ \text{kHz})(0.01\ \mu\text{F})} = 3.95\ \text{k}\Omega$$

$$X_L = 2\pi fL = 2\pi(4.03\ \text{kHz})(100\ \text{mH}) = 2.53\ \text{k}\Omega$$

Therefore, the total reactance and the impedance at $f_r - 1$ kHz are

$$X_{tot} = |X_L - X_C| = |2.53\ \text{k}\Omega - 3.95\ \text{k}\Omega| = 1.42\ \text{k}\Omega$$

$$Z = \sqrt{R^2 + X_{tot}^2} = \sqrt{(100\ \Omega)^2 + (1.42\ \text{k}\Omega)^2} = \mathbf{1.42\ k\Omega}$$

(c) At 1 kHz above f_r,

$$f = 5.03\ \text{kHz} + 1\ \text{kHz} = 6.03\ \text{kHz}$$

$$X_C = \frac{1}{2\pi(6.03\ \text{kHz})(0.01\ \mu\text{F})} = 2.64\ \text{k}\Omega$$

$$X_L = 2\pi(6.03\ \text{kHz})(100\ \text{mH}) = 3.79\ \text{k}\Omega$$

Therefore, the total reactance and the impedance at $f_r + 1$ kHz are

$$X_{tot} = |3.79\,\text{k}\Omega - 2.64\,\text{k}\Omega| = 1.15\,\text{k}\Omega$$

$$Z = \sqrt{(100\,\Omega)^2 + (1.15\,\text{k}\Omega)^2} = \mathbf{1.15\,k\Omega}$$

In part (b), Z is capacitive; in part (c), Z is inductive.

Related Problem What happens to the impedance if f is decreased below 4.03 kHz? Above 6.03 kHz?

 Open Multisim file E13-07 on your CD-ROM. Measure the current and the voltage across each element at the resonant frequency, 1 kHz below resonance, and 1 kHz above resonance.

The Phase Angle of a Series *RLC* Circuit

At frequencies below resonance, $X_C > X_L$, and the current leads the source voltage, as indicated in Figure 13–18(a). The phase angle decreases as the frequency approaches the resonant value and is 0° at resonance, as indicated in part (b). At frequencies above resonance, $X_L > X_C$, and the current lags the source voltage, as indicated in part (c). As the frequency goes higher, the phase angle approaches 90°. A plot of phase angle versus frequency is shown in Figure 13–18(d).

▶ FIGURE 13–18

The phase angle as a function of frequency in a series *RLC* circuit.

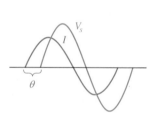

(a) Below f_r, I leads V_s.

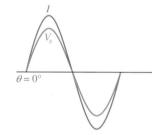

(b) At f_r, I is in phase with V_s.

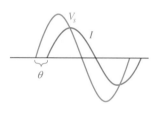

(c) Above f_r, I lags V_s.

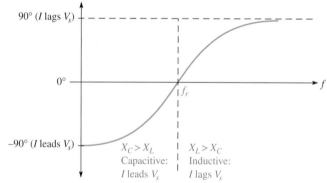

(d) Phase angle versus frequency.

**SECTION 13–3
REVIEW**

1. What is the condition for series resonance?
2. Why is the current maximum at the resonant frequency?
3. Calculate the resonant frequency for $C = 1000$ pF and $L = 1000\ \mu$H.
4. In Question 3, is the circuit inductive, capacitive, or resistive at 50 kHz?

13–4 SERIES RESONANT FILTERS

A common use of series *RLC* circuits is in filter applications. In this section, you will learn the basic configurations for passive band-pass and band-stop filters and several important filter characteristics.

After completing this section, you should be able to

- ◆ **Analyze series resonant filters**
  - ◆ Identify a basic series resonant band-pass filter
  - ◆ Define and determine *bandwidth*
  - ◆ Define the *half-power frequency*
  - ◆ Discuss dB measurement
  - ◆ Define *selectivity*
  - ◆ Discuss filter quality factor (Q)
  - ◆ Identify a series resonant band-stop filter

The Band-Pass Filter

A basic series resonant band-pass filter is shown in Figure 13–19. Notice that the series *LC* portion is placed between the input and the output and that the output is taken across the resistor.

▲ FIGURE 13–19

A basic series resonant band-pass filter.

A **band-pass filter** allows signals at the resonant frequency and at frequencies within a certain band (or range) extending below and above the resonant value to pass from input to output without a significant reduction in amplitude. Signals at frequencies lying outside this specified band (called the **passband**) are reduced in amplitude to below a certain level and are considered to be rejected by the filter.

The filtering action is the result of the impedance characteristic of the filter. As you learned in Section 13–3, the impedance is minimum at resonance and has increasingly higher values below and above the resonant frequency. At very low frequencies, the impedance is very high and tends to block the current. As the frequency increases, the impedance drops, allowing more current and thus more voltage across the output resistor. At the resonant frequency, the impedance is very low and equal to the winding resistance of the coil. At this point there is maximum current and the resulting output voltage is maximum. As the frequency goes above resonance, the impedance again increases, causing the current and the resulting output voltage to drop. Figure 13–20 illustrates the general frequency response of a series resonant band-pass filter.

(a) As the frequency increases to f_1, V_{out} increases to 7.07 V.

(b) As the frequency increases from f_1 to f_r, V_{out} increases from 7.07 V to 10 V.

(c) As the frequency increases from f_r to f_2, V_{out} decreases from 10 V to 7.07 V.

(d) As the frequency increases above f_2, V_{out} decreases below 7.07 V.

▲ **FIGURE 13–20**

Example of the frequency response of a series resonant band-pass filter with the input voltage at a constant 10 V rms. The winding resistance of the coil is neglected.

Bandwidth of the Passband

The bandwidth (*BW*) of a band-pass filter is the range of frequencies for which the current (or output voltage) is equal to or greater than 70.7% of its value at the resonant frequency. Figure 13–21 shows the bandwidth on the response curve for a band-pass filter.

The frequencies at which the output of a filter is 70.7% of its maximum are the **cutoff frequencies**. Notice in Figure 13–21 that frequency f_1, which is below f_r, is the frequency at which I (or V_{out}) is 70.7% of the resonant value (I_{max}); f_1 is commonly called the *lower cutoff frequency*. At frequency f_2, above f_r, the current (or V_{out}) is again 70.7% of its maximum; f_2

▶ **FIGURE 13–21**

Generalized response curve of a series resonant band-pass filter.

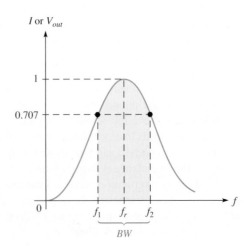

is called the *upper cutoff frequency*. Other names for f_1 and f_2 are −3 dB *frequencies*, *critical frequencies*, *band frequencies*, and *half-power frequencies*. (The term *decibel*, abbreviated dB, is defined later in this section.)

The formula for calculating the bandwidth is

$$BW = f_2 - f_1$$

Equation 13–5

The unit of bandwidth is the hertz (Hz), the same as for frequency.

EXAMPLE 13–8

A certain series resonant band-pass filter has a maximum current of 100 mA at the resonant frequency. What is the value of the current at the cutoff frequencies?

Solution   Current at the cutoff frequencies is 70.7% of maximum.

$$I_{f1} = I_{f2} = 0.707I_{max} = 0.707(100\,\text{mA}) = \textbf{70.7 mA}$$

Related Problem   Will a change in the cutoff frequencies affect the current at the new cutoff frequencies if the maximum current remains 100 mA?

EXAMPLE 13–9

A resonant circuit has a lower cutoff frequency of 8 kHz and an upper cutoff frequency of 12 kHz. Determine the bandwidth.

Solution $$BW = f_2 - f_1 = 12\,\text{kHz} - 8\,\text{kHz} = \textbf{4 kHz}$$

Related Problem   What is the bandwidth when $f_1 = 1\,\text{MHz}$ and $f_2 = 1.2\,\text{MHz}$?

Half-Power Points of the Filter Response

As previously mentioned, the upper and lower cutoff frequencies are sometimes called the **half-power frequencies**. This term is derived from the fact that the true power from the source at these frequencies is one-half the power delivered at the resonant frequency. The following steps show that this relationship is true for a series resonant circuit.

At resonance,

$$P_{max} = I_{max}^2 R$$

The power at f_1 (or f_2) is

$$P_{f1} = I_{f1}^2 R = (0.707I_{max})^2 R = (0.707)^2 I_{max}^2 R = 0.5I_{max}^2 R = 0.5P_{max}$$

Decibel (dB) Measurement

As previously mentioned, another common term for the upper and lower cutoff frequencies is −3 dB *frequencies*. The **decibel (dB)** is ten times the logarithmic ratio of two powers, which can be used to express the input-to-output relationship of a filter. The following equation expresses a power ratio in decibels:

$$\text{dB} = 10\log\left(\frac{P_{out}}{P_{in}}\right)$$

Equation 13–6

The decibel formula using a voltage ratio is based on the previous formula for the power ratio with voltages measured across equal resistances.

$$\text{dB} = 20\log\left(\frac{V_{out}}{V_{in}}\right)$$

Equation 13–7

EXAMPLE 13–10

At a certain frequency, the output power of a filter is 5 W and the input power is 10 W. Express the power ratio in decibels.

Solution

$$10 \log\left(\frac{P_{out}}{P_{in}}\right) = 10 \log\left(\frac{5 \text{ W}}{10 \text{ W}}\right) = 10 \log(0.5) = \mathbf{-3.01 \text{ dB}}$$

Related Problem

Express the ratio $V_{out}/V_{in} = 0.2$ in decibels.

The −3 dB Frequencies The output of a filter is said to be down 3 dB at the cutoff frequencies. As you know, this frequency is the point at which the output voltage is 70.7% of the maximum voltage at resonance. We can show that the 70.7% point is the same as 3 dB below maximum (or −3 dB) as follows. The maximum voltage is the 0 dB reference.

$$20 \log\left(\frac{0.707V_{max}}{V_{max}}\right) = 20 \log(0.707) = -3 \text{ dB}$$

Selectivity of a Band-Pass Filter

The response curve in Figure 13–21 is also called a *selectivity curve*. **Selectivity** defines how well a resonant circuit responds to a certain frequency and discriminates against all others. *The narrower the bandwidth, the greater the selectivity.*

We ideally assume that a resonant circuit accepts frequencies within its bandwidth and completely eliminates frequencies outside the bandwidth. Such is not actually the case, however, because signals with frequencies outside the bandwidth are not completely eliminated. Their magnitudes, however, are greatly reduced. The further the frequencies are from the cutoff frequencies, the greater the reduction, as illustrated in Figure 13–22(a). An ideal selectivity curve is shown in Figure 13–22(b).

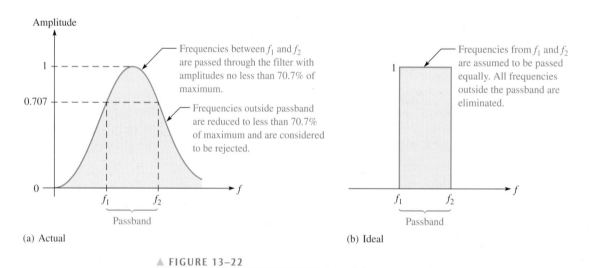

▲ FIGURE 13–22

Generalized selectivity curve of a band-pass filter.

As you can see in Figure 13–23, another factor that influences selectivity is the steepness of the slopes of the curve. The faster the curve drops off at the cutoff frequencies, the more selective the circuit is because the frequencies outside the passband are more quickly reduced (attenuated).

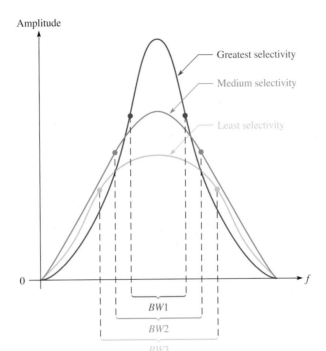

The Quality Factor (Q) of a Resonant Circuit

The quality factor (Q) of a circuit is the ratio of the reactive power in the inductor to the true power in the winding resistance of the coil and any other resistance in series with the coil. It is a ratio of the power in L to the power in R. The quality factor is important in resonant circuits. A formula for Q is developed as follows:

$$Q = \frac{\text{energy stored}}{\text{energy dissipated}} = \frac{\text{reactive power}}{\text{true power}} = \frac{I^2 X_L}{I^2 R}$$

The I^2 terms cancel, leaving

$$Q = \frac{X_L}{R}$$

Equation 13–8

Since Q varies with frequency because X_L varies, we are interested mainly in Q at resonance. Note that Q is a ratio of like units (ohms) which cancel and, therefore, Q has no unit itself. The quality factor is also known as unloaded Q because it is defined with no load across the coil.

EXAMPLE 13–11

Determine Q at resonance for the circuit in Figure 13–24.

▶ FIGURE 13–24

f_r 1.007 kHz

C 4.7 μF

L 5 mH

R 10 Ω

Solution   Determine the inductive reactance.

$$X_L = 2\pi f_r L = 2\pi(1.007 \text{ kHz})(5 \text{ mH}) = 31.6 \ \Omega$$

The quality factor is

$$Q = \frac{X_L}{R} = \frac{31.6 \ \Omega}{10 \ \Omega} = \mathbf{3.16}$$

Related Problem   Calculate Q at resonance if C in Figure 13–24 is halved. The resonant frequency will increase.

How Q Affects Bandwidth   A higher value of circuit Q results in a smaller bandwidth. A lower value of Q causes a larger bandwidth. A formula for the bandwidth of a resonant circuit in terms of Q is

Equation 13–9

$$BW = \frac{f_r}{Q}$$

EXAMPLE 13–12   What is the bandwidth of the filter in Figure 13–25?

▶ FIGURE 13–25

Solution   The total resistance is

$$R_{tot} = R + R_W = 51 \ \Omega + 50 \ \Omega = 101 \ \Omega$$

Determine the bandwidth as follows:

$$f_r = \frac{1}{2\pi\sqrt{LC}} = \frac{1}{2\pi\sqrt{(10 \text{ mH})(0.0047 \ \mu\text{F})}} = 23.2 \text{ kHz}$$

$$X_L = 2\pi f_r L = 2\pi(23.2 \text{ kHz})(10 \text{ mH}) = 1.46 \text{ k}\Omega$$

$$Q = \frac{X_L}{R_{tot}} = \frac{1.46 \text{ k}\Omega}{101 \ \Omega} = 14.5$$

$$BW = \frac{f_r}{Q} = \frac{23.2 \text{ kHz}}{14.5} = \mathbf{1.60 \text{ kHz}}$$

Related Problem   Determine the bandwidth if L is changed to 50 mH in Figure 13–25.

 Open Multisim file E13-12 on your CD-ROM. Determine the bandwidth by measurement. How closely does this result compare to the calculated value?

The Band-Stop Filter

The basic series resonant band-stop filter is shown in Figure 13–26. Notice that the output voltage is taken across the *LC* portion of the circuit. This filter is still a series *RLC* circuit, just as the band-pass filter is. The difference is that in this case, the output voltage is taken across the combination of *L* and *C* rather than across *R*.

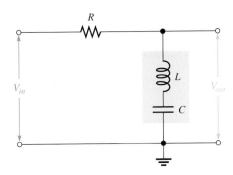

▲ FIGURE 13–26

A basic series resonant band-stop filter.

The **band-stop filter** rejects signals with frequencies between the lower and upper cutoff frequencies and passes those signals with frequencies below and above the cutoff values, as shown in the response curve of Figure 13–27. The range of frequencies between the lower and upper cutoff points is called the **stopband.** This type of filter is also referred to as a *band-elimination filter, band-reject filter,* or a *notch filter.*

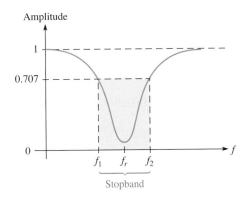

▲ FIGURE 13–27

Generalized response curve for a band-stop filter.

All the characteristics that have been discussed in relation to the band-pass filter apply equally to the band-stop filter, with the exception that the response curve of the output voltage is opposite. For the band-pass filter, V_{out} is maximum at resonance. For the band-stop filter, V_{out} is minimum at resonance.

At very low frequencies, the *LC* combination appears as a near open due to the high X_C, thus allowing most of the input voltage to pass through to the output. As the frequency increases, the impedance of the *LC* combination decreases until, at resonance, it is zero (ideally). Thus, the input signal is shorted to ground, and there is very little output voltage. As the frequency goes its resonant value, the *LC* impedance increases, allowing an increasing amount of voltage to be dropped across it. The general frequency response of a series resonant band-stop filter is illustrated in Figure 13–28.

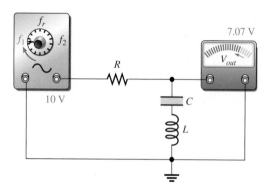

(a) As frequency increases to f_1, V_{out} decreases from 10 V to 7.07 V.

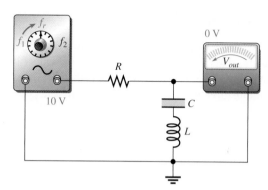

(b) As frequency increases from f_1 to f_r, V_{out} decreases from 7.07 V to 0 V.

(c) As frequency increases from f_r to f_2, V_{out} increases from 0 V to 7.07 V.

(d) As frequency increases above f_2, V_{out} increases toward 10 V.

▲ FIGURE 13–28

Example of the frequency response of a series resonant band-stop filter with V_{in} at a constant 10 V rms. The winding resistance is neglected.

EXAMPLE 13–13

Find the output voltage at f_r and the bandwidth in Figure 13–29.

R_1
47 Ω
100 mV
C
0.01 μF
$R_W = 30\ \Omega$
L
100 mH
V_{out}

▲ FIGURE 13–29

Solution Since $X_L = X_C$ at resonance, then

$$V_{out} = \left(\frac{R_W}{R_1 + R_W}\right)V_{in} = \left(\frac{30\ \Omega}{77\ \Omega}\right)100\ \text{mV} = \mathbf{39.0\ mV}$$

Determine the bandwidth as follows:

$$f_r = \frac{1}{2\pi\sqrt{LC}} = \frac{1}{2\pi\sqrt{(100\,\text{mH})(0.01\,\mu\text{F})}} = 5.03\,\text{kHz}$$

$$X_L = 2\pi f_r L = 2\pi(5.03\,\text{kHz})(100\,\text{mH}) = 3160\,\Omega$$

$$Q = \frac{X_L}{R} = \frac{X_L}{R_1 + R_W} = \frac{3160\,\Omega}{77\,\Omega} = 41$$

$$BW = \frac{f_r}{Q} = \frac{5.03\,\text{kHz}}{41} = \mathbf{123\,Hz}$$

Related Problem   What happens to V_{out} if the frequency is increased above resonance? Below resonance?

Open Multisim file E13-13 on your CD-ROM. Verify the calculated value of the resonant frequency and then measure the output voltage at resonance. Determine the bandwidth by measurement.

SECTION 13–4
REVIEW

1. The output voltage of a certain band-pass filter is 15 V at the resonant frequency. What is its value at the cutoff frequencies?
2. For a certain band-pass filter, $f_r = 120\,\text{kHz}$ and $Q = 12$. What is the bandwidth of the filter?
3. In a band-stop filter, is the current minimum or maximum at resonance? Is the output voltage minimum or maximum at resonance?

13–5   PARALLEL *RLC* CIRCUITS

In this section, you will learn how to determine the impedance and phase angle of a parallel *RLC* circuit. Current relationships and series-parallel to parallel conversions are discussed.

After completing this section, you should be able to

◆ **Analyze parallel *RLC* circuits**

  ◆ Calculate the impedance

  ◆ Calculate the phase angle

  ◆ Determine all currents

  ◆ Convert from a series-parallel *RLC* circuit to an equivalent parallel form

Impedance and Phase Angle

The circuit in Figure 13–30 consists of the parallel combination of *R*, *L*, and *C*. To find the admittance, add the conductance (G) and the total susceptance (B_{tot}) as phasor quantities. B_{tot} is the difference of the inductive susceptance and the capacitive susceptance.

$$B_{tot} = |B_L - B_C|$$

▶ FIGURE 13–30

▶ FIGURE 13–30

Parallel *RLC* circuit.

Therefore, the formula for admittance is

Equation 13–10

Equation 13–10

$$Y = \sqrt{G^2 + B_{tot}^2}$$

The total impedance is the reciprocal of the admittance.

$$Z_{tot} = \frac{1}{Y}$$

The phase angle of the circuit is given by the following formula:

Equation 13–11

$$\theta = \tan^{-1}\left(\frac{B_{tot}}{G}\right)$$

When the frequency is above its resonant value ($X_C < X_L$), the impedance of the circuit in Figure 13–30 is predominantly capacitive because the capacitive current is greater, and the total current leads the source voltage. When the frequency is below its resonant value ($X_L < X_C$), the impedance of the circuit is predominantly inductive, and the total current lags the source voltage.

EXAMPLE 13–14

Determine the total impedance and the phase angle for the parallel *RLC* circuit in Figure 13–31.

▶ FIGURE 13–31

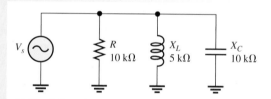

Solution   First, determine the admittance as follows:

$$G = \frac{1}{R} = \frac{1}{10\,k\Omega} = 100\,\mu S$$

$$B_C = \frac{1}{X_C} = \frac{1}{10\,k\Omega} = 100\,\mu S$$

$$B_L = \frac{1}{X_L} = \frac{1}{5\,k\Omega} = 200\,\mu S$$

$$B_{tot} = |B_L - B_C| = 100\,\mu S$$

$$Y = \sqrt{G^2 + B_{tot}^2} = \sqrt{(100\,\mu S)^2 + (100\,\mu S)^2} = 141.4\,\mu S$$

From Y, you can get Z_{tot}.

$$Z_{tot} = \frac{1}{Y} = \frac{1}{141.4\,\mu S} = \mathbf{7.07\,k\Omega}$$

The phase angle is

$$\theta = \tan^{-1}\left(\frac{B_{tot}}{G}\right) = \tan^{-1}\left(\frac{100 \; \mu S}{100 \; \mu S}\right) = \textbf{45}°$$

Related Problem   Is the impedance of the circuit in Figure 13–31 predominantly inductive or predominantly capacitive?

Current Relationships

In a parallel *RLC* circuit, the current in the capacitive branch and the current in the inductive branch are always 180° out of phase with each other (neglecting any coil resistance). For this reason, I_C and I_L subtract from each other, and thus the total current into the parallel branches of *L* and *C* is always less than the largest individual branch current, as illustrated in Figure 13–32 and in the waveform diagram of Figure 13–33. Of course, the current in the resistive branch is always 90° out of phase with both reactive currents, as shown in the current phasor diagram of Figure 13–34. The total current can be expressed as

$$I_{tot} = \sqrt{I_R^2 + I_{CL}^2}$$

Equation 13–12

▲ FIGURE 13–32

The total current into the parallel combination of *C* and *L* is the difference of the two branch currents $(I_{CL} = |I_C - I_L|)$.

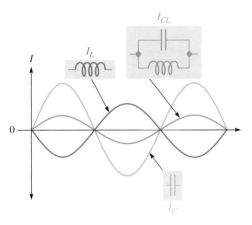

▲ FIGURE 13–33

I_C and I_L effectively subtract.

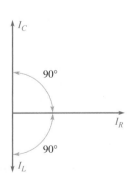

▲ FIGURE 13–34

Current phasor diagram for a parallel *RLC* circuit.

where I_{CL} is the absolute value of the difference of the two currents, $|I_C - I_L|$, and is the total current into the L and C branches.

The phase angle can also be expressed in terms of the branch currents as

Equation 13–13

$$\theta = \tan^{-1}\left(\frac{I_{CL}}{I_R}\right)$$

EXAMPLE 13–15

Find each branch current and the total current in Figure 13–35. Draw a diagram of their relationship.

▶ FIGURE 13–35

Solution   Apply Ohm's law to find each branch current.

$$I_R = \frac{V_s}{R} = \frac{5\text{ V}}{2.2\text{ k}\Omega} = \textbf{2.27 mA}$$

$$I_C = \frac{V_s}{X_C} = \frac{5\text{ V}}{5\text{ k}\Omega} = \textbf{1 mA}$$

$$I_L = \frac{V_s}{X_L} = \frac{5\text{ V}}{10\text{ k}\Omega} = \textbf{0.5 mA}$$

The total current is the phasor sum of the branch currents.

$$I_{CL} = |I_C - I_L| = 0.5\text{ mA}$$

$$I_{tot} = \sqrt{I_R^2 + I_{CL}^2} = \sqrt{(2.27\text{ mA})^2 + (0.5\text{ mA})^2} = \textbf{2.32 mA}$$

The phase angle is

$$\theta = \tan^{-1}\left(\frac{I_{CL}}{I_R}\right) = \tan^{-1}\left(\frac{0.5\text{ mA}}{2.27\text{ mA}}\right) = 12.4°$$

The total current is 2.32 mA, leading V_s by 12.4°. Figure 13–36 is the current phasor diagram for the circuit.

▶ FIGURE 13–36

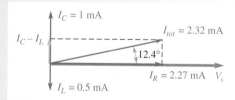

Related Problem   Will the total current increase or decrease if the frequency in Figure 13–35 is increased? Why?

Conversion of Series-Parallel to Parallel

The particular series-parallel configuration shown in Figure 13–37 is important because it represents a circuit having parallel L and C branches, with the winding resistance of the coil taken into account as a series resistance in the L branch.

The series-parallel circuit in Figure 13–37 can be viewed in an equivalent purely parallel form, as indicated in Figure 13–38. This equivalent form will simplify the analysis of parallel resonant characteristics that will be discussed in Section 13–6.

▲ FIGURE 13–37

A series-parallel *RLC* circuit
($Q = X_L/R_W$).

▲ FIGURE 13–38

Parallel equivalent form of the
circuit in Figure 13–37.

The equivalent inductance, L_{eq}, and the equivalent parallel resistance, $R_{p(eq)}$, are given by the following formulas:

$$L_{eq} = L\left(\frac{Q^2 + 1}{Q^2}\right)$$

Equation 13–14

$$R_{p(eq)} = R_W(Q^2 + 1)$$

Equation 13–15

where Q is the quality factor of the coil, X_L/R_W. Derivations of these formulas are quite involved and thus are not given here. Notice in the equations that for a $Q \geq 10$, the value of L_{eq} is approximately the same as the original value of L. For example, if $L = 10\,\text{mH}$ and $Q = 10$, then

$$L_{eq} = 10\,\text{mH}\left(\frac{10^2 + 1}{10^2}\right) = 10\,\text{mH}(1.01) = 10.1\,\text{mH}$$

The equivalency of the two circuits means that at a given frequency, when the same value of voltage is applied to both circuits, the same total current is in both circuits and the phase angles are the same. Basically, an equivalent circuit simply makes circuit analysis more convenient.

EXAMPLE 13–16

Convert the series-parallel circuit in Figure 13–39 to an equivalent parallel form at the given frequency.

FIGURE 13–39

Solution Determine the inductive reactance.

$$X_L = 2\pi fL = 2\pi(15.9\,\text{kHz})(5\,\text{mH}) = 500\,\Omega$$

The Q of the coil is

$$Q = \frac{X_L}{R_W} = \frac{500\ \Omega}{25\ \Omega} = 20$$

Since $Q > 10$, then $L_{eq} \cong L = 5$ mH.
The equivalent parallel resistence is

$$R_{p(eq)} = R_W(Q^2 + 1) = (25\ \Omega)(20^2 + 1) = 10.0\ \text{k}\Omega$$

This equivalent resistance ($R_{p(eq)}$) appears in parallel with R_1 as shown in Figure 13–40(a). When combined, they give a total parallel resistance ($R_{p(tot)}$) of 3.38 kΩ, as indicated in Figure 13–40(b).

(a) Parallel equivalent of the circuit in Figure 13–39   (b) $R_{p(tot)} = R_1 \parallel R_{p(eq)} = 3.38$ kΩ

▲ FIGURE 13–40

Related Problem   Find the equivalent parallel circuit if $R_W = 10\ \Omega$ in Figure 13–39.

**SECTION 13–5
REVIEW**

1. In a three-branch parallel circuit, $R = 150\ \Omega$, $X_C = 100\ \Omega$, and $X_L = 50\ \Omega$ at a certain frequency. Determine the current in each branch when $V_s = 12$ V.
2. Is the circuit in Question 1 capacitive or inductive? Why?
3. Find the equivalent parallel inductance and resistance for a 20 mH coil with a winding resistance of 10 Ω at a frequency of 1 kHz.

13–6 PARALLEL RESONANCE

In this section, we will first look at the resonant condition in an ideal parallel *LC* circuit. Then, we will examine the more realistic case where the resistance of the coil is taken into account.

After completing this section, you should be able to

◆ **Analyze a circuit for parallel resonance**

  ◆ Describe parallel resonance in an ideal circuit

  ◆ Describe parallel resonance in a nonideal circuit

  ◆ Explain how impedance varies with frequency

◆ Determine current and phase angle at resonance

◆ Determine parallel resonant frequency

◆ Discuss the effects of loading a parallel resonant circuit

Condition for Ideal Parallel Resonance

Ideally, **parallel resonance** occurs when $X_L = X_C$. The frequency at which resonance occurs is called the *resonant frequency,* just as in the series resonant circuit. When $X_L = X_C$, the two branch currents, I_C and I_L, are equal in magnitude, and, of course, they are always 180° out of phase with each other. Thus, the two currents cancel and the total current is zero, as presented in Figure 13–41. In this ideal case, the winding resistance of the coil is assumed to be zero.

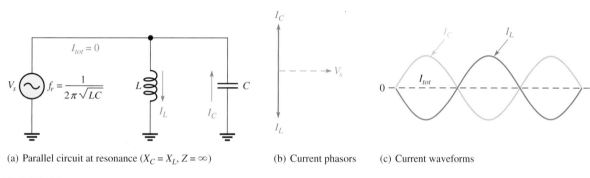

(a) Parallel circuit at resonance ($X_C = X_L, Z = \infty$)   (b) Current phasors   (c) Current waveforms

▲ FIGURE 13–41

An ideal parallel *LC* circuit at resonance.

Since the total current is zero, the impedance of the parallel *LC* circuit is infinitely large (∞). These ideal resonant conditions are stated as follows:

$$X_L = X_C$$
$$Z_r = \infty$$

Parallel Resonant Frequency

For an ideal parallel resonant circuit, the frequency at which resonance occurs is determined by the same formula as in series resonant circuits.

$$f_r = \frac{1}{2\pi\sqrt{LC}}$$

Equation 13–16

Currents in a Parallel Resonant Circuit

The currents in a parallel *LC* circuit vary as the frequency is increased from below the resonant value, through resonance, and then above the resonant value. Figure 13–42 illustrates the general response of an ideal circuit in terms of changes in the currents.

Below the Resonant Frequency   Figure 13–42(a) indicates the response as the source frequency is increased from zero toward f_r. At very low frequencies, X_C is very high and X_L is very low, so most of the current is through L. As the frequency increases, the current

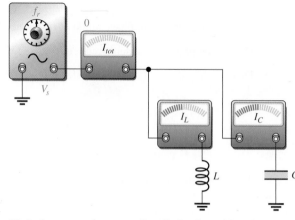

(a) As frequency is increased below resonance: $X_C > X_L$, $I_L > I_C$, I_L decreases, I_C increases, and I_{tot} decreases.

(b) At the resonant frequency: $X_C = X_L$, $I_L = I_C$, and $I_{tot} = 0$.

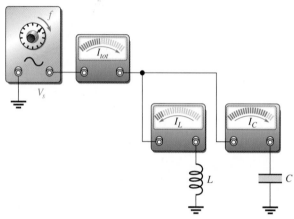

(c) As frequency is increased above resonance: $X_L > X_C$, $I_L < I_C$, I_L decreases, I_C increases, and I_{tot} increases.

▲ FIGURE 13–42

An illustration of how the currents respond in a parallel *LC* circuit as the frequency is varied from below resonance to above resonance. The source voltage amplitude is constant.

HANDS ON TIP

When you check the resonant frequency of an *LC* circuit using a function generator, the Thevenin resistance of the generator increases the Q of the circuit. A generator with an internal resistance of 600 Ω can significantly broaden the bandwidth of the resonant circuit. To reduce the Q and obtain a narrower bandwidth, a small parallel resistor can be placed across the generator output. The drawback of this method is that the signal amplitude from the generator is reduced.

through L decreases and the current through C increases, causing the total current to decrease. At all times, I_L and I_C are 180° out of phase with each other, and thus the total current is the difference of the two branch currents. During this time, the impedance is increasing, as indicated by the decrease in total current.

At the Resonant Frequency When the frequency reaches its resonant value, f_r, as shown in Figure 13–42(b), X_C and X_L are equal, so I_C and I_L cancel because they are equal in magnitude but opposite in phase. At this point the total current is at its minimum value of zero. Since I_{tot} is zero, Z is infinite. Thus, the ideal parallel *LC* circuit appears as an open at f_r.

Above the Resonant Frequency As the frequency is increased above resonance, as indicated in Figure 13–42(c), X_C continues to decrease and X_L continues to increase, causing the branch currents again to be unequal, with I_C being larger. As a result, total current increases and impedance decreases. As the frequency becomes very high, the impedance becomes very small due to the dominance of a very small X_C in parallel with a very large X_L.

In summary, the current dips to a minimum as the impedance peaks to a maximum at parallel resonance. The expression for the total current into the L and C branches is

Equation 13–17

$$I_{tot} = |I_L - I_C|$$

EXAMPLE 13–17

Find the resonant frequency and the branch currents in the ideal (winding resistance neglected) parallel *LC* circuit of Figure 13–43.

▲ FIGURE 13–43

Solution   The resonant frequency is

$$f_r = \frac{1}{2\pi\sqrt{LC}} = \frac{1}{2\pi\sqrt{(100\ \text{mH})(0.047\ \mu\text{F})}} = \textbf{2.32 kHz}$$

Determine the branch currents as follows:

$$X_L = 2\pi f_r L = 2\pi(2.32\ \text{kHz})(100\ \text{mH}) = 1.46\ \text{k}\Omega$$
$$X_C = X_L = 1.46\ \text{k}\Omega$$
$$I_L = \frac{V_s}{X_L} = \frac{10\ \text{V}}{1.46\ \text{k}\Omega} = \textbf{6.85 mA}$$
$$I_C = I_L = \textbf{6.85 mA}$$

The total current into the parallel *LC* circuit is

$$I_{tot} = |I_L - I_C| = \textbf{0 A}$$

Related Problem   Find f_r and all the currents at resonance in Figure 13–43 if *C* is changed to 0.022 μF.

Open Multisim file E13-17 on your CD-ROM. Determine the resonant frequency by measurement. Determine the currents through *L* and *C* at the resonant frequency.

Tank Circuit

The parallel resonant *LC* circuit is often called a **tank circuit.** The term *tank circuit* refers to the fact that the parallel resonant circuit stores energy in the magnetic field of the coil and in the electric field of the capacitor. The stored energy is transferred back and forth between the capacitor and the coil on alternate half-cycles as the current goes first one way and then the other when the inductor deenergizes and the capacitor charges, and vice versa. This concept is illustrated in Figure 13–44.

(a) The coil deenergizes as the capacitor charges.

(b) The capacitor discharges as the coil energizes.

◀ FIGURE 13–44

Energy storage in an ideal parallel resonant tank circuit.

Parallel Resonant Conditions in a Nonideal Circuit

So far, the resonance of an ideal parallel *LC* circuit has been examined. Now let's consider resonance in a tank circuit with the winding resistance taken into account. Figure 13–45 shows a nonideal tank circuit and its parallel *RLC* equivalent.

▶ FIGURE 13–45

A practical treatment of parallel resonant circuits includes the winding resistance.

(a) Nonideal tank circuit   (b) Parallel *RLC* equivalent

If the winding resistance is the only resistance in the circuit, the quality factor, *Q*, of the circuit at resonance is simply the *Q* of the coil.

$$Q = \frac{X_L}{R_W}$$

In terms of circuit component values, the *Q* can also be expressed as

$$Q = \frac{1}{R}\sqrt{\frac{L}{C}}$$

The expressions for the equivalent inductance and the equivalent parallel resistance were given in Equations 13–14 and 13–15 as

$$L_{eq} = L\left(\frac{Q^2 + 1}{Q^2}\right)$$

$$R_{p(eq)} = R_W(Q^2 + 1)$$

Recall that for $Q \geq 10, L_{eq} \cong L$.

At parallel resonance,

$$X_{L(eq)} = X_C$$

In the parallel equivalent circuit, $R_{p(eq)}$ is in parallel with an ideal coil and a capacitor, so the *L* and *C* branches act as an ideal tank circuit that has an infinite impedance at resonance, as shown in Figure 13–46. Therefore, the total impedance of the nonideal tank circuit at resonance can be expressed as simply the equivalent parallel resistance.

Equation 13–18

$$Z_r = R_W(Q^2 + 1)$$

▶ FIGURE 13–46

At resonance, the parallel *LC* portion appears open and the source sees only $R_{p(eq)}$, which equals $R_W(Q^2 + 1)$.

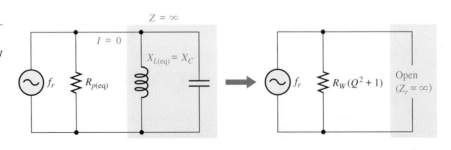

EXAMPLE 13–18

Determine the impedance of the circuit in Figure 13–47 at the resonant frequency ($f_r \cong 17{,}794$ Hz).

▶ **FIGURE 13–47**

Solution   Before you can calculate the impedance using Equation 13–18, you must find the quality factor. To get Q, first find the inductive reactance.

$$X_L = 2\pi f_r L = 2\pi(17{,}794 \text{ Hz})(8 \text{ mH}) = 894 \ \Omega$$

$$Q = \frac{X_L}{R_W} = \frac{894 \ \Omega}{50 \ \Omega} = 17.9$$

$$Z_r = R_W(Q^2 + 1) = 50 \ \Omega(17.9^2 + 1) = \mathbf{16.0 \ k\Omega}$$

Related Problem   Determine Z_r in Figure 13–47 if the winding resistance is $10 \ \Omega$.

Variation of the Impedance with Frequency

The impedance of a parallel resonant circuit is maximum at the resonant frequency and decreases at lower and higher frequencies, as indicated by the curve in Figure 13–48.

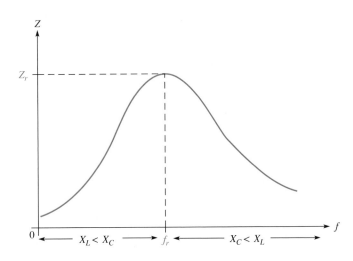

◀ **FIGURE 13–48**

Generalized impedance curve for a parallel resonant circuit. The circuit is inductive below f_r, resistive at f_r, and capacitive above f_r.

At very low frequencies, X_L is very small and X_C is very high, so the total impedance is essentially equal to that of the inductive branch. As the frequency goes up, the impedance also increases, and the inductive reactance dominates (because it is less than X_C) until the resonant frequency is reached. At this point, of course, $X_L \cong X_C$ (for $Q > 10$) and the impedance is at its maximum. As the frequency goes above resonance, the capacitive reactance dominates (because it is less than X_L) and the impedance decreases.

Current and Phase Angle at Resonance

In the ideal tank circuit, the total current from the source at resonance is zero because the impedance is infinite. In the nonideal case, there is some total current at the resonant frequency, and it is determined by the impedance at resonance.

Equation 13–19

$$I_{tot} = \frac{V_s}{Z_r}$$

The phase angle of the parallel resonant circuit is 0° because the impedance is purely resistive at the resonant frequency.

Parallel Resonant Frequency in a Nonideal Circuit

As you know, when the winding resistance is considered, the resonant condition is

$$X_{L(eq)} = X_C$$

which can be expressed as

$$2\pi f_r L \left(\frac{Q^2 + 1}{Q^2} \right) = \frac{1}{2\pi f_r C}$$

Solving for f_r in terms of Q yields

$$f_r = \frac{1}{2\pi \sqrt{LC}} \sqrt{\frac{Q^2}{Q^2 + 1}}$$

When $Q \geq 10$, the term with the Q factors is approximately 1.

$$\sqrt{\frac{Q^2}{Q^2 + 1}} = \sqrt{\frac{100}{101}} = 0.995 \cong 1$$

Therefore, the parallel resonant frequency is approximately the same as the series resonant frequency as long as Q is equal to or greater than 10.

$$f_r \cong \frac{1}{2\pi \sqrt{LC}} \qquad \text{for } Q \geq 10$$

For the case where the R_W of the coil is the only resistance in the circuit, a precise expression for f_r in terms of the circuit component values is

Equation 13–20

$$f_r = \frac{\sqrt{1 - (R_W^2 C / L)}}{2\pi \sqrt{LC}}$$

This precise formula is seldom necessary and for most practical situations the simpler equation $f_r = 1/(2\pi \sqrt{LC})$ is sufficient. However, the next example illustrates the use of Equation 13–20.

EXAMPLE 13–19

Find the frequency, impedance, and total current at resonance for the circuit in Figure 13–49 using Equation 13–20.

▶ FIGURE 13–49

Solution   The precise resonant frequency is

$$f_r = \frac{\sqrt{1 - (R_W^2 C/L)}}{2\pi\sqrt{LC}} = \frac{\sqrt{1 - [(100\ \Omega)^2(0.047\ \mu F)/0.1\ H]}}{2\pi\sqrt{(0.047\ \mu F)(0.1\ H)}} = \textbf{2.32 kHz}$$

Calculate impedance as follows:

$$X_L = 2\pi f_r L = 2\pi(2.32\ \text{kHz})(0.1\ \text{H}) = 1.46\ \text{k}\Omega$$

$$Q = \frac{X_L}{R_W} = \frac{1.46\ \text{k}\Omega}{100\ \Omega} = 14.6$$

$$Z_r = R_W(Q^2 + 1) = 100\ \Omega(14.6^2 + 1) = \textbf{21.4 k}\Omega$$

The total current is

$$I_{tot} = \frac{V_s}{Z_r} = \frac{10\ \text{V}}{21.4\ \text{k}\Omega} = \textbf{467 }\mu\textbf{A}$$

Related Problem   Repeat this example using the formula $f_r = 1/(2\pi\sqrt{LC})$ and compare the results.

 Open Multisim file E13-19 on your CD-ROM. Determine the resonant frequency by measurement. Determine the total current and the currents through L and C at the resonant frequency. How do these results compare with the calculated values?

An External Load Resistance Affects a Tank Circuit

In most practical situations an external load resistance appears in parallel with a nonideal tank circuit, as shown in Figure 13–50(a). Obviously, the external resistor (R_L) will dissipate more of the energy delivered by the source and thus will lower the overall Q of the circuit. The external resistor effectively appears in parallel with the equivalent parallel resistance of the coil, $R_{p(eq)}$, and both are combined to determine a total parallel resistance, $R_{p(tot)}$, as indicated in Figure 13–50(b).

$$R_{p(tot)} = R_L \| R_{p(eq)}$$

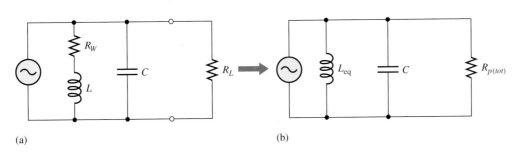

(a)   (b)

▲ FIGURE 13–50

Tank circuit with a load resistor and its equivalent circuit.

The overall Q, designated Q_O, for a parallel RLC circuit is expressed differently from the Q of a series circuit.

$$Q_O = \frac{R_{p(tot)}}{X_{L(eq)}}$$

Equation 13–21

As you can see, the effect of loading the tank circuit is to reduce its overall Q (which is equal to the coil Q when unloaded).

SECTION 13–6
REVIEW

1. Is the impedance minimum or maximum at parallel resonance?
2. Is the current minimum or maximum at parallel resonance?
3. At ideal parallel resonance, $X_L = 1.5$ kΩ. What is X_C?
4. A tank circuit has the following values: $R_W = 4.0$ Ω, $L = 50$ mH, and $C = 10$ pF. Calculate f_r and Z_r.
5. If $Q = 25$, $L = 50$ mH, and $C = 1000$ pF, what is f_r?
6. In Question 5, if $Q = 2.5$, what is f_r?
7. In a certain tank circuit, the coil resistance is 20 Ω. What is the total impedance at resonance if $Q = 20$?

13–7 PARALLEL RESONANT FILTERS

Parallel resonant circuits are commonly applied to band-pass and band-stop filters. In this section, we examine these applications.

After completing this section, you should be able to

◆ **Analyze the operation of parallel resonant filters**

- ◆ Show how a band-pass filter is implemented
- ◆ Define *bandwidth*
- ◆ Explain how loading affects selectivity
- ◆ Show how a band-stop filter is implemented
- ◆ Determine the resonant frequency, bandwidth, and output voltage of band-pass and band-stop parallel resonant filters

The Band-Pass Filter

A basic parallel resonant band-pass filter is shown in Figure 13–51. Notice that the output is taken across the tank circuit in this application.

The bandwidth and cutoff frequencies for a parallel resonant band-pass filter are defined in the same way as for the series resonant circuit, and the formulas given in Section 13–4 still apply. General band-pass frequency response curves showing both V_{out} and I_{tot} versus frequency are given in Figures 13–52(a) and 13–52(b), respectively.

The filtering action is as follows: At very low frequencies, the impedance of the tank circuit is very low, and therefore only a small amount of voltage is dropped across it. As the frequency increases, the impedance of the tank circuit increases, and, as a result, the output voltage increases. When the frequency reaches its resonant value, the impedance is at its maximum and so is the output voltage. As the frequency goes above resonance, the impedance begins to decrease, causing the output voltage to decrease. The general response of a

▶ FIGURE 13–51

A basic parallel resonant band-pass filter.

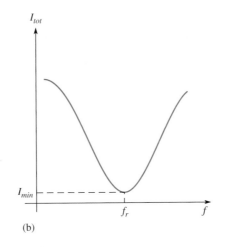

Generalized frequency response curves for a parallel resonant band-pass filter.

(a)

(b)

parallel resonant band-pass filter is illustrated in Figure 13–53. This illustration shows how the current and the output voltage change with frequency.

(a) As the frequency increases to f_1, V_{out} increases to 7.07 V, and I_{tot} decreases.

(b) As the frequency increases from f_1 to f_r, V_{out} increases from 7.07 V to 10 V, and I_{tot} decreases to its minimum value.

(c) As the frequency increases from f_r to f_2, V_{out} decreases from 10 V to 7.07 V, and I_{tot} increases from its minimum.

(d) As the frequency increases above f_2, V_{out} decreases below 7.07 V, and I_{tot} continues to increase.

▲ FIGURE 13–53

Example of the response of a parallel resonant band-pass filter with the input voltage at a constant 10 V rms.

EXAMPLE 13–20

A certain parallel resonant band-pass filter has a maximum output voltage of 4 V at f_r. What is the value of V_{out} at the cutoff frequencies?

Solution V_{out} at the cutoff frequencies is 70.7% of maximum.

$$V_{out(1)} = V_{out(2)} = 0.707V_{out(max)} = 0.707(4 \text{ V}) = \mathbf{2.828 \text{ V}}$$

Related Problem   What is V_{out} at the cutoff frequencies if V_{out} at the resonant frequency is 10 V?

EXAMPLE 13–21

A parallel resonant circuit has a lower cutoff frequency of 3.5 kHz and an upper cutoff frequency of 6 kHz. What is the bandwidth?

Solution $$BW = f_2 - f_1 = 6 \text{ kHz} - 3.5 \text{ kHz} = \mathbf{2.5 \text{ kHz}}$$

Related Problem   A filter has a lower cutoff frequency of 520 kHz and a bandwidth of 10 kHz. What is the upper cutoff frequency?

EXAMPLE 13–22

A certain parallel resonant band-pass filter has a resonant frequency of 12 kHz and a Q of 10. What is its bandwidth?

Solution $$BW = \frac{f_r}{Q} = \frac{12 \text{ kHz}}{10} = \mathbf{1.2 \text{ kHz}}$$

Related Problem   A certain parallel resonant band-pass filter has a resonant frequency of 100 MHz and a bandwidth of 4 MHz. What is its Q?

Loading Effects   When a resistive load is connected across the output of a filter as shown in Figure 13–54(a), the Q of the filter is reduced. Since $BW = f_r/Q$, the bandwidth is

R_s and $R_{p(tot)}$ act as a voltage divider.

$Z = \infty$ (open)

(a) Tank circuit with load

$$V_{out} = \left(\frac{R_{p(tot)}}{R_{p(tot)} + R_s}\right)V_s$$

(b) Equivalent circuit

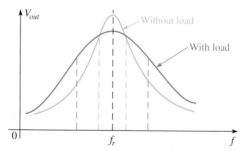

(c) Loading widens the bandwidth and reduces the output.

▲ **FIGURE 13–54**

Effects of loading on a parallel resonant band-pass filter.

increased, thus reducing the selectivity. Also, the impedance of the filter at resonance is decreased because R_L effectively appears in parallel with $R_{p(eq)}$. Thus, the maximum output voltage is reduced by the voltage-divider effect of $R_{p(tot)}$ and the internal source resistance R_s, as illustrated in Figure 13–54(b). Figure 13–54(c) shows the general effect of a load on the filter response curve.

EXAMPLE 13–23

(a) Determine f_r, BW, and V_{out} at resonance for the unloaded filter in Figure 13–55. The source resistance is 600 Ω.

(b) Repeat part (a) when the filter is loaded with a 50 kΩ resistance, and compare the results.

▶ FIGURE 13–55

Solution   (a) $f_r \cong \dfrac{1}{2\pi\sqrt{LC}} = \dfrac{1}{2\pi\sqrt{(100\ \text{mH})(0.1\ \mu\text{F})}} = \textbf{1.59 kHz}$

Calculate the bandwidth at resonance as follows:

$$X_L = 2\pi f_r L = 2\pi(1.59\ \text{kHz})(100\ \text{mH}) = 999\ \Omega$$

$$Q = \frac{X_L}{R_W} = \frac{999\ \Omega}{50\ \Omega} = 20$$

$$BW = \frac{f_r}{Q} = \frac{1.59\ \text{kHz}}{20} = \textbf{79.5 Hz}$$

Calculate the output voltage.

$$R_{p(eq)} = R_W(Q^2 + 1) = 50\ \Omega(20^2 + 1) = 20.1\ \text{k}\Omega$$

$$V_{out} = \left(\frac{R_{p(eq)}}{R_{p(eq)} + R_s}\right)V_s = \left(\frac{20.1\ \text{k}\Omega}{20.7\ \text{k}\Omega}\right)5\ \text{V} = \textbf{4.86 V}$$

(b) When a 50 kΩ load resistance is connected, you obtain the following values. The resonant frequency is not affected.

$$R_{p(tot)} = R_{p(eq)} \| R_L = 20.1\ \text{k}\Omega \| 50\ \text{k}\Omega = 14.3\ \text{k}\Omega$$

$$Q_O = \frac{R_{p(tot)}}{X_L} = \frac{14.3\ \text{k}\Omega}{999\ \Omega} = 14.3$$

$$BW = \frac{f_r}{Q_O} = \frac{1.59\ \text{kHz}}{14.3} = \textbf{111 Hz}$$

$$V_{out} = \left(\frac{R_{p(tot)}}{R_{p(tot)} + R_s}\right)V_s = \left(\frac{14.3\ \text{k}\Omega}{14.9\ \text{k}\Omega}\right)5\ \text{V} = \textbf{4.80 V}$$

The result of adding the load resistance is an increased bandwidth and a decreased output voltage at resonance.

Related Problem   How does load resistance affect the Q_O?

The Band-Stop Filter

A basic parallel resonant band-stop filter is shown in Figure 13–56. The output is taken across a load resistor in series with the tank circuit.

The variation of the tank circuit impedance with frequency produces the familiar current response that has been previously discussed; that is, the current is minimum at resonance and increases on both sides of resonance. Since the output voltage is across the series load resistor, the output voltage follows the current, thus creating the band-stop response characteristic, as indicated in Figure 13–57.

▲ **FIGURE 13–56**

A basic parallel resonant band-stop filter.

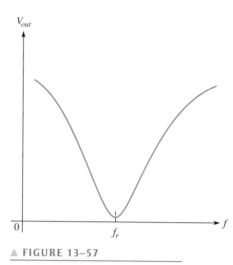

▲ **FIGURE 13–57**

Band-stop filter response.

Actually, the band-stop filter in Figure 13–56 can be viewed as a voltage divider created by Z_r of the tank and the load resistance. Thus, the output voltage at f_r is

$$V_{out} = \left(\frac{R_L}{R_L + Z_r}\right)V_{in}$$

EXAMPLE 13–24

Find f_r and the output voltage across R_L at resonance for the band-stop filter in Figure 13–58.

▶ **FIGURE 13–58**

Solution Calculate the resonant frequency and impedance as follows:

$$f_r = \frac{\sqrt{1 - (R_W^2 C/L)}}{2\pi\sqrt{LC}} = \frac{\sqrt{1 - [(250\ \Omega)^2(1\ \mu F)/330\ \text{mH}]}}{2\pi\sqrt{(330\ \text{mH})(1\ \mu F)}} = \textbf{249 Hz}$$

$$X_L = 2\pi f_r L = 2\pi(249\ \text{Hz})(330\ \text{mH}) = 516\ \Omega$$

$$Q = \frac{X_L}{R_W} = \frac{516\ \Omega}{250\ \Omega} = 2.06$$

$$Z_r = R_W(Q^2 + 1) = 250\ \Omega(2.06^2 + 1) = 1.31\ \text{k}\Omega$$

At resonance,

$$V_{out} = \left(\frac{R_L}{R_L + Z_r}\right)V_s = \left(\frac{1.0\ \text{k}\Omega}{2.31\ \text{k}\Omega}\right)12\ \text{V} = \textbf{5.19 V}$$

Related Problem Why wouldn't the formula for ideal resonant frequency $[f_r = 1/(2\pi\sqrt{LC})]$ work in this particular case?

Open Multisim file E13-24 on your CD-ROM. Determine the resonant frequency and the voltage across R_L at resonance.

SECTION 13–7 REVIEW

1. How can the bandwidth of a parallel resonant filter be increased?
2. The resonant frequency of a certain high-Q ($Q > 10$) filter is 5 kHz. If the Q is lowered to 2, does f_r change and, if so, to what value?
3. What is the impedance of a tank circuit at its resonant frequency if $R_W = 75\ \Omega$ and $Q = 25$?

13–8 APPLICATIONS

Resonant circuits are used in a wide variety of applications, particularly in communication systems. In this section, we will look briefly at a few common communication systems applications to illustrate the importance of resonant circuits in electronic communication.

After completing this section, you should be able to

◆ **Discuss some applications of resonant circuits**

  ◆ Describe a tuned amplifier application

  ◆ Describe antenna coupling

  ◆ Describe tuned amplifiers

  ◆ Describe signal separation in a receiver

  ◆ Describe a radio receiver

Tuned Amplifiers

A *tuned amplifier* is a circuit that amplifies signals within a specified band. Typically, a parallel resonant circuit is used in conjunction with an amplifier to achieve the selectivity. In terms of the general operation, input signals with frequencies that range over a wide band are accepted on the amplifier's input and are amplified. The resonant circuit allows only a relatively narrow band of those frequencies to be passed on. The variable capacitor allows tuning over the range of input frequencies so that a desired frequency can be selected, as indicated in Figure 13–59.

▲ FIGURE 13–59

A basic tuned band-pass amplifier.

Antenna Input to a Receiver

Radio signals are sent out from a transmitter via electromagnetic waves that propagate through the atmosphere. When the electromagnetic waves cut across the receiving antenna, small voltages are induced. Out of the wide range of electromagnetic frequencies, only one frequency or a limited band of frequencies must be extracted. Figure 13–60 shows a typical arrangement of an antenna coupled to the receiver input by a transformer (covered in Chapter 14). A variable capacitor is connected across the transformer secondary to form a parallel resonant circuit.

▶ FIGURE 13–60

Resonant coupling from an antenna.

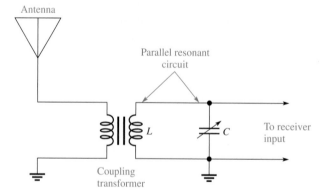

Double-Tuned Transformer Coupling in a Receiver

In some types of communication receivers, tuned amplifiers are transformer-coupled together to increase the amplification. Capacitors can be placed in parallel with the primary and secondary windings of the transformer, effectively creating two parallel resonant bandpass filters that are coupled together. This technique, illustrated in Figure 13–61, can result in a wider bandwidth and steeper slopes on the response curve, thus increasing the selectivity for a desired band of frequencies.

▲ FIGURE 13–61

Double-tuned amplifiers.

Signal Reception and Separation in a TV Receiver

A standard broadcast band television receiver must handle both video (picture) signals and audio (sound) signals. Each TV transmitting station is allotted a 6 MHz bandwidth. Channel 2 is allotted a band from 54 MHz through 59 MHz, channel 3 is allotted a band from 60 MHz through 65 MHz, on up to channel 13, which has a band from 210 MHz through 215 MHz. You can tune the front end of the TV receiver to select any one of these channels by using tuned amplifiers. The signal output of the front end of the receiver has a bandwidth from 41 MHz through 46 MHz, regardless of the channel that is tuned in. This band, called the *intermediate frequency* (IF) band, contains both video and audio. Amplifiers tuned to the IF band boost the signal and feed it to the video amplifier.

Before the output of the video amplifier is applied to the cathode-ray tube, the audio signal is removed by a 4.5 MHz band-stop resonant circuit (called a *wave trap*), as shown in Figure 13–62. This trap keeps the sound signal from interfering with the picture. The video amplifier output is also applied to band-pass circuits that are tuned to the sound carrier frequency of 4.5 MHz. The sound signal is then processed and applied to the speaker as indicated in Figure 13–62.

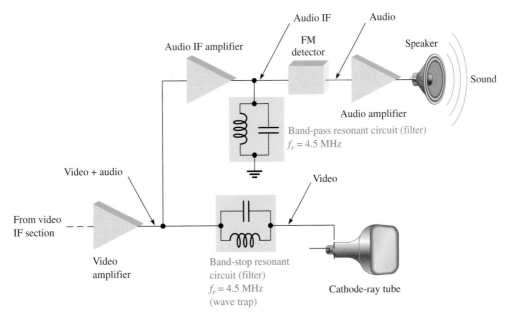

▲ FIGURE 13–62

A simplified portion of a TV receiver showing filter usage.

Superheterodyne Receiver

Another good example of resonant circuit applications is in the common AM (amplitude modulation) receiver. The AM broadcast band ranges from 535 kHz to 1605 kHz. Each AM station is assigned a 10 kHz bandwidth within that range. The tuned circuits are designed to pass only the signals from the desired radio station, rejecting all others. To reject stations outside the one that is tuned, the tuned circuits must be selective, passing on only the signals in the 10 kHz band and rejecting all others. Too much selectivity is not desirable either however. If the bandwidth is too narrow, some of the higher frequency modulated signals will be rejected, resulting in a loss of fidelity. Ideally, the resonant circuit must reject signals that are not in the desired pass-band. A simplified block diagram of a superheterodyne AM receiver is shown in Figure 13–63.

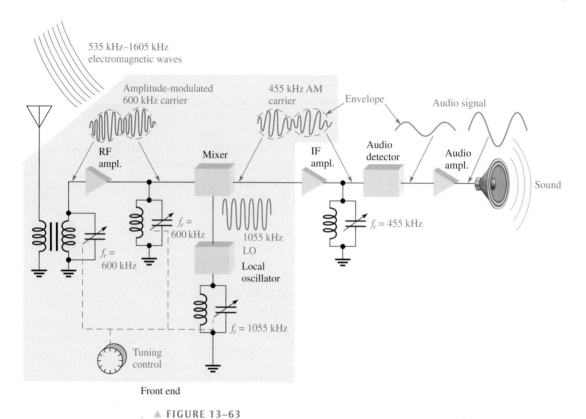

▲ FIGURE 13-63

A simplified diagram of a superheterodyne AM radio broadcast receiver showing the application of tuned resonant circuits.

There are basically three parallel resonant circuits in the front end of the receiver. Each of these resonant circuits is gang-tuned by capacitors; that is, the capacitors are mechanically or electronically linked together so that they change together as a station is selected. The front end is tuned to receive a desired station, for example, one that transmits at 600 kHz. The input resonant circuit from the antenna and the RF (radio frequency) amplifier resonant circuit select only a frequency of 600 kHz out of all the frequencies crossing the antenna.

The actual audio (sound) signal is carried by the 600 kHz carrier frequency by modulating the amplitude of the carrier so that it follows the audio signal as indicated. The variation in the amplitude of the carrier corresponding to the audio signal is called the *envelope*. The 600 kHz is then applied to a circuit called the *mixer*.

The local oscillator (LO) is tuned to a frequency that is 455 kHz above the selected frequency (1055 kHz, in this case). By a process called *heterodyning* or *beating*, the AM signal and the local oscillator signal are mixed together, and the 600 kHz AM signal is converted by the mixer to a 455 kHz AM signal (1055 kHz − 600 kHz = 455 kHz).

The 455 kHz is the intermediate frequency (IF) for standard AM receivers. No matter which station within the broadcast band is selected, its frequency is always converted to the 455 kHz IF. The amplitude-modulated IF is amplified by the IF amplifier which is tuned to 455 kHz. The output of the IF amplifier is applied to an audio detector which removes the IF, leaving only the envelope which is the audio signal. The audio signal is then amplified and applied to the speaker.

SECTION 13–8
REVIEW

1. Generally, why is a tuned resonant circuit necessary when a signal is coupled from an antenna to the input of a receiver?

2. What is a wave trap?

3. What is meant by *ganged tuning?*

Application Assignment

PUTTING YOUR KNOWLEDGE TO WORK

In the application assignment from the last chapter, you identified two types of filters in sealed housings. In this application assignment, you have another filter to evaluate, which is some type of resonant filter with no specifications available. Your assignment is to develop a frequency response curve and determine the resonant frequency and the bandwidth.

You will use oscilloscope measurements to determine the frequency response characteristics of the filter. The internal circuitry and component values are of no concern in this case.

Step 1: Measuring the Frequency Response

Based on the series of five oscilloscope measurements in Figure 13–64, create a frequency response curve (plot of output voltage versus frequency) for the filter.

Step 2: Analyzing the Response Curve

Specify the type of filter and determine the resonant frequency and the bandwidth.

Review

1. What are the half-power frequencies for the filter in this assignment?

2. From the measurements in Figure 13–64, can you determine the circuit arrangement or component values?

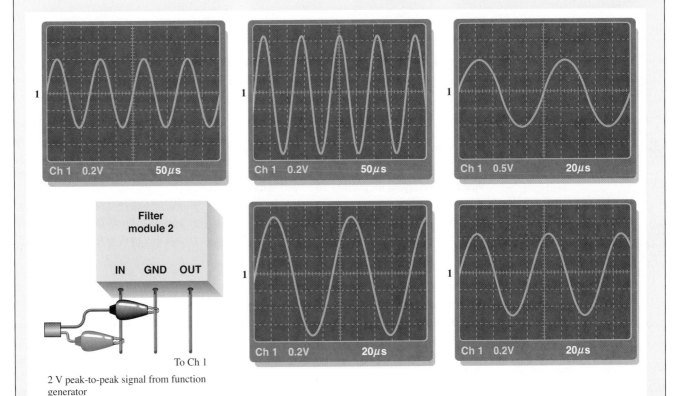

▲ FIGURE 13–64

Frequency response measurements.

SUMMARY

◆ X_L and X_C have opposing effects in an *RLC* circuit.

◆ In a series *RLC* circuit, the larger reactance determines the net reactance of the circuit.

◆ In a parallel *RLC* circuit, the smaller reactance determines the net reactance of the circuit.

Series Resonance

◆ The reactances are equal.

◆ The impedance is minimum and equal to the resistance.

◆ The current is maximum.

◆ The phase angle is zero.

◆ The voltages across *L* and *C* are equal in magnitude and, as always, 180° out of phase with each other and thus they cancel.

Parallel Resonance

◆ The reactances are approximately equal for $Q \geq 10$.

◆ The impedance is maximum.

◆ The current is minimum and, ideally, equal to zero.

◆ The phase angle is zero.

◆ The currents in the *L* and *C* branches are equal in magnitude and, as always, 180° out of phase with each other and thus they cancel.

◆ A band-pass filter passes frequencies between the lower and upper critical frequencies and rejects all others.

◆ A band-stop filter rejects frequencies between its lower and upper critical frequencies and passes all others.

◆ The bandwidth of a resonant filter is determined by the quality factor (Q) of the circuit and the resonant frequency.

◆ Cutoff frequencies are also called −3 dB frequencies or critical frequencies.

◆ The output voltage is 70.7% of its maximum at the cutoff frequencies.

KEY TERMS

Key terms and other bold terms in the chapter are defined in the end-of-book glossary.

Band-pass filter   A resonant circuit that passes a range of frequencies lying between two cutoff frequencies and rejects frequencies above and below the range.

Band-stop filter   A resonant circuit that rejects a range of frequencies lying between two cutoff frequencies and passes frequencies above and below the range.

Cutoff frequency (f_c)   The frequency at which the output voltage of a filter is 70.7% of the maximum output voltage.

Decibel (dB)   A unit of logarithmic expression ten times the logarithm of the ratio of two powers or twenty times the logarithm of the ratio of two voltages measured across equal resistances.

Half-power frequency   The frequency at which the output of a filter is 70.7% of maximum.

Parallel resonance   In a parallel *RLC* circuit, the condition where the impedance is maximum and the reactances are equal.

Resonant frequency   The frequency at which a resonant condition occurs in a series or parallel *RLC* circuit.

Selectivity   A measure of how effectively a resonant circuit passes certain frequencies and rejects others. The narrower the bandwidth, the greater the selectivity.

Series resonance   In a series *RLC* circuit, the condition where the impedance is minimum and the reactances are equal.

FORMULAS

13–1	$X_{tot} = \lvert X_L - X_C \rvert$	Total series reactance (absolute value)
13–2	$Z_{tot} = \sqrt{R^2 + X_{tot}^2}$	Total series RLC impedance
13–3	$\theta = \tan^{-1}\left(\dfrac{X_{tot}}{R}\right)$	Series RLC phase angle
13–4	$f_r = \dfrac{1}{2\pi\sqrt{LC}}$	Series resonant frequency
13–5	$BW = f_2 - f_1$	Bandwidth
13–6	$dB = 10\log\left(\dfrac{P_{out}}{P_{in}}\right)$	Decibel formula for voltage ratio
13–7	$dB = 20\log\left(\dfrac{V_{out}}{V_{in}}\right)$	Decibel formula for power ratio
13–8	$Q = \dfrac{X_L}{R}$	Series resonant quality factor
13–9	$BW = \dfrac{f_r}{Q}$	Bandwidth
13–10	$Y = \sqrt{G^2 + B_{tot}^2}$	Parallel RLC admittance
13–11	$\theta = \tan^{-1}\left(\dfrac{B_{tot}}{G}\right)$	Parallel RLC phase angle
13–12	$I_{tot} = \sqrt{I_R^2 + I_{CL}^2}$	Total parallel RLC current
13–13	$\theta = \tan^{-1}\left(\dfrac{I_{CL}}{I_R}\right)$	Parallel RLC phase angle
13–14	$L_{eq} = L\left(\dfrac{Q^2 + 1}{Q^2}\right)$	Equivalent parallel inductance
13–15	$R_{p(eq)} = R_W(Q^2 + 1)$	Equivalent parallel resistance
13–16	$f_r = \dfrac{1}{2\pi\sqrt{LC}}$	Ideal parallel resonant frequency
13–17	$I_{tot} = \lvert I_L - I_C \rvert$	Total parallel LC current (absolute value)
13–18	$Z_r = R_W(Q^2 + 1)$	Impedance at parallel resonance
13–19	$I_{tot} = \dfrac{V_s}{Z_r}$	Total current at parallel resonance
13–20	$f_r = \dfrac{\sqrt{1 - (R_W^2 C/L)}}{2\pi\sqrt{LC}}$	Parallel resonant frequency (exact)
13–21	$Q_O = \dfrac{R_{p(tot)}}{X_{L(eq)}}$	Q of a parallel RLC circuit

SELF-TEST

Answers are at the end of the chapter.

1. The total reactance of a series RLC circuit at resonance is
   (a) zero   (b) equal to the resistance   (c) infinity   (d) capacitive

2. The phase angle of a series RLC circuit at resonance is
   (a) $-90°$ (b) $+90°$ (c) $0°$ (d) dependent on the reactance

3. The impedance at the resonant frequency of a series RLC circuit with $L = 15$ mH, $C = 0.015\ \mu F$, and $R_W = 80\ \Omega$ is
   (a) $15\ k\Omega$ (b) $80\ \Omega$ (c) $30\ \Omega$ (d) $0\ \Omega$

4. In a series RLC circuit that is operating below the resonant frequency, the current
   (a) is in phase with the source voltage   (b) lags the source voltage
   (c) leads the source voltage

5. If the value of C in a series RLC circuit is increased, the resonant frequency
   (a) is not affected   (b) increases   (c) remains the same   (d) decreases

6. In a certain series resonant circuit, $V_C = 150$ V, $V_L = 150$ V, and $V_R = 50$ V. The value of the source voltage is
   (a) 150 V   (b) 300 V   (c) 50 V   (d) 350 V

7. A certain series resonant band-pass filter has a bandwidth of 1 kHz. If the existing coil is replaced with one having a lower value of Q, the bandwidth will
   (a) increase   (b) decrease   (c) remain the same   (d) be more selective

8. At frequencies below resonance in a parallel RLC circuit, the current
   (a) leads the source voltage   (b) lags the source voltage
   (c) is in phase with the source voltage

9. The total current into the L and C branches of a parallel circuit at resonance is ideally
   (a) maximum   (b) low   (c) high   (d) zero

10. To tune a parallel resonant circuit to a lower frequency, the capacitance should be
    (a) increased   (b) decreased   (c) left alone   (d) replaced with inductance

11. The resonant frequency of a parallel circuit is the same as a series circuit using the same components when
    (a) the Q is very low   (b) the Q is very high   (c) there is no resistance

12. If the resistance in parallel with a parallel resonant filter is reduced, the bandwidth
    (a) disappears   (b) decreases   (c) becomes sharper   (d) increases

PROBLEMS

Answers to odd-numbered problems are at the end of the book.

BASIC PROBLEMS

SECTION 13–1 Impedance and Phase Angle of Series *RLC* Circuits

1. A certain series RLC circuit operates at a frequency of 5 kHz and has the following values: $R = 10\ \Omega$, $C = 0.047\ \mu$F, and $L = 5$ mH. Determine the impedance and phase angle. What is the total reactance?

2. Find the impedance in Figure 13–65.

3. If the frequency of the source voltage in Figure 13–65 is doubled from the value that produces the indicated reactances, how does the impedance change?

▶ FIGURE 13–65

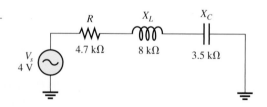

SECTION 13–2 Analysis of Series *RLC* Circuits

4. For the circuit in Figure 13–65, find I_{tot}, V_R, V_L, and V_C.

5. Draw the voltage phasor diagram for the circuit in Figure 13–65.

6. Analyze the circuit in Figure 13–66 for the following ($f = 25\,\text{kHz}$):

    (a) I_{tot} **(b)** P_{true} **(c)** P_r **(d)** P_a

▶ FIGURE 13–66

SECTION 13–3   Series Resonance

7. For the circuit in Figure 13–65, is the resonant frequency higher or lower than the value indicated by the reactances?

8. For the circuit in Figure 13–67, determine the voltage across R at resonance.

▶ FIGURE 13–67

9. Find X_L, X_C, Z, and I at the resonant frequency in Figure 13–67.

10. A certain series resonant circuit has a maximum current of 50 mA and a V_L of 100 V. The source voltage is 10 V. What is Z? What are X_L and X_C?

11. For the *RLC* circuit in Figure 13–68, determine the resonant frequency and the cutoff frequencies.

▶ FIGURE 13–68

12. What is the value of the current at the half-power points in Figure 13–68?

SECTION 13–4   Series Resonant Filters

13. Determine the resonant frequency for each filter in Figure 13–69. Are these filters band-pass or band-stop types?

▶ FIGURE 13–69

    (a)   (b)

14. Assuming that the coils in Figure 13–69 have a winding resistance of 10 Ω, find the bandwidth for each filter.

15. Determine f_r and BW for each filter in Figure 13–70.

► FIGURE 13–70

(a)   (b)

SECTION 13–5   Parallel *RLC* Circuits

16. Find the total impedance of the circuit in Figure 13–71.

17. Is the circuit in Figure 13–71 capacitive or inductive? Explain.

18. For the circuit in Figure 13–71, find all the currents and voltages.

19. Find the total impedance for the circuit in Figure 13–72.

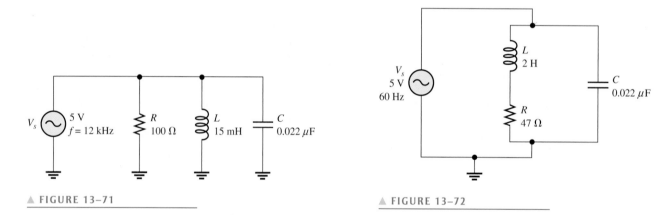

▲ FIGURE 13–71   ▲ FIGURE 13–72

SECTION 13–6   Parallel Resonance

20. What is the impedance of an ideal parallel resonant circuit (no resistance in either branch)?

21. Find Z at resonance and f_r for the tank circuit in Figure 13–73.

22. How much current is drawn from the source in Figure 13–73 at resonance? What are the inductive current and the capacitive current at the resonant frequency?

► FIGURE 13–73

SECTION 13–7   Parallel Resonant Filters

23. At resonance, $X_L = 2$ kΩ and $R_W = 25$ Ω in a parallel resonant band-pass filter. The resonant frequency is 5 kHz. Determine the bandwidth.

24. If the lower cutoff frequency is 2400 Hz and the upper cutoff frequency is 2800 Hz, what is the bandwidth?

25. In a certain resonant circuit, the power at resonance is 2.75 W. What is the power at the lower and upper cutoff frequencies?

26. What values of L and C should be used in a tank circuit to obtain a resonant frequency of 8 kHz? The bandwidth must be 800 Hz. The winding resistance of the coil is 10 Ω.

27. A parallel resonant circuit has a Q of 50 and a BW of 400 Hz. If Q is doubled, what is the bandwidth for the same f_r?

ADVANCED PROBLEMS

28. For each following case, express the voltage ratio in decibels:

    (a) $V_{in} = 1$ V, $V_{out} = 1$ V   (b) $V_{in} = 5$ V, $V_{out} = 3$ V

    (c) $V_{in} = 10$ V, $V_{out} = 7.07$ V   (d) $V_{in} = 25$ V, $V_{out} = 5$ V

29. Find the current through each component in Figure 13–74. Find the voltage across each component.

30. Determine whether there is a value of C that will make $V_{ab} = 0$ V in Figure 13–75. If not, explain.

31. If the value of C is 0.22 μF, how much current is through each branch in Figure 13–75? What is the total current?

▲ FIGURE 13–74

▲ FIGURE 13–75

32. Determine the resonant frequencies in Figure 13–76 and find V_{out} at each resonant frequency.

▲ FIGURE 13–76

33. Design a band-pass filter using a parallel resonant circuit to meet the following specifications: $BW = 500$ Hz, $Q = 40$, $I_{C(max)} = 20$ mA, $V_{C(max)} = 2.5$ V.

34. Design a circuit in which the following series resonant frequencies are switch-selectable: 500 kHz, 1000 kHz, 1500 kHz, 2000 kHz.

35. Design a parallel-resonant network using a single coil and switch-selectable capacitors to produce the following resonant frequencies: 8 MHz, 9 MHz, 10 MHz, and 11 MHz. Assume a 10 μH coil with a winding resistance of 5 Ω.

MULTISIM TROUBLESHOOTING PROBLEMS

36. Open file P13-36. Determine if there is a fault and, if so, identify it.

37. Open file P13-37. Determine if there is a fault and, if so, identify it.

38. Open file P13-38. Determine if there is a fault and, if so, identify it.

39. Open file P13-39. Determine if there is a fault and, if so, identify it.

40. Open file P13-40. Determine if there is a fault and, if so, identify it.

41. Open file P13-41. Determine if there is a fault and, if so, identify it.

ANSWERS

SECTION REVIEWS

SECTION 13–1 **Impedance and Phase Angle of Series *RLC* Circuits**

1. The circuit is inductive if $X_L > X_C$ and capacitive if $X_C > X_L$.

2. $X_{tot} = |X_L - X_C| = 70\ \Omega$; The circuit is capacitive.

3. $Z = \sqrt{R^2 + X_{tot}^2} = 83.2\ \Omega$; $\theta = \tan^{-1}(X_{tot}/R) = 57.3°$; Current is leading V_s.

SECTION 13–2 **Analysis of Series *RLC* Circuits**

1. $V_s = \sqrt{V_R^2 + (V_C - V_L)^2} = 38.4\ \text{V}$

2. Current leads V_s because the circuit is capacitive.

3. $X_{tot} = |X_L - X_C| = 6\ \text{k}\Omega$

SECTION 13–3 **Series Resonance**

1. Series resonance occurs when $X_L = X_C$.

2. The current is maximum because the impedance is minimum.

3. $f_r = 1/(2\pi\sqrt{LC}) = 159\ \text{kHz}$

4. It is capacitive because $X_C > X_L$.

SECTION 13–4 **Series Resonant Filters**

1. $V_{out} = 0.707(15\ \text{V}) = 10.6\ \text{V}$

2. $BW = f_r/Q = 10\ \text{kHz}$

3. Current is maximum; output voltage is minimum.

SECTION 13–5 **Parallel *RLC* Filters**

1. $I_R = V_s/R = 80\ \text{mA}$; $I_C = V_s/X_C = 120\ \text{mA}$; $I_L = V_s/X_L = 240\ \text{mA}$

2. The circuit is inductive ($X_L < X_C$).

3. $L_{eq} = L[(Q^2 + 1)/Q^2] = 20.1\ \text{mH}$; $R_{p(eq)} = R_W(Q^2 + 1) = 1589\ \Omega$

SECTION 13–6 **Parallel Resonance**

1. The impedance is maximum.

2. The current is minimum.

3. At ideal parallel resonance, $X_C = X_L = 1.5\ \text{k}\Omega$.

4. $f_r = \sqrt{1 - (R_W^2 C/L)}/2\pi\sqrt{LC} = 225\ \text{kHz}$; $Z_r = R_W(Q^2 + 1) = 1250\ \text{M}\Omega$

5. $f_r = 1/(2\pi\sqrt{LC}) = 22.5\ \text{kHz}$

6. $f_r = \sqrt{Q^2/(Q^2 + 1)}/2\pi\sqrt{LC} = 20.9\ \text{kHz}$

7. $Z_r = R_W(Q^2 + 1) = 8.02\ \text{k}\Omega$

SECTION 13–7 **Parallel Resonant Filters**

1. The bandwidth can be increased by reducing the parallel resistance.

2. f_r changes to 4.47 kHz.

3. $Z_r = R_W(Q^2 + 1) = 47.0\,\text{k}\Omega$

SECTION 13–8 **Applications**

1. A tuned resonant circuit is used to select a narrow band of frequencies.

2. A wave trap is a band-stop filter.

3. Several variable capacitors (or inductors) whose values can be varied simultaneously with a common control is an example of ganged tuning.

Application Assignment

1. $f_{c(1)} = 8\,\text{kHz}; f_{c(2)} = 11.6\,\text{kHz}$

2. The circuit or component values cannot be determined from the data given.

RELATED PROBLEMS FOR EXAMPLES

13–1 $1.25\,\text{k}\Omega; 63.4°$

13–2 $4.71\,\text{k}\Omega$

13–3   Current increases, reaches a maximum at resonance, and then decreases.

13–4   More capacitive

13–5   71.2 kHz

13–6   2.27 mA

13–7 Z increases; Z increases

13–8   No

13–9   200 kHz

13–10 -14 dB

13–11   4.61

13–12   322 Hz

13–13 V_{out} increases; V_{out} increases

13–14   Inductive

13–15   Increase. X_C will decrease and approach 0.

13–16 $R_{p(eq)} = 25\,\text{k}\Omega; L_{eq} = 5\,\text{mH}; C = 0.022\,\mu\text{F}, R_{p(tot)} = 4.24\,\text{k}\Omega$

13–17 $f_r = 3.39\,\text{kHz}; I_L = 4.69\,\text{mA}; I_C = 4.69\,\text{mA}; I_{tot} = 0\,\text{A}$

13–18 $80.0\,\text{k}\Omega$

13–19   The differences are negligible.

13–20   7.07 V

13–21   530 kHz

13–22   25

13–23 Q_O decreases with less load resistance.

13–24   The Q is less than 10.

SELF-TEST

1. (a)   2. (c)   3. (b)   4. (c)   5. (d)   6. (c)   7. (a)

8. (b)   9. (d)   10. (a)   11. (b)   12. (d)

14

TRANSFORMERS

CHAPTER OBJECTIVES

Explain mutual inductance

Describe how a transformer is constructed and how it works

Describe how transformers increase and decrease voltage

Discuss the effect of a resistive load across the secondary winding

Discuss the concept of a reflected load in a transformer

Discuss impedance matching with transformers

Describe a practical transformer

Describe several types of transformers

Troubleshoot transformers

KEY TERMS

◆ Electrical isolation
◆ Mutual inductance (L_M)
◆ Transformer
◆ Primary winding
◆ Secondary winding
◆ Magnetic coupling

◆ Turns ratio (n)
◆ Reflected resistance
◆ Impedance matching
◆ Maximum power transfer
◆ Apparent power rating
◆ Center tap

APPLICATION ASSIGNMENT PREVIEW

The assignment will be to troubleshoot a type of dc power supply that uses a transformer to couple the ac voltage from a standard electrical outlet. By making voltage measurements at various points, you can determine if there is a fault and be able to specify the part of the power supply that is faulty. After studying this chapter, you should be able to complete the application assignment.

VISIT THE COMPANION WEBSITE

Study aids for this chapter are available at
http://www.prenhall.com/floyd

INTRODUCTION

In Chapter 11, you learned about self-inductance. In this chapter, you will study mutual inductance, which is the basis for the operation of transformers. Transformers are used in all types of applications such as power supplies, electrical power distribution, and signal coupling in communications systems.

The operation of the transformer is based on the principle of mutual inductance, which occurs when two or more coils are in close proximity. A simple transformer is actually two coils that are electromagnetically coupled by their mutual inductance. Because there is no electrical contact between two magnetically coupled coils, the transfer of energy from one coil to the other can be achieved in a situation of complete electrical isolation. In relation to transformers, the term *winding* or *coil* is commonly used to describe the primary or secondary.

14–1 MUTUAL INDUCTANCE

When two coils are placed close to each other, a changing electromagnetic field produced by the current in one coil will cause an induced voltage in the second coil because of the mutual inductance between the two coils.

After completing this section, you should be able to

◆ **Explain mutual inductance**

  ◆ Discuss magnetic coupling

  ◆ Define *electrical isolation*

  ◆ Define *coefficient of coupling*

  ◆ Identify the factors that affect mutual inductance and state the formula

Recall that the electromagnetic field surrounding a coil of wire expands, collapses, and reverses as the current increases, decreases, and reverses. When a second coil is placed very close to the first coil so that the changing magnetic lines of force cut through the second coil, the coils are magnetically coupled and a voltage is induced, as indicated in Figure 14–1.

Lines of force cutting second coil as the electromagnetic field expands, collapses, and reverses in response to the sinusoidal input.

◀ **FIGURE 14–1**

A voltage is induced in the second coil as a result of the changing current in the first coil, producing a changing magnetic field that links the second coil.

When two coils are magnetically coupled, they provide **electrical isolation** because there is no electrical connection between them, only a magnetic link. If the current in the first coil is a sine wave, the voltage induced in the second coil is also a sine wave. The amount of voltage induced in the second coil as a result of the current in the first coil is dependent on the **mutual inductance, LM**.

The mutual inductance is established by the inductance of each coil (L_1 and L_2) and by the amount of coupling (k) between the two coils. To maximize coupling, the two coils are wound on a common core. The three factors that influence mutual inductance (k, L_1, and L_2) are shown in Figure 14–2. The formula for mutual inductance is

$$L_M = k\sqrt{L_1 L_2}$$

Equation 14–1

◀ **FIGURE 14–2**

The mutual inductance of two coils.

Coefficient of Coupling

The **coefficient of coupling, k,** between the primary and secondary windings of a transformer is the ratio of the flux (lines of force) produced by the primary linking the secondary ($\phi_{1\text{-}2}$) to the total flux produced by the primary (ϕ_1).

Equation 14–2

$$k = \frac{\phi_{1\text{-}2}}{\phi_1}$$

For example, if half of the total flux produced by coil 1 links coil 2, then $k = 0.5$. A greater value of k means that more voltage is induced in coil 2 for a certain rate of change of current in coil 1. Note that k has no units. Recall that the unit of magnetic lines of force (flux) is the weber, abbreviated Wb.

The coefficient of coupling, k, depends on the physical closeness of the coils and the type of core material on which they are wound. Also, the construction and shape of the cores are factors.

EXAMPLE 14–1

Two coils are wound on a single core, and the coefficient of coupling is 0.3. The inductance of coil 1 is $10\,\mu\text{H}$, and the inductance of coil 2 is $15\,\mu\text{H}$. What is L_M?

Solution

$$L_M = k\sqrt{L_1 L_2} = 0.3\sqrt{(10\,\mu\text{H})(15\,\mu\text{H})} = \mathbf{3.67\,\mu\text{H}}$$

Related Problem*   Determine the mutual inductance when $k = 0.5$, $L_1 = 1\,\text{mH}$, and $L_2 = 600\,\mu\text{H}$.

---

*Answers are at the end of the chapter.

EXAMPLE 14–2

One coil produces a total magnetic flux of $50\,\mu\text{Wb}$, and $20\,\mu\text{Wb}$ link coil 2. What is k?

Solution

$$k = \frac{\phi_{1\text{-}2}}{\phi_1} = \frac{20\,\mu\text{Wb}}{50\,\mu\text{Wb}} = \mathbf{0.4}$$

Related Problem   Determine k when $\phi_1 = 500\,\mu\text{Wb}$ and $\phi_{1\text{-}2} = 375\,\mu\text{Wb}$.

**SECTION 14–1
REVIEW**
Answers are at the end of the chapter.

1. Define *mutual inductance.*
2. Two 50 mH coils have $k = 0.9$. What is L_M?
3. If k is increased, what happens to the voltage induced in one coil as a result of a current change in the other coil?

14–2 THE BASIC TRANSFORMER

A basic **transformer** is an electrical device constructed of two coils of wire (windings) electromagnetically coupled to each other so that there is a mutual inductance for the transfer of power from one winding to the other.

After completing this section, you should be able to

◆ **Describe how a transformer is constructed and how it works**

  ◆ Identify the parts of a basic transformer

◆ Discuss the importance of the core material

◆ Define *primary winding* and *secondary winding*

◆ Define *turns ratio*

◆ Discuss how the direction of windings affects voltage polarities

A schematic of a transformer is shown in Figure 14–3(a). One coil is called the **primary winding** and the other coil is called the **secondary winding** as indicated. For standard operation, the source voltage is applied to the primary winding, and a load is connected to the secondary winding, as shown in Figure 14–3(b). The primary winding is the input winding, and the secondary winding is the output winding. It is common to refer to the side of the transformer that has the source voltage as the *primary,* and the side that has the induced voltage as the *secondary.*

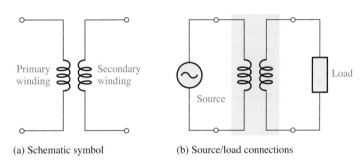

(a) Schematic symbol   (b) Source/load connections

◀ FIGURE 14–3

The basic transformer.

The windings of a transformer are formed around the core. The core provides both a physical structure for placement of the windings and a magnetic path so that the magnetic flux is concentrated close to the coils. Three general categories of core material are air, ferrite, and iron. The schematic symbol for each type is shown in Figure 14–4.

(a) Air core   (b) Ferrite core   (c) Iron core

◀ FIGURE 14–4

Schematic symbols specify the type of core.

Air-core and ferrite-core transformers generally are used for high-frequency applications and consist of windings on an insulating shell that is hollow (air) or constructed of ferrite, such as depicted in Figure 14–5. The wire is typically covered by a varnish-type coating to prevent the windings from shorting together. The amount of **magnetic coupling** between the primary winding and the secondary winding is set by the type of core material and by the relative positions of the windings. In Figure 14–5(a), the windings are loosely coupled because they are separated, and in part (b) they are tightly coupled because they are overlapping. The tighter the coupling, the greater the induced voltage in the secondary for a given current in the primary.

Iron-core transformers generally are used for audio frequency (AF) and power applications. These transformers consist of windings on a core constructed from laminated sheets of

▶ FIGURE 14–5

Transformers with cylindrical-shaped cores.

Air or ferrite core

(a) Loosely coupled windings

(b) Tightly coupled windings. Cutaway view shows both windings.

ferromagnetic material insulated from each other, as shown in Figure 14–6. This construction provides an easy path for the magnetic flux and increases the amount of coupling between the windings. The figure also shows the basic construction of two major configurations of iron-core transformers. In the core-type construction, shown in Figure 14–6(a), the windings are on separate legs of the laminated core. In the shell-type construction, shown in part (b), both windings are on the same leg. Each type has certain advantages. In general, the core type has more room for insulation and can handle higher voltages. The shell type can produce higher core flux, so fewer turns are required.

A variety of transformers is shown in Figure 14–7.

Primary winding

Laminated iron core

Secondary winding

Laminated iron core

(a) Core type has each winding on a separate leg.

(b) Shell type has both windings on the same leg.

▲ FIGURE 14–6

Iron-core transformer construction with multilayer windings.

▲ FIGURE 14–7

Some common types of transformers.

Turns Ratio

A transformer parameter that is useful in understanding how a transformer operates is the turns ratio. In this text, the **turns ratio, (n)** is defined as the ratio of the number of turns in the secondary winding (N_{sec}) to the number of turns in the primary winding (N_{pri}).

$$n = \frac{N_{sec}}{N_{pri}}$$

Equation 14–3

This definition of turns ratio is based on the IEEE standard for electronics power transformers as specified in the IEEE dictionary. Other categories of transformer may have a different definition, so some sources define the turns ratio as N_{pri}/N_{sec}. Either definition is correct as long as it is clearly stated and used consistently. The turns ratio of a transformer is rarely if ever given as a transformer specification. Generally, the input and output voltages and the power rating are the key specifications. However, the turns ratio is useful in studying the operating principle of a transformer.

EXAMPLE 14–3   A certain transformer used in a radar system has a primary winding with 100 turns and a secondary winding with 400 turns. What is the turns ratio?

Solution $N_{sec} = 400$ and $N_{pri} = 100$; therefore, the turns ratio is

$$n = \frac{N_{sec}}{N_{pri}} = \frac{400}{100} = \textbf{4}$$

A turns ratio of 4 can be expressed as 1:4 on a schematic.

Related Problem   A certain transformer has a turns ratio of 10. If $N_{pri} = 500$, what is N_{sec}?

Direction of Windings

Another important transformer parameter is the direction in which the windings are placed around the core. As illustrated in Figure 14–8, the direction of the windings determines the polarity of the voltage across the secondary winding (secondary voltage) with respect to the voltage across the primary winding (primary voltage). Phase dots can be used on the schematic symbols to indicate polarities, as shown in Figure 14–9.

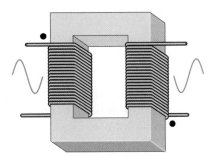

(a) The primary and secondary voltages are in phase when the windings are in the same effective direction around the magnetic path.

(b) The primary and secondary voltages are 180° out of phase when the windings are in the opposite direction.

▲ FIGURE 14–8

The direction of the windings determines the relative polarities of the voltages.

▶ FIGURE 14–9

Phase dots indicate corresponding polarities of primary and secondary voltages.

Phase dots

(a) Voltages are in phase.

(b) Voltages are out of phase.

SECTION 14–2 REVIEW	1. Upon what principle is the operation of a transformer based?
	2. Define *turns ratio.*
	3. Why are the directions of the windings of a transformer important?
	4. A certain transformer has a primary winding with 500 turns and a secondary winding with 250 turns. What is the turns ratio?

14–3 STEP-UP AND STEP-DOWN TRANSFORMERS

A step-up transformer has more turns in its secondary winding than in its primary winding and is used to increase ac voltage. A step-down transformer has more turns in its primary winding than in its secondary winding and is used to decrease ac voltage.

After completing this section, you should be able to

◆ **Describe how transformers increase and decrease voltage**

  ◆ Explain how a step-up transformer works

  ◆ Identify a step-up transformer by its turns ratio

  ◆ State the relationship between primary and secondary voltages and the turns ratio

  ◆ Explain how a step-down transformer works

  ◆ Identify a step-down transformer by its turns ratio

The Step-Up Transformer

A transformer in which the secondary voltage is greater than the primary voltage is called a **step-up transformer.** The amount that the voltage is stepped up depends on the turns ratio. For any transformer,

The ratio of secondary voltage (V_{sec}) to primary voltage (V_{pri}) is equal to the ratio of the number of turns in the secondary winding (N_{sec}) to the number of turns in the primary winding (N_{pri}).

Equation 14–4

$$\frac{V_{sec}}{V_{pri}} = \frac{N_{sec}}{N_{pri}}$$

Recall that N_{sec}/N_{pri} defines the turns ratio, n. Therefore, from this relationship, V_{sec} can be expressed as

Equation 14–5

$$V_{sec} = nV_{pri}$$

Equation 14–5 shows that the secondary voltage is equal to the turns ratio times the primary voltage. This condition assumes that the coefficient of coupling is 1, and a good iron-core transformer approaches this value.

The turns ratio for a step-up transformer is always greater than 1 because the number of turns in the secondary winding (N_{sec}) is always greater than the number of turns in the primary winding (N_{pri}).

EXAMPLE 14–4

The transformer in Figure 14–10 has a turns ratio of 3. What is the voltage across the secondary?

▶ FIGURE 14–10

Solution The secondary voltage is

$$V_{sec} = nV_{pri} = 3(120\text{ V}) = \textbf{360 V}$$

Note that the turns ratio of 3 is indicated on the schematic as 1:3, meaning that there are three secondary turns for each primary turn.

Related Problem The transformer in Figure 14–10 is changed to one with a turns ratio of 4. Determine V_{sec}.

Open Multisim file E14-04 on your CD-ROM and measure the secondary voltage.

The Step-Down Transformer

A transformer in which the secondary voltage is less than the primary voltage is called a **step-down transformer.** The amount by which the voltage is stepped down depends on the turns ratio. Equation 14–5 also applies to a step-down transformer.

The turns ratio of a step-down transformer is always less than 1 because the number of turns in the secondary winding (N_{sec}) is always less than the number of turns in the primary winding (N_{pri}).

EXAMPLE 14–5

The transformer in Figure 14–11 is part of a laboratory power supply and has a turns ratio of 0.2. What is the secondary voltage?

▶ FIGURE 14–11

Solution   The secondary voltage is

$$V_{sec} = nV_{pri} = 0.2(120 \text{ V}) = \textbf{24 V}$$

Related Problem   The transformer in Figure 14–11 is changed to one with a turns ratio of 0.48. Determine the secondary voltage.

Open Multisim file E14-05 on your CD-ROM and measure the secondary voltage.

DC Isolation

If there is a nonchanging direct current through the primary circuit of a transformer, nothing happens in the secondary circuit, as indicated in Figure 14–12(a). A changing current in the primary winding is necessary in order to create a changing magnetic field. This will cause voltage to be induced in the secondary circuit, as indicated in Figure 14–12(b). Therefore, the transformer isolates the secondary circuit from any dc voltage in the primary circuit. A transformer that is used strictly for isolation has a turns ratio of 1.

(a)   (b)

▲ FIGURE 14–12

DC isolation and ac coupling.

In a typical application, a small transformer can be used to keep the dc voltage on the output of an amplifier stage from affecting the dc bias of the next amplifier stage. Only the ac signal is coupled through the transformer from one stage to the next, as Figure 14–13 illustrates.

▶ FIGURE 14–13

Audio amplifier stages with trans-former coupling for dc isolation.

SECTION 14–3 REVIEW

1. What does a step-up transformer do?
2. If the turns ratio is 5, how much greater is the secondary voltage than the primary voltage?
3. When 240 V ac are applied to a transformer with a turns ratio of 10, what is the secondary voltage?

4. What does a step-down transformer do?

5. A voltage of 120 V ac is applied to the primary winding of a transformer with a turns ratio of 0.5. What is the secondary voltage?

6. A primary voltage of 120 V ac is reduced to 12 V ac. What is the turns ratio?

7. Can a dc voltage be coupled through a transformer?

14–4 LOADING THE SECONDARY

When a resistive load is connected to the secondary winding of a transformer, the relationship of the load (secondary) current and the current in the primary circuit is determined by the turns ratio.

After completing this section, you should be able to

◆ **Discuss the effect of a resistive load across the secondary winding**

   ◆ Discuss power in a transformer

   ◆ Determine the current delivered by the secondary when a step-up transformer is loaded

   ◆ Determine the current delivered by the secondary when a step-down transformer is loaded

When a load is connected to the secondary winding of a transformer, the power delivered to the load can never be greater than the power delivered by the primary winding. For an ideal transformer, the power delivered by the secondary winding (P_{sec}) equals the power delivered by the primary winding (P_{pri}). When losses are considered, the power delivered by the secondary is always less.

Power is dependent on voltage and current, and there can be no increase in power in a transformer. Therefore, if the voltage is stepped up, the current is stepped down and vice versa. In an ideal transformer, the power delivered by the secondary to the load is the same as the power delivered by the primary regardless of the turns ratio.

The power delivered by the primary is

$$P_{pri} = V_{pri}I_{pri}$$

The power delivered by the secondary is

$$P_{sec} = V_{sec}I_{sec}$$

Ideally, $P_{pri} = P_{sec}$; therefore,

$$V_{pri}I_{pri} = V_{sec}I_{sec}$$

Transposing terms,

$$\frac{I_{pri}}{I_{sec}} = \frac{V_{sec}}{V_{pri}}$$

From Equation 14–4,

$$\frac{V_{sec}}{V_{pri}} = \frac{N_{sec}}{N_{pri}}$$

Therefore, since N_{sec}/N_{pri} equals the turns ratio, n, the relationship of primary current to secondary current in a transformer is

Equation 14–6

$$\frac{I_{pri}}{I_{sec}} = n$$

Inverting both sides of Equation 14–6 and solving for I_{sec},

Equation 14–7

$$I_{sec} = \left(\frac{1}{n}\right)I_{pri}$$

Figure 14–14 illustrates the effects of voltages and currents in a transformer. In part (a), for a step-up transformer in which n is greater than 1, the secondary current is less than the primary current because $1/n$ is less than 1. For a step-down transformer, shown in Figure 14–14(b), n is less than 1, and I_{sec} is greater than I_{pri} because $1/n$ is greater than 1.

▶ FIGURE 14–14

Illustration of voltages and currents in a transformer with a loaded secondary winding.

(a) Step-up transformer: $V_{sec} > V_{pri}$ and $I_{sec} < I_{pri}$

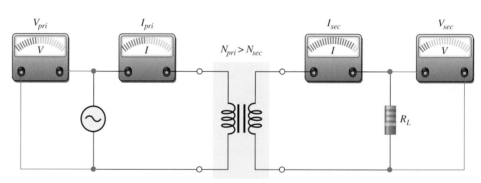

(b) Step-down transformer: $V_{sec} < V_{pri}$ and $I_{sec} > I_{pri}$

EXAMPLE 14–6

The two transformers shown in Figure 14–15 have loaded secondaries. If, as a result of the loaded secondary, the primary current is 100 mA in each case, what is the current through the load?

▶ FIGURE 14–15

(a)   (b)

Solution   In part (a), the turns ratio is 10. Therefore, the secondary load current is

$$I_L = I_{sec} = \left(\frac{1}{n}\right)I_{pri} = \left(\frac{1}{10}\right)I_{pri} = 0.1(100\,\text{mA}) = \mathbf{10\,mA}$$

In part (b), the turns ratio is 0.5. Therefore, the secondary load current is

$$I_L = I_{sec} = \left(\frac{1}{n}\right)I_{pri} = \left(\frac{1}{0.5}\right)I_{pri} = 2(100\,\text{mA}) = \mathbf{200\,mA}$$

Related Problem   What is the secondary current in Figure 14–15(a) if the turns ratio is doubled? What is the secondary current in Figure 14–15(b) if the turns ratio is halved? Assume the load resistances are changed so that I_{pri} remains at 100 mA in both cases.

SECTION 14–4 REVIEW

1. If the turns ratio of a transformer is 2, is the secondary current greater than or less than the primary current? By how much?
2. A transformer has 100 primary turns and 25 secondary turns, and I_{pri} is 0.5 A. What is the turns ratio? What is the value of I_{sec}?
3. In Question 2, what is the primary current when there is a secondary load current of 10 A?

14–5 REFLECTED LOAD

From the viewpoint of the primary, a load connected across the secondary winding of a transformer appears to have a resistance that is not necessarily equal to the actual resistance of the load. The actual load is "reflected" into the primary as determined by the turns ratio. This reflected load is what the source effectively sees, and it determines the amount of primary current.

After completing this section, you should be able to

◆ **Discuss the concept of a reflected load in a transformer**

  ◆ Define *reflected resistance*

  ◆ Explain how the turns ratio affects the reflected resistance

  ◆ Calculate reflected resistance

The concept of a reflected load is illustrated in Figure 14–16. The load (R_L) in the secondary of a transformer is reflected into the primary by transformer action. The load appears to the source in the primary to be a resistance (R_{pri}) with a value determined by the turns ratio and the actual value of the load resistance. The resistance R_{pri} is called the **reflected resistance**.

The resistance in the primary of Figure 14–16 is $R_{pri} = V_{pri}/I_{pri}$. The resistance in the secondary is $R_L = V_{sec}/I_{sec}$. From Equations 14–4 and 14–6, you know that $V_{sec}/V_{pri} = n$ and $I_{pri}/I_{sec} = n$. Using these relationships, a formula for R_{pri} in terms of R_L is determined as follows:

$$\frac{R_{pri}}{R_L} = \frac{V_{pri}/I_{pri}}{V_{sec}/I_{sec}} = \left(\frac{V_{pri}}{V_{sec}}\right)\left(\frac{I_{sec}}{I_{pri}}\right) = \left(\frac{1}{n}\right)\left(\frac{1}{n}\right) = \left(\frac{1}{n}\right)^2$$

▶ FIGURE 14–16

Reflected load in a transformer circuit.

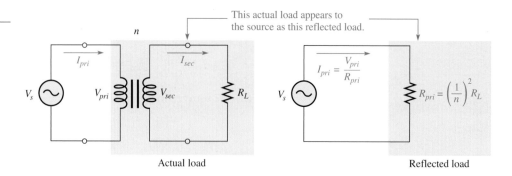

This actual load appears to the source as this reflected load.

Actual load

Reflected load

Solving for R_{pri} yields

Equation 14–8

$$R_{pri} = \left(\frac{1}{n}\right)^2 R_L$$

Equation 14–8 shows that the resistance reflected into the primary is the square of the reciprocal of the turns ratio times the load resistance.

In a step-up transformer ($n > 1$), the reflected resistance is less than the actual load resistance; in a step-down transformer ($n < 1$), the reflected resistance is greater than the load resistance. This is illustrated in Examples 14–7 and 14–8, respectively.

EXAMPLE 14–7

Figure 14–17 shows a source that is transformer-coupled to a load resistor of 100 Ω. The transformer has a turns ratio of 4. What is the reflected resistance seen by the source?

▶ FIGURE 14–17

R_L
100 Ω

Solution   The reflected resistance is

$$R_{pri} = \left(\frac{1}{n}\right)^2 R_L = \left(\frac{1}{4}\right)^2 100 \ \Omega = \left(\frac{1}{16}\right) 100 \ \Omega = \mathbf{6.25 \ \Omega}$$

The source sees a resistance of 6.25 Ω just as if it were connected directly, as shown in the equivalent circuit of Figure 14–18.

▶ FIGURE 14–18

Resistance "reflected" from secondary

R_{pri}
6.25 Ω

Related Problem   If the turns ratio in Figure 14–17 is 10 and R_L is 600 Ω, what is the reflected resistance?

EXAMPLE 14–8

In Figure 14–17, if a transformer that has a turns ratio of 0.25 is used, what is the reflected resistance?

Solution The reflected resistance is

$$R_{pri} = \left(\frac{1}{n}\right)^2 R_L = \left(\frac{1}{0.25}\right)^2 100 \ \Omega = (4)^2 100 \ \Omega = \mathbf{1600 \ \Omega}$$

Related Problem To achieve a reflected resistance of 800 Ω, what turns ratio is required in Figure 14–17?

SECTION 14–5 REVIEW

1. Define *reflected resistance*.
2. What transformer characteristic determines the reflected resistance?
3. A given transformer has a turns ratio of 10, and the load is 50 Ω. How much resistance is reflected into the primary?
4. What is the turns ratio required to reflect a 4 Ω load resistance into the primary as 400 Ω?

14–6 IMPEDANCE MATCHING

One application of transformers is in the matching of a load impedance to a source impedance to achieve maximum transfer of power or other results. This technique is called **impedance matching**. In audio systems, special wide-band transformers are often used to get the maximum amount of available power from the amplifier to the speaker by proper selection of the turns ratio. Transformers designed specifically for impedance matching usually show the input and output impedance they are designed to match.

After completing this section, you should be able to

- ◆ **Discuss impedance matching with transformers**
  - ◆ Give a general definition of impedance
  - ◆ Discuss the maximum power transfer theorem
  - ◆ Define *impedance matching*
  - ◆ Explain the purpose of impedance matching
  - ◆ Describe a practical application

As you have learned, impedance is the opposition to current, including the effects of both resistance and reactance combined. We will confine our usage in this chapter to resistance only.

The concept of **maximum power transfer** is illustrated in the basic circuit of Figure 14–19. Part (a) shows an ac voltage source with a series resistance representing its internal resistance. Some fixed internal resistance is inherent in all sources due to their internal circuitry. When the source is connected directly to a load, as shown in part (b), generally the objective is to transfer as much of the power produced by the source to the load as possible. However, a certain amount of the power produced by the source is dissipated in its internal resistance, and the remaining power goes to the load.

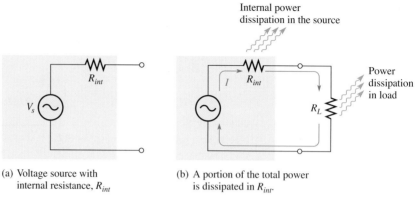

(a) Voltage source with
internal resistance, R_{int}

(b) A portion of the total power
is dissipated in R_{int}.

▲ FIGURE 14–19

Power transfer from a nonideal voltage source to a load.

The maximum power transfer theorem is important when you need to know the value of the load at which the most power is delivered from the source. The theorem was introduced in Chapter 6 and is restated as follows:

When a source is connected to a load, maximum power is delivered to the load when the load resistance is equal to the fixed internal source resistance.

As mentioned before, in most practical situations the internal source resistance of various types of sources is fixed and cannot be changed. Also, in many cases, the resistance of a device that acts as a load is fixed and cannot be altered. If you need to connect a given source to a given load, remember that only by chance will their resistances match. In this situation, a special type of wide-band transformer comes in handy. You can use the reflected-resistance characteristic provided by a transformer to make the load resistance appear to have the same value as the source resistance. This technique is called *impedance matching,* and the transformer is called an impedance-matching transformer because it also transforms reactances as well as resistances.

Let's take a practical, everyday situation to illustrate the concept of impedance matching. Assume that the input resistance of a TV receiver is 300 Ω. An antenna must be connected to this input by a lead-in cable in order to receive TV signals. In this situation, the antenna and the lead-in act as the source, and the input resistance of the TV receiver is the load, as illustrated in Figure 14–20.

(a) The antenna/lead-in is the source; the TV input is the load.

(b) Circuit equivalent of antenna and TV receiver system

▲ FIGURE 14–20

An antenna directly coupled to a TV receiver.

It is common for an antenna system to have a characteristic resistance of 75 Ω. Thus, if the 75 Ω source (antenna and lead-in) is connected directly to the 300 Ω TV input, maximum power will not be delivered to the input of the TV, and you will have poor signal reception. The solution is to use a matching transformer, connected as indicated in Figure 14–21, in order to match the 300 Ω load resistance to the 75 Ω source resistance.

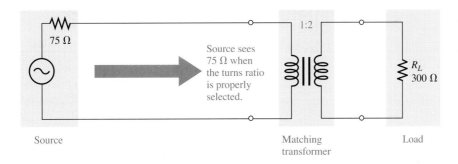

◀ FIGURE 14–21

Example of a load matched to a source by transformer coupling for maximum power transfer.

Source   Matching   Load
              transformer

To match the resistances, that is, to reflect the load resistance (R_L) into the primary so that it appears to have a value equal to the internal source resistance (R_{int}), you must select a proper value of turns ratio. You want the 300 Ω load resistance to look like 75 Ω to the source. Use Equation 14–8 to obtain a formula to determine the turns ratio, n, when you know the values for R_L and R_{pri}.

$$R_{pri} = \left(\frac{1}{n}\right)^2 R_L$$

Transpose terms and divide both sides by R_L.

$$\left(\frac{1}{n}\right)^2 = \frac{R_{pri}}{R_L}$$

Then take the square root of both sides.

$$\frac{1}{n} = \sqrt{\frac{R_{pri}}{R_L}}$$

Invert both sides to get the following formula for the turns ratio:

$$n = \sqrt{\frac{R_L}{R_{pri}}}$$

Equation 14–9

Finally, solve for the particular turns ratio to match a 300 Ω load to a 75 Ω source.

$$n = \sqrt{\frac{300\ \Omega}{75\ \Omega}} = \sqrt{4} = 2$$

Therefore, a matching transformer with a turns ratio of 2 must be used in this application.

EXAMPLE 14–9

An amplifier has an 800 Ω internal resistance. In order to provide maximum power to an 8 Ω speaker, what turns ratio must be used in the coupling transformer?

Solution   The reflected resistance must equal 800 Ω. Thus, from Equation 14–9, the turns ratio can be determined.

$$n = \sqrt{\frac{R_L}{R_{pri}}} = \sqrt{\frac{8\ \Omega}{800\ \Omega}} = \sqrt{0.01} = \mathbf{0.1}$$

The diagram and its equivalent reflected circuit are shown in Figure 14–22.

FIGURE 14–22

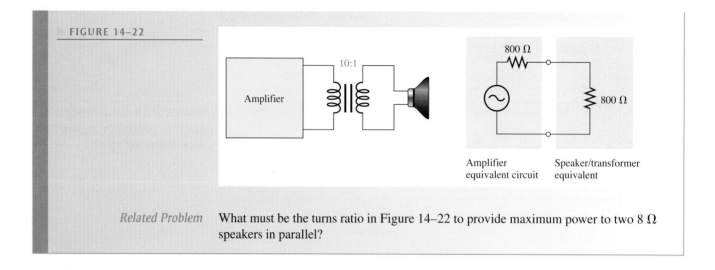

Amplifier
equivalent circuit

Speaker/transformer
equivalent

Related Problem   What must be the turns ratio in Figure 14–22 to provide maximum power to two 8 Ω speakers in parallel?

**SECTION 14–6
REVIEW**

1. What does impedance matching mean?
2. What is the advantage of matching the load resistance to the resistance of a source?
3. A transformer has a turns ratio of 0.5. What is the reflected resistance with 100 Ω across the secondary?

14–7 NONIDEAL TRANSFORMER CHARACTERISTICS

Transformer operation has been discussed from an ideal point of view. That is, the winding resistance, the winding capacitance, and nonideal core characteristics were all neglected and the transformer was treated as if it had an efficiency of 100%. For studying the basic concepts and in many applications, the ideal model is valid. However, the practical transformer has several nonideal characteristics of which you should be aware.

After completing this section, you should be able to

◆ **Describe a practical transformer**

   ◆ List and describe the nonideal characteristics

   ◆ Explain power rating of a transformer

   ◆ Define *efficiency* of a transformer

▲ FIGURE 14–23

Winding resistance in a practical transformer.

Winding Resistance

Both the primary and the secondary windings of a practical transformer have winding resistance. (You learned about the winding resistance of inductors in Chapter 11.) The winding resistances of a practical transformer are represented as resistors in series with the windings as shown in Figure 14–23.

Winding resistance in a practical transformer results in less voltage across a secondary load. Voltage drops due to the winding resistance effectively subtract from the primary and secondary voltages and result in a load voltage that is less than that predicted by the relationship $V_{sec} = nV_{pri}$. In most cases the effect is relatively small and can be neglected.

Losses in the Core

There is always some energy conversion in the core material of a practical transformer. This conversion is seen as a heating of ferrite and iron cores, but conversion does not occur in air cores. Part of this energy conversion is because of the continuous reversal of the magnetic field due to the changing direction of the primary current; this component of the energy conversion is called *hysteresis loss*. The rest of the energy conversion to heat is caused by eddy currents produced when voltage is induced in the core material by the changing magnetic flux, according to Faraday's law. The eddy currents occur in circular patterns in the core resistance, thus producing heat. This conversion to heat is greatly reduced by the use of laminated construction of iron cores. The thin layers of ferromagnetic material are insulated from each other to minimize the buildup of eddy currents by confining them to a small area and to keep core losses to a minimum.

Magnetic Flux Leakage

In an ideal transformer, all the magnetic flux produced by the primary current is assumed to pass through the core to the secondary winding and vice versa. In a practical transformer, some of the magnetic flux lines break out of the core and pass through the surrounding air back to the other end of the winding, as illustrated in Figure 14–24 for the magnetic field produced by the primary current. Magnetic flux leakage results in a reduced secondary voltage.

Leakage flux

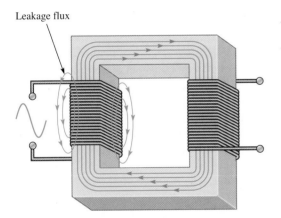

◀ **FIGURE 14–24**

Flux leakage in a practical transformer.

The percentage of magnetic flux that actually reaches the secondary winding determines the coefficient of coupling of the transformer. For example, if nine out of ten flux lines remain inside the core, the coefficient of coupling is 0.90 or 90%. Most iron-core transformers have very high coefficients of coupling (greater than 0.99), whereas ferrite-core and air-core devices have lower values.

Winding Capacitance

As you learned in Chapter 11, there is always some stray capacitance between adjacent turns of a winding. These stray capacitances result in an effective capacitance in parallel with each winding of a transformer, as indicated in Figure 14–25.

These stray capacitances have very little effect on the transformer's operation at low frequencies because the reactances (X_C) are very high. However, at higher frequencies, the reactances decrease and begin to produce a bypassing effect across the primary winding and across the secondary load. As a result, less of the total primary current is through the primary winding, and less of the total secondary current is through the load. This effect reduces the load voltage as the frequency goes up.

HANDS ON TIP

If you have an unmarked small transformer, you can use a signal generator with a relatively low output voltage to check the voltage ratio and thus the turns ratio between the input (primary) and the output (secondary). This is safer than applying 110 V ac and holding your breath. Typically, the primary wires are black, a low-voltage secondary is green, and a high-voltage secondary is red. A striped wire usually indicates a center tap. Unfortunately, all transformers do not have colored wires or the wires are not always standard colors.

▶ FIGURE 14–25

Winding capacitance in a practical transformer.

Transformer Power Rating

A power transformer is typically rated in volt-amperes (VA), primary/secondary voltage, and operating frequency. For example, a given transformer rating may be specified as 2 kVA, 500/50, 60 Hz. The 2 kVA value is the **apparent power rating**. The 500 and the 50 can be either secondary or primary voltages. The 60 Hz is the operating frequency.

The transformer rating can be helpful in selecting the proper transformer for a given application. Let's assume, for example, that 50 V is the secondary voltage. In this case the load current is

$$I_L = \frac{P_{sec}}{V_{sec}} = \frac{2\,\text{kVA}}{50\,\text{V}} = 40\,\text{A}$$

On the other hand, if 500 V is the secondary voltage, then

$$I_L = \frac{P_{sec}}{V_{sec}} = \frac{2\,\text{kVA}}{500\,\text{V}} = 4\,\text{A}$$

These are the maximum currents that the secondary can handle in either case.

The reason that the power rating is in volt-amperes (apparent power) rather than in watts (true power) is as follows: If the transformer load is purely capacitive or purely inductive, the true power (watts) delivered to the load is ideally zero. However, the current for $V_{sec} = 500$ V and $X_C = 100\,\Omega$ at 60 Hz, for example, is 5 A. This current exceeds the maximum of 4 A that the 2 kVA secondary can handle, and even though the true power is zero, the transformer may be damaged. So it is meaningless to specify power in watts for transformers.

Transformer Efficiency

Recall that the secondary power is equal to the primary power in an ideal transformer. Because the nonideal characteristics just discussed result in a power loss in the transformer, the secondary (output) power is always less than the primary (input) power. The **efficiency,** symbolized by the Greek letter eta (η), of a transformer is a measure of the percentage of the input power that is delivered to the output.

Equation 14–10

$$\eta = \left(\frac{P_{out}}{P_{in}}\right)100\%$$

Most power transformers have efficiencies in excess of 95%.

EXAMPLE 14–10

A certain type of transformer has a primary current of 5 A and a primary voltage of 4800 V. The secondary current is 90 A and the secondary voltage is 240 V. Determine the efficiency of this transformer.

Solution   The input power is

$$P_{in} = V_{pri}I_{pri} = (4800\,\text{V})(5\,\text{A}) = 24\,\text{kVA}$$

The output power is

$$P_{out} = V_{sec}I_{sec} = (240\text{ V})(90\text{ A}) = 21.6\text{ kVA}$$

The efficiency is

$$\eta = \left(\frac{P_{out}}{P_{in}}\right)100\% = \left(\frac{21.6\text{ kVA}}{24\text{ kVA}}\right)100\% = \mathbf{90\%}$$

Related Problem A transformer has a primary current of 8 A with a primary voltage of 440 V. The secondary current is 30 A and the secondary voltage is 100 V. What is the efficiency?

SECTION 14–7
REVIEW

1. Explain how a practical transformer differs from the ideal model.
2. The coefficient of coupling of a certain transformer is 0.85. What does this mean?
3. A certain transformer has a rating of 10 kVA. If the secondary voltage is 250 V, how much load current can the transformer handle?

14–8 TAPPED AND MULTIPLE-WINDING TRANSFORMERS

The basic transformer has several important variations. They include tapped transformers, multiple-winding transformers, and autotransformers.

After completing this section, you should be able to

◆ **Describe several types of transformers**

  ◆ Describe center-tapped transformers

  ◆ Describe multiple-winding transformers

  ◆ Describe autotransformers

Tapped Transformers

A schematic of a transformer with a center-tapped secondary winding is shown in Figure 14–26(a). The **center tap (CT)** is equivalent to two secondary windings with half the total voltage across each.

The voltages between either end of the secondary winding and the center tap are, at any instant, equal in magnitude but opposite in polarity, as illustrated in Figure 14–26(b). Here, for example, at some instant on the sinusoidal voltage, the polarity across the entire secondary winding is as shown (top end +, bottom −). At the center tap, the voltage is less positive than

(a) Center-tapped transformer

(b) Output voltages with respect to the center tap are 180° out of phase with each other and are one-half the magnitude of the secondary voltage.

▲ FIGURE 14–26

Operation of a center-tapped transformer.

▶ FIGURE 14–27

Application of a center-tapped transformer in ac-to-dc conversion.

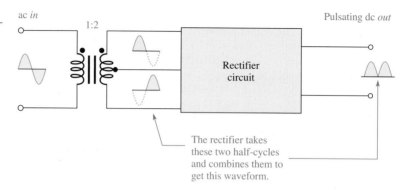

▶ FIGURE 14–27

Application of a center-tapped transformer in ac-to-dc conversion.

The rectifier takes these two half-cycles and combines them to get this waveform.

the top end but more positive than the bottom end of the secondary. Therefore, measured with respect to the center tap, the top end of the secondary is positive, and the bottom end is negative. This center-tapped feature is used in many power supply rectifiers in which the ac voltage is converted to dc, as illustrated in Figure 14–27 and also in impedance-matching transformers.

Some tapped transformers have taps on the secondary winding at points other than the electrical center. Also, multiple primary and secondary taps are sometimes used in certain applications. Examples of these types of transformers are shown in Figure 14–28.

▶ FIGURE 14–28

Tapped transformers.

(a)   (b)   (c)

One example of a transformer with a multiple-tap primary winding and a center-tapped secondary winding is the utility-pole transformer used by power companies to step down the high voltage from the power line to 110 V/220 V service for residential and commercial customers, as shown in Figure 14–29. The multiple taps on the primary winding are used for minor adjustments in the turns ratio in order to overcome line voltages that are slightly too high or too low.

▶ FIGURE 14–29

Utility-pole transformer in a typical power distribution system.

Multiple-Winding Transformers

Some transformers are designed to operate from either 110 V ac or 220 V ac lines. These transformers usually have two primary windings, each of which is designed for 110 V ac. When the two are connected in series, the transformer can be used for 220 V ac operation, as illustrated in Figure 14–30.

(a) Two primary windings

(b) Primary windings in parallel for 110 V ac operation

(c) Primary windings in series for 220 V ac operation

◀ FIGURE 14–30

Multiple-primary transformers.

More than one secondary winding can be wound on a common core. Transformers with several secondary windings are often used to achieve several voltages by either stepping up or stepping down the primary voltage. These types are commonly used in power supply applications in which several voltage levels are required for the operation of an electronic instrument.

A typical schematic of a transformer with multiple secondary windings is shown in Figure 14–31; this transformer has three secondary windings. Sometimes you will find combinations of multiple primary windings, multiple secondary windings, and tapped transformers all in one unit.

▲ FIGURE 14–31

A multiple-secondary transformer.

EXAMPLE 14–11

The transformer shown in Figure 14–32 has the turns ratios for each secondary relative to the primary as indicated. One of the secondary windings is also center tapped. If 110 V ac are connected to the primary winding, determine each secondary voltage and the voltages with respect to the center tap (CT) on the middle secondary winding.

▶ FIGURE 14–32

Solution

$$V_{AB} = n_{AB}V_{pri} = (0.05)110\text{ V} = \textbf{5.5 V}$$

$$V_{CD} = n_{CD}V_{pri} = (2)110\text{ V} = \textbf{220 V}$$

$$V_{(CT)C} = V_{(CT)D} = \frac{220\text{ V}}{2} = \textbf{110 V}$$

$$V_{EF} = n_{EF}V_{pri} = (0.1)110\text{ V} = \textbf{11 V}$$

Related Problem Repeat the calculations if the primary winding is halved.

Autotransformers

Applications of the autotransformer include starting industrial induction motors and regulating transmission line voltages. In an **autotransformer,** one winding serves as both the primary and the secondary windings. The winding is tapped at the proper points to achieve the desired turns ratio for stepping up or stepping down the voltage.

Autotransformers differ from conventional transformers in that there is no electrical isolation between the primary and the secondary circuits because both are on one winding. Autotransformers normally are smaller and lighter than equivalent conventional transformers because they require a much lower kVA rating for a given load. Many autotransformers provide an adjustable tap using a sliding contact mechanism so that the output voltage can be varied (these are often called *variacs*.) Figure 14–33 shows schematic symbols for various types of autotransformers.

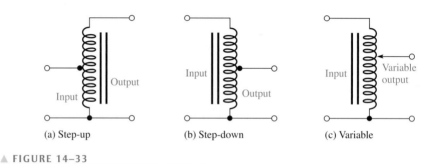

(a) Step-up   (b) Step-down   (c) Variable

▲ **FIGURE 14–33**

Variable autotransformers.

SECTION 14–8 REVIEW	1. A certain transformer has two secondary windings. The turns ratio from the primary winding to the first secondary winding is 10. The turns ratio from the primary winding to the other secondary winding is 0.2. If 220 V ac are applied to the primary winding, what are the secondary voltages?
	2. Name one advantage and one disadvantage of an autotransformer over a conventional transformer.

14–9 TROUBLESHOOTING

Transformers are reliable devices when operated within their specified range. Common failures in a transformer are opens in either the primary or the secondary windings. One cause of an open is the operation of the device under conditions that exceed its ratings. Normally, when a transformer fails, it is very difficult to repair, and therefore the simplest procedure is to replace it. A few transformer failures and the associated symptoms are covered in this section.

After completing this section, you should be able to

◆ **Troubleshoot transformers**

    ◆ Find an open primary or secondary winding

    ◆ Find a shorted or partially shorted primary or secondary winding

Open Primary Winding

When there is an open primary winding, there is no primary current and, therefore, no induced voltage or current in the secondary. This condition is illustrated in Figure 14–34(a), and the method of checking with an ohmmeter is shown in part (b).

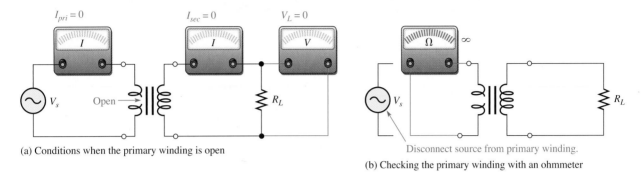

(a) Conditions when the primary winding is open

(b) Checking the primary winding with an ohmmeter

▲ FIGURE 14–34

Open primary winding.

Open Secondary Winding

When there is an open secondary winding, there is no current in the secondary circuit and, as a result, no voltage across the load. Also, an open secondary winding causes the primary current to be very small (there is only a small magnetizing current). In fact, the primary current may be practically zero. This condition is illustrated in Figure 14–35(a), and the ohmmeter check is shown in part (b).

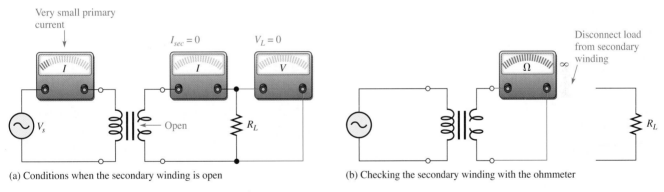

(a) Conditions when the secondary winding is open

(b) Checking the secondary winding with the ohmmeter

▲ FIGURE 14–35

Open secondary winding.

Shorted or Partially Shorted Windings

Shorted windings are very rare and if they do occur are difficult to find unless there is a visual indication or a large number of windings are shorted. A completely shorted primary winding will draw excessive current from the source; and unless there is a breaker or a fuse in the circuit, either the source or the transformer or both will burn out. A partial short in the primary winding can cause higher than normal or even excessive primary current.

In the case of a shorted or partially shorted secondary winding, there is an excessive primary current because of the low reflected resistance due to the short. Often, this excessive current will burn out the primary winding and result in an open. The short-circuit current in the secondary winding causes the load current to be zero (full short) or smaller than normal (partial short), as demonstrated in Figure 14–36(a) and (b). The ohmmeter check for this condition is shown in part (c).

(a) Secondary winding completely shorted

(b) Secondary winding partially shorted

(c) Checking the secondary winding with the ohmmeter

▲ **FIGURE 14–36**

Shorted secondary winding.

SECTION 14–9 REVIEW

1. What is the most probable failure in a transformer?
2. What is often the cause of transformer failure?

Application Assignment

PUTTING YOUR KNOWLEDGE TO WORK

A common application of the transformer is in dc power supplies. The transformer is used to couple the ac line voltage into the power supply circuitry where it is converted to a dc voltage. You will troubleshoot four identical transformer-coupled dc power supplies and, based on a series of measurements, determine the fault, if any, in each.

The transformer (T_1) in the power supply schematic of Figure 14–37 steps the 110 V rms at the ac outlet down to 10 V rms which is converted by the diode bridge rectifier, filtered, and regulated to obtain a 6 V dc output. The diode rectifier changes the ac to a pulsating full-wave dc voltage that is smoothed by the capacitor filter C_1. The voltage regulator is an integrated circuit that takes the filtered voltage and provides a

▶ **FIGURE 14–37**

Basic transformer-coupled dc power supply.

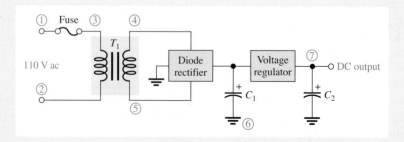

constant 6 V dc over a range of load values and line voltage variations. Additional filtering is provided by capacitor C_2. You will learn about these circuits in a later course. The circled numbers in Figure 14–37 correspond to measurement points on the power supply unit.

Step 1: Familiarization with the Power Supply

You have four identical power supply boards to troubleshoot like the one shown in Figure 14–38. The power line to the primary winding of the transformer (T_1) is protected by a fuse. The secondary winding is connected to the circuit containing the recti-

fier, filter, and regulator. Measurement points are indicated by the circled numbers.

Step 2: Measuring Voltages on Power Supply Board 1

After plugging the power supply into a standard wall outlet, an autoranging portable multimeter is used to measure the voltages. In an autoranging meter, the appropriate measurement range is automatically selected instead of being manually selected as in a standard multimeter.

Determine from the meter readings in Figure 14–39 whether or not the power supply is operating properly. If it is not, isolate the

▲ FIGURE 14–38

Power supply board (top view).

▲ FIGURE 14–39

Voltage measurements on power supply board 1.

problem to one of the following: the circuit containing the recti-fier, filter, and regulator; the transformer; the fuse; or the power source. The circled numbers on the meter inputs correspond to the numbered points on the power supply in Figure 14–38.

Step 3: Measuring Voltages on Power Supply Boards 2, 3, and 4

Determine from the meter readings for boards 2, 3, and 4 in Figure 14–40 whether or not each power supply is operating properly. If it is not, isolate the problem to one of the following:

the circuit containing the rectifier, filter, and regulator; the trans-former; the fuse; or the power source. Only the meter displays and corresponding measurement points are shown.

Review

1. In the case where the transformer was found to be faulty, how can you determine the specific fault (open windings or shorted windings)?

2. What type of fault in the transformer could cause the fuse to blow?

▲ FIGURE 14–40

Measurements for power supply boards 2, 3, and 4.

SUMMARY

◆ A transformer generally consists of two or more coils that are magnetically coupled on a common core.

◆ There is mutual inductance between two magnetically coupled coils.

◆ When current in one coil changes, voltage is induced in the other coil.

◆ The primary is the winding connected to the source, and the secondary is the winding connected to the load.

◆ The number of turns in the primary winding and the number of turns in the secondary winding determine the turns ratio.

◆ The relative polarities of the primary and secondary voltages are determined by the direction of the windings around the core.

◆ A step-up transformer has a turns ratio greater than 1.

◆ A step-down transformer has a turns ratio less than 1.

◆ A transformer cannot increase power.

◆ In an ideal transformer, the power from the source (input power) is equal to the power delivered to the load (output power).

◆ If the voltage is stepped up, the current is stepped down, and vice versa.

◆ A load connected across the secondary winding of a transformer appears to the source as a reflected load having a value dependent on the reciprocal of the turns ratio squared.

◆ An impedance-matching transformer can match a load resistance to an internal source resistance to achieve maximum power transfer to the load by selection of the proper turns ratio.

◆ A transformer does not respond to constant dc.

◆ Conversion of electrical energy to heat in an actual transformer results from winding resistances, hysteresis loss in the core, eddy currents in the core, and flux leakage.

KEY TERMS

Key terms and other bold terms in the chapter are defined in the end-of-book glossary.

Apparent power rating   The method of rating transformers in which the power capability is expressed in volt-amperes (VA).

Center tap (CT)   A connection at the midpoint of a winding in a transformer.

Electrical isolation   The condition that exists when two coils are magnetically linked but have no electrical connection between them.

Impedance matching   A technique used to match a load resistance to a source resistance in order to achieve maximum transfer of power.

Magnetic coupling   The magnetic connection between two coils as a result of the changing magnetic flux lines of one coil cutting through the second coil.

Maximum power transfer   The condition, when the load resistance equals the source resistance, under which maximum power is transferred from source to load.

Mutual inductance (L_M)   The inductance between two separate coils, such as in a transformer.

Primary winding   The input winding of a transformer; also called *primary*.

Reflected resistance   The resistance in the secondary circuit reflected into the primary circuit.

Secondary winding   The output winding of a transformer; also called *secondary*.

Transformer   An electrical device constructed of two coils of wire (windings) that are electromagnetically coupled to each other so that there is mutual inductance from one winding to another.

Turns ratio (n)   The ratio of turns in the secondary winding to turns in the primary winding.

FORMULAS

14–1	$L_M = k \sqrt{L_1 L_2}$	Mutual inductance
14–2	$k = \dfrac{\phi_{1\text{-}2}}{\phi_1}$	Coefficient of coupling
14–3	$n = \dfrac{N_{sec}}{N_{pri}}$	Turns ratio
14–4	$\dfrac{V_{sec}}{V_{pri}} = \dfrac{N_{sec}}{N_{pri}}$	Voltage ratio
14–5	$V_{sec} = nV_{pri}$	Secondary voltage
14–6	$\dfrac{I_{pri}}{I_{sec}} = n$	Current ratio
14–7	$I_{sec} = \left(\dfrac{1}{n}\right)I_{pri}$	Secondary current
14–8	$R_{pri} = \left(\dfrac{1}{n}\right)^2 R_L$	Reflected resistance
14–9	$n = \sqrt{\dfrac{R_L}{R_{pri}}}$	Turns ratio for impedance matching
14–10	$\eta = \left(\dfrac{P_{out}}{P_{in}}\right)100\%$	Transformer efficiency

SELF-TEST

Answers are at the end of the chapter.

1. A transformer is used for
   (a) dc voltages   (b) ac voltages
   (c) both dc and ac

2. Which one of the following is affected by the turns ratio of a transformer?
   (a) primary voltage
   (b) dc voltage
   (c) secondary voltage
   (d) none of these

3. If the windings of a certain transformer with a turns ratio of 1 are in opposite directions around the core, the secondary voltage is
   (a) in phase with the primary voltage
   (b) less than the primary voltage
   (c) greater than the primary voltage
   (d) out of phase with the primary voltage

4. When the turns ratio of a transformer is 10 and the primary ac voltage is 6 V, the secondary voltage is
   (a) 60 V   (b) 0.6 V   (c) 6 V   (d) 36 V

5. When the turns ratio of a transformer is 0.5 and the primary ac voltage is 100 V, the secondary voltage is
   (a) 200 V   (b) 50 V   (c) 10 V   (d) 100 V

6. A certain transformer has 500 turns in the primary winding and 2500 turns in the secondary winding. The turns ratio is
   (a) 0.2   (b) 2.5   (c) 5   (d) 0.5

7. If 10 W of power are applied to the primary winding of an ideal transformer with a turns ratio of 5, the power delivered to the secondary load is
   (a) 50 W   (b) 0.5 W   (c) 0 W   (d) 10 W

8. In a certain loaded transformer, the secondary voltage is one-third the primary voltage. Ideally, the secondary current is
   (a) one-third the primary current
   (b) three times the primary current
   (c) equal to the primary current
   (d) less than the primary current

9. When a 1.0 kΩ load resistor is connected across the secondary winding of a transformer with a turns ratio of 2, the source "sees" a reflected load of
   (a) 250 Ω   (b) 2 kΩ   (c) 4 kΩ   (d) 1.0 kΩ

10. In Question 9, if the turns ratio is 0.5, the source "sees" a reflected load of
    (a) 1.0 kΩ   (b) 2 kΩ   (c) 4 kΩ   (d) 500 Ω

11. The turns ratio required to match a 50 Ω source to a 200 Ω load is
    (a) 0.25   (b) 0.5   (c) 4   (d) 2

12. Maximum power is transferred from a source to a load when
    (a) $R_L > R_{int}$ (b) $R_L < R_{int}$ (c) $R_L = R_{int}$ (d) $R_L = nR_{int}$

13. When a 12 V battery is connected across the primary winding of a transformer with a turns ratio of 4, the secondary voltage is
    (a) 0 V   (b) 12 V   (c) 48 V   (d) 3 V

14. A certain transformer has a turns ratio of 1 and a 0.95 coefficient of coupling. When 1 V ac is applied to the primary, the secondary voltage is
    (a) 1 V   (b) 1.95 V   (c) 0.95 V

PROBLEMS

Answers to odd-numbered problems are at the end of the book.

BASIC PROBLEMS

SECTION 14–1 Mutual Inductance

1. What is the mutual inductance when $k = 0.75$, $L_1 = 1\,\mu H$, and $L_2 = 4\,\mu H$?

2. Determine the coefficient of coupling when $L_M = 1\,\mu H$, $L_1 = 8\,\mu H$, and $L_2 = 2\,\mu H$.

SECTION 14–2 The Basic Transformer

3. What is the turns ratio of a transformer having 120 turns in its primary winding and 360 turns in its secondary winding?

4. **(a)** What is the turns ratio of a transformer having 250 turns in its primary winding and 1000 turns in its secondary winding?

   (b) What is the turns ratio when the primary winding has 400 turns and the secondary winding has 100 turns?

5. Determine the phase of the secondary voltage with respect to the primary voltage for each transformer in Figure 14–41.

(a)   (b)   (c)

▲ FIGURE 14–41

SECTION 14–3 Step-Up and Step-Down Transformers

6. If 120 V ac are connected to the primary of a transformer with a turns ratio of 1.5, what is the secondary voltage?

7. A certain transformer has 250 turns in its primary winding. In order to double the secondary voltage, how many turns must be in the secondary winding?

8. How many primary volts must be applied to a transformer with a turns ratio of 10 to obtain a secondary voltage of 60 V ac?

9. For each transformer in Figure 14–42, draw the secondary voltage showing its relationship to the primary voltage. Also indicate the amplitude.

▶ FIGURE 14–42

(a)   (b)

10. To step 120 V down to 30 V, what must be the turns ratio?

11. The primary winding of a transformer has 1200 V across it. What is the secondary voltage if the turns ratio is 0.2?

12. How many primary volts must be applied to a transformer with a turns ratio of 0.1 to obtain a secondary voltage of 6 V ac?

13. What is the voltage across the load in each circuit in Figure 14–43?

14. If the bottom of each secondary winding in Figure 14–43 were grounded, would the values of the load voltages be changed?

▲ FIGURE 14–43

15. Determine the unspecified meter readings in Figure 14–44.

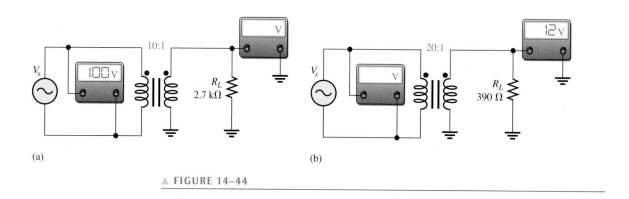

▲ FIGURE 14–44

16. If R_L is doubled in the circuit of Figure 14–44(a), what would the secondary meter read?

SECTION 14–4 **Loading the Secondary**

17. Determine I_{sec} in Figure 14–45.

18. Determine the following quantities in Figure 14–46:

    (a) secondary voltage

    (b) secondary current

    (c) primary current

    (d) power in the load

▲ FIGURE 14–45

▲ FIGURE 14–46

SECTION 14–5 Reflected Load

19. What is the load resistance as seen by the source in Figure 14–47?

20. What is the resistance reflected into the primary circuit in Figure 14–48?

▲ FIGURE 14–47   ▲ FIGURE 14–48

21. What is the primary current (rms) in Figure 14–48 if the rms source voltage is 115 V?

22. What must be the turns ratio in Figure 14–49 in order to reflect 300 Ω into the primary circuit?

▶ FIGURE 14–49

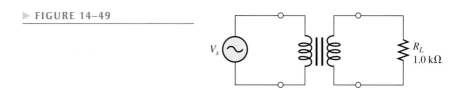

SECTION 14–6 Impedance Matching

23. For the circuit in Figure 14–50, find the turns ratio required to deliver maximum power to the 4 Ω speaker.

24. In Figure 14–50, what is the maximum power in watts delivered to the speaker?

25. Determine the value to which R_L must be adjusted in Figure 14–51 for maximum power transfer. The internal source resistance is 50 Ω.

▲ FIGURE 14–50   ▲ FIGURE 14–51

26. Plot the power curve for values of R_L in Figure 14–51 ranging from 1 kΩ to 10 kΩ in 1 kΩ increments. $R_L = 50$ Ω and $V_s = 10$ V.

SECTION 14–7 Nonideal Transformer Characteristics

27. In a certain transformer, the input power to the primary is 100 W. If 5.5 W are dissipated in the winding resistances, what is the output power to the load, neglecting any other losses?

28. What is the efficiency of the transformer in Problem 27?

29. Determine the coefficient of coupling for a transformer in which 2% of the total flux generated in the primary does not pass through the secondary.

30. A certain transformer is rated at 1 kVA. It operates on 60 Hz, 120 V ac. The secondary voltage is 600 V.

(a) What is the maximum load current?

(b) What is the smallest R_L that you can drive?

(c) What is the largest capacitor that can be connected as a load?

31. What kVA rating is required for a transformer that must handle a maximum load current of 10 A with a secondary voltage of 2.5 kV?

SECTION 14–8   **Tapped and Multiple-Winding Transformers**

32. Determine each unknown voltage indicated in Figure 14–52.

▶ FIGURE 14–52

33. Using the indicated secondary voltages in Figure 14–53, determine the turns ratio of the primary winding to each tapped section.

34. In Figure 14–54, each primary winding can accommodate 120 V ac. Show how the primaries should be connected for 240 V ac operation. Determine each secondary voltage.

35. Determine the turns ratios from each primary to each secondary in Figure 14–54.

▲ FIGURE 14–53   ▲ FIGURE 14–54

SECTION 14–9   **Troubleshooting**

36. When you apply 120 V ac across the primary winding of a transformer and check the voltage across the secondary winding, you get 0 V. Further investigation shows no primary or secondary current. List the possible faults. What is your next step in isolating the problem?

37. What is likely to happen if the primary winding of a transformer shorts?

38. In checking out a transformer circuit you find the secondary voltage is less than it should be, although it is not zero. What is the most likely cause?

ADVANCED PROBLEMS

39. For the loaded, tapped-secondary transformer in Figure 14–55, determine the following:

  (a) all load voltages and currents

  (b) the resistance looking into the primary

▶ FIGURE 14–55

40. A certain transformer is rated at 5 kVA, 2400/120 V, at 60 Hz.

  (a) What is the turns ratio if the 120 V is the secondary voltage?

  (b) What is the current rating of the secondary if 2400 V is the primary voltage?

  (c) What is the current rating of the primary if 2400 V is the primary voltage?

41. Determine the voltage measured by each voltmeter in Figure 14–56. The bench-type meters have one terminal that connects to ground as indicated.

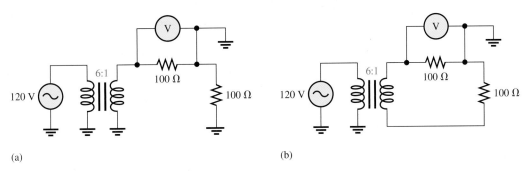

(a)

(b)

▲ **FIGURE 14–56**

42. Find the appropriate turns ratio for each switch position in Figure 14–57 in order to transfer the maximum power to each load when the internal source resistance is 10 Ω. Specify the number of turns for the secondary winding if the primary winding has 100 turns.

▶ **FIGURE 14–57**

43. What must the turns ratio be in Figure 14–48 to limit the primary current to 3 mA with a source voltage of 115 V? Assume an ideal transformer and source.

44. Assume 110 V is applied to the primary of a transformer with a VA rating of 10 VA. The output voltage is 12.6 V. What is the smallest resistor that can be connected across the secondary?

45. A step-down transformer uses 110 V on the primary and 10 V on the secondary. If the secondary is rated for a maximum of 1 A, what fuse rating should be selected on the primary side?

MULTISIM TROUBLESHOOTING PROBLEMS

46. Open file P14-46 and test the circuit. If there is a fault, identify it.

47. Open file P14-47 and test the circuit. If there is a fault, identify it.

48. Determine if there is a fault in the circuit in file P14-48. If so, identify it.

49. Find and specify any faulty component in the circuit in file P14-49.

ANSWERS

SECTION REVIEWS

SECTION 14–1   Mutual Inductance

1. Mutual inductance is the inductance between two coils, established by the amount of coupling between the coils.

2. $L_M = k\sqrt{L_1 L_2} = 45$ mH

3. Induced voltage increases when k is increased.

SECTION 14–2   **The Basic Transformer**

1. Transformer operation is based on the principle of mutual inductance.

2. Turns ratio is the ratio of turns in the secondary to turns in the primary.

3. Directions of the windings determine the relative voltage polarities.

4. $n = N_{sec}/N_{pri} = 0.5$

SECTION 14–3   **Step-Up and Step-Down Transformers**

1. A step-up transformer increases voltage.

2. The secondary voltage is five times greater.

3. $V_{sec} = nV_{pri} = 2400\,\text{V}$

4. A step-down transformer decreases voltage.

5. $V_{sec} = nV_{pri} = 60\,\text{V}$

6. $n = 12\,\text{V}/120\,\text{V} = 0.1$

7. No

SECTION 14–4   **Loading the Secondary**

1. The secondary current is half the primary current.

2. $n = 0.25; I_{sec} = (1/n)I_{pri} = 2\,\text{A}$

3. $I_{pri} = nI_{sec} = 2.5\,\text{A}$

SECTION 14–5   **Reflected Load**

1. Reflected resistance is the resistance in the secondary circuit as seen from the primary circuit as a function of the turns ratio.

2. The reciprocal of the turns ratio determines reflected resistance.

3. $R_{pri} = (1/n)^2 R_L = 0.5\,\Omega$

4. $n = \sqrt{R_L/R_{pri}} = 0.1$

SECTION 14–6   **Impedance Matching**

1. Impedance matching is making the load resistance equal the source resistance.

2. Maximum power is delivered to the load when $R_L = R_{int}$.

3. $R_{pri} = (1/n)^2 R_L = 400\,\Omega$

SECTION 14–7   **Nonideal Transformer Characteristics**

1. In a practical transformer, conversion of electrical energy to heat reduces the efficiency. An ideal transformer has an efficiency of 100%.

2. When the coefficient of coupling is 0.85, 85% of the magnetic flux generated in the primary winding passes through the secondary winding.

3. $I_L = 10\,\text{kVA}/250\,\text{V} = 40\,\text{A}$

SECTION 14–8   **Tapped and Multiple-Winding Transformers**

1. $V_{sec} = 10(220\,\text{V}) = 2200\,\text{V}; V_{sec} = 0.2(220\,\text{V}) = 44\,\text{V}$

2. Autotransformers are smaller and lighter for the same rating. Autotransformers provide no electrical isolation.

SECTION 14–9   **Troubleshooting**

1. The most probable failure is an open winding.

2. Operating above rated values causes transformer failure.

Application Assignment

1. Use an ohmmeter to check for open windings. Shorted windings are indicated by an incorrect secondary voltage.

2. A short will cause the fuse to blow.

RELATED PROBLEMS FOR EXAMPLES

14–1   387 μH

14–2   0.75

14–3   5000 turns

14–4   480 V

14–5   57.6 V

14–6   5 mA; 400 mA

14–7   6 Ω

14–8   0.354

14–9   0.0707 or 14.14:1

14–10   85.2%

14–11 $V_{AB} = 11$ V; $V_{CD} = 440$ V; $V_{(CT)C} = V_{(CT)D} = 220$ V; $V_{EF} = 22$ V

SELF-TEST

1. (b)   **2.** (c)   **3.** (d)   **4.** (a)   **5.** (b)   **6.** (c)   **7.** (d)

8. (b)   **9.** (a)   **10.** (c)   **11.** (d)   **12.** (c)   **13.** (a)   **14.** (c)

15

TIME RESPONSE OF REACTIVE CIRCUITS

CHAPTER OBJECTIVES

◆ Explain the operation of an *RC* integrator

◆ Analyze an *RC* integrator with a single-pulse input

◆ Analyze an *RC* integrator with a repetitive-pulse input

◆ Analyze an *RC* differentiator with a single-pulse input

◆ Analyze an *RC* differentiator with a repetitive-pulse input

◆ Analyze the operation of an *RL* integrator

◆ Analyze the operation of an *RL* differentiator

◆ Discuss some applications of integrators and differentiators

◆ Troubleshoot *RC* integrators and *RC* differentiators

KEY TERMS

◆ Integrator
◆ Time constant
◆ Transient time
◆ Steady state
◆ Differentiator

APPLICATION ASSIGNMENT PREVIEW

For the application assignment in this chapter, you will determine the component values required to meet certain specifications in a time-delay circuit. You will also determine how to test the circuit for proper operation using a pulse generator and an oscilloscope. After studying this chapter, you should be able to complete the application assignment.

VISIT THE COMPANION WEBSITE

Study aids for this chapter are available at
http://www.prenhall.com/floyd

INTRODUCTION

In Chapters 10 and 12, the frequency response of *RC* and *RL* circuits was covered. In this chapter, the time response of *RC* and *RL* circuits with pulse inputs is examined.

Before starting this chapter, you should review the material in Sections 9–5 and 11–4. Understanding exponential changes in voltages and currents in capacitors and inductors is crucial to the study of the time response of reactive circuits. Exponential formulas that were given in Chapter 9 are used throughout this chapter.

With pulse inputs, the time response of the circuits is of primary importance. In the areas of pulse and digital circuits, technicians are often concerned with how a circuit responds over an interval of time to rapid changes in voltage or current. The relationship of the circuit time constant to the input pulse characteristics, such as pulse width and period, determines the wave shapes of the voltages in the circuit.

Integrator and *differentiator,* terms used throughout this coverage, refer to mathematical functions that are approximated by these circuits under certain conditions. Mathematical integration is an averaging process, and mathematical differentiation is a process for establishing an instantaneous rate of change of a quantity. We will not deal with the purely mathematical aspects of integration and differentiation at this level of coverage.

15–1 THE *RC* INTEGRATOR

In terms of time response, a series *RC* circuit in which the output voltage is taken across the capacitor is known as an **integrator**. Recall that in terms of frequency response, this particular series *RC* circuit is a low-pass filter. The term, *integrator,* is derived from a mathematical function which this type of circuit approximates under certain conditions.

After completing this section, you should be able to

◆ **Explain the operation of an *RC* integrator**

◆ Describe how the capacitor charges and discharges

◆ Explain how a capacitor reacts to an instantaneous change in voltage or current

◆ Describe the basic output voltage waveform

Charging and Discharging of a Capacitor

When a pulse generator is connected to the input of an *RC* integrator, as shown in Figure 15–1, the capacitor will charge and discharge in response to the pulses. When the input goes from its low level to its high level, the capacitor charges toward the high level of the pulse through the resistor. This charging action is analogous to connecting a battery through a switch to the *RC* circuit, as illustrated in Figure 15–2(a). When the pulse goes from its high level back to its low level, the capacitor discharges back through the source. Compared to the resistance of the resistor, *R*, the resistance of the source is assumed to be negligible. This discharging action is analogous to replacing the source with a closed switch, as illustrated in Figure 15–2(b).

◀ **FIGURE 15–1**

An *RC* integrator with a pulse generator connected.

(a) When the input pulse goes HIGH, the source effectively acts as a battery in series with a closed switch, thereby charging the capacitor.

(b) When the input pulse goes back LOW, the source effectively acts as a closed switch, providing a discharge path for the capacitor.

▲ FIGURE 15–2

The equivalent action when a pulse source charges and discharges the capacitor.

A capacitor will charge and discharge following an exponential curve. Its rate of charging and discharging depends on the *RC* **time constant**, a fixed time interval determined by *R* and *C* ($\tau = RC$).

For an ideal pulse, both edges are considered to be instantaneous. Two basic rules of capacitor behavior help in understanding the response of *RC* circuits to pulse inputs.

1. The capacitor appears as a short to an instantaneous change in current and as an open to dc.

2. The voltage across the capacitor cannot change instantaneously—it can change only exponentially.

The Capacitor Voltage

In an *RC* integrator, the output is the capacitor voltage. The capacitor charges during the time that the input pulse is high. If the pulse is at its high level long enough, the capacitor will fully charge to the voltage amplitude of the pulse, as illustrated in Figure 15–3. The capacitor discharges during the time that the pulse is low. If the low time between pulses is long enough, the capacitor will fully discharge to zero, as shown in the figure. Then when the next pulse occurs, it will charge again.

▶ FIGURE 15–3

Illustration of a capacitor fully charging and discharging in response to a pulse input. A pulse generator is connected to the input, but the symbol is not shown, only the waveform.

| SECTION 15–1 REVIEW | 1. Define the term *integrator* in relation to an *RC* circuit. |
| Answers are at the end of the chapter. | 2. What causes a capacitor in an *RC* circuit to charge and discharge? |

15–2   RESPONSE OF *RC* INTEGRATORS TO A SINGLE PULSE

From the previous section, you have a general idea of how an *RC* integrator responds over time to a pulse input. In this section, the time response to a single pulse is examined in detail.

After completing this section, you should be able to

◆ **Analyze an *RC* integrator with a single-pulse input**

  ◆ Discuss the importance of the circuit time constant

  ◆ Define *transient time*

  ◆ Determine the response when the pulse width is equal to or greater than five time constants

  ◆ Determine the response when the pulse width is less than five time constants

Two conditions of response to a single-pulse input must be considered:

1. When the input pulse width (t_W) is equal to or greater than five time constants ($t_W \geq 5\tau$)

2. When the input pulse width is less than five time constants ($t_W < 5\tau$)

Recall that five time constants is accepted as the time a capacitor needs to fully charge or fully discharge; this time is often called the **transient time**. A capacitor will fully charge if the pulse width is equal to or greater than five time constants (5τ). This condition is expressed as $t_W \geq 5\tau$. At the end of the pulse, the capacitor fully discharges back through the source.

Figure 15–4 illustrates the output waveforms for various *RC* transient times and a fixed input pulse width. Notice that as the transient time becomes shorter, compared to the pulse width, the shape of the output pulse approaches that of the input. In each case, the output reaches the full amplitude of the input.

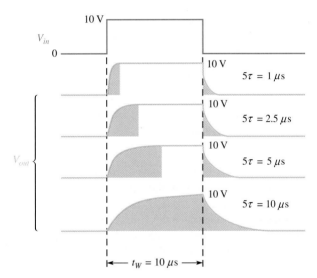

◀ **FIGURE 15–4**

Variation of an integrator's output pulse shape with transient time. The shaded areas indicate when the capacitor is charging and discharging.

Figure 15–5 shows how a fixed time constant and a variable input pulse width affect the integrator output. Notice that as the pulse width is increased, the shape of the output pulse approaches that of the input. Again, this means that the transient time is short compared to the pulse width. The rise and fall times of the output remain constant.

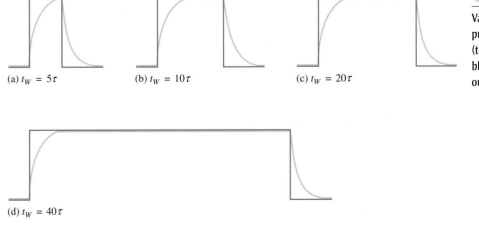

◀ **FIGURE 15–5**

Variation of an integrator's output pulse shape with input pulse width (the time constant is fixed). Dark blue is input and light blue is output.

Now let's examine the case in which the width of the input pulse is less than five time constants of the RC integrator. This condition is expressed as $t_W < 5\tau$. As you know, a capacitor charges for the duration of the pulse and the pulse width is the time it has for charging. However, because the pulse width is less than the time the capacitor needs to fully charge (5τ), the output voltage will *not* reach the full input voltage before the end of the pulse. The capacitor only partially charges, as illustrated in Figure 15–6 for several values of RC time constants. Notice that for longer time constants, the output reaches a lower voltage because the capacitor cannot charge as much during the pulse width. Of course, in the examples with a single-pulse input, the capacitor fully discharges after the pulse ends.

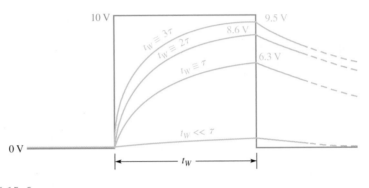

▲ FIGURE 15–6

Capacitor voltage for various time constants that are longer than the input pulse width. Dark blue is input and light blue is output.

When the time constant is much greater than the input pulse width, the capacitor charges very little, and, as a result, the output voltage becomes a very small almost constant value, as indicated in Figure 15–6.

Figure 15–7 illustrates the effect of reducing the input pulse width for a fixed time constant value. As the pulse width is reduced, the output voltage becomes smaller because the capacitor has less time to charge. However, it takes the capacitor the same length of time (5τ) to discharge back to zero for each condition after the pulse is removed.

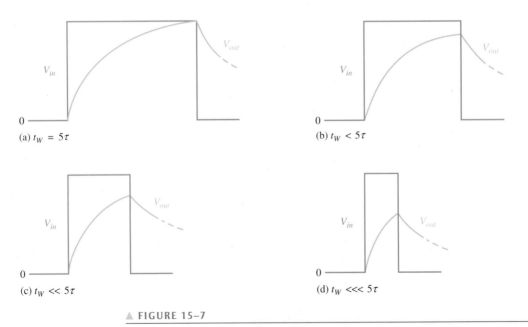

▲ FIGURE 15–7

The capacitor charges less and less as the input pulse width is reduced. The time constant is fixed.

EXAMPLE 15–1

A single 10 V pulse with a width of 100 μs is applied to the *RC* integrator in Figure 15–8. The source resistance is assumed to be zero.

(a) To what voltage will the capacitor charge?

(b) How long will it take the capacitor to discharge?

(c) Show the output voltage waveform.

▲ FIGURE 15–8

Solution   **(a)** The circuit time constant is

$$\tau = RC = (100\text{ k}\Omega)(0.001\ \mu\text{F}) = 100\ \mu\text{s}$$

Notice that the pulse width is exactly equal to one time constant. Thus, the capacitor will charge approximately 63% of the full input amplitude in one time constant, so the output will reach a maximum voltage of

$$V_{out} = (0.63)10\text{ V} = \textbf{6.3 V}$$

(b) The capacitor discharges back through the source when the pulse ends. The total discharge time is

$$5\tau = 5(100\ \mu\text{s}) = \textbf{500}\ \boldsymbol{\mu}\textbf{s}$$

(c) The output charging and discharging curve is shown in Figure 15–9.

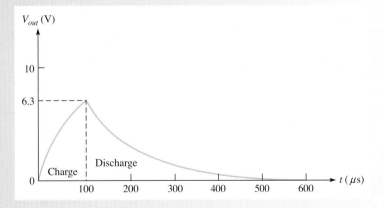

▲ FIGURE 15–9

*Related Problem**   If the input pulse width in Figure 15–8 is increased to 200 μs, to what voltage will the capacitor charge?

*Answers are at the end of the chapter.

EXAMPLE 15–2

Determine to what voltage the capacitor in Figure 15–10 will charge when a single pulse is applied to the input. Assume C is initially uncharged and the source resistance is zero.

▶ FIGURE 15–10

Solution   Calculate the time constant.

$$\tau = RC = (2.2\text{ k}\Omega)(1\ \mu\text{F}) = 2.2\text{ ms}$$

Because the pulse width is 5 ms, the capacitor charges for approximately 2.27 time constants (5 ms/2.2 ms = 2.27). Use the exponential formula, Equation 9–15, to find the voltage to which the capacitor will charge. With $V_F = 25$ V and $t = 5$ ms, the calculation is as follows:

$$v = V_F(1 - e^{-t/RC}) = (25\text{ V})(1 - e^{-5\text{ms}/2.2\text{ms}}) = \textbf{22.4 V}$$

These calculations show that the capacitor charges to 22.4 V during the 5 ms duration of the input pulse. It will discharge back to zero when the pulse goes back to zero.

Related Problem   Determine how much C will charge if the pulse width is increased to 10 ms.

**SECTION 15–2
REVIEW**

1. When an input pulse is applied to an *RC* integrator, what condition must exist in order for the output voltage to reach the full amplitude of the input?

2. For the circuit in Figure 15–11, which has a single-pulse input, find the maximum output voltage and determine how long the capacitor will discharge.

3. For Figure 15–11, draw the approximate shape of the output voltage with respect to the input pulse.

▶ FIGURE 15–11

4. If the integrator time constant equals the input pulse width, will the capacitor fully charge?

5. Describe the condition in an integrator under which the output voltage has the approximate shape of a rectangular input pulse.

15–3   RESPONSE OF *RC* INTEGRATORS TO REPETITIVE PULSES

In electronic systems, you will encounter waveforms with repetitive pulses much more often than with single pulses. However, an understanding of the integrator's response to single pulses is necessary in order to understand how these circuits respond to repeated pulses.

After completing this section, you should be able to

◆ **Analyze an *RC* integrator with a repetitive-pulse input**

   ◆ Determine the response when the capacitor does not fully charge or discharge

   ◆ Define *steady state*

   ◆ Describe the effect of a change in time constant on circuit response

If a periodic pulse waveform is applied to an *RC* integrator, as shown in Figure 15–12, the output waveshape depends on the relationship of the circuit time constant and the frequency of the input pulses. The capacitor, of course, charges and discharges in response to a pulse input. The amount of charge and discharge of the capacitor depends both on the circuit time constant and on the input frequency, as mentioned.

If the pulse width and the time between pulses are each equal to or greater than five time constants, the capacitor will fully charge and fully discharge during each period of the input waveform. This case is shown in Figure 15–12.

▲ FIGURE 15–12

RC integrator with a repetitive-pulse waveform input.

When the pulse width and the time between pulses are shorter than 5 time constants, as illustrated in Figure 15–13 for a square wave, the capacitor will *not* completely charge or discharge. We will now examine the effects of this situation on the output voltage of the *RC* integrator.

◀ FIGURE 15–13

Input waveform that does not allow full charge or discharge of the integrator capacitor.

For illustration, let's use an *RC* integrator with a charging and discharging time constant equal to the pulse width of a 10 V square wave input, as in Figure 15–14. This choice will simplify the analysis and will demonstrate the basic action of the integrator under these conditions. At this point, you really do not care what the exact time constant value is because an *RC* circuit charges 63.2% during one time constant interval.

▶ FIGURE 15–14

Integrator with a square wave input having a period equal to two time constants ($T = 2\tau$).

Let's assume that the capacitor in Figure 15–14 begins initially uncharged and examine the output voltage on a pulse-by-pulse basis. The results of this analysis are shown in Figure 15–15.

▶ FIGURE 15–15

Input and output for the initially uncharged integrator in Figure 15–14.

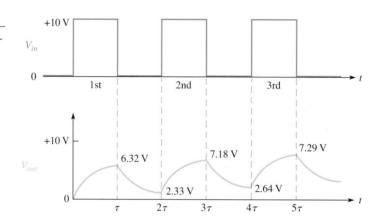

First pulse   During the first pulse, the capacitor charges. The output voltage reaches 6.32 V, which is 63.2% of 10 V, as shown in Figure 15–15.

Between first and second pulses   The capacitor discharges, and the voltage decreases to 36.8% of the voltage at the beginning of this interval: 0.368(6.32 V) = 2.33 V.

Second pulse   The capacitor voltage begins at 2.33 V and increases 63.2% of the way to 10 V. The total charging range is 10 V − 2.33 V = 7.67 V. The capacitor voltage will increase an additional 63.2% of 7.67 V, which is 4.85 V. Thus, at the end of the second pulse, the output voltage is 2.33 V + 4.85 V = 7.18 V, as indicated in Figure 15–15. Notice that the average is building up.

Between second and third pulses   The capacitor discharges during this time, and therefore the voltage decreases to 36.8% of the initial voltage by the end of the second pulse: 0.368(7.18 V) = 2.64 V.

Third pulse   At the start of the third pulse, the capacitor voltage is 2.64 V. The capacitor charges 63.2% of the way from 2.64 V to 10 V: 0.632(10 V − 2.64 V) = 4.65 V. Therefore, the voltage at the end of the third pulse is 2.64 V + 4.65 V = 7.29 V.

Steady-State Time Response

In the preceding discussion, the output voltage gradually built up and then began leveling off. It takes approximately 5τ for the output voltage to build up to 99% of its final value, regardless of the number of pulses that may occur during that time interval. This interval is the transient time of the circuit. Once the output voltage reaches the average value of the input voltage, a **steady-state** condition is reached, which continues as long as the periodic input continues. This condition is illustrated in Figure 15–16 based on the approximate values obtained after the first three pulses.

HANDS ON TIP

When you view pulse waveforms on an oscilloscope, set the scope to be DC coupled, not AC coupled. The reason is that AC coupling places a capacitor in series and can cause distortion in low-frequency pulse signals. Also, DC coupling allows you to observe the dc level of the pulse.

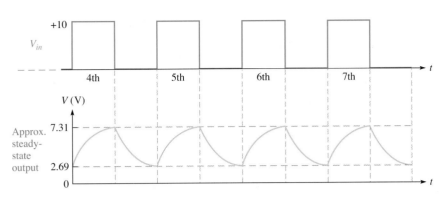

Output reaches steady state after 5τ and stabilizes at the values indicated.

The transient time for our example circuit is the time from the beginning of the first pulse to the end of the third pulse. The capacitor voltage at the end of the third pulse is 7.29 V, which is about 99% of its final value.

The Effect of an Increase in Time Constant

What happens to the output voltage if the *RC* time constant of the integrator is increased with a variable resistor, as indicated in Figure 15–17? As the time constant is increased, the capacitor charges less during a pulse and discharges less between pulses. The result is a smaller fluctuation in the output voltage for increasing values of time constant, as shown in Figure 15–18.

As the time constant becomes extremely long compared to the pulse width, the output voltage approaches a constant dc voltage, as shown in Figure 15–18(c). This value is the average value of the input. For a square wave, it is one-half the amplitude.

◀ **FIGURE 15–17**

Integrator with a variable time constant.

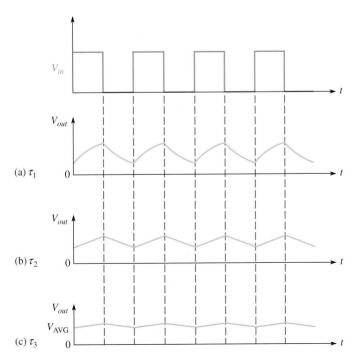

◀ **FIGURE 15–18**

Effect of increasing time constants on the output of an integrator $(\tau_3 > \tau_2 > \tau_1)$.

EXAMPLE 15–3

Determine the output voltage waveform for the first two pulses applied to the integrator circuit in Figure 15–19. Assume that the capacitor is initially uncharged.

▶ FIGURE 15–19

Solution   First, calculate the circuit time constant.

$$\tau = RC = (4.7 \text{ k}\Omega)(0.01 \text{ } \mu\text{F}) = 47 \text{ } \mu\text{s}$$

Obviously, the time constant is much longer than the input pulse width or the interval between pulses (notice that the input is not a square wave). Thus, in this case, the exponential formulas must be applied, and the analysis is relatively difficult. Follow the solution carefully.

1. *Calculation for first pulse:*   Use the equation for an increasing exponential (Eq. 9–15) because C is charging. Note that V_F is 5 V, and t equals the pulse width of 10 μs. Therefore,

$$v_C = V_F(1 - e^{-t/RC}) = (5 \text{ V})(1 - e^{-10\mu s/47\mu s}) = 958 \text{ mV}$$

This result is plotted in Figure 15–20(a).

▶ FIGURE 15–20

2. *Calculation for interval between first and second pulse:*   Use the equation for a decreasing exponential (Eq. 9–16) because C is discharging. Note that V_i is 958 mV because C begins to discharge from this value at the end of the first pulse. The discharge time is 15 μs. Therefore,

$$v_C = V_i e^{-t/RC} = (958 \text{ mV})e^{-15\mu s/47\mu s} = 696 \text{ mV}$$

This result is shown in Figure 15–20(b).

3. *Calculation for second pulse:* At the beginning of the second pulse, the output voltage is 696 mV. During the second pulse, the capacitor will again charge. In this case it does not begin at zero volts. It already has 696 mV from the previous charge and discharge. To handle this situation, you must use the general exponential formula (Eq. 9–13).

$$v = V_F + (V_i - V_F)e^{-t/\tau}$$

Using this equation, you can calculate the voltage across the capacitor at the end of the second pulse.

$$v_C = V_F + (V_i - V_F)e^{-t/RC} = 5\,\text{V} + (696\,\text{mV} - 5\,\text{V})e^{-10\mu s/47\mu s} = 1.52\,\text{V}$$

This result is shown in Figure 15–20(c).

Notice that the output waveform builds up on successive input pulses. After approximately 5τ, it will reach its steady state and will fluctuate between a constant maximum and a constant minimum, with an average equal to the average value of the input. You can demonstrate this pattern by carrying the analysis in this example further.

Related Problem   Determine V_{out} at the beginning of the third pulse.

Open Multisim file E15-03 on your CD-ROM. Measure the steady-state output waveform in terms of its minimum, maximum, and average values.

**SECTION 15–3
REVIEW**

1. What conditions allow an *RC* integrator capacitor to fully charge and discharge when a periodic pulse waveform is applied to the input?
2. What will the output waveform look like if the circuit time constant is extremely small compared to the pulse width of a square wave input?
3. What is the time called that is required for the output voltage to build up to a constant average value when 5τ is greater than the pulse width of an input square wave?
4. Define *steady-state response.*
5. What does the average value of the output voltage of an integrator equal during steady state?

15–4   RESPONSE OF *RC* DIFFERENTIATORS TO A SINGLE PULSE

In terms of time response, a series *RC* circuit in which the output voltage is taken across the resistor is known as a **differentiator**. Recall that in terms of frequency response, this particular series *RC* circuit is a high-pass filter. The term, *differentiator,* is derived from a mathematical function which this type of circuit approximates under certain conditions.

After completing this section, you should be able to

◆ **Analyze an *RC* differentiator with a single-pulse input**

   ◆ Describe the response at the rising edge of the input pulse

   ◆ Determine the response during and at the end of a pulse for various pulse width–time constant relationships

Figure 15–21 shows an *RC* differentiator with a pulse input. The same action occurs in the differentiator as in the integrator, except the output voltage is taken across the resistor rather than the capacitor. The capacitor charges exponentially at a rate depending on the *RC* time constant. The shape of the differentiator's resistor voltage is determined by the charging and discharging action of the capacitor.

▶ FIGURE 15–21

An *RC* differentiator with a pulse generator connected.

Pulse Response

To understand how the output voltage is shaped by a differentiator, you must consider the following:

1. The response to the rising pulse edge

2. The response between the rising and falling edges

3. The response to the falling pulse edge

Response to the Rising Edge of the Input Pulse   Let's assume that the capacitor is initially uncharged prior to the rising pulse edge. Prior to the pulse, the input is zero volts. Thus, there are zero volts across the capacitor and also zero volts across the resistor, as indicated in Figure 15–22(a).

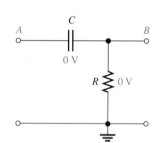

(a) Before pulse is applied

(b) At rising edge of input pulse

(c) During level part of pulse when $t_W \geq 5\tau$

(d) At falling edge of pulse when $t_W \geq 5\tau$

(e) During level part of pulse when $t_W < 5\tau$

(f) At falling edge of pulse when $t_W < 5\tau$

▲ FIGURE 15–22

Examples of the response of a differentiator to a single-pulse input under two conditions: $t_W \geq 5\tau$ and $t_W < 5\tau$. A pulse generator is connected to the input, but the symbol is not shown, only the pulses.

Let's also assume that a 10 V pulse is applied to the input. When the rising edge occurs, the voltage at point *A* goes to +10 V. Recall that the voltage across a capacitor cannot change instantaneously, and thus the capacitor appears instantaneously as a short. Therefore, if the voltage at point *A* goes instantly to +10 V, then the voltage at point *B must* also go instantly to +10 V, keeping the capacitor voltage zero for the instant of the rising edge. The capacitor voltage is the voltage from point *A* to point *B*.

The voltage at point *B* with respect to ground is the voltage across the resistor (and the output voltage). Thus, the output voltage suddenly goes to +10 V in response to the rising pulse edge, as indicated in Figure 15–22(b).

Response During Pulse When $t_W \geq 5\tau$ While the pulse is at its high level between the rising edge and the falling edge, the capacitor is charging. When the pulse width is equal to or greater than five time constants ($t_W \geq 5\tau$), the capacitor has time to fully charge.

As the voltage across the capacitor builds up exponentially, the voltage across the resistor decreases exponentially until it reaches zero volts at the time the capacitor reaches full charge (+10 V in this case). This decrease in the resistor voltage occurs because the sum of the capacitor voltage and the resistor voltage at any instant must be equal to the source voltage, in compliance with Kirchhoff's voltage law ($v_C + v_R = v_{in}$). This part of the response is illustrated in Figure 15–22(c).

Response to Falling Edge When $t_W \geq 5\tau$ Let's examine the case in which the capacitor is fully charged at the end of the pulse ($t_W \geq 5\tau$). Refer to Figure 15–22(d). On the falling edge, the input pulse suddenly goes from +10 V back to zero. An instant before the falling edge, the capacitor is charged to 10 V, so the voltage at point *A* is +10 V and the voltage at point *B* is 0 V. The voltage across a capacitor cannot change instantaneously, so when the voltage at point *A* makes a transition from +10 V to zero on the falling edge, the voltage at point *B must* also make a 10 V transition from zero to −10 V. This keeps the voltage across the capacitor at 10 V for the instant of the falling edge.

The capacitor now begins to discharge exponentially. As a result, the resistor voltage goes from −10 V to zero in an exponential curve, as indicated in Figure 15–22(d).

Response During Pulse When $t_W < 5\tau$ When the pulse width is less than five time constants ($t_W < 5\tau$), the capacitor does not have time to fully charge. Its partial charge depends on the relation of the time constant and the pulse width.

Because the capacitor does not reach the full +10 V, the resistor voltage will not reach zero volts by the end of the pulse. For example, if the capacitor charges to +5 V during the pulse interval, the resistor voltage will decrease to +5 V, as illustrated in Figure 15–22(e).

Response to Falling Edge When $t_W < 5\tau$ Now, let's examine the case in which the capacitor is only partially charged at the end of the pulse ($t_W < 5\tau$). For example, if the capacitor charges to +5 V, the resistor voltage at the instant before the falling edge is also +5 V because the capacitor voltage plus the resistor voltage must add up to +10 V, as illustrated in Figure 15–22(e).

When the falling edge occurs, the voltage at point *A* goes from +10 V to zero. As a result, the voltage at point *B* goes from +5 V to −5 V, as illustrated in Figure 15–22(f). This decrease occurs, of course, because the capacitor voltage cannot change at the instant of the falling edge. Immediately after the falling edge, the capacitor begins to discharge to zero. As a result, the resistor voltage goes from −5 V to zero, as shown.

Summary of *RC* Differentiator Response to a Single Pulse

A good way to summarize this section is to look at the general output waveforms of a differentiator as the time constant is varied from one extreme, when 5τ is much less than the pulse width, to the other extreme, when 5τ is much greater than the pulse width. These situations are illustrated in Figure 15–23. In part (a), the output consists of narrow positive and negative "spikes." In part (e), the output approaches the shape of the input. Various conditions between these extremes are illustrated in parts (b), (c), and (d).

(a) 5τ much less than t_W

(b) $5\tau = 0.5t_W$

V_{out} { (c) $5\tau = t_W$

(d) 5τ greater than t_W

(e) 5τ much greater than t_W

▲ FIGURE 15–23

Effects of a change in time constant on the shape of the output voltage of an *RC* differentiator.

EXAMPLE 15–4

Show the output voltage for the circuit in Figure 15–24.

▲ FIGURE 15–24

Solution First , calculate the time constant.

$$\tau = RC = (15\,\text{k}\Omega)(120\,\text{pF}) = 1.8\,\mu\text{s}$$

In this case, $t_W > 5\tau$, so the capacitor reaches full charge in 9 μs (before the end of the pulse).

On the rising edge, the resistor voltage jumps to +5 V and then decreases exponentially to zero before the end of the pulse. On the falling edge, the resistor voltage jumps to −5 V and then goes back to zero exponentially. The resistor voltage is, of course, the output, and its shape is shown in Figure 15–25.

▶ FIGURE 15–25

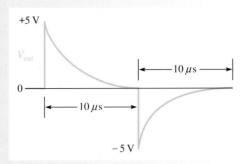

Related Problem   Show the output voltage if $R = 18 \text{ k}\Omega$ and $C = 47 \text{ pF}$ in Figure 15–24.

EXAMPLE 15–5   Determine the output voltage waveform for the differentiator in Figure 15–26.

▶ FIGURE 15–26

Solution   First, calculate the time constant.

$$\tau = (2.2 \text{ k}\Omega)(1 \ \mu\text{F}) = 2.2 \text{ ms}$$

On the rising edge, the resistor voltage immediately jumps to $+25$ V. Because the pulse width is 5 ms, the capacitor charges for approximately 2.27 time constants during the pulse, and therefore does not reach full charge. Thus, you must use the formula for a decreasing exponential (Eq. 9–16) in order to calculate to what voltage the output decreases by the end of the pulse.

$$v_{out} = V_i e^{-t/RC} = (25 \text{ V})e^{-5\text{ms}/2.2\text{ms}} = 2.58 \text{ V}$$

where $V_i = 25$ V and $t = 5$ ms. This calculation gives the resistor voltage at the end of the 5 ms pulse width interval.

On the falling edge, the resistor voltage immediately jumps from $+2.58$ V down to -22.4 V (a 25 V transition). The resulting waveform of the output voltage is shown in Figure 15–27.

▶ FIGURE 15–27

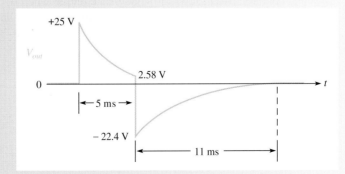

Related Problem   Determine the voltage at the end of the pulse in Figure 15–26 if R is $1.5 \text{ k}\Omega$.

SECTION 15–4
REVIEW

1. Show the output of a differentiator for a 10 V input pulse when $5\tau = 0.5t_W$.

2. Under what condition does the output pulse shape most closely resemble the input pulse for a differentiator?

3. What does the differentiator output look like when 5τ is much less than the pulse width of the input?

4. If the resistor voltage in a differentiating circuit is down to $+5$ V at the end of a 15 V input pulse, to what negative value will the resistor voltage go in response to the falling edge of the input?

15–5 Response of *RC* Differentiators to Repetitive Pulses

The *RC* differentiator response to a single pulse, covered in the last section, is extended in this section to repetitive pulses.

After completing this section, you should be able to

◆ **Analyze an *RC* differentiator with a repetitive-pulse input**

   ◆ Determine the response when the pulse width is less than five time constants

If a periodic pulse waveform is applied to an *RC* differentiating circuit, two conditions again are possible: $t_W \geq 5\tau$ or $t_W < 5\tau$. Figure 15–28 shows the output when $t_W = 5\tau$. As the time constant is reduced, both the positive and the negative portions of the output become narrower. Notice that the average value of the output is zero; the waveform has equal positive and negative portions. The average value of a waveform is its **dc component.** Because a capacitor blocks dc, the dc component of the input is prevented from passing through to the output.

▶ FIGURE 15–28

Example of differentiator response when $t_W = 5\tau$.

Figure 15–29 shows the steady-state output when $t_W < 5\tau$. As the time constant is increased, the positively and negatively sloping portions become flatter. For a very long time constant, the output approaches the shape of the input, but with an average value of zero.

▶ FIGURE 15–29

Example of differentiator response when $t_W < 5\tau$.

Analysis of a Repetitive Waveform

Like the integrator, the differentiator output takes time (5τ) to reach steady state. To illustrate the response, let's take an example in which the time constant equals the input pulse width. At this point, we do not care what the value of the circuit time constant is because we know that the resistor voltage will decrease to 36.8% of its maximum value during one pulse (1τ). Let's assume that the capacitor in Figure 15–30 begins initially uncharged and examine the output voltage on a pulse-by-pulse basis. The results of this analysis are shown in Figure 15–31.

◀ FIGURE 15–30

RC differentiator with $T = 2\tau$.

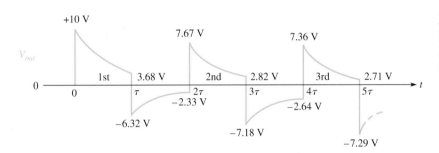

◀ FIGURE 15–31

Differentiator output waveform during transient time for the circuit in Figure 15–30.

First pulse   On the rising edge, the output instantaneously jumps to +10 V. Then the capacitor partially charges to 63.2% of 10 V, which is 6.32 V. Thus, the output voltage must decrease to 3.68 V, as shown in Figure 15–31.

On the falling edge, the output instantaneously makes a negative-going 10 V transition to −6.32 V because 3.68 V − 10 V = −6.32 V.

Between first and second pulses   The capacitor discharges to 36.8% of 6.32 V, which is 2.33 V. Thus, the resistor voltage, which starts at −6.32 V, must increase to −2.33 V. Why? Because at the instant prior to the next pulse, the input voltage is zero. Therefore, the sum of v_C and v_R must be zero (+2.33 V − 2.33 V = 0). Remember that $v_C + v_R = v_{in}$ at all times, in accordance with Kirchhoff's voltage law.

Second pulse   On the rising edge, the output makes an instantaneous, positive-going, 10 V transition from −2.33 V to 7.67 V. Then by the end of the pulse the capacitor charges 0.632 (10 V − 2.33 V) = 4.85 V. Thus, the capacitor voltage increases from 2.33 V to 2.33 V + 4.85 V = 7.18 V. The output voltage drops to 0.368(7.67 V) = 2.82 V.

On the falling edge, the output instantaneously makes a negative-going transition from 2.82 V to −7.18 V, as shown in Figure 15–31.

Between second and third pulses   The capacitor discharges to 36.8% of 7.18 V, which is 2.64 V. Thus, the output voltage starts at −7.18 V and increases to −2.64 V because the capacitor voltage and the resistor voltage must add up to zero at the instant prior to the third pulse (the input is zero).

Third pulse   On the rising edge, the output makes an instantaneous 10 V transition from −2.64 V to +7.36 V. Then the capacitor charges 0.632(10 V − 2.64 V) = 4.65 V to 2.64 V + 4.65 V = +7.29 V. As a result, the output voltage drops to 0.368(7.36 V) = 2.71 V. On the falling edge, the output instantly goes from +2.71 V down to −7.29 V.

After the third pulse, five time constants have elapsed, and the output voltage is close to its steady state. Thus, the waveform in Figure 15–31 will continue to vary from a positive maximum of about +7.3 V to a negative maximum of about −7.3 V, with an average value of zero.

SECTION 15–5 REVIEW

1. What conditions allow an *RC* differentiator to fully charge and discharge when a periodic pulse waveform is applied to the input?
2. What will the output waveform look like if the circuit time constant is extremely small compared to the pulse width of a square wave input?
3. What does the average value of the differentiator output voltage equal during steady state?

15–6 RESPONSE OF *RL* INTEGRATORS TO PULSE INPUTS

A series *RL* circuit in which the output voltage is taken across the resistor is known as an integrator in terms of time response. The response to a single pulse is discussed but can be extended to repetitive pulses as was done for the case of *RC* integrators.

After completing this section, you should be able to

◆ **Analyze the operation of an *RL* integrator**

   ◆ Determine the response to a single-pulse input

Figure 15–32 shows an *RL* integrator. The output waveform is taken across the resistor and, under equivalent conditions, is the same shape as that for the *RC* integrator. Recall that in the *RC* case, the output was across the capacitor.

▶ **FIGURE 15–32**

An *RL* integrator with a pulse generator connected.

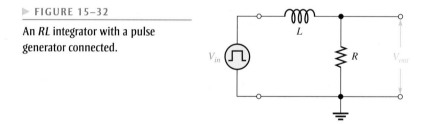

As you know, each edge of an ideal pulse is considered to occur instantaneously. Two basic rules for inductor behavior will aid in analyzing *RL* circuit responses to pulse inputs:

1. The inductor appears as an open to an instantaneous change in current and as a short (ideally) to dc.

2. The current in an inductor cannot change instantaneously—it can change only exponentially.

Response of the *RL* Integrator to a Single Pulse

When a pulse generator is connected to the input of an *RL* integrator and the voltage pulse goes from its low level to its high level, the inductor prevents a sudden change in current. As a result, the inductor acts as an open, and all the input voltage is across it at the instant of the rising pulse edge. This situation is indicated in Figure 15–33(a).

After the rising edge, the current builds up, and the output voltage follows the current as it increases exponentially, as shown in Figure 15–33(b). The current can reach a maximum

(a) At rising edge of pulse ($i = 0$)

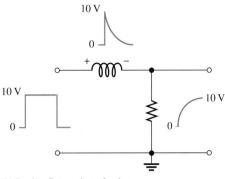

(b) During flat portion of pulse

(c) At falling edge of pulse and after

▲ **FIGURE 15–33**

Illustration of the pulse response of an *RL* integrator ($t_W > 5\tau$). A pulse generator is connected to the input but its symbol is not shown, only the pulses.

of V_p/R if the transient time is shorter than the pulse width ($V_p = 10$ V in this example where V_p is pulse amplitude).

When the pulse goes from its high level to its low level, an induced voltage with reversed polarity is created across the coil in an effort to keep the current equal to V_p/R. The output voltage begins to decrease exponentially, as shown in Figure 15–33(c).

The exact shape of the output depends on the L/R time constant as summarized in Figure 15–34 for various relationships between the time constant and the pulse width. You should note that the response of this *RL* circuit in terms of the shape of the output is

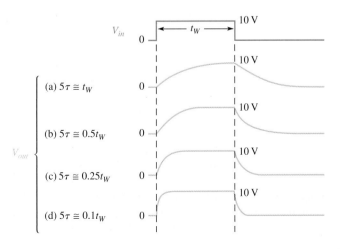

◀ **FIGURE 15–34**

Illustration of the variation in integrator output pulse shape with time constant.

identical to that of the *RC* integrator. The relationship of the *L/R* time constant to the input pulse width has the same effect as the *RC* time constant that we discussed earlier in this chapter. For example, when $t_W < 5\tau$, the output voltage will not reach its maximum possible value.

EXAMPLE 15–6

Determine the maximum output voltage for the integrator in Figure 15–35 when a single pulse is applied as shown.

▶ FIGURE 15–35

Solution   Calculate the time constant.

$$\tau = \frac{L}{R} = \frac{100\text{ mH}}{4.7\text{ k}\Omega} = 21.3\ \mu\text{s}$$

Because the pulse width is 50 μs, the inductor charges for approximately 2.35τ; (50 μs/21.3 μs = 2.35). Use the exponential formula to calculate the voltage.

$$v_{out(max)} = V_F(1 - e^{-t/\tau}) = (25\text{ V})(1 - e^{-50\mu s/21.3\mu s}) = \textbf{22.6 V}$$

Related Problem   What value must *R* be for the output voltage to reach 25 V by the end of the input pulse in Figure 15–35?

EXAMPLE 15–7

A pulse is applied to the *RL* integrator in Figure 15–36. Determine the waveforms and the values for *I*, V_R, and V_L.

▶ FIGURE 15–36

Solution   The circuit time constant is

$$\tau = \frac{L}{R} = \frac{5\text{ mH}}{1.5\text{ k}\Omega} = 3.33\ \mu\text{s}$$

Since $5\tau = 16.7\ \mu$s is less than t_W, the current will reach its maximum value and remain there until the end of the pulse.

At the rising edge of the pulse,

$$i = 0 \, \text{A}$$
$$v_R = 0 \, \text{V}$$
$$v_L = 10 \, \text{V}$$

The inductor appears as an open, so all of the input voltage appears across *L*. During the pulse,

$$i \text{ increases exponentially to } \frac{V_p}{R} = \frac{10 \, \text{V}}{1.5 \, \text{k}\Omega} = 6.67 \, \text{mA in } 16.7 \, \mu\text{s}$$

v_R increases exponentially to 10 V in 16.7 μs

v_L increases exponentially to zero in 16.7 μs

At the falling edge of the pulse,

$$i = 6.67 \, \text{mA}$$
$$v_R = 10 \, \text{V}$$
$$v_L = -10 \, \text{V}$$

After the pulse,

i decreases exponentially to zero in 16.7 μs

v_R decreases exponentially to zero in 16.7 μs

v_L decreases exponentially to zero in 16.7 μs

The waveforms are shown in Figure 15–37.

FIGURE 15–37

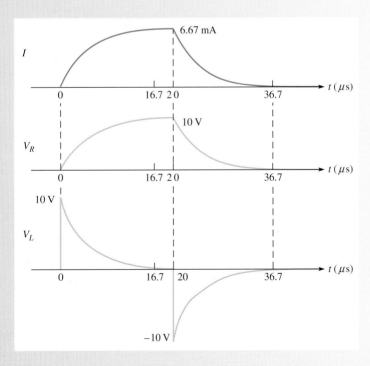

Related Problem   What will be the maximum output voltage if the amplitude of the input pulse is increased to 20 V in Figure 15–36?

EXAMPLE 15–8

A 10 V pulse with a width of 10 μs is applied to the integrator in Figure 15–38. Determine the voltage level that the output will reach during the pulse. If the source has an internal resistance of 300 Ω, how long will it take the output to decrease to zero? Show the output voltage waveform.

▶ FIGURE 15–38

Solution The coil charges through the 300 Ω source resistance plus the 4700 Ω external resistor. The time constant is

$$\tau = \frac{L}{R_{tot}} = \frac{50\,\text{mH}}{4700\,\Omega\,+\,300\,\Omega} = \frac{50\,\text{mH}}{5\,\text{k}\Omega} = 10\,\mu\text{s}$$

Notice that in this case the pulse width is exactly equal to τ. Thus, the output V_R will reach approximately 63% of the full input amplitude in 1τ. Therefore, the output voltage gets to **6.3 V** at the end of the pulse.

After the pulse is gone, the inductor discharges back through the 300 Ω source resistance and the 4700 Ω resistor. The output voltage takes 5τ to completely decrease to zero.

$$5\tau = 5(10\,\mu\text{s}) = \textbf{50}\,\boldsymbol{\mu}\textbf{s}$$

The output voltage is shown in Figure 15–39.

▲ FIGURE 15–39

Related Problem To what approximate maximum value must R be changed in Figure 15–38 to allow the output voltage to reach the input level during the pulse?

SECTION 15–6 REVIEW

1. In an RL integrator, across which component is the output voltage taken?
2. When a pulse is applied to an RL integrator, what condition must exist in order for the output voltage to reach the amplitude of the input?
3. Under what condition will the output voltage have the approximate shape of the input pulse?

15–7 RESPONSE OF *RL* DIFFERENTIATORS TO PULSE INPUTS

A series *RL* circuit in which the output voltage is taken across the inductor is known as a differentiator in terms of time response. The response to a single pulse is discussed but can be extended to repetitive pulses as was done for the case of *RC* differentiators.

After completing this section, you should be able to

◆ **Analyze the operation of an *RL* differentiator**

   ◆ Determine the response to a single-pulse input

Response of the *RL* Differentiator to a Single Pulse

Figure 15–40 shows an *RL* differentiator with a pulse generator connected to the input.

◀ FIGURE 15–40

An *RL* differentiator with a pulse generator connected.

Initially, before the pulse, there is no current in the circuit. When the input pulse goes from its low level to its high level, the inductor prevents a sudden change in current. It does this, as you know, with an induced voltage equal and opposite to the input. As a result, *L* looks like an open, and all of the input voltage appears across it at the instant of the rising edge, as shown in Figure 15–41(a) with a 10 V pulse.

During the pulse, the current exponentially builds up. As a result, the inductor voltage decreases, as shown in Figure 15–41(b). The rate of decrease, as you know, depends on the

(a) At rising edge of pulse

(b) During flat portion of pulse

(c) At falling edge when $t_W < 5\tau$

(d) At falling edge when $t_W \geq 5\tau$

▲ FIGURE 15–41

Illustration of the response of an *RL* differentiator for both time constant conditions. The pulse generator is connected to the input, but its symbol is not shown, only the pulses.

L/R time constant. When the falling edge of the input occurs, the inductor reacts to keep the current as is, by creating an induced voltage in a direction as indicated in Figure 15–41(c). This reaction is seen as a sudden negative-going transition of the inductor voltage, as indicated in parts (c) and (d).

Two conditions are possible, as indicated in Figure 15–41(c) and (d). In part (c), 5τ is greater than the input pulse width, and the output voltage does not have time to decrease to zero. In part (d), 5τ is less than or equal to the pulse width, and so the output decreases to zero before the end of the pulse. In this case a full -10 V transition occurs at the falling edge.

Keep in mind that as far as the input and output waveforms are concerned, the *RL* integrator and differentiator perform the same as their *RC* counterparts.

A summary of the *RL* differentiator response for relationships of various time constants and pulse widths is shown in Figure 15–42. Compare this figure to Figure 15–23 for an *RC* differentiator and you will see that the responses are identical.

▶ FIGURE 15–42

Illustration of the variation in output pulse shape with the time constant.

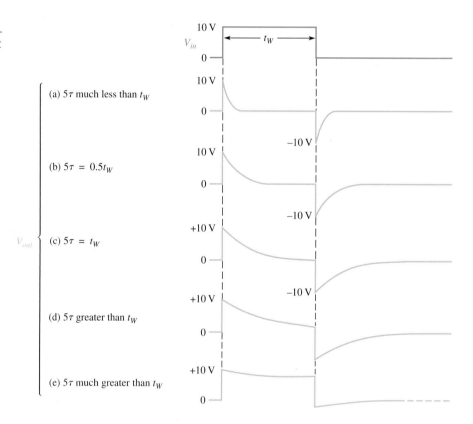

EXAMPLE 15–9

Show the output voltage waveform for the *RL* differentiator in Figure 15–43.

FIGURE 15–43

Solution   First, calculate the time constant.

$$\tau = \frac{L}{R} = \frac{20\,\mu\text{H}}{10\,\text{k}\Omega} = 2\,\text{ns}$$

In this case, $t_W = 5\tau$, so the output will decay to zero at the end of the pulse.

On the rising edge, the inductor voltage jumps to $+5$ V and then decays exponentially to zero. It reaches approximately zero at the instant of the falling edge. On the falling edge of the input, the inductor voltage jumps to -5 V and then goes back to zero. The output waveform is shown in Figure 15–44.

▶ FIGURE 15–44

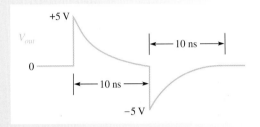

Related Problem   Show the output voltage if the input pulse width is reduced to 5 ns in Figure 15–43.

EXAMPLE 15–10   Determine the output voltage waveform for the *RL* differentiator in Figure 15–45.

▶ FIGURE 15–45

Solution   First, calculate the time constant.

$$\tau = \frac{L}{R} = \frac{20\,\text{mH}}{10\,\text{k}\Omega} = 2\,\mu\text{s}$$

On the rising edge, the inductor voltage immediately jumps to $+25$ V. Because the pulse width is 5 μs, the inductor charges for only two and a half time constants (2.5τ), so you must use the formula for a decreasing exponential.

$$v_L = V_i e^{-t/\tau} = (25\,\text{V})e^{-5\mu\text{s}/2/\mu\text{s}} = (25\,\text{V})e^{-2.5} = 2.05\,\text{V}$$

This result is the inductor voltage at the end of the 5 μs input pulse.

On the falling edge, the output immediately drops from $+2.05$ V to -22.95 V (a 25 V negative-going transition). The complete output waveform is shown in Figure 15–46.

▶ FIGURE 15–46

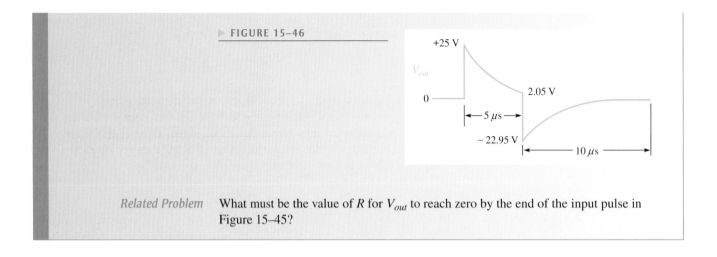

+25 V

V_{out}

0

2.05 V

5 μs

− 22.95 V

10 μs

Related Problem   What must be the value of R for V_{out} to reach zero by the end of the input pulse in Figure 15–45?

SECTION 15–7 REVIEW

1. In an *RL* differentiator, across which component is the output taken?
2. Under what condition does the output pulse shape most closely resemble the input pulse?
3. If the inductor voltage in an *RL* differentiator is down to +2 V at the end of a +10 V input pulse, to what negative voltage will the output voltage go in response to the falling edge of the input?

15–8 APPLICATIONS

Although integrators and differentiators are found in many different kinds of applications, only three basic ones are discussed in this section.

After completing this section, you should be able to

◆ **Discuss some applications of integrators and differentiators**

◆ Describe how *RC* integrators are used in timing circuits

◆ Describe how an integrator can be used for converting pulse waveforms to dc

◆ Describe how a differentiator can be used as a trigger pulse generator

Timing Circuits

RC integrators can be used in timing circuits to set a specified time interval for various purposes. By changing the time constant, the interval can be adjusted. For example, the *RC* integrator circuit in Figure 15–47(a) is used to provide a delay between the time a power-on switch is closed and the time a certain event is activated by a threshold circuit. The threshold circuit is designed to respond to the input voltage only when the input reaches a certain specified level. Don't worry how the threshold circuit works at this point; you will learn about this type of circuit in a later course.

When the switch is thrown, the capacitor begins to charge at a rate set by the *RC* time constant. After a certain time, the capacitor voltage reaches the threshold value and triggers (turns on) the circuit to activate a device such as a motor, relay, or lamp, depending on the particular application. This action is illustrated by the waveforms in Figure 15–47(b).

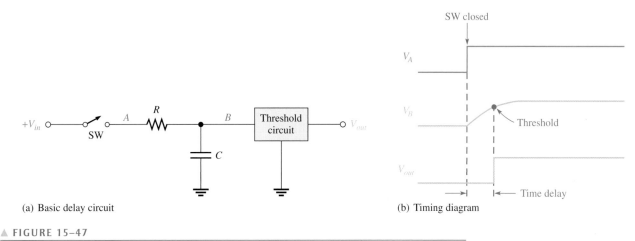

(a) Basic delay circuit

(b) Timing diagram

▲ FIGURE 15–47

A basic time delay application of an *RC* integrator.

EXAMPLE 15–11

What is the time delay in the circuit of Figure 15–47(a) with $V_{in} = 9$ V, $R = 10$ MΩ, and $C = 0.47$ μF? Assume the threshold voltage is 5 V.

Solution   Use the exponential formula, Equation 9–15, and solve for time as follows:

$$v = V_F(1 - e^{-t/RC}) = V_F - V_F e^{-t/RC}$$

$$V_F - v = V_F e^{-t/RC}$$

$$e^{-t/RC} = \frac{V_F - v}{V_F}$$

Taking the natural log (ln) of both sides of the equation yields

$$-\frac{t}{RC} = \ln\left(\frac{V_F - v}{V_F}\right)$$

$$t = -RC \ln\left(\frac{V_F - v}{V_F}\right)$$

V_F is the final voltage to which C will charge and equals V_{in}. Substituting values and solving for t yields

$$t = -(10\ \text{M}\Omega)(0.47\ \mu\text{F})\ln\left(\frac{9\ \text{V} - 5\ \text{V}}{9\ \text{V}}\right) = -(10\ \text{M}\Omega)(0.47\ \mu\text{F})\ln\left(\frac{4\ \text{V}}{9\ \text{V}}\right) = \mathbf{3.8\ s}$$

Related Problem   Find the time delay for the circuit in Figure 15–47 for $V_{in} = 24$ V, $R = 10$ kΩ, and $C = 1500$ pF.

A Pulse Waveform-to-DC Converter

An integrating circuit can be used to convert a pulse waveform to a constant dc value equal to the average of the waveform. This is accomplished by using a time constant that is extremely large compared to the period of the pulse waveform, as illustrated in Figure 15–48(a). Actually, there will be a slight ripple on the output as the capacitor charges and discharges a little. This ripple becomes less as the time constant becomes larger and can approach a constant level, as shown in Figure 15–48(b). In terms of sinusoidal response, this circuit is a low-pass filter.

A Positive and Negative Trigger Pulse Generator

A differentiator circuit can be used to produce very short duration pulses (spikes) with both positive and negative polarities, as illustrated in Figure 15–49(a). When the time constant is

(a)

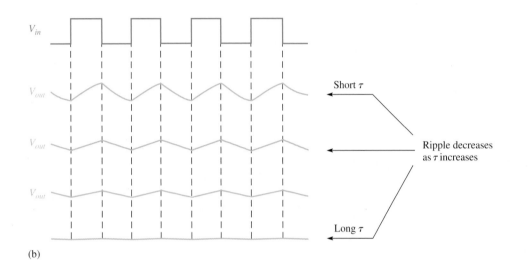

(b)

▲ FIGURE 15–48

A long time constant integrator acts as a pulse-to-dc converter.

(a)

(b)

▲ FIGURE 15–49

A very short time constant differentiator generates positive and negative spikes.

small compared to the pulse width of the input, the differentiator produces a positive spike on each positive-going edge of the input and a negative spike on each negative-going edge.

To separate the positive and negative spikes, two clipping circuits are used, as shown in Figure 15–49(b). Each clipping circuit consists of a diode, which is a semiconductor device. The negative clipper removes the negative spike and passes the positive spike. The positive clipper does just the opposite.

SECTION 15–8 REVIEW	1. How can the delay time in the circuit of Figure 15–47 be increased?
	2. Reducing the value of *R* in Figure 15–48 will (increase, decrease) the amount of ripple on the output.
	3. What characteristic must the differentiator in Figure 15–49 have in order to produce very short duration spikes on its output?

15–9 TROUBLESHOOTING

In this section, *RC* circuits with pulse inputs are used to demonstrate the effects of common component failures in selected cases. The concepts can then be easily related to *RL* circuits.

After completing this section, you should be able to

◆ **Troubleshoot *RC* integrators and *RC* differentiators**

   ◆ Recognize the effect of an open capacitor

   ◆ Recognize the effect of a shorted capacitor

   ◆ Recognize the effect of an open resistor

Open Capacitor

If the capacitor in an *RC* integrator opens, the output has the same waveshape as the input, as shown in Figure 15–50(a). If the capacitor in an *RC* differentiator opens, the output is zero because it is held at ground through the resistor, as illustrated in part (b).

(a) Integrator

(b) Differentiator

◀ FIGURE 15–50

Examples of the effect of an open capacitor.

Shorted Capacitor

If the capacitor in an *RC* integrator shorts, the output is at ground as shown in Figure 15–51(a). If the capacitor in an *RC* differentiator shorts, the output is the same as the input, as shown in part (b).

Examples of the effect of a shorted capacitor.

(a)

(b)

Open Resistor

If the resistor in an *RC* integrator opens, the capacitor has no discharge path, and, ideally, it will hold any charge it may have. In an actual situation, any charge will gradually leak off or the capacitor will discharge slowly through a measuring instrument connected to the output. This is illustrated in Figure 15–52(a).

If the resistor in an *RC* differentiator opens, the output looks like the input except for the dc level because the capacitor now must charge and discharge through the extremely high resistance of the oscilloscope, as shown in Figure 15–52(b).

Examples of the effect of an open resistor.

(a)

(b)

SECTION 15–9 REVIEW

1. An *RC* integrator has a zero output with a square wave input. What are the possible causes of this problem?
2. If the integrator capacitor is open, what is the output for a square wave input?
3. If the capacitor in a differentiator is shorted, what is the output for a square wave input?

Application Assignment

PUTTING YOUR KNOWLEDGE TO WORK

You have been given the assignment of breadboarding and testing a time-delay circuit that will provide five switch-selectable delay times. An *RC* integrator is selected for this application. The input is a 5 V pulse of long duration which begins the time delay. The exponential output voltage goes to a threshold trigger circuit that is used to turn the power on to a portion of a system after any one of the five selectable time delays.

A schematic of the selectable time-delay integrator is shown in Figure 15–53. The *RC* integrator is driven by a positive pulse input, and the output is the exponential voltage across the selected capacitor. The output voltage triggers a threshold circuit at the 3.5 V level, which then turns on the power to a portion of a system. The basic concept of operation is shown in Figure 15–54. In this application, the delay time of the integrator is specified as the time from the rising edge of the input pulse to the point where the output voltage reaches 3.5 V. The specified time delays are listed in Table 15–1.

◀ **FIGURE 15–53**

Integrator delay circuit.

▲ **FIGURE 15–54**

Illustration of the time-delay operation.

TABLE 15–1

SWITCH POSITION	DELAY TIME
A	10 ms
B	25 ms
C	40 ms
D	65 ms
E	85 ms

Step 1: Capacitor Values

Determine a value for each of the five capacitors in the time-delay circuit that will provide a delay time within 10% of the specified delay time. Select from the following list of standard values (all are in μF): 0.1, 0.12, 0.15, 0.18, 0.22, 0.27, 0.33, 0.39, 0.47, 0.56, 0.68, 0.82, 1.0, 1.2, 1.5, 1.8, 2.2, 2.7, 3.3, 3.9, 4.7, 5.6, 6.8, and 8.2.

Step 2: Circuit Connections

Refer to Figure 15–55. The components for the time-delay circuit are assembled, but not connected, on the breadboard. Using

▲ FIGURE 15–55

Time-delay circuit breadboard and test instruments.

the circled numbers, develop a point-to-point wiring list to show how the circuit and measurement instruments should be connected.

Step 3: Test Procedure and Instrument Settings

Develop a procedure for fully testing the time-delay circuit. Specify the amplitude, frequency, and duty cycle settings for the function generator in order to test each delay time. Specify the oscilloscope sec/div settings for measuring each of the five specified delay times.

Step 4: Measurement

Explain how you will verify that each switch setting produces the proper output delay time.

Review

1. Explain why the input pulse to the time-delay circuit must be of sufficiently long duration.

2. Indicate how you would modify the time-delay circuit so that each selected time delay had some adjustment range.

SUMMARY

- ◆ In an *RC* integrator, the output voltage is taken across the capacitor.
- ◆ In an *RC* differentiator, the output voltage is taken across the resistor.
- ◆ In an *RL* integrator, the output voltage is taken across the resistor.
- ◆ In an *RL* differentiator, the output voltage is taken across the inductor.
- ◆ In an integrator, when the pulse width (t_W) of the input is much less than the transient time, the output voltage approaches a constant level equal to the average value of the input.
- ◆ In an integrator, when the pulse width of the input is much greater than the transient time, the output voltage approaches the shape of the input.
- ◆ In a differentiator, when the pulse width of the input is much less than the transient time, the output voltage approaches the shape of the input but with an average value of zero.
- ◆ In a differentiator, when the pulse width of the input is much greater than the transient time, the output voltage consists of narrow, positive-going and negative-going spikes occurring on the leading and trailing edges of the input pulses.

KEY TERMS

Key terms and other bold terms in the chapter are defined in the end-of-book glossary.

Differentiator   A circuit producing an output that approaches the mathematical derivative of the input.

Integrator   A circuit producing an output that approaches the mathematical integral of the input.

Steady state   The equilibrium condition of a circuit that occurs after an initial transient time.

Time constant   A fixed-time interval, set by *R* and *C*, or *R* and *L* values, that determines the time response of a circuit.

Transient time   An interval equal to approximately five time constants.

SELF-TEST

Answers are at the end of the chapter.

1. The output of an *RC* integrator is taken across the

   (a) resistor   **(b)** capacitor   **(c)** source   **(d)** coil

2. When a 10 V input pulse with a width equal to one time constant is applied to an *RC* integrator, the capacitor charges to

   (a) 10 V   **(b)** 5 V   **(c)** 6.3 V   **(d)** 3.7 V

3. When a 10 V input pulse with a width equal to one time constant is applied to an *RC* differentiator, the capacitor charges to

   (a) 6.3 V   **(b)** 10 V   **(c)** 5 V   **(d)** 3.7 V

4. In an *RC* integrator, the output pulse closely resembles the input pulse when
   (a) τ is much larger than the pulse width
   (b) τ is equal to the pulse width
   (c) τ is less than the pulse width
   (d) τ is much less than the pulse width

5. In an *RC* differentiator, the output pulse closely resembles the input when
   (a) τ is much larger than the pulse width
   (b) τ is equal to the pulse width
   (c) τ is less than the pulse width
   (d) τ is much less than the pulse width

6. The positive and negative portions of a differentiator's output voltage are maximum when
   (a) $5\tau < t_W$ (b) $5\tau > t_W$ (c) $5\tau = t_W$ (d) $5\tau > 0$

7. The output of an *RL* integrator is taken across the
   (a) resistor   (b) coil   (c) source   (d) capacitor

8. The maximum current in an *RL* differentiator is
   (a) $I = \dfrac{V_p}{X_L}$ (b) $I = \dfrac{V_p}{Z}$ (c) $I = \dfrac{V_p}{R}$

9. The current in an *RL* differentiator reaches its maximum possible value when
   (a) $5\tau = t_W$ (b) $5\tau < t_W$ (c) $5\tau > t_W$ (d) $\tau = 0.5t_W$

10. If you have an *RC* and an *RL* differentiator with equal time constants sitting side-by-side and you apply the same input pulse to both,
    (a) the *RC* has the widest output pulse
    (b) the *RL* has the most narrow spikes on the output
    (c) the output of one is an increasing exponential and the output of the other is a decreasing exponential
    (d) you can't tell the difference by observing the output waveforms

PROBLEMS

Answers to odd-numbered problems are at the end of the book.

BASIC PROBLEMS

SECTION 15–1 The *RC* Integrator

1. An integrator has $R = 2.2\,\text{k}\Omega$ in series with $C = 0.047\,\mu\text{F}$. What is the time constant?

2. Determine how long it takes the capacitor in an integrating circuit to reach full charge for each of the following series *RC* combinations:
   (a) $R = 47\,\Omega, C = 47\,\mu\text{F}$ (b) $R = 3300\,\Omega, C = 0.015\,\mu\text{F}$
   (c) $R = 22\,\text{k}\Omega, C = 100\,\text{pF}$ (d) $R = 4.7\,\text{M}\Omega, C = 10\,\text{pF}$

3. It is required that an integrator have a time constant of approximately 6 ms. If $C = 0.22\,\mu\text{F}$, what standard value of *R* must be used?

4. For the capacitor in the integrator of Problem 3 to fully charge during a pulse, what must be the minimum width of the pulse?

SECTION 15–2 Response of *RC* Integrators to a Single Pulse

5. A 20 V pulse is applied to an *RC* integrator. The pulse width equals one time constant. To what voltage does the capacitor charge during the pulse? Assume that it is initially uncharged.

6. Repeat Problem 5 for the following values of t_W:
   (a) 2τ (b) 3τ (c) 4τ (d) 5τ

7. Show the approximate shape of an integrator output voltage where 5τ is much less than the pulse width of a 10 V square wave input. Repeat for the case in which 5τ is much larger than the pulse width.

8. Determine the output voltage for an integrator with a single-pulse input, as shown in Figure 15–56. For repetitive pulses, how long will it take this circuit to reach steady state?

▶ FIGURE 15–56

SECTION 15–3 Response of *RC* Integrators to Repetitive Pulses

9. Draw the integrator output in Figure 15–57 showing maximum voltages.

10. A 1 V, 10 kHz pulse waveform with a duty cycle of 25% is applied to an integrator with $\tau = 25\ \mu s$. Graph the output voltage for three initial pulses. *C* is initially uncharged.

▶ FIGURE 15–57

11. What is the steady-state output voltage of the *RC* integrator with a square wave input shown in Figure 15–58?

▶ FIGURE 15–58

SECTION 15–4 Response of *RC* Differentiators to a Single Pulse

12. Repeat Problem 7 for an *RC* differentiator.

13. Redraw the circuit in Figure 15–56 to make it a differentiator, and repeat Problem 8.

SECTION 15–5 Response of *RC* Differentiators to Repetitive Pulses

14. Draw the differentiator output in Figure 15–59, showing maximum voltages.

▶ FIGURE 15–59

15. What is the steady-state output voltage of the differentiator with the square wave input shown in Figure 15–60?

▶ FIGURE 15–60

SECTION 15–6 Response of *RL* Integrators to Pulse Inputs

16. Determine the output voltage for the circuit in Figure 15–61. A single-pulse input is applied as shown.

17. Draw the integrator output in Figure 15–62, showing maximum voltages.

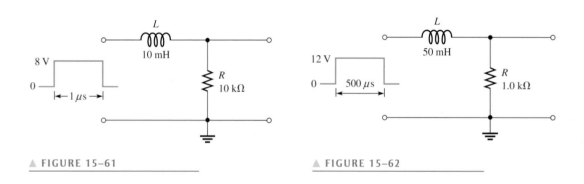

▲ FIGURE 15–61   ▲ FIGURE 15–62

SECTION 15–7 Response of *RL* Differentiators to Pulse Inputs

18. (a) What is τ in Figure 15–63?

    (b) Draw the output voltage.

19. Draw the output waveform if a periodic pulse waveform with $t_W = 25$ ns and $T = 60$ ns is applied to the circuit in Figure 15–63.

▶ FIGURE 15–63

SECTION 15–8 Applications

20. What is the instantaneous voltage at point *B* in Figure 15–47 440 μs after the switch is closed for $R = 22$ kΩ and $C = 0.001$ μF? $V_{in} = 10$ V.

21. Ideally, what is the output of an *RC* integrator when the input is a square wave with an amplitude of 12 V? Assume that the time constant is much greater than the period of the input signal?

SECTION 15–9   Troubleshooting

22. Determine the most likely fault(s) in the circuit of Figure 15–64(a) for each set of waveforms in parts (b) and (c). V_{in} is a square wave with a period of 8 ms.

(a)

(b)

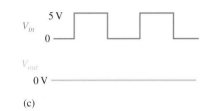

(c)

▲ **FIGURE 15–64**

23. Determine the most likely fault(s), if any, in the circuit of Figure 15–65(a) for each set of waveforms in parts (b) and (c). V_{in} is a square wave with a period of 8 ms.

(a)

(b)

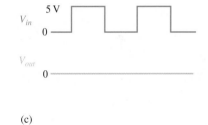

(c)

▲ **FIGURE 15–65**

ADVANCED PROBLEMS

24. (a) What is τ in Figure 15–66?

    (b) Draw the output voltage.

▷ **FIGURE 15–66**

25. (a) What is τ in Figure 15–67?

    (b) Draw the output voltage.

▷ **FIGURE 15–67**

26. Determine the time constant in Figure 15–68. Is this circuit an integrator or a differentiator?

▶ FIGURE 15–68

27. In a time-delay circuit like that of Figure 15–47, what time constant will produce a 1 s delay if the threshold of the circuit is 2.5 V and the amplitude of the input is 5 V?

28. Draw the schematic for the circuit in Figure 15–69 and determine if the oscilloscope presentation is correct.

(a) Oscilloscope display

(b) Circuit board with instrument leads connected

▲ FIGURE 15–69

MULTISIM TROUBLESHOOTING PROBLEMS

29. Open file P15-29 and test the circuit. If there is a fault, identify it.

30. Open file P15-30 and test the circuit. If there is a fault, identify it.

31. Determine if there is a fault in the circuit in file P15-31. If so, identify it.

32. Identify any faulty component in the circuit in file P15-32.

ANSWERS

SECTION REVIEWS

SECTION 15–1   The *RC* Integrator

1. An integrator is a series *RC* circuit with a pulse input in which the output is across the capacitor.

2. A voltage applied to the input causes the capacitor to charge. Zero volts across the input causes the capacitor to discharge.

SECTION 15–2   Response of *RC* Integrators to a Single Pulse

1. The output of an integrator reaches full amplitude when $5\tau \leq t_W$.

2. $V_{out} = (0.632)1 \text{ V} = 0.632 \text{ V}$; $t_{\text{disch}} = 5\tau = 51.7 \text{ ms}$.

3. See Figure 15–70.

4. No, *C* will not fully charge.

5. The output is approximately the shape of the input when $5\tau \ll t_W$ (5τ much less than t_W).

▶ **FIGURE 15–70**

SECTION 15–3   Response of *RC* Integrators to Repetitive Pulses

1. An integrator capacitor will fully charge and discharge when $5\tau \leq t_W$ and $5\tau \leq$ time between pulses.

2. The output looks like the input.

3. transient time

4. Steady state is the response after the transient time has passed.

5. The average value of the output voltage equals the average value of the input voltage.

SECTION 15–4   Response of *RC* Differentiators to a Single Pulse

1. See Figure 15–71.

▶ **FIGURE 15–71**

2. The output approximates the input when $5\tau \gg t_W$.

3. The output consists of a positive and a negative spike.

4. $V_R = +5\,\text{V} - 15\,\text{V} = -10\,\text{V}$

SECTION 15–5   Response of *RC* Differentiators to Repetitive Pulses

1. *C* fully charges and discharges when $5\tau \leq t_W$ and $5\tau \leq$ time between pulses.

2. The output consists of positive and negative spikes.

3. $V_{out} = 0\,\text{V}$

SECTION 15–6   Response of *RL* Integrators to Pulse Inputs

1. The output is across the resistor.

2. The output reaches the input amplitude when $5\tau \leq t_W$.

3. The output approximates the input when $5\tau \ll t_W$.

SECTION 15–7   Response of *RL* Differentiators to Pulse Inputs

1. The output is across the inductor.

2. The output approximates the input when $5\tau \gg t_W$.

3. $V_{out} = 2\,\text{V} - 10\,\text{V} = -8\,\text{V}$

SECTION 15–8   Applications

1. Increase the time constant to increase delay time.

2. Reducing *R* will increase ripple.

3. A very short time constant produces very short duration spikes.

SECTION 15–9 **Troubleshooting**

1. Zero output of *RC* integrator indicates shorted capacitor, open resistor, no source voltage, or open contact.

2. An open integrator capacitor results in an output exactly like the input.

3. A shorted differentiator capacitor results in an output exactly like the input.

Application Assignment

1. The input pulse must be sufficiently long to allow the output to reach 3.5 V for the longest time-constant setting.

2. Add a series potentiometer to adjust the total resistance.

RELATED PROBLEMS FOR EXAMPLES

15–1 8.65 V

15–2 24.7 V

15–3 1.10 V

15–4 See Figure 15–72.

▶ FIGURE 15–72

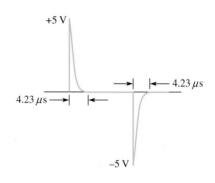

15–5 892 mV

15–6 10 kΩ

15–7 20 V

15–8 24.7 kΩ (assuming $R_s = 300\ \Omega$)

15–9 See Figure 15–73.

▶ FIGURE 15–73

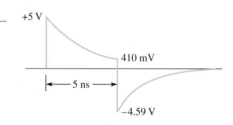

15–10 20 kΩ

15–11 3.5 μs

SELF-TEST

1. (b)   **2.** (c)   **3.** (a)   **4.** (d)   **5.** (a)

6. (a)   **7.** (a)   **8.** (c)   **9.** (b)   **10.** (d)

TABLE OF STANDARD RESISTOR VALUES

Resistance Tolerance (±%)

0.1% 0.25% 0.5%	1%	2% 5%	10%	0.1% 0.25% 0.5%	1%	2% 5%	10%	0.1% 0.25% 0.5%	1%	2% 5%	10%	0.1% 0.25% 0.5%	1%	2% 5%	10%	0.1% 0.25% 0.5%	1%	2% 5%	10%	0.1% 0.25% 0.5%	1%	2% 5%	10%
10.0	10.0	10	10	14.7	14.7	—	—	21.5	21.5	—	—	31.6	31.6	—	—	46.4	46.4	—	—	68.1	68.1	68	68
10.1	—	—	—	14.9	—	—	—	21.8	—	—	—	32.0	—	—	—	47.0	—	47	47	69.0	—	—	—
10.2	10.2	—	—	15.0	15.0	15	15	22.1	22.1	22	22	32.4	32.4	—	—	47.5	47.5	—	—	69.8	69.8	—	—
10.4	—	—	—	15.2	—	—	—	22.3	—	—	—	32.8	—	—	—	48.1	—	—	—	70.6	—	—	—
10.5	10.5	—	—	15.4	15.4	—	—	22.6	22.6	—	—	33.2	33.2	33	33	48.7	48.7	—	—	71.5	71.5	—	—
10.6	—	—	—	15.6	—	—	—	22.9	—	—	—	33.6	—	—	—	49.3	—	—	—	72.3	—	—	—
10.7	10.7	—	—	15.8	15.8	—	—	23.2	23.2	—	—	34.0	34.0	—	—	49.9	49.9	—	—	73.2	73.2	—	—
10.9	—	—	—	16.0	—	16	—	23.4	—	—	—	34.4	—	—	—	50.5	—	—	—	74.1	—	—	—
11.0	11.0	11	—	16.2	16.2	—	—	23.7	23.7	—	—	34.8	34.8	—	—	51.1	51.1	51	—	75.0	75.0	75	—
11.1	—	—	—	16.4	—	—	—	24.0	—	24	—	35.2	—	—	—	51.7	—	—	—	75.9	—	—	—
11.3	11.3	—	—	16.5	16.5	—	—	24.3	24.3	—	—	35.7	35.7	—	—	52.3	52.3	—	—	76.8	76.8	—	—
11.4	—	—	—	16.7	—	—	—	24.6	—	—	—	36.1	—	36	—	53.0	—	—	—	77.7	—	—	—
11.5	11.5	—	—	16.9	16.9	—	—	24.9	24.9	—	—	36.5	36.5	—	—	53.6	53.6	—	—	78.7	78.7	—	—
11.7	—	—	—	17.2	—	—	—	25.2	—	—	—	37.0	—	—	—	54.2	—	—	—	79.6	—	—	—
11.8	11.8	—	—	17.4	17.4	—	—	25.5	25.5	—	—	37.4	37.4	—	—	54.9	54.9	—	—	80.6	80.6	—	—
12.0	—	12	12	17.6	—	—	—	25.8	—	—	—	37.9	—	—	—	56.2	—	—	—	81.6	—	—	—
12.1	12.1	—	—	17.8	17.8	—	—	26.1	26.1	—	—	38.3	38.3	—	—	56.6	56.6	56	56	82.5	82.5	82	82
12.3	—	—	—	18.0	—	18	18	26.4	—	—	—	38.8	—	—	—	56.9	—	—	—	83.5	—	—	—
12.4	12.4	—	—	18.2	18.2	—	—	26.7	26.7	—	—	39.2	39.2	39	39	57.6	57.6	—	—	84.5	84.5	—	—
12.6	—	—	—	18.4	—	—	—	27.1	—	27	27	39.7	—	—	—	58.3	—	—	—	85.6	—	—	—
12.7	12.7	—	—	18.7	18.7	—	—	27.4	27.4	—	—	40.2	40.2	—	—	59.0	59.0	—	—	86.6	86.6	—	—
12.9	—	—	—	18.9	—	—	—	27.7	—	—	—	40.7	—	—	—	59.7	—	—	—	87.6	—	—	—
13.0	13.0	13	—	19.1	19.1	—	—	28.0	28.0	—	—	41.2	41.2	—	—	60.4	60.4	—	—	88.7	88.7	—	—
13.2	—	—	—	19.3	—	—	—	28.4	—	—	—	41.7	—	—	—	61.2	—	—	—	89.8	—	—	—
13.3	13.3	—	—	19.6	19.6	—	—	28.7	28.7	—	—	42.2	42.2	—	—	61.9	61.9	62	—	90.9	90.9	91	—
13.5	—	—	—	19.8	—	—	—	29.1	—	—	—	42.7	—	—	—	62.6	—	—	—	92.0	—	—	—
13.7	13.7	—	—	20.0	20.0	20	—	29.4	29.4	—	—	43.2	43.2	43	—	63.4	63.4	—	—	93.1	93.1	—	—
13.8	—	—	—	20.3	—	—	—	29.8	—	—	—	43.7	—	—	—	64.2	—	—	—	94.2	—	—	—
14.0	14.0	—	—	20.5	20.5	—	—	30.1	30.1	30	—	44.2	44.2	—	—	64.9	64.9	—	—	95.3	95.3	—	—
14.2	—	—	—	20.8	—	—	—	30.5	—	—	—	44.8	—	—	—	65.7	—	—	—	96.5	—	—	—
14.3	14.3	—	—	21.0	21.0	—	—	30.9	30.9	—	—	45.3	45.3	—	—	66.5	66.5	—	—	97.6	97.6	—	—
14.5	—	—	—	21.3	—	—	—	31.2	—	—	—	45.9	—	—	—	67.3	—	—	—	98.8	—	—	—

NOTE: These values are generally available in multiples of 0.1, 1, 10, 100, 1 k, and 1 M.

CAPACITOR COLOR CODING AND MARKING

Capacitor Color

Some capacitors have color-coded designations. The color code used for capacitors is basically the same as that used for resistors. Some variations occur in tolerance designation. The basic color codes are shown in Table B–1, and some typical color-coded capacitors are illustrated in Figure B–1.

▶ TABLE B–1

Typical composite color codes for capacitors (picofarads).

COLOR	DIGIT	MULTIPLIER	TOLERANCE
Black	0	1	20%
Brown	1	10	1%
Red	2	100	2%
Orange	3	1000	3%
Yellow	4	10000	
Green	5	100000	5% (EIA)
Blue	6	1000000	
Violet	7		
Gray	8		
White	9		
Gold		0.1	5% (JAN)
Silver		0.01	10%
No color			20%

NOTE: EIA stands for Electronic Industries Association, and JAN stands for Joint Army-Navy, a military standard.

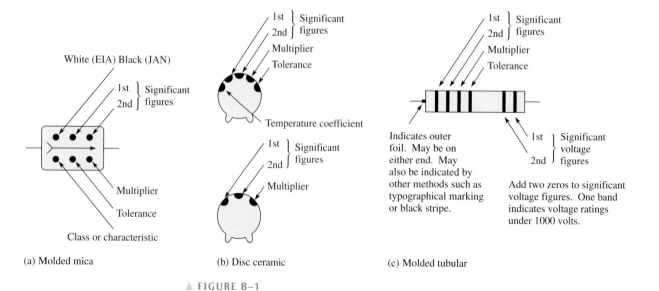

(a) Molded mica

(b) Disc ceramic

(c) Molded tubular

▲ FIGURE B–1

Typical color-coded capacitors.

Marking Systems

A capacitor, as shown in Figure B–2, has certain identifying features.

◆ Body of one solid color (off-white, beige, gray, tan or brown).

◆ End electrodes completely enclose ends of part.

◆ Many different sizes:

1. Type 1206: 0.125 inch long by 0.063 inch wide (3.2 mm × 1.6 mm) with variable thickness and color.

2. Type 0805: 0.080 inch long by 0.050 inch wide (2.0 mm × 1.25 mm) with variable thickness and color.

3. Variably sized with a single color (usually translucent tan or brown). Sizes range from 0.059 inch (1.5 mm) to 0.220 inch (5.6 mm) in length and in width from 0.032 inch (0.8 mm) to 0.197 inch (5.0 mm).

◆ Three different marking systems:

1. Two place (letter and number only).

2. Two place (letter and number or two numbers).

3. One place (letter of varying color).

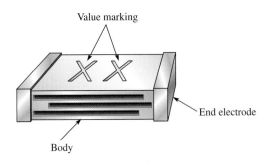

▲ FIGURE B–2

Capacitor marking.

Standard Two-Place Code

Refer to Table B–2.

$= 2.2 \times 10^3 = 2200$ pF

Multiplier (0–9)

Value (1st and 2nd significant digits)

Examples: S2 = 4.7 × 100 = 470 pF
b0 = 3.5 × 1.0 = 3.5 pF

▶ TABLE B–2

	VALUE*			MULTIPLIER
A 1.0	L 2.7	T 5.1		0 = ×1.0
B 1.1	M 3.0	U 5.6		1 = ×10
C 1.2	N 3.3	m 6.0		2 = ×100
D 1.3	b 3.5	V 6.2		3 = ×1000
E 1.5	P 3.6	W 6.8		4 = ×10000
F 1.6	Q 3.9	n 7.0		5 = ×100000
G 1.8	d 4.0	X 7.5		etc.
H 2.0	R 4.3	t 8.0		
J 2.2	e 4.5	Y 8.2		
K 2.4	S 4.7	y 9.0		
a 2.5	f 5.0	Z 9.1		

*Note uppercase and lowercase letters.

Alternate Two-Place Code

Refer to Table B–3.

◆ Values below 100 pF—Value read directly

◆ Values 100 pF and above—Letter/Number code

$$A1 = 10 \times 10 = 100 \text{ pF}$$

Multiplier (1–9)

Value (1st and 2nd significant digits)

$$N3 = 33 \times 1000$$
$$= 33000 \text{ pF} = .033 \ \mu\text{F}$$

▶ TABLE B–3

	VALUE*			MULTIPLIER
A 10	J 22	S 47		1 = ×10
B 11	K 24	T 51		2 = ×100
C 12	L 27	U 56		3 = ×1000
D 13	M 30	V 62		4 = ×10000
E 15	N 33	W 68		5 = ×100000
F 16	P 36	X 75		
G 18	Q 39	Y 82		etc.
H 20	R 43	Z 91		

*Note uppercase letters only.

Standard Single-Place Code

Refer to Table B–4.

$$= 4.7 \times 1.0 = 4.7 \text{ pF}$$

—— Color-multiplier

—— Value symbol

Examples: R (Green) $= 3.3 \times 100 = 330$ pF
7 (Blue) $= 8.2 \times 1000 = 8200$ pF

◀ TABLE B–4

VALUE						MULTIPLIER (COLOR)
A	1.0	K	2.2	W	4.7	Orange = ×1.0
B	1.1	L	2.4	X	5.1	Black = ×10
C	1.2	N	2.7	Y	5.6	Green = ×100
D	1.3	O	3.0	Z	6.2	Blue = ×1000
E	1.5	R	3.3	3	6.8	Violet = ×10000
H	1.6	S	3.6	4	7.5	Red = ×100000
I	1.8	T	3.9	7	8.2	
J	2.0	V	4.3	9	9.1	

NORTON'S THEOREM AND MILLMAN'S THEOREM

Norton's Theorem

▲ FIGURE C–1

The form of Norton's equivalent circuit.

Like Thevenin's theorem, Norton's theorem provides a method of reducing a more complex circuit to a simpler form. The basic difference is that Norton's theorem gives an equivalent current source in parallel with an equivalent resistance. The form of Norton's equivalent circuit is shown in Figure C–1. Regardless of how complex the original circuit is, it can always be reduced to this equivalent form. The equivalent current source is designated I_N, and the equivalent resistance is designated R_N.

To apply Norton's theorem, you must know how to find the two quantities I_N and R_N. Once you know them for a given circuit, simply connect them in parallel to get the complete Norton circuit.

Norton's Equivalent Current (I_N) As stated, I_N is one part of the complete Norton equivalent circuit; R_N is the other part. I_N is defined to be the short-circuit current between two points in a circuit. Any component connected between these two points effectively "sees" a current source of value I_N in parallel with R_N.

To illustrate, suppose that a resistive circuit of some kind has a resistor connected between two points in the circuit, as shown in Figure C–2(a). We wish to find the Norton circuit that is equivalent to the one shown as "seen" by R_L. To find I_N, calculate the current between points A and B with these two points shorted, as shown in Figure C–2(b). Example C–1 demonstrates how to find I_N.

▶ FIGURE C–2

Determining the Norton equivalent current, I_N.

(a) Original circuit   (b) Short the terminals to get I_N.

EXAMPLE C–1

Determine I_N for the circuit within the shaded area in Figure C–3(a).

▶ FIGURE C–3

(a)   (b)

Solution   Short terminals A and B as shown in Figure C–3(b). I_N is the current through the short and is calculated as follows: First, the total resistance seen by the voltage source is

$$R_T = R_1 + \frac{R_2 R_3}{R_2 + R_3} = 47\ \Omega + \frac{(47\ \Omega)(100\ \Omega)}{147\ \Omega} = 79\ \Omega$$

The total current from the source is

$$I_T = \frac{V_S}{R_T} = \frac{83.3\ \text{V}}{79\ \Omega} = 1.05\ \text{A}$$

Now apply the current-divider formula to find I_N (the current through the short).

$$I_N = \left(\frac{R_2}{R_2 + R_3}\right)I_T = \left(\frac{47\ \Omega}{147\ \Omega}\right)1.05\ \text{A} = \mathbf{336\ mA}$$

This is the value for the equivalent Norton current source.

Norton's Equivalent Resistance (R_N)   We define R_N in the same way as R_{TH}: it is the total resistance appearing between two terminals in a given circuit with all sources replaced by their internal resistances. Example C–2 demonstrates how to find R_N.

EXAMPLE C–2

Find R_N for the circuit within the shaded area of Figure C–3(a) (see Example C–1).

Solution   First reduce V_S to zero by shorting it, as shown in Figure C–4.
Looking in at terminals A and B, you can see that the parallel combination of R_1 and R_2 is in series with R_3. Thus,

$$R_N = R_3 + \frac{R_1}{2} = 100\ \Omega + \frac{47\ \Omega}{2} = \mathbf{124\ \Omega}$$

▲ FIGURE C–4

The two examples have shown how to find the two equivalent components of a Norton equivalent circuit, I_N and R_N. Keep in mind that these values can be found for any linear circuit. Once these are known, they must be connected in parallel to form the Norton equivalent circuit, as illustrated in Example C–3.

EXAMPLE C–3

Draw the complete Norton circuit for the original circuit in Figure C–3 (Example C–1).

Solution In Examples C–1 and C–2 you found that $I_N = 336$ mA and $R_N = 124$ Ω. The Norton equivalent circuit is shown in Figure C–5.

▶ FIGURE C–5

Summary of Norton's Theorem Any load resistor connected between the terminals of a Norton equivalent circuit will have the same current through it and the same voltage across it as if it were connected to the terminals of the original circuit. A summary of steps for theoretically applying Norton's theorem is as follows:

1. Short the two terminals between which you want to find the Norton equivalent circuit.

2. Determine the current (I_N) through the shorted terminals.

3. Determine the resistance (R_N) between the two terminals (opened) with all voltage sources shorted and all current sources opened ($R_N = R_{TH}$).

4. Connect I_N and R_N in parallel to produce the complete Norton equivalent for the original circuit.

Norton's equivalent circuit can also be derived from Thevenin's equivalent circuit by use of the source conversion method.

Millman's Theorem

Millman's theorem permits any number of parallel voltage sources to be reduced to a single equivalent voltage source. It simplifies finding the voltage across or current through a load. Millman's theorem gives the same results as Thevenin's theorem for the special case of parallel voltage sources. A conversion by Millman's theorem is illustrated in Figure C–6.

▲ FIGURE C–6

Reduction of parallel voltage sources to a single equivalent voltage source.

Millman's Equivalent Voltage (V_{EQ}) and Equivalent Resistance (R_{EQ}) Millman's theorem gives us a formula for calculating the equivalent voltage, V_{EQ}. To find V_{EQ}, convert each of the parallel voltage sources into the current sources, as shown in Figure C–7.

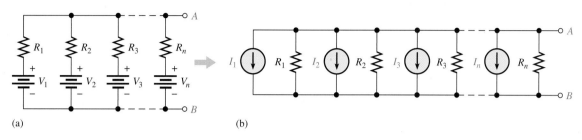

(a)   (b)

▲ FIGURE C–7

Parallel voltage sources converted to current sources.

In Figure C–7(b), the total current from the parallel current sources is

$$I_T = I_1 + I_2 + I_3 + \cdots + I_n$$

The total conductance between terminals A and B is

$$G_T = G_1 + G_2 + G_3 + \cdots + G_n$$

where $G_T = 1/R_T$, $G_1 = 1/R_1$, and so on. Remember, the current sources are effectively open. Therefore, by Millman's theorem, the equivalent resistance, R_{EQ}, is the total resistance R_T.

$$R_{EQ} = \frac{1}{G_T} = \frac{1}{(1/R_1) + (1/R_2) + (1/R_3) + \cdots + (1/R_n)}$$

Equation C–1

By Millman's theorem, the equivalent voltage is $I_T R_{EQ}$, where I_T is expressed as follows:

$$I_T = I_1 + I_2 + I_3 + \cdots + I_n = \frac{V_1}{R_1} + \frac{V_2}{R_2} + \frac{V_3}{R_3} + \cdots + \frac{V_n}{R_n}$$

The following is the formula for the equivalent voltage:

$$V_{EQ} = \frac{(V_1/R_1) + (V_2/R_2) + (V_3/R_3) + \cdots + (V_n/R_n)}{(1/R_1) + (1/R_2) + (1/R_3) + \cdots + (1/R_n)}$$

Equation C–2

Equations C–1 and C–2 are the two Millman formulas. The equivalent voltage source has a polarity such that the total current through a load will be in the same direction as in the original circuit.

EXAMPLE C–4

Use Millman's theorem to find the voltage across R_L and the current through R_L in Figure C–8.

▶ FIGURE C–8

Solution Apply Millman's theorem as follows:

$$R_{EQ} = \frac{1}{(1/R_1) + (1/R_2) + (1/R_3)}$$

$$= \frac{1}{(1/22\ \Omega) + (1/22\ \Omega) + (1/10\ \Omega)} = \frac{1}{0.19} = 5.24\ \Omega$$

$$V_{EQ} = \frac{(V_1/R_1) + (V_2/R_2) + (V_3/R_3)}{(1/R_1) + (1/R_2) + (1/R_3)}$$

$$= \frac{(10\ \text{V}/22\ \Omega) + (5\ \text{V}/22\ \Omega) + (15\ \text{V}/10\ \Omega)}{(1/22\ \Omega) + (1/22\ \Omega) + (1/10\ \Omega)} = \frac{2.18\ \text{A}}{0.19\ \text{S}} = 11.5\ \text{V}$$

The single equivalent voltage source is shown in Figure C–9.
Now calculate I_L and V_L for the load resistor.

$$I_L = \frac{V_{EQ}}{R_{EQ} + R_L} = \frac{11.5\ \text{V}}{52.2\ \Omega} = \textbf{220 mA}$$

$$V_L = I_L R_L = (220\ \text{mA})(47\ \Omega) = \textbf{10.3 V}$$

▶ FIGURE C–9

ANSWERS TO ODD-NUMBERED PROBLEMS

Chapter 1

1. (a) 3×10^3 (b) 7.5×10^4 (c) 2×10^6

3. (a) 8.4×10^3 (b) 9.9×10^4 (c) 2×10^5

5. (a) 0.0000025   (b) 500   (c) 0.39

7. (a) 4.32×10^7 (b) 5.00085×10^3 (c) 6.06×10^{-8}

9. (a) 2.0×10^9 (b) 3.6×10^{14} (c) 1.54×10^{-14}

11. (a) 89×10^3 (b) 450×10^3 (c) 12.04×10^{12}

13. (a) 345×10^{-6} (b) 25×10^{-3} (c) 1.29×10^{-9}

15. (a) 7.1×10^{-3} (b) 101×10^6 (c) 1.50×10^6

17. (a) 22.7×10^{-3} (b) 200×10^6 (c) 848×10^{-3}

19. (a) $345 \, \mu A$ (b) $25 \, mA$ (c) $1.29 \, nA$

21. (a) $3 \, \mu F$ (b) $3.3 \, M\Omega$ (c) $350 \, nA$

23. (a) $5000 \, \mu A$ (b) $3.2 \, mW$
    (c) $5 \, MV$ (d) $10,000 \, kW$

25. (a) $50.68 \, mA$ (b) $2.32 \, M\Omega$ (c) $0.0233 \, \mu F$

27. (a) 3   (b) 4   (c) 5   (d) 6   (e) 3   (f) 2

Chapter 2

1. $80 \times 10^{12} \, C$

3. $4.64 \times 10^{-18} \, C$

5. (a) $10 \, V$ (b) $2.5 \, V$ (c) $4 \, V$

7. $20 \, V$

9. (a) $75 \, A$ (b) $20 \, A$ (c) $2.5 \, A$

11. $2 \, s$

13. A: $6800 \, \Omega \pm 10\%$
    B: $33 \, \Omega \pm 10\%$
    C: $47,000 \, \Omega \pm 5\%$

15. (a) Red, violet, brown, gold
    (b) B: $330 \, \Omega$, D: $2.2 \, k\Omega$, A: $39 \, k\Omega$, L: $56 \, k\Omega$, F: $100 \, k\Omega$

17. (a) $10 \, \Omega \pm 5\%$
    (b) $5.1 \, M\Omega \pm 10\%$
    (c) $68 \, \Omega \pm 5\%$

19. (a) $28.7 \, k\Omega \pm 1\%$
    (b) $60.4 \, \Omega \pm 1\%$
    (c) $9.31 \, k\Omega \pm 1\%$

21. (a) $22 \, \Omega$ (b) $4.7 \, k\Omega$ (c) $82 \, k\Omega$
    (d) $3.3 \, k\Omega$ (e) $56 \, \Omega$ (f) $10 \, M\Omega$

23. There is current through lamp 2.

25. Ammeter in series with resistors, with its negative terminal to the negative terminal of source and its positive terminal to one side of R_1. Voltmeter placed across (in parallel with) the source (negative to negative, positive to positive).

27. Position 1: $V1 = 0, V2 = V_S$
    Position 2: $V1 = V_S, V2 = 0$

29. $250 \, V$

31. (a) $200 \, \Omega$ (b) $150 \, M\Omega$ (c) $4500 \, \Omega$

33. $33.3 \, V$

35. AWG #27

37. Circuit (b)

39. One ammeter in series with battery. One ammeter in series with each resistor (seven total).

41. See Figure P–1.

▲ FIGURE P–1

Chapter 3

1. (a) $3 \, A$ (b) $0.2 \, A$ (c) $1.5 \, A$

3. $15 \, mA$

5. (a) $3.33 \, mA$ (b) $550 \, \mu A$ (c) $588 \, \mu A$
   (d) $500 \, mA$ (e) $6.60 \, mA$

7. (a) $2.50 \, mA$ (b) $2.27 \, \mu A$ (c) $8.33 \, mA$

9. $I = 0.642 \, A$, so the 0.5 A fuse will blow.

11. (a) $10 \, mV$ (b) $1.65 \, V$ (c) $14.1 \, kV$
    (d) $3.52 \, V$ (e) $250 \, mV$ (f) $750 \, kV$
    (g) $8.5 \, kV$ (h) $3.53 \, mV$

13. (a) $81 \, V$ (b) $500 \, V$ (c) $117.5 \, V$

15. (a) $2\,k\Omega$ (b) $3.5\,k\Omega$ (c) $2\,k\Omega$

    (d) $100\,k\Omega$ (e) $1\,M\Omega$

17. (a) $4\,\Omega$ (b) $3\,k\Omega$ (c) $200\,k\Omega$

19. 417 mW

21. (a) 1 MW   (b) 3 MW   (c) 150 MW   (d) 8.7 MW

23. (a) 2,000,000 μW   (b) 500 μW

    (c) 250 μW   (d) 6.67 μW

25. $P = W/t$ in watts; $V = W/Q$; $I = Q/t$. $P = VI = W/t$, so (1 V)(1 A) = 1 watt

27. 16.5 mW

29. 1.18 kW

31. 5.81 W

33. 25 Ω

35. 0.00186 kWh

37. 156 mW

39. 1 W

41. (a) positive at top   (b) positive at bottom

    (c) positive at right

43. 36 Ah

45. 13.5 mA

47. 4.25 W

49. Five

51. 150 Ω

53. $V = 0\,V, I = 0\,A$; $V = 10\,V, I = 100\,mA$;

    $V = 20\,V, I = 200\,mA$; $V = 30\,V, I = 300\,mA$;

    $V = 40\,V, I = 400\,mA$; $V = 50\,V, I = 500\,mA$;

    $V = 60\,V, I = 600\,mA$; $V = 70\,V, I = 700\,mA$;

    $V = 80\,V, I = 800\,mA$; $V = 90\,V, I = 900\,mA$;

    $V = 100\,V, I = 1\,A$

55. $R_1 = 0.5\,\Omega$; $R_2 = 1\,\Omega$; $R_3 = 2\,\Omega$

57. 10 V; 30 V

59. $I_{MAX} = 3.83\,mA$; $I_{MIN} = 3.46\,mA$

61. 216 kWh

63. 12 W

65. 2.5 A

67. No fault

69. Lamp 4 is shorted.

Chapter 4

1. See Figure P–2.

3. $170\,k\Omega$

5. $138\,\Omega$

7. (a) $7.9\,k\Omega$ (b) $33\,\Omega$ (c) $13.24\,M\Omega$

The series circuit is disconnected from the source, and the ohmmeter is connected across the circuit terminals.

9. $1126\,\Omega$

11. (a) $170\,k\Omega$ (b) $50\,\Omega$

    (c) $12.4\,k\Omega$ (d) $1.97\,k\Omega$

13. 0.1 A

15. (a) $625\,\mu A$

    (b) $4.26\,\mu A$. The ammeter is connected in series.

17. (a) 34.0 mA   (b) 16 V   (c) 0.543 W

19. 14 V

21. 26 V

23. (a) $V_2 = 6.8\,V$

    (b) $V_R = 8\,V$, $V_{2R} = 16\,V$, $V_{3R} = 24\,V$, $V_{4R} = 32\,V$

The voltmeter is connected across (in parallel with) each resistor for which the voltage is unknown.

25. (a) 3.84 V   (b) 6.77 V

27. 3.80 V; 9.38 V

29. $V_{5.6k\Omega} = 10\,V$; $V_{1k\Omega} = 1.79\,V$; $V_{560\Omega} = 1\,V$; $V_{10k\Omega} = 17.9\,V$

31. 55 mW

33. Measure V_A and V_B individually with respect to ground; then $V_{R2} = V_A - V_B$.

35. (a) R_4 open   (b) R_4 and R_5 shorted

37. $780\,\Omega$

39. $V_A = 10\,V$; $V_B = 7.72\,V$; $V_C = 6.68\,V$;

    $V_D = 1.81\,V$; $V_E = 0.57\,V$; $V_F = 0\,V$

41. $500\,\Omega$

43. (a) 19.1 mA   (b) 45.8 V

    (c) $R(\tfrac{1}{8}\,W) = 343\,\Omega$, $R(\tfrac{1}{4}\,W) = 686\,\Omega$,
      $R(\tfrac{1}{2}\,W) = 1371\,\Omega$

45. See Figure P–3.

▲ FIGURE P–3

▶ FIGURE P–2

47. $R_1 + R_7 + R_8 + R_{10} = 4.23 \, \text{k}\Omega$;

$R_2 + R_4 + R_6 + R_{11} = 23.6 \, \text{k}\Omega$;

$R_3 + R_5 + R_9 + R_{12} = 19.9 \, \text{k}\Omega$

49. *A*: 5.45 mA; *B*: 6.06 mA; *C*: 7.95 mA; *D*: 12 mA

51. *A*: $V_1 = 6.03 \, \text{V}, V_2 = 3.35 \, \text{V}, V_3 = 2.75 \, \text{V}$,
$V_4 = 1.88 \, \text{V}, V_5 = 4.0 \, \text{V}$;

B: $V_1 = 6.71 \, \text{V}, V_2 = 3.73 \, \text{V}, V_3 = 3.06 \, \text{V}, V_5 = 4.5 \, \text{V}$;

C: $V_1 = 8.1 \, \text{V}, V_2 = 4.5 \, \text{V}, V_5 = 5.4 \, \text{V}$;

D: $V_1 = 10.8 \, \text{V}, V_5 = 7.2 \, \text{V}$

53. Yes, R_3 and R_5 are shorted.

55. **(a)** R_{11} has burned open due to excessive power.

(b) Replace R_{11} (10 kΩ).

(c) 338 V

57. R_6 is shorted.

59. Lamp 4 is open.

61. The 82 Ω resistor is shorted.

Chapter 5

1. See Figure P–4.

▲ FIGURE P–4

3. 3.43 kΩ

5. **(a)** 25.6 Ω **(b)** 359 Ω

(c) 819 Ω **(d)** 996 Ω

7. 2 kΩ

9. 12 V; 5 mA

11. **(a)** 909 μA **(b)** 76 mA

13. Circuit (a)

15. 1350 mA

17. $I_2 = I_3 = 7.5 \, \text{mA}$. Connect an ammeter in series with each resistor in each branch.

19. $I_1 = 2.19 \, \text{A}; I_2 = 811 \, \text{mA}$

21. 200 mW

23. 682 mA; 4.09 A

25. The 1.0 kΩ resistor is open.

27. R_2 is open.

29. $R_2 = 25 \, \Omega; R_3 = 100 \, \Omega; R_4 = 12.5 \, \Omega$

31. $I_R = 4.8 \, \text{A}; I_{2R} = 2.4 \, \text{A}; I_{3R} = 1.6 \, \text{A}; I_{4R} = 1.2 \, \text{A}$

33. **(a)** $R_1 = 100 \, \Omega, R_2 = 200 \, \Omega, I_2 = 50 \, \text{mA}$

(b) $I_1 = 125 \, \text{mA}, I_2 = 74.9 \, \text{mA}, R_1 = 80 \, \Omega, R_2 = 134 \, \Omega$,
$V_S = 10 \, \text{V}$

(c) $I_1 = 253 \, \text{mA}, I_2 = 147 \, \text{mA}, I_3 = 100 \, \text{mA}, R_1 = 395 \, \Omega$

35. 53.7 Ω

37. 3.92 A; 1.08 A

39. $R_1 \| R_2 \| R_5 \| R_9 \| R_{10} \| R_{12} = 100 \, \text{k}\Omega \| 220 \, \text{k}\Omega \| 560 \, \text{k}\Omega \|$
$390 \, \text{k}\Omega \| 1.2 \, \text{M}\Omega \| 100 \, \text{k}\Omega = 33.6 \, \text{k}\Omega$

$R_4 \| R_6 \| R_7 \| R_8 = 270 \, \text{k}\Omega \| 1.0 \, \text{M}\Omega \| 820 \, \text{k}\Omega \| 680 \, \text{k}\Omega =$
$135.2 \, \text{k}\Omega$

$R_3 \| R_{11} = 330 \, \text{k}\Omega \| 1.8 \, \text{M}\Omega = 278.9 \, \text{k}\Omega$

41. $R_2 = 750 \, \Omega; R_4 = 423 \, \Omega$

43. The 4.7 kΩ resistor is open.

45. **(a)** One of the resistors has opened due to excessive power dissipation.

(b) 30 V

(c) Replace the 1.8 kΩ resistor.

47. **(a)** 940 Ω **(b)** 518 Ω **(c)** 518 Ω **(d)** 422 Ω

49. R_3 is open.

51. **(a)** *R* from pin 1 to pin 4 agrees with calculated value.

(b) *R* from pin 2 to pin 3 agrees with calculated value.

Chapter 6

1. R_2, R_3, and R_4 are in parallel, and this parallel combination is in series with both R_1 and R_5.

3. See Figure P–5.

(a)

(b)

▲ FIGURE P–5

5. 2003 Ω

7. **(a)** 128 Ω **(b)** 791 Ω

9. (a) $I_1 = I_4 = 11.7$ mA, $I_2 = I_3 = 5.85$ mA; $V_1 = 655$ mV, $V_2 = V_3 = 585$ mV, $V_4 = 257$ mV

(b) $I_1 = 3.8$ mA, $I_2 = 618\ \mu$A, $I_3 = 1.27$ mA, $I_4 = 1.91$ mA; $V_1 = 2.58$ V, $V_2 = V_3 = V_4 = 420$ mV

11. 2.22 mA

13. 7.5 V unloaded; 7.29 V loaded

15. 56 kΩ load

17. 22 kΩ

19. 2 V

21. 360 Ω

23. 7.33 kΩ

25. $R_{TH} = 18$ kΩ; $V_{TH} = 2.7$ V

27. 1.06 V; 226 μA

29. 75 Ω

31. 21 mA

33. No, the meter should read 4.39 V. The 680 Ω resistor is open.

35. The 7.62 V and 5.24 V readings are incorrect, indicating that the 3.3 kΩ resistor is open.

37. (a) $V_1 = -10$ V, all others 0 V

(b) $V_1 = -2.33$ V, $V_4 = -7.67$ V, $V_2 = -7.67$ V, $V_3 = 0$ V

(c) $V_1 = -2.33$ V, $V_4 = -7.67$ V, $V_2 = 0$ V, $V_3 = -7.67$ V

(d) $V_1 = -10$ V, all others 0 V

39. See Figure P–6.

41. $R_T = 5.76$ kΩ; $V_A = 3.3$ V; $V_B = 1.7$ V; $V_C = 850$ mV

43. $V_1 = 1.61$ V; $V_2 = 6.77$ V; $V_3 = 1.72$ V; $V_4 = 3.33$ V; $V_5 = 378$ mV; $V_6 = 2.57$ V; $V_7 = 378$ mV; $V_8 = 1.72$ V; $V_9 = 1.61$ V

45. 110 Ω

47. $R_1 = 180\ \Omega$; $R_2 = 60\ \Omega$. Output across R_2.

49. 845 μA

51. 11.7 V

53. See Figure P–7.

55. Pos 1: $V_1 = 88.0$ V, $V_2 = 58.7$ V, $V_3 = 29.3$ V
Pos 2: $V_1 = 89.1$ V, $V_2 = 58.2$ V, $V_3 = 29.1$ V
Pos 3: $V_1 = 89.8$ V, $V_2 = 59.6$ V, $V_3 = 29.3$ V

57. One of the 12 kΩ resistors is open.

59. The 2.2 kΩ resistor is open.

61. $V_A = 0$ V; $V_B = 11.1$ V

63. R_2 is shorted.

65. No fault

67. R_4 is shorted.

69. R_5 is shorted.

Chapter 7

1. Decrease

3. 37.5 μWb

5. 1000 G

7. 597

9. 1500 At

11. (a) Electromagnetic force   **(b)** Spring force

13. Electromagnetic force

15. Change the current.

17. Material A

▶ FIGURE P–6

▶ FIGURE P–7

19. 1 mA

21. To electrically connect the loop to the external circuit

23. The output voltage appears as the solid blue curve in Figure 7–40 with a frequency of 120 Hz and a peak of 10 V.

25. Design is flawed. Twelve volts is not enough voltage to operate two 12 V relays in series; 24 V is too much voltage to operate a 12 V lamp. Install a separate 12 V power supply for the lamp and change the 12 V to 24 V for the relays.

Chapter 8

1. **(a)** 1 Hz   **(b)** 5 Hz   **(c)** 20 Hz

    (d) 1 kHz   **(e)** 2 kHz   **(f)** 100 kHz

3. 2 μs

5. 250 Hz

7. 200 rps

9. **(a)** 7.07 mA   **(b)** 4.5 mA   **(c)** 14.14 mA

11. **(a)** 17.7 V   **(b)** 25 V   **(c)** 0 V   **(d)** −17.7 V

13. 15°, A leads.

15. See Figure P–8.

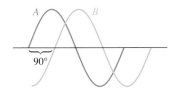

▲ FIGURE P–8

17. **(a)** 22.5°   **(b)** 60°   **(c)** 90°

    (d) 108°   **(e)** 216°   **(f)** 324°

19. **(a)** 57.4 mA   **(b)** 99.6 mA   **(c)** −17.4 mA

    (d) −57.4 mA   **(e)** −99.6 mA   **(f)** 0 mA

21. 30°: 13.0 V; 45°: 14.5 V; 90°: 13.0 V; 180°: −7.5 V; 200°: −11.5 V; 300°: −7.5 V

23. **(a)** 7.07 mA   **(b)** 0 A   **(c)** 10 mA

    (d) 20 mA   **(e)** 10 mA

25. 7.38 V

27. 4.24 V

29. $t_r \cong$ 3.0 ms; t_f 3.0 ms; $t_W \cong$ 12.0 ms; Ampl. = 5 V

31. **(a)** −0.375 V   **(b)** 3.01 V

33. **(a)** 50 kHz   **(b)** 10 Hz

35. 25 kHz

37. 0.424 V; 2 Hz

39. 1.4 V; 120 ms; 30%

41. I_{max} = 2.38 A; V_{avg} = 136 V; See Figure P–9.

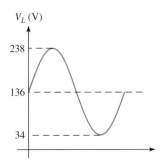

▲ FIGURE P–9

43. **(a)** 2.5   **(b)** 3.96 V   **(c)** 12.5 kHz

45. See Figure P–10.

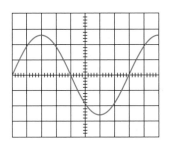

▲ FIGURE P–10

47. $V_{p(in)}$ = 4.44 V; f_{in} = 2 Hz

49. R_3 is open.

51. 5 V; 1 ms

Chapter 9

1. **(a)** 5 μF   **(b)** 1 μC   **(c)** 10 V

3. **(a)** 0.001 μF   **(b)** 0.0035 μF   **(c)** 0.00025 μF

5. 2 μF

7. 88.5 pF

9. 0.0249 μF

11. A 12.5 pF increase

13. Ceramic

15. **(a)** 0.022 μF   **(b)** 0.047 μF

    (c) 0.001 μF   **(d)** 22 pF

17. **(a)** Encapsulation

    (b) Dielectric (ceramic disk)

    (c) Plate (metal disk)

    (d) Leads

19. **(a)** 0.69 μF   **(b)** 69.7 pF   **(c)** 2.6 μF

21. V_1 = 2.13 V; V_2 = 10 V; V_3 = 4.55 V; V_4 = 1 V

23. **(a)** 2.62 μF   **(b)** 689 pF   **(c)** 1.6 μF

25. (a) $100\,\mu s$ (b) $560\,\mu s$ (c) $22.1\,\mu s$ (d) $15\,ms$

27. (a) $9.48\,V$ (b) $13.0\,V$ (c) $14.3\,V$

     (d) $14.7\,V$ (e) $14.9\,V$

29. (a) $2.72\,V$ (b) $5.90\,V$ (c) $11.7\,V$

31. (a) $339\,k\Omega$ (b) $13.5\,k\Omega$

     (c) $677\,\Omega$ (d) $33.9\,\Omega$

33. (a) $30.4\,\Omega$ (b) $115\,k\Omega$ (c) $49.7\,\Omega$

35. $200\,\Omega$

37. $P_{true} = 0\,W;\ P_r = 3.39\,mVAR$

39. $0\,\Omega$

41. $3.18\,ms$

43. $3.24\,\mu s$

45. (a) Charges to $3.32\,V$ in $10\,ms$, then discharges to $0\,V$ in $215\,ms$.

     (b) Charges to $3.32\,V$ in $10\,ms$, then discharges to $2.96\,V$ in $5\,ms$, then charges toward $20\,V$.

47. $0.0056\,\mu F$

49. $V_1 = 7.25\,V;\ V_2 = 2.76\,V;\ V_3 = 0.79\,V;$
$V_5 = 1.19\,V;\ V_6 = 0.79\,V;\ V_4 = 1.98\,V$

51. C_2 is open.

53. No fault

Chapter 10

1. $8\,kHz;\ 8\,kHz$

3. (a) $288\,\Omega$ (b) $1209\,\Omega$

5. (a) $726\,k\Omega$ (b) $155\,k\Omega$

     (c) $91.5\,k\Omega$ (d) $63.0\,k\Omega$

7. (a) $34.7\,mA$ (b) $4.14\,mA$

9. $I_{tot} = 12.3\,mA;\ V_{C1} = 1.31\,V;\ V_{C2} = 0.595\,V;\ V_R = 0.616\,V;$
$\theta = 72.0°\ (V_s\ lagging\ I_{tot})$

11. $808\,\Omega;\ -36.1°$

13. (a) $90°$ (b) $86.4°$ (c) $57.8°$ (d) $9.04°$

15. $326\,\Omega;\ 64.3°$

17. $245\,\Omega;\ 80.5°$

19. $I_{C1} = 118\,mA;\ I_{C2} = 55.3\,mA;\ I_{R1} = 36.4\,mA;\ I_{R2} = 44.4\,mA;\ I_{tot} = 191\,mA;\ \theta = 65.0°\ (V_s\ lagging\ I_{tot})$

21. (a) $3.86\,k\Omega$ (b) $21.3\,\mu A$ (c) $14.8\,\mu A$

     (d) $25.9\,\mu A$ (e) $34.8°\ (V_s\ lagging\ I_{tot})$

23. $V_{C1} = 8.74\,V;\ V_{C2} = 3.26\,V;\ V_{C3} = 3.26\,V;\ V_{R1} = 2.11\,V;$
$V_{R2} = 1.15\,V;\ \theta = 85.5°$

25. $I_{tot} = 82.4\,mA;\ I_{C2} = 14.4\,mA;\ I_{C3} = 67.6\,mA;$
$I_{R1} = I_{R2} = 6.39\,mA$

27. $4.03\,VA$

29. 0.915

31. Use the formula, $V_{out} = \left(\dfrac{X_C}{Z_{tot}}\right)1\,V$. See Figure P–11.

FREQUENCY (kHz)	X_C (kΩ)	Z_{tot} (kΩ)	V_{out} (V)
0			1.000
1	4.08	5.64	0.723
2	2.04	4.40	0.464
3	1.36	4.13	0.329
4	1.02	4.03	0.253
5	0.816	3.98	0.205
6	0.680	3.96	0.172
7	0.583	3.94	0.148
8	0.510	3.93	0.130
9	0.453	3.93	0.115
10	0.408	3.92	0.104

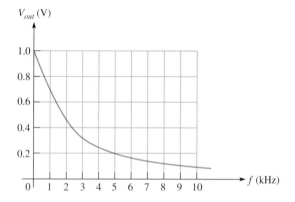

▲ FIGURE P–11

33. See Figure P–12.

◀ FIGURE P–12

(a) For Figure 10–75   (b) For Figure 10–76

35. Figure 10–75: 1.05 kHz; Figure 10–76: 1.59 kHz

37. No leakage: $V_{out} = 3.21$ V; $\theta = 18.7°$;

Leakage: $V_{out} = 2.83$ V, $\theta = 33.3°$

39. **(a)** 0 V   **(b)** 0.321 V   **(c)** 0.5 V   **(d)** 0 V

41. **(a)** $I_{L(A)} = 4.4$ A; $I_{L(B)} = 3.06$ A

(b) $P_{r(A)} = 509$ VAR; $P_{r(B)} = 211$ VAR

(c) $P_{true(A)} = 823$ W; $P_{true(B)} = 641$ W

(d) $P_{a(A)} = 968$ VA; $P_{a(B)} = 675$ VA

(e) Load A

43. 11.4 kΩ

45. $P_r = 1.32$ kVAR; $P_a = 2$ kVA

47. 0.103 μF

49. C is leaky.

51. No fault

53. R_2 is open.

Chapter 11

1. **(a)** 1000 mH   **(b)** 0.25 mH

(c) 0.01 mH   **(d)** 0.5 mH

3. 3450 turns

5. 50 mJ

7. 155 μH

9. 7.14 μH

11. **(a)** 4.33 H   **(b)** 50 mH   **(c)** 57 μH

13. **(a)** 1 μs   **(b)** 2.13 μs   **(c)** 2 μs

15. **(a)** 5.52 V   **(b)** 2.03 V   **(c)** 0.747 V

(d) 0.275 V   **(e)** 0.101 V

17. **(a)** 136 kΩ   **(b)** 1.57 kΩ   **(c)** 1.79 Ω

19. $I_{tot} = 10.1$ mA; $I_{L2} = 6.7$ mA; $I_{L3} = 3.37$ mA

21. 101 mVAR

23. **(a)** 0.427 mA   **(b)** 0.569 mA

25. 26.1 mA

27. L_3 is open.

29. No fault

31. L_3 is shorted.

Chapter 12

1. 15 kHz

3. **(a)** 112 Ω   **(b)** 1.8 kΩ

5. **(a)** 17.4 Ω   **(b)** 64 Ω   **(c)** 127 Ω   **(d)** 251 Ω

7. 0.302 V

9. **(a)** 89.3 mA   **(b)** 2.78 mA

11. 38.7°

13. See Figure P–13.

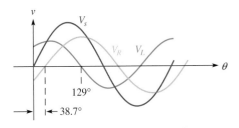

▲ **FIGURE P–13**

15. **(a)** 0.092°   **(b)** 9.15°   **(c)** 58.2°   **(d)** 86.4°

17. 7.69 Ω

19. 2.39 kHz

21. **(a)** 274 Ω   **(b)** 89.3 mA   **(c)** 159 mA

(d) 183 mA   **(e)** 60.7° (I_{tot} lagging V_s)

23. $V_{R1} = 7.92$ V; $V_{R2} = V_L = 20.8$ V

25. $I_{tot} = 36$ mA; $I_L = 33.2$ mA; $I_{R2} = 13.9$ mA

27. 13.0 mW; 10.4 mVAR

29. $PF = 0.386$; $P_{true} = 347$ mW; $P_r = 692$ mVAR;

$P_a = 900$ mVA

31. See Figure P–14.

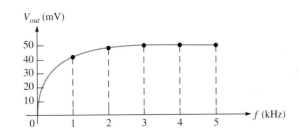

▲ **FIGURE P–14**

33. $V_{R1} = V_{L1} = 18$ V; $V_{R2} = V_{R3} = V_{L2} = 0$ V

35. 5.57 V

37. 343 mA

39. **(a)** 405 mA   **(b)** 228 mA   **(c)** 333 mA   **(d)** 335 mA

41. 0.133

43. See Figure P–15.

▲ **FIGURE P–15**

45. L_2 is open.

47. R_2 is open.

49. L_1 is shorted.

Chapter 13

1. 520 Ω, 88.9° (V_s lagging I); 520 Ω capacitive

3. Impedance increases.

5. See Figure P–16.

▲ FIGURE P–16

7. f_r is lower.

9. $X_L = 4.61$ kΩ; $X_C = 4.61$ kΩ; $Z = 220$ Ω; $I = 54.5$ mA

11. $f_r = 459$ kHz; $f_1 = 360$ kHz; $f_2 = 559$ kHz

13. (a) 14.5 kHz; band-pass   (b) 24.0 kHz; band-pass

15. (a) $f_r = 339$ kHz, $BW = 239$ kHz

     (b) $f_r = 10.4$ kHz, $BW = 2.61$ kHz

17. Capacitive, $X_C < X_L$.

19. 758 Ω

21. 53.1 MΩ; 104 kHz

23. 62.5 Hz

25. 1.38 W

27. 200 Hz

29. $I_{R1} = I_C = 2.11$ mA; $I_{L1} = 1.33$ mA; $I_{L2} = 667$ μA;
$I_{R2} = 667$ μA; $V_{R1} = 6.96$ V; $V_C = 2.11$ V;
$V_{L1} = V_{L2} = V_{R2} = 6.67$ V

31. $I_{R1} = I_{L1} = 41.5$ mA; $I_C = I_{L2} = 133$ mA; $I_{tot} = 104$ mA

33. $L = 989$ μH; $C = 0.064$ μF

35. Neglecting R_W, 8 MHz: $C = 40$ pF; 9 MHz: $C = 31$ pF;
10 MHz: $C = 25$ pF; 11 MHz: $C = 21$ pF

37. No fault

39. L is shorted.

41. L is shorted.

Chapter 14

1. 1.5 μH

3. 3

5. (a) In phase   (b) Out of phase   (c) Out of phase

7. 500 turns

9. (a) Same polarity, 100 V rms

     (b) Opposite polarity, 100 V rms

11. 240 V

13. (a) 6 V   (b) 0 V   (c) 40 V

15. (a) 10 V   (b) 240 V

17. 33.3 mA

19. 27.2 Ω

21. 5.75 mA

23. 0.5

25. 5 kΩ

27. 94.5 W

29. 0.98

31. 25 kVA

33. Secondary 1: 2; Secondary 2: 0.5; Secondary 3: 0.25

35. Top secondary: $n = 100/1000 = 0.1$

     Next secondary: $n = 200/1000 = 0.2$

     Next secondary: $n = 500/1000 = 0.5$

     Bottom secondary: $n = 1000/1000 = 1$

37. Excessive primary current is drawn, potentially burning out the source and/or the transformer, unless the primary is protected by a fuse.

39. (a) $V_{L1} = 35$ V, $I_{L1} = 2.92$ A, $V_{L2} = 15$ V, $I_{L2} = 1.5$ A

     (b) 28.9 Ω

41. (a) 20 V   (b) 10 V

43. 0.0145 (69.2:1)

45. 90 mA or less

47. Secondary is open.

49. Primary is open.

Chapter 15

1. 103 μs

3. 27 kΩ

5. 12.6 V

7. See Figure P–17.

▲ FIGURE P–17

9. See Figure P–18.

▲ FIGURE P–18

11. 15 V dc level with a very small charge/discharge fluctuation

13. Exchange positions of *R* and *C*. See Figure P–19 for the output voltage. $5\tau = 5$ ms (repeating Problem 8)

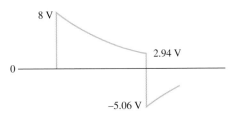

▲ FIGURE P–19

15. Approximately the same shape as input, but with an average value of 0 V

17. See Figure P–20.

▲ FIGURE P–20

19. See Figure P–21.

▲ FIGURE P–21

21. A 6 V dc level

23. **(b)** No fault   **(c)** Open *C* or shorted *R*

25. **(a)** 23.5 ms

    (b) See Figure P–22.

▲ FIGURE P–22

27. 1.44 s

29. Capacitor is open.

31. No fault

GLOSSARY

accuracy An indication of the range of error in a measurement.

admittance (Y) A measure of the ability of a reactive circuit to permit current; the reciprocal of impedance. The unit is the siemens (S).

ammeter An electrical instrument used to measure current.

ampere (A or amp) The unit of electrical current.

ampere-hour rating A number given in ampere-hours (Ah) determined by multiplying the current in amps (A) times the length of time in hours (h) a battery can deliver that current to a load.

ampere-turn The SI unit of magnetomotive force (mmf).

amplification The process of producing a larger voltage, current, or power using a smaller input signal as a pattern.

amplifier An electronic circuit having the capability of amplification and designed specifically for that purpose.

amplitude The maximum value of a voltage or current.

apparent power (P_a) The product of the voltage times the current, expressed in volt-amperes (VA). In a purely resistive circuit it is the same as the true power.

apparent power rating The method of rating transformers in which the power capability is expressed in volt-amperes (VA).

atom The smallest particle of an element possessing the unique characteristics of that element.

atomic number The number of protons in the nucleus of an atom.

attenuation A gain less than unity.

autotransformer A transformer in which the primary and secondary windings are in a single winding.

average value The average of a sine wave over one half-cycle. It is 0.637 times the peak value.

AWG (American wire gauge) A standardization based on wire diameter.

balanced bridge A bridge circuit that is in the balanced state as indicated by zero volts across the bridge.

band-pass filter A resonant circuit that passes a range of frequencies lying between two cutoff frequencies and rejects frequencies above and below the range.

band-stop filter A resonant circuit that rejects a range of frequencies lying between two cutoff frequencies and passes frequencies above and below the range.

bandwidth (_BW_) The characteristic of certain electronic circuits that specifies the usable range of frequencies for which signals pass from input to output without significant reduction in amplitude.

baseline The normal level of a pulse waveform; the voltage level in the absence of a pulse.

battery An energy source that uses a chemical reaction to convert chemical energy into electrical energy.

bias The application of a dc voltage to a diode or other electronic device to produce a desired mode of operation.

bleeder current The current left after the total load current is subtracted from the total current into the circuit.

branch One current path in a parallel circuit.

bypass A capacitor connected from a point to ground to remove the ac signal without affecting the dc voltage. A special case of decoupling.

capacitance The ability of a capacitor to store electrical charge.

capacitive reactance The opposition of a capacitor to sinusoidal current. The unit is the ohm (Ω).

capacitive susceptance (B_C) The ability of a capacitor to permit current; the reciprocal of capacitive reactance. The unit is the siemens (S).

capacitor An electrical device consisting of two conductive plates separated by an insulating material and possessing the property of capacitance.

capacitor-input filter A power supply filter that uses a capacitor from the rectifier output to ground to eliminate most of the variation in the rectifier output voltage.

center tap (CT) A connection at the midpoint of the secondary winding of a transformer.

charge An electrical property of matter that exists because of an excess or a deficiency of electrons. Charge can be either positive or negative.

charging The process in which a current removes charge from one plate of a capacitor and deposits it on the other plate, making one plate more positive than the other.

choke An inductor. The term is used more commonly in connection with inductors used to block or choke off high frequencies.

circuit An interconnection of electrical components designed to produce a desired result. A basic circuit consists of a source, a load, and an interconnecting current path.

circuit breaker A resettable protective device used for interrupting excessive current in an electric circuit.

circular mil (CM) The unit of the cross-sectional area of a wire.

closed circuit A circuit with a complete current path.

coefficient of coupling (k) A constant associated with transformers that is the ratio of secondary magnetic flux to primary magnetic flux. The ideal value of 1 indicates that all the flux in the primary winding is coupled into the secondary winding.

coil A common term for an inductor.

color code A system of color bands or dots that identify the value of a resistor or other component.

common Reference ground.

conductance (G) The ability of a circuit to allow current; the reciprocal of resistance. The unit is the siemens (S).

conductor A material in which electrical current is established with relative ease. An example is copper.

core The structure around which the winding of an inductor is formed. The core material influences the electromagnetic characteristics of the inductor.

coulomb (C) The unit of electrical charge; the total charge possessed by 6.25×10^{18} electrons.

Coulomb's law A law that states a force exists between two charged bodies that is directly proportional to the product of the two charges and inversely proportional to the square of the distance between them.

coupling The method of connecting a capacitor from between two points in a circuit to allow ac to pass from one point to the other while blocking dc.

current The rate of flow of charge (free electrons).

current divider A parallel circuit in which the total current divides among the branches.

current source A device that produces a constant current for a varying load.

cutoff frequency (f_c) The frequency at which the output voltage of a filter is 70.7% of the maximum output voltage.

cycle One repetition of a periodic waveform.

dc component The average value of a pulse waveform.

dc power supply An electronic instrument that produces voltage, current, and power from the ac power line or batteries in a form suitable for use in powering electronic equipment.

decibel (dB) A unit of logarithmic expression ten times the logarithm of the ratio of two powers or twenty times the logarithm of the ratio of two voltages measured across equal resistances.

decoupling The method of connecting a capacitor from one point, usually the dc power supply line, to ground to short ac to ground without affecting the dc voltage.

degree The unit of angular measure corresponding to 1/360 of a complete revolution.

dielectric The insulating material between the plates of a capacitor.

dielectric constant A measure of the ability of a dielectric material to establish an electric field.

dielectric strength A measure of the ability of a dielectric material to withstand voltage without breaking down.

differentiator A circuit that produces an inverted output that approaches the mathematical derivative of the input, which is the rate of change.

discrete device An individual electrical or electronic component that must be used in combination with other components to form a complete functional circuit.

DMM Digital multimeter; an electronic instrument that combines meters for the measurement of voltage, current, and resistance.

duty cycle A characteristic of a pulse waveform that indicates the percentage of time that a pulse is present during a cycle; the ratio of pulse width to period.

effective value A measure of the heating effect of a sine wave; also known as the *rms* (root mean square) *value.*

efficiency The ratio of the output power to the input power of a circuit, usually expressed as a percentage.

electrical Related to the use of electrical voltage and current to achieve desired results.

electrical isolation The condition that exists when two coils are magnetically linked but have no electrical connection between them.

electrical shock The physical sensation resulting from current through the body.

electromagnetic field A formation of a group of magnetic lines of force surrounding a conductor created by electrical current in the conductor.

electromagnetic induction The phenomenon or process by which a voltage is produced in a conductor when there is relative motion between the conductor and a magnetic or electromagnetic field.

electromagnetism The production of a magnetic field by current in a conductor.

electron A basic particle of electrical charge in matter. The electron possesses negative charge.

electronic Related to the movement and control of free electrons in semiconductors or vacuum devices.

element One of the unique substances that make up the known universe. Each element is characterized by a unique atomic structure.

energy The ability to do work. The unit is the joule (J).

engineering notation A system for representing any number as a one-, two-, or three-digit number times a power of ten with an exponent that is a multiple of 3.

error The difference between the true or best-accepted value of some quantity and the measured value.

exponent The number to which a base number is raised.

exponential A mathematical function described by a natural logarithm (base). Increasing and decreasing current and voltage for a capacitor or inductor are described by exponential functions.

falling edge The negative-going transition of a pulse.

fall time (t_f) The time interval required for a pulse to change from 90% to 10% of its amplitude.

farad (F) The unit of capacitance.

Faraday's law A law stating that the voltage induced across a coil of wire equals the number of turns in the coil times the rate of change of the magnetic flux.

filter A type of circuit that passes certain frequencies and rejects all others.

free electron A valence electron that has broken away from its parent atom and is free to move from atom to atom within the atomic structure of a material.

frequency A measure of the rate of change of a periodic function; the number of cycles completed in 1 s. The unit of frequency is the hertz.

frequency response In electrical circuits, the variation in the output voltage (or current) over a specified range of frequencies.

function generator An instrument that produces more than one type of waveform.

fundamental frequency The repetition rate of a waveform.

fuse A protective device that burns open when there is excessive current in a circuit.

gauss A CGS unit of flux density.

generator An energy source that produces electrical signals.

germanium A semiconductive material.

ground The common or reference point in a circuit.

half-power frequency The frequency at which the output of a filter is 70.7% of maximum.

half-splitting A troubleshooting procedure where one starts in the middle of a circuit or system and, depending on the first measurement, works toward the output or toward the input to find the fault.

harmonics The frequencies contained in a composite waveform, which are integer multiples of the repetition frequency (fundamental).

henry (H) The unit of inductance.

hertz (Hz) The unit of frequency. One hertz equals one cycle per second.

high-pass circuit A certain type of circuit whereby higher frequencies are passed and lower frequencies are rejected.

hypotenuse The longest side of a right triangle.

hysteresis A characteristic of a magnetic material whereby a change in magnetization lags the application of a magnetic force.

impedance (Z) The total opposition to sinusoidal current expressed in ohms.

impedance matching A technique used to match a load resistance to an internal source resistance in order to achieve a maximum transfer of power.

induced current (i_{ind}) A current induced in a conductor as a result of a changing magnetic field.

induced voltage (v_{ind}) Voltage produced as a result of a changing magnetic field.

inductance (L) The property of an inductor that produces an opposition to any change in current.

inductive reactance (X_L) The opposition of an inductor to sinusoidal current. The unit is the ohm.

inductive susceptance (B_L) The ability of an inductor to permit current; the reciprocal of inductive reactance. The unit is the siemens.

inductor An electrical device formed by a wire wound in a coil around a core having the property of inductance and the capability to store energy in its electromagnetic field; also known as a coil or, in some applications, a choke.

input The voltage, current, or power applied to an electrical circuit to produce a desired result.

instantaneous power The value of power in a circuit at any given instant of time.

instantaneous value The voltage or current value of a waveform at a given instant in time.

insulator A material that does not allow current under normal conditions.

integrated circuit (IC) A type of circuit in which all the components are constructed on a single tiny chip of silicon.

integrator A circuit that produces an output that approaches the mathematical integral of the input.

interface To make the output of one type of circuit compatible with the input of another so that they can operate properly together.

ion An atom that has gained or lost a valence electron resulting in a net positive or negative charge.

joule (J) The SI unit of energy.

kilowatt-hour (kWh) A large unit of energy used mainly by utility companies.

Kirchhoff's current law A law stating that the total current into a node equals the total current out of the node.

Kirchhoff's voltage law A law stating that (1) the sum of the voltage drops around a single closed loop (path) equals the source voltage in that loop or (2) the algebraic sum of all the voltages (drops and sources) around a single closed path is zero.

lag To be behind; describes a condition of the phase or time relationship of waveforms in which one waveform is behind the other in phase or time.

lead To be ahead; describes a condition of the phase or time relationship of waveforms in which one waveform is ahead of the other in phase or time; also, a wire or cable connection to a device or instrument.

leading edge The first step or transition of a pulse.

Lenz's law A law that states when the current through a coil changes, the polarity of the induced voltage created by the changing magnetic field is such that it always opposes the change that caused it. The current cannot change instantaneously.

linear Characterized by a straight-line relationship.

lines of force Magnetic flux lines that exist in a magnetic field radiating from the north pole to the south pole.

load An element (resistor or other component) connected across the output terminals of a circuit that draws current from the source and upon which work is done.

load current The output current of a circuit supplied to a load.

loading The effect on a circuit when an element that draws current from the circuit is connected across the output terminals.

low-pass circuit A certain type of circuit in which lower frequencies are passed and higher frequencies are rejected.

magnetic coupling The magnetic connection between two coils as a result of the changing magnetic flux lines of one coil cutting through the second coil.

magnetic field A force field radiating from the north pole to the south pole of a magnet.

magnetic field intensity The amount of mmf per unit length of magnetic material. The unit is the ampere-turns/meter (At/m); also called *magnetizing force*.

magnetic flux The lines of force between the north and south poles of a permanent magnet or an electromagnet.

magnetic flux density The number of lines of force per unit area perpendicular to a magnetic field.

magnetomotive force The cause of a magnetic field; measured in ampere-turns.

magnitude The value of a quantity, such as the number of volts of voltage or the number of amperes of current.

maximum power transfer The condition, when the load resistance equals the source resistance, under which maximum power is transferred from source to load.

maximum power transfer theorem A theorem that states the maximum power is transferred from a source to a load when the load resistance equals the internal source resistance.

metric prefix A symbol that is used to replace the power of ten in numbers expressed in engineering notation.

modulation The process in which a signal containing information is used to modify a characteristic of another signal such as amplitude, frequency, or pulse width so that the information on the first is also contained on the second.

multimeter An instrument that measures voltage, current, and resistance.

mutual inductance (L_M) The inductance between two separate coils, such as in a transformer.

neutron An atomic particle having no electrical charge.

node A point or junction in a circuit at which two or more components are connected.

nucleus The central part of an atom containing protons and neutrons.

ohm (Ω) The unit of resistance.

ohmmeter An instrument for measuring resistance.

Ohm's law A law stating that current is directly proportional to voltage and inversely proportional to resistance.

open A circuit condition in which the current path is interrupted.

open circuit A circuit in which there is not a complete current path.

orbit The path an electron takes as it circles around the nucleus of an atom.

oscillator A circuit that produces a repetitive waveform on its output with only the dc supply voltage as an input.

oscilloscope A measurement instrument that displays signal waveforms on a screen.

parallel The relationship in electric circuits in which two or more current paths are connected between the same two points.

parallel resonance In a parallel *RLC* circuit, the condition where the impedance is maximum and the reactances are equal.

passband The range of frequencies passed by a filter.

peak-to-peak value The voltage or current value of a waveform measured from its minimum to its maximum points.

peak value The voltage or current value of a waveform at its maximum positive or negative points.

period (T) The time interval of one complete cycle of a given sine wave or any periodic waveform.

periodic Characterized by a repetition at fixed time intervals.

permeability The measure of ease with which a magnetic field can be established in a material.

phase The relative displacement of a time-varying waveform in terms of its occurrence with respect to a reference.

phase angle The angle between the source voltage and the total current in a reactive circuit.

phasor A representation of a sine wave in terms of both magnitude and phase angle.

photoconductive cell A type of variable resistor that is light-sensitive.

photovoltaic effect The process whereby light energy is converted directly into electrical energy.

piezoelectric effect The property of a crystal whereby a changing mechanical stress produces a voltage across the crystal.

pole In practical terms, a single *RC* circuit in a filter or amplifier that causes the response to change at a 20 dB per decade rate above or below a certain frequency.

potentiometer A three-terminal variable resistor.

power The rate of energy usage.

power factor The relationship between volt-amperes and true power or watts. Volt-amperes multiplied by the power factor equals true power.

power of ten A numerical representation consisting of a base of 10 and an exponent; the number 10 raised to a power.

power rating The maximum amount of power that a resistor can dissipate without being damaged by excessive heat buildup.

power supply A device that provides power to a load.

precision A measure of the repeatability (or consistency) of a series of measurements.

primary winding The input winding of a transformer; also called *primary*.

probe An accessory used to connect a voltage to the input of an oscilloscope or other instrument.

proton A positively charged atomic particle.

pulse A type of waveform that consists of two equal and opposite steps in voltage or current separated by a time interval.

pulse repetition frequency The fundamental frequency of a repetitive pulse waveform; the rate at which the pulses repeat expressed in either hertz or pulses per second.

pulse width (t_W) The time interval between the opposite steps of an ideal pulse. For a nonideal pulse, the time between the 50% points on the leading and trailing edges.

quality factor (Q) The ratio of reactive power to true power in an inductor or a resonant circuit.

radian A unit of angular measurement. There are 2π radians in one complete revolution. One radian equals 57.3°.

ramp A type of waveform characterized by a linear increase or decrease in voltage or current.

RC lag circuit A phase shift circuit in which the output voltage, taken across the capacitor, lags the input voltage by a specified angle.

RC lead circuit A phase shift circuit in which the output voltage, taken across the resistor, leads the input voltage by a specified angle.

RC time constant A fixed time interval set by the values of R and C that determines the time response of a series RC circuit. It equals the product of the resistance and the capacitance.

reactive power (P_r) The rate at which energy is stored and alternately returned to the source by a capacitor or inductor. The unit is the VAR.

rectifier An electronic circuit that converts ac into pulsating dc; one part of a power supply.

reference ground The metal chassis that houses the assembly or a large conducive area on a printed circuit board used as the common or reference point.

reflected load The load as it appears to the source in the primary of a transformer.

reflected resistance The resistance in the secondary circuit reflected into the primary circuit.

relay An electromagnetically controlled mechanical device in which electrical contacts are open or closed by a magnetizing current.

reluctance The opposition to the establishment of a magnetic field in a material.

resistance Opposition to current. The unit is the ohm (Ω).

resistor An electrical component designed specifically to have a certain amount of resistance.

resolution The smallest increment of a quantity that a meter can measure.

resonant frequency The frequency at which a resonant condition occurs in a series or parallel RLC circuit.

retentivity The ability of a material, once magnetized, to maintain a magnetized state without the presence of a magnetizing force.

RFI Radio frequency interference; high frequencies produced when high values of current and voltage are switched on and off.

rheostat A two-terminal variable resistor.

right triangle A triangle with a 90° angle.

ripple voltage The small variation in the dc voltage on the output of a filtered rectifier caused by the slight charging and discharging action of the filter capacitor.

rise time (t_r) The time interval required for a pulse to change from 10% to 90% of its amplitude.

rising edge The positive-going transition of a pulse.

RL lag circuit A phase shift circuit in which the output voltage, taken across the resistor, lags the input voltage by a specified angle.

RL lead circuit A phase shift circuit in which the output voltage, taken across the inductor, leads the input voltage by a specified angle.

RL time constant A fixed time interval set by the values of R and L that determines the time response of a circuit and is equal to L/R.

rms value The value of a sine wave that indicates its heating effect, also known as the *effective value*. It is equal to 0.707 times the peak value. RMS stands for root mean square.

round off The process of dropping one or more digits to the right of the last significant digit in a number.

sawtooth waveform A type of electrical waveform composed of ramps; a special case of a triangular waveform in which one ramp is much shorter than the other.

schematic A symbolized diagram of an electrical or electronic circuit.

scientific notation A system for representing any number as a number between 1 and 10 times an appropriate power of ten.

secondary winding The output winding of a transformer; also called *secondary*.

Seebeck effect The generation of a voltage at the junction of two different metals that have a temperature difference between them.

selectivity A measure of how effectively a resonant circuit passes certain frequencies and rejects others. The narrower the bandwidth, the greater the selectivity.

semiconductor A material that has a conductance value between that of a conductor and that of an insulator. Silicon and germanium are examples.

sensitivity factor The ohms-per-volt rating of a voltmeter.

series In an electric circuit, a relationship of components in which the components are connected such that they provide a single current path between two points.

series-aiding An arrangement of two or more series voltage sources with polarities in the same direction.

series-opposing An arrangement of two series voltage sources with polarities in the opposite direction.

series resonance In a series RLC circuit, the condition where the impedance is minimum and the reactances are equal.

shell An energy band in which electrons orbit the nucleus of an atom.

short A circuit condition in which there is a zero or abnormally low resistance between two points; usually an inadvertent condition.

SI Standardized international system of units used for all engineering and scientific work; abbreviation for French *Le Système International d'Unites*.

siemens The unit of conductance.

significant digit A digit known to be correct in a number.

silicon A semiconductive material used in diodes and transistors.

sine wave A type of electrical waveform that is based on the mathematical sine function.

solenoid An electromagnetically controlled device in which the mechanical movement of a shaft or plunger is activated by a magnetizing current.

solenoid valve An electrically controlled valve for control of air, water, steam, oils, refrigerants, and other fluids.

speaker An electromagnetic device that converts electrical signals to sound waves.

steady state The equilibrium condition of a circuit that occurs after an initial transient time.

step-down transformer A transformer in which the secondary voltage is less than the primary voltage.

step-up transformer A transformer in which the secondary voltage is greater than the primary voltage.

stopband The range of frequencies between the upper and lower cutoff points.

superposition A method for analyzing circuits with two or more sources by examining the effects of each source by itself and then combining the effects.

switch An electrical or electronic device for opening and closing a current path.

tank circuit A parallel resonant circuit.

tapered Nonlinear, such as a tapered potentiometer.

temperature coefficient A constant specifying the amount of change in the value of a quantity for a given change in temperature.

terminal An external contact point on an electric circuit or an electronic device.

terminal equivalency A condition that occurs when two circuits produce the same load voltage and load current where the same value of load resistance is connected to either circuit.

tesla The SI unit of flux density.

thermistor A type of temperature transducer in which resistance is inversely proportional to temperature.

Thevenin's theorem A circuit theorem that provides for reducing any two-terminal resistive circuit to a single equivalent voltage source in series with an equivalent resistance.

time constant A fixed-time interval set by R and C, or R and L values, that determines the time response of a circuit.

tolerance The limits of variation in the value of a component.

trailing edge The second step or transition of a pulse.

transducer A device that converts a physical parameter into an electrical quantity.

transformer An electrical device constructed of two or more coils (windings) that are electromagnetically coupled to each other to provide a transfer of power from one coil to another.

transient A temporary passing condition in a circuit; a sudden or temporary change in circuit conditions.

transient time An interval equal to approximately five time constants.

transistor A semiconductor device that controls current between two terminals based on the current or voltage at a third terminal and is used for amplification and switching of electrical signals.

triangular waveform A type of electrical waveform that consists of two ramps.

trigger The activating mechanism of some electronic devices or instruments.

trimmer A small variable capacitor.

troubleshooting A systematic process of isolating, identifying, and correcting a fault in a circuit or system; the application of logical thinking combined with a thorough knowledge of circuit or system operation to find and correct a malfunction.

true power The power that is dissipated in a circuit, usually in the form of heat.

turns ratio The ratio of turns in the secondary winding to turns in the primary winding.

unbalanced bridge A bridge circuit that is in the unbalanced state as indicated by a voltage across the bridge proportional to the amount of deviation from the balanced state.

valence Related to the outer shell or orbit of an atom.

valence electron An electron that is present in the outermost shell of an atom.

VAR (volt-ampere reactive) The unit of reactive power.

volt The unit of voltage or electromotive force.

voltage The amount of energy available to move a certain number of electrons from one point to another in an electric circuit.

voltage divider A circuit consisting of series resistors across which one or more output voltages are taken.

voltage drop The decrease in the voltage across a resistor due to loss of energy.

voltage source A device that produces a constant voltage for a varying load.

voltmeter An instrument used to measure voltage.

watt (W) The unit of power.

Watt's law A law that states the relationships of power to current, voltage, and resistance.

waveform The pattern of variations of a voltage or current showing how the quantity changes with time.

weber (Wb) The SI unit of magnetic flux, which represents 10^8 lines.

Wheatstone bridge A 4-legged type of bridge circuit with which an unknown resistance can be accurately measured using the balanced state of the bridge. Deviations in resistance can be measured using the unbalanced state.

winding The loops or turns of wire in an inductor.

winding resistance The resistance of the length of wire that makes up a coil.

wiper The sliding contact in a potentiometer.

INDEX